Julie Vermilya 546893
693 S. Wonders
353-2582

A GEOGRAPHY OF MAN

THIRD EDITION

PRESTON E. JAMES, *Syracuse University*

WITH THE COLLABORATION OF
HIBBERD V. B. KLINE, JR.
University of Pittsburgh

A GEOGRAPHY OF MAN

GINN–BLAISDELL

A XEROX COMPANY

WALTHAM, MASSACHUSETTS • TORONTO • LONDON

CONSULTING EDITORS

John F. Kolars and Melvin G. Marcus, *University of Michigan,*
and Ann E. Larimore

No man can reveal to you aught but that which already lies
  half asleep in the dawning of your knowledge.
For the vision of one man lends not its wings to another man.

And even as each one of you stands alone in God's knowledge,
  so must each one of you be alone in his knowledge
  of God and in his understanding of the earth.

KAHLIL GIBRAN

Preface

A Geography of Man is designed for an elementary college-level course in world geography. The book is specifically concerned with the interrelations of man and his natural surroundings. The purpose is to develop geographic concepts, and to illustrate the methods of geographic analysis. Adequate factual content is presented to permit the application of geographic ideas, but the ideas are presumed to be more important than completeness of content. Two different kinds of concepts are developed: (1) concepts concerning the character and arrangement over the earth of the major physical-biotic systems that constitute the natural surroundings of man—the human habitats; and (2) concepts regarding the significance to man of these natural surroundings.

A system is made up of interdependent elements so organized that a change in any one element results in changes in all the others. Geography deals with spatial systems—that is, systems that occupy space on the face of the earth. To be sure, the whole surface of the earth, including its animal and human inhabitants, constitutes the only complete system. But the totality of interaction is far too complex for meaningful analysis. It is necessary, therefore, to proceed toward an understanding of the interrelations between man and habitat through the study of subsystems. Geography, as a professional field, deals with many kinds of spatial systems, but for the purposes of this book attention is first directed to the physical-biotic systems that are called habitats.

These physical-biotic systems, or ecosystems, must be simplified to provide a useful conceptual framework for the development of an elementary picture of world geography. This simplification involves the definition of categories of interrelated parts at the same degree of generalization. For the purposes of this book a habitat is considered to be made up of associations of five elements: (1) surface features; (2) climates; (3) water; (4) wild vegetation; and (5) soils.

Nine groups of habitat regions are recognized, and these form the basis of organization for the main part of the text.   Each is defined in terms of the association of these five elements in specific segments of earth-space. The nine habitat groups are listed on page 22.   In previous editions of this book—and of its predecessor, *An Outline of Geography*—eight groups of regions were presented.   Continued field studies indicate that the savannas and tropical woodlands (tropical scrub forests) do in fact constitute a system of related parts of special significance to man and therefore merit recognition as a separate group.

These nine habitats are arranged on the earth's land masses in a predictable pattern. The pattern involves the interplay of two principles: (1) that all habitat features causally related to climate are arranged in a regular, repeated pattern in relation to latitude and continental position; and (2) that all habitat features causally related to surface features are irregularly arranged with reference to latitude and continental position.   If the earth were all land or all water, the world's climates would form simple latitudinal zones.   But the differences between climates over the land and climates over the water modify the simple latitudinal arrangement.   The irregular pattern of high mountains on the continents further modifies and distorts the simple climatic patterns as they would develop on flat continents.   The actual arrangement of habitats, therefore, is described by the interplay of the principle of climatic regularity and surface irregularity.

Nevertheless, the proper study of the text and its accompanying maps should prepare the student to pass the "thumb test."   With his back to a globe the student is asked to indicate with his thumb some part of the earth's surface.   He then turns to see what part he has indicated.   From looking at the globe he knows two facts about the general area he has indicated: He knows its position in latitude; and he knows whether it is located on the eastern side of an ocean basin, the western side of an ocean basin, the eastern side of a continent, the interior of a continent, or the western side of a continent.   With this information he should be able to predict the kind of habitat system he would find in that part of the earth.   If a student is unable to say anything about the physical-biotic character of any major part of the earth's surface, he fails the test.

Geography is also concerned with the interrelations between man and habitat.   What does the habitat mean to the people who must live and work in it?   Is the habitat favorable or unfavorable?   In examining these questions we come to one of the core concepts of modern geography: that the significance to man of the physical and biotic features of his habitat is a function of the attitudes, objectives, and technical skills of man himself.

The habitat that is favorable to one group of people may prove unfavorable to another. A change in any of the elements of a culture, or way of living of a people, makes necessary the reappraisal of the habitat.

This concept is demonstrated, for selected places within each of the nine groups of regions, by examining the experience of man with the problems of making a living from earth resources. Man's experience with a particular habitat is examined historically. With each change in attitudes or objectives, or especially in technology, the significance of the habitat is reexamined. This is a method of study that the geographers describe as *sequent occupance*. For each period during which the culture remains essentially unchanged, the geography of man in relation to habitat is reconstructed. When changes in the culture take place, for whatever reason, the differences in the man–habitat relations are identified.

The student who lacks the background of technical, systematic studies that would be provided by proper courses in secondary school is aided by use of the appendixes. Appendix A, by Hibberd V. B. Kline Jr., presents a general, elementary picture of the nature and use of maps. The other appendixes present in condensed outline form the principles of climatology, geomorphology, hydrography, and vegetation geography. At the end of the section of appendixes there is an up-to-date bibliography of geographic writings, together with a discussion of bibliographic sources.

The author expresses his appreciation to Professor Hibberd V. B. Kline Jr., who collaborated in the critical appraisal of many sections of the book, especially those dealing with Africa. The author is also indebted to his wife, Eileen W. James, who prepared some of the new maps for this third edition.

PRESTON E. JAMES

Syracuse University

Contents

Reference Maps

xvii

A GEOGRAPHY OF MAN

The Habitat

MOST LITERATE PEOPLE are aware of the existence of a world-wide population problem. For many decades specialists in the study of population have been warning that mankind is headed for disaster; but during these same decades in the United States food has become more plentiful, and most Americans have improved their living conditions in terms of material comforts. The dimensions of the world population problem, and what it can mean with regard to the capacity of man to support himself from earth resources, are not widely understood even now. Yet among all the complex and disturbing situations that modern man must face, none is more fundamental than that of the increasing pressure of people on the land. This book deals with that problem.

In 1963 the population of the world was 3,180,000,000. In 1950 there were about 2,406,000,000 people in the world. Between 1950 and 1960 the population of the world increased by about 500,000,000. As each minute went by during this decade there were 80 new mouths to feed, and 80 new pairs of hands to employ. Estimates of the world population by the year 2000 offer figures such as five billion.

The population is very unevenly spread over the earth. Vast areas are only very thinly populated, with small concentrations of people separated by many miles of empty country. In southern and eastern Asia, on the other hand, about half of all the people in the world are packed into less than a tenth of the world's habitable area. In Europe a little less than a fifth of mankind occupies an area that amounts to less than one-twentieth of the habitable world.

Yet to draw the conclusion that a great movement to the empty lands of the earth is about to take place would be quite wrong. People are concentrated in certain parts of the earth's surface as a result of historical processes.   These processes are not simple: the fact is that the concentrations of people in Asia took place for very different reasons than those that explain the concentrations in Europe.   Furthermore, in this second half of the twentieth century, the tendency is for the densely populated areas to become even more densely populated, and for the thinly populated areas to lose population.

Since all food, clothing, shelter, and other material things that surround civilized man are derived from things produced by the earth, it becomes critical to examine the natural surroundings of man—the human habitat. To understand what the habitats of the earth mean to its human inhabitants requires a long view of how, over the centuries, man has brought the earth resources into use.   Furthermore, since man–land relations change through time, and also vary in major ways from place to place at any one time, generalizations about population and resources in the world as a whole are less useful than those that divide the world into distinct areas, in each of which the experience of man in making a living from earth resources has differed.

THE FACE OF THE EARTH

What kind of a place is this world into which so many people are crowded?   Among the other planets that move around our medium-sized sun, the earth is neither the largest nor the smallest; it is neither very far away from the sun nor very close to it.   Yet the surface of the earth is unique in the known universe.   Of all the possible temperatures that exist in nature, here at the surface of the earth temperatures occur within the narrow range between the boiling point and the freezing point of water. On the earth water can exist as a liquid.   The first living organisms appeared in the shallow margins of the oceans.   When living creatures moved out onto the land they were equipped with skins so that they could carry their water environment with them—much as astronauts today carry an atmosphere with them inside their space suits.   Without water in liquid form, life, as we know it, would be impossible.

Water and sunlight are essential conditions for the growth of plants, and plants provide the support of other living organisms, including man.   In the presence of liquid water, plants have the capacity to make use of the energy from the sun to transform the lifeless minerals of the earth's crust into organic matter.   Animals live on plants, or on other animals that live on plants.   From plants and animals man also gets his supply of food.

The essential elements for the support of life, including human life, are not evenly distributed over the surface of the earth.   The amount of energy received from the sun is greatest in the lower latitudes; it decreases in higher latitudes toward the poles.   Water, too, is very unevenly spread over the land. There are parts of the earth that receive an abundance, even a superabundance of rainfall; but there are other parts that remain dry most of the time. Furthermore there are places where the water is locked up in the great ice caps and glaciers. These differences in sunlight and water are not arranged in a haphazard manner: rather, they form regular patterns on the face of the earth that can be explained in terms of the processes producing them.

The uneven distribution of sunlight and water must be seen against the background of another kind of uneven distribution. The land itself varies from place to place in the nature of its rocks and minerals, in elevation above sea level, and in the steepness and form of the slopes. The rock crust is cracked and broken where it is in contact with the atmosphere, forming a mantle of loose rock fragments. In this mantle the inorganic materials are mixed with organic materials derived from the decay of plants. The result is a soil. In complex but predictable relationships with the patterns of sunlight, water, rocks, slopes, and soils are the various associations of plants known collectively as vegetation, and the groups of animals that live on the vegetation and on each other. All of these things together form the natural surroundings of man—the human habitat.

To make matters more complicated, all these interrelated features of the face of the earth are constantly changing. The "everlasting hills" only seem to be everlasting because they change so slowly in relation to the span of a human lifetime. Other changes go on rapidly. There are changes resulting from the processes of physics and chemistry; there are changes resulting from the processes of biology; and there are economic, social, and political processes resulting from the activities of man. In fact, during the past few centuries man has become a major agent of change as he transforms the patterns of plants and animals, digs out the earth's minerals, diverts the flow of water, rebuilds the soils, and even modifies for his own convenience the shape of the surface features. The landscapes in areas of human concentration are largely man-made.

This book is concerned with the interacting processes that produce the diverse habitats of the earth. We seek to understand how and why one part of the earth differs from another. But we also seek to understand what these differences mean to the human inhabitants. Is a habitat favorable or unfavorable for settlement by a particular human group? Does it present special difficulties? It is important to understand that in spite of the advanced engineering skill of modern man, life on the earth is still dependent on energy and light from the sun and on the availability of water. The greatest material achievements of man are still fashioned from the materials of the earth.

The study of man's experience in making a living from earth resources illuminates an important principle: that the habitat by itself cannot be termed either favorable or unfavorable. It is dependent on the particular human group. Repeatedly, history offers examples of the varying habitability of specific regions. The same countries which to one people seem to be inhospitable and lacking in resources, to another people may seem to offer great advantages for the development of human society; and the same countries which once provided support for a flourishing civilization, may now appear as difficult places in which to make a living. What is the difference? In some cases, perhaps, there have been climatic changes, or shifts in the courses of rivers, or other natural phenomena that do actually change the physical character of the land; but in many other instances there is no evidence of such change. The difference is in the human group. For a people without steel plows, railroads, or great urban markets, the world's grasslands, for example, were rated as lands of low productivity; but for a people armed with the mechanical equipment and possessing the economic institutions of the industrial era, these same lands became major sources of wheat and meat.

The story does not always run in the direction of progress, however. There are many regions in which a human society armed with primitive tools was once able to form a workable connection with the resources of the land, but in which men with machines have been unable to survive because of the rapid destruction of the resources. What degree of slope is too steep for agriculture? The answer to this question depends on the technique of farming, for slopes which can be cultivated with hoes may be much too steep for plows. In other words, the significance of the physical conditions of the land depends on the attitudes, objectives, and technical abilities of the inhabitants.

This principle illustrates that modern man is not necessarily emancipated from dependence on the resources of the earth. For primitive peoples with relatively simple cultures the connections with the habitat were local, direct, and easily observable. Modern industrial society, on the other hand, derives its earth-born materials from widely separated places. The magic of modern transportation makes possible the shipment of bulky raw materials from great distances, as well as the shipment of finished products. There are many city people whose understanding of the sources of food fails to extend beyond the supermarket. But in reality man is still closely tied to earth resources.

THE PATTERN OF SURFACE FEATURES

For the purposes of presenting a global view of man's relations to the habitat it is possible to define certain habitat regions. The elements that combine to differentiate the face of the earth into human habitats include the pattern of surface features, the pattern of climates, the pattern of water,

the pattern of vegetation, and the pattern of soils. There are cerain recurring associations of these five elements that define the groups of habitat
regions.

The pattern of surface features forms the major lineaments of the face
of the earth. The largest relief features are the continents and ocean
basins. The continents are composed of relatively upstanding masses of
the earth's crust. The difference of elevation above the center of the earth
between the continents and ocean basins averages only about three miles.
Since the radius of the earth at the equator is 3968 miles, this difference
of only three miles of surface relief is small indeed—only about 1/1300 of
the radius. If an ordinary 12-inch globe were made to scale, it would
scarcely be possible to feel the continents and ocean basins with finger tips.
The maximum difference in elevation on the earth's surface is about 12
miles (between Mount Everest, 29,028 feet above sea level, and the Chal-
lenger Deep in the Mariana Trench in the Pacific Ocean, 35,800 feet below sea level). But even this is only 1/330 of the earth's radius. On
a 12-inch globe you might feel some roughness by running fingers over
these places. Water fills the ocean basins, and submerges the margins of
the continents. Of the whole surface of the earth, only 29.4 per cent
is land.

The continents and ocean basins are irregularly arranged on the earth.
There is much more land north of the equator than south of it, and 90 per
cent of the land, outside of ice-covered Antarctica, is located in the hemisphere that centers in western France—the Land Hemisphere. But the
continents and oceans have not always been outlined as they are today.
For some million years parts of the continents were covered with thick
masses of ice, as Greenland and Antarctica still are. The ice sheets only
melted back about 25,000 years ago, and some geologists think we are now
in one of the inter-glacial epochs between advances of the ice. Normally,
when rain or snow falls on the land it drains off again to the sea, seeping
through the soil and running through the rivers. But during the glacial
period large quantities of the earth's water were locked up in the ice, so
that sea level was some 300 feet lower than today. It is estimated that if
the ice caps of Greenland and Antarctica should melt, sea level would rise
another 200 feet. When the sea level was lower, North America and Asia
were connected by dry land where today there is Bering Strait; and dry
land also extended from Southeast Asia through the islands to Australia
and beyond. Most of the continental shelves (the submerged continental
margins) were exposed.

Many geologists, furthermore, accept the evidence that the continents
have been drifting apart (Map 1). Some two hundred million years ago
all the land masses were concentrated in one place on the globe. This
continental mass was composed of relatively light rocks, floating on the

CONTINENTAL DRIFT

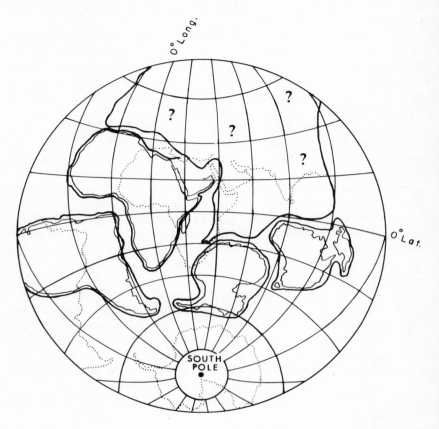

About 130 Million Years Ago

Map 1.

heavier rocks that make up most of the earth's crust.   For reasons not fully
understood, the continental mass broke apart.   North and South America
drifted to the west, wrinkling up mountains along their western edge.   Today rock structures in eastern North America closely resemble those
of Scotland and Scandinavia; and the rock structures of the Brazilian
Highlands resemble those of southern Africa.   In fact the coast of Brazil
seems to fit quite well into the western coast of Africa.   Madagascar and
India drifted eastward, as also did Australia.   India drifted into the southern part of Asia, wrinkling up some of the world's highest mountains along

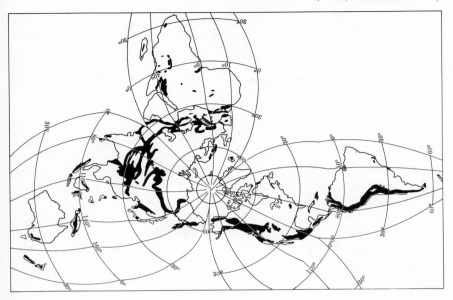

Map 2. The arrangements of mountains and continents.

the line of impact. Regardless of whether this hypothesis (known as the Wegener Hypothesis after its German author) is or is not true, it serves to indicate that even the outlines of the continents and of the surface features that give each continent a distinctive pattern are in process of slow change.

At present the seven continents are tied together by more or less continuous chains of high mountains (Map 2). These mountain ranges, passing from continent to continent or festooned around the oceans in strings of islands, form a framework to which are joined the other major lineaments of the earth's face. Without regard to the complexity of detail at this time, the general distribution pattern of high mountains is one of relative simplicity but profound significance. In a sense the central and southeastern part of Asia is the core of the world's lands, and in the present-day world it is composed of a complex knot of towering mountain ranges. From this core mountain axes extend in three directions: one westward through southern Asia, southern Europe, and northern Africa to the edge of the Atlantic Ocean basin; and one northward and one southward to form, through the American continents and the Pacific margins of the Antarctic Continent, a broken ring of mountains around the basin of the Pacific Ocean. The manner in which the several continental masses are joined to this framework gives to each its own peculiar shape. Yet these various lands, when plotted on a polar projection, appear as three peninsulas radiating from the Asian core (Map 2): Europe and Africa, depending from the western limb of the mountain system; the East Indies, Australia, and New Zealand, depending from the southern limb; and the American continents, attached to the limb which starts northeastward through eastern Asia and crosses into the Western Hemisphere through Alaska. The land masses of the world, therefore, are irregularly arranged with reference to the poles and the divisions of latitude and longitude.

THE PATTERN OF CLIMATES

These major lineaments of the face of the earth are produced by the characteristics of the lithosphere, the rock crust of the earth, and the hydrosphere, the earth's water. Overlying these two spheres is a third one, the atmosphere. This is a thin film of gases clinging to the earth's surface. It is made up of nitrogen (about 78 per cent), oxygen (about 21 per cent), and small amounts of water vapor, carbon dioxide, and other gases. Artificial satellites lifted a few hundred miles above the earth go beyond this film of gases. It is important to keep in mind that if a circle were printed on this page to represent the earth, the whole atmosphere would lie within the width of the black line. Yet it is the average condition of this film of gases that produces the earth's pattern of climates.

The climatic features, unlike the land masses, are regularly arranged with reference to the poles and the divisions of latitude and longitude. If you know the latitude of a place and its longitudinal position (eastern or western side of an ocean; eastern, interior, or western part of a continent), you can describe in a general way the nature of its climate.

Latitude. Because the earth's axis is tilted 66½° from the plane of the earth's orbit around the sun, all the latitudes from 23½° N. (the Tropic of Cancer) to 23½° S. (the Tropic of Capricorn) receive the sun's rays vertically twice during a year. As one proceeds northward from the Tropic of Cancer or southward from the Tropic of Capricorn, the sun's rays reach the surface of the earth at larger and larger angles from the vertical or zenith. Much more energy is received at the earth's surface when the sun's rays are vertical than when they reach the earth at an angle. Very little energy is received when the sun rises only a little above the horizon even at noon.

The atmosphere receives most of its heat from the surface of the earth. The sun's radiant energy passes through the gases of the atmosphere, affecting their temperature only to a small degree. But direct contact with the earth or radiation from the earth does affect the air temperature. Therefore the air has a higher temperature close to the earth, and temperature decreases with altitude. And since the earth is heated more in the low latitudes (within 30° of the equator) than in the high latitudes (60° to the poles), the average annual air temperatures are generally higher at the earth's surface the lower the latitude. If the earth were all land or all water, temperature would correspond quite closely to latitude.

Land and Water. The surface of the earth, however, is anything but uniform. The simple arrangement of temperature by latitude is modified by the irregular arrangement of land and water bodies. Land and water react to the impact of energy from the sun in different ways. Land heats up by day and in summer much more rapidly than does water.* And at night and in winter the land radiates its heat faster than does water. Air over the water, therefore, has more equable temperature than does air over the land. At any given latitude the summers are hotter and the winters are colder over the land than over the water. The greatest extremes of summer heat and winter cold are found in the continental interiors, distant from the moderating effect of the oceans. Ranges of temperature between summer and winter increase with increasing latitude and distance from the sea. A distinction is recognized between *marine* climates and *continental* climates.

There are important differences, also, in the character of ocean water from place to place. Plate 10 (p. 564) shows that the oceans are regularly marked off into regions of warm and cold water, as well as water of moderate temperature. In the Northern Hemisphere the ocean water circulates in a clockwise direction, and in the Southern Hemisphere counterclockwise. Where ocean currents swing away from the continental margins there are back-eddies from the opposite direction, or cold water wells up from underneath. The arrangement of cold and warm water in the oceans is one element of the regularity of climatic features on the earth.

The Jet Streams. Another element of regularity is found in the general circulation of the atmosphere. Much new knowledge concerning the wind currents of the earth has been gained as a result of the development of high-flying airplanes and rockets. The traditional description of the world's wind systems now requires revision in the light of modern knowledge, much of it derived from the International Geophysical Year (1957–1958), when the nations of the world collaborated in simultaneous observations of elements of the world's physical character.

Basic to an understanding of the circulation of the atmosphere are two facts. First is the fact that from the equator as far as 38° of latitude in both hemispheres more energy is received from the sun than is lost by radiation. This is a zone of net build-up of energy. From 38° to the poles more energy is lost by radiation than is received from the sun. This is a zone of net loss of energy. Some mechanism has to exist to equalize

*The reasons for this are outlined in Appendix B, p. 466.

the resulting differences of energy, and this mechanism consists of a transfer of heat from lower to higher latitudes, partly through the ocean currents, partly through movements of the atmosphere.

The second fact is that the earth is a rotating ball, and the atmosphere is a thin film of gases held to the earth by gravity. Because of the earth's rotation, any freely moving body in the Northern Hemisphere tends to curve to the right, and any freely moving body in the Southern Hemisphere tends to curve to the left (see Appendix B, p. 469). On the equator the deflective effect of the earth's rotation is zero, and within ten degrees of the equator the effect is negligible. But beyond 10° of latitude in both hemispheres, if air currents do not move in tight curves it is because some condition of the atmosphere exists to stop the swing to the right or to the left.

The condition that makes air movement in more or less straight lines possible is the uneven distribution of pressure. All moving masses of air in the Northern Hemisphere tend to throw out air to the right, and in the Southern Hemisphere to throw out air to the left. Therefore air piles up and pressure increases to the right of an air current in the Northern Hemisphere, and to the left of an air current in the Southern Hemisphere. The amount of curvature an air current follows before it is held to a more or less straight course by high pressure to the right or left depends on the speed of the air flow and the speed of the rotation of the earth.

The air that starts moving toward higher latitudes in both hemispheres curves to the right or left until further deflection is stopped by a ridge of high pressure—to the right of the air stream in the Northern Hemisphere, and to the left in the Southern Hemisphere. The result is the development of the *subtropical jet streams*. In both hemispheres these jet streams flow eastward between latitudes 30° and 40°, moving farther poleward in summer of the hemisphere and farther equatorward in winter of the hemisphere. The jet streams are flat, ribbon-like flows, moving at speeds of 200 to 300 miles per hour, at elevations between 20,000 and 40,000 feet above the surface of the earth. There are periods when the jet streams move in fairly straight courses toward the east, but there are other periods when the courses are wavy, or when the streams break up into detached pieces (Map 98, p. 418).

Meteorologists have identified two other jet streams in each hemisphere in addition to the well-developed subtropical jet streams. One is the *polar front jet stream*, moving from west to east poleward of latitude 40°, which is strongest in winter of the hemisphere. The other is the *polar night jet stream* which is to be found in winter at very high altitudes moving toward the east along the Arctic Circle and the Antarctic Circle. There is a close connection between the irregular shifts of these jet streams and the weather changes at the surface of the earth.

The Oceanic Whirls. The subtropical jet streams tend to create ridges of high pressure around the world about latitude 30° in both hemispheres. These ridges are the result of the piling up of air to the right of the jet stream in the Northern Hemisphere, and to the left in the Southern Hemisphere. But the ridges of high pressure are broken up over land areas, and are well-developed only over the oceans. The great expanse of the south Pacific Ocean permits the development of a fairly continuous pressure ridge. But even in the Southern Hemisphere, and conspicuously in the Northern Hemisphere, the ridge is broken into cells, each located over the eastern sides of the oceans at about latitude 30°. The maintenance of high pressure in these cells over the oceans not only results from the piling up of air from the jet streams, but also from the periodic arrival at these latitudes of cold air masses of polar origin that have traveled over the surface of the earth.

From these cells of high pressure, surface air moves out in all directions (Plate 12, p. 568). Again because of the deflective effect of the earth's rotation, in the Northern Hemisphere a vast whirl of air results with pressures high to the right of the wind. This is a clockwise whirl. In the Southern Hemisphere pressures are high to the left and the whirls rotate counterclockwise. These great whirls of air, centering over the eastern sides of the ocean basins at about latitude 30° and sweeping over the margins of the continents, are known as *oceanic whirls*. They constitute one of the two basic elements of regularity in the world's prevailing surface winds.

The oceanic whirls are easily identified on the wind maps (Plate 12, p. 568). In the North Atlantic, for example, the air rotating around the high pressure cell forms northeast winds from latitude 30° almost to the equator. North of latitude 10° N., these winds continue to circle around the pressure cell. As they cross the ocean they come from the east rather than the northeast. They approach the southeast coast of the United States from the southeast, and they flow from the Gulf of Mexico onto the continent from the south. North of latitude 30° the air masses of maritime origin forming part of the oceanic whirl continue to curve to the right, coming first from the southwest, then the west, then the northwest. They cross the North Atlantic Ocean as strong westerly and northwesterly winds, and sweep onto the continent of Europe. Continuing to curve to the right they become north winds over the eastern Mediterranean, and northeast again over the Sahara.

Oceanic whirls can be identified in five positions on the earth: centering in the North Atlantic, the South Atlantic, the North Pacific, the South Pacific, and the South Indian. In the North Indian Ocean there is no oceanic whirl, for the continent of Asia occupies the latitudes where the high pressure cell would otherwise form.

The zone of intertropical convergence, where the oceanic whirls of the opposite hemispheres come together, is a zone of much cloudiness and heavy rainfall. The zone of convergence shifts southward in January, corresponding to the southward shift of the jet streams and the high pressure cells. At this season air from the northeast crosses the equator into South America; and northeast winds also cross the equator along the eastern coast of Africa. In July the zone of convergence is north of the equator. At this season an east-moving current of air is generated in the zone of convergence along the eastern sides of the ocean basins—the *equatorial westerlies*. In the eastern Pacific these westerlies strike the Pacific coast of Central America. In the eastern Atlantic a strong westerly current crosses the Guinea Coast of Africa, and then continues across Africa to bring the heavy summer rains to the highlands of East Africa and Ethiopia. In the North Indian Ocean in July, the equatorial westerlies finding no oceanic whirl to impede their movement, reach the southern part of Asia, forming the summer monsoon of that region. In these zones of convergence the violent tropical storms—hurricanes and typhoons—are born.

The Polar Outbursts. The second major element of the world's surface winds is made up of the irregular surges of cold air of polar origin. Over the ice caps of Antarctica and Greenland, over the ice-covered Arctic Ocean, and over the snow-covered northern continents in winter, the air is chilled. When air is chilled it becomes more compact and heavy. This cold heavy air lies close to the ground, piling up as a lens-shaped accumulation over the cold surfaces. The cold air accumulates in this manner until it begins to slide out. The outward movements come in the form of surges, since cold air masses moving away from the center of accumulation will exhaust the pile of cold air. These surges of cold polar air are called *polar outbursts*. They are especially strong and frequent around the margins of Antarctica, but they are also strong in winter around Greenland and the northern continents. There is a close connection between the irregular shifts of the polar-front jet streams and the surges of cold air.

The polar outbursts move over the surface of the earth like drops of water on a window pane. They have steep, rolling fronts, and streamlined tops. The polar outbursts burrow into the poleward parts of the oceanic whirls, and because the cold air is relatively heavy, the lighter maritime air is pushed up. The maritime air climbs part way up the back slopes of the cold air masses. Along the advancing cold fronts there are eddies of maritime air. These eddies rotate counterclockwise in the Northern Hemisphere, and clockwise in the Southern Hemisphere. The cold air masses, pushing forward under these rotating eddies, force a rapid rise of the maritime air. These are the *cyclonic storms*, the whirling storms that form irregularly recurring features of the daily weather maps, and that bring the variable weather characteristic of the middle latitudes.* The movement of a typical cold air mass across North America on successive days is shown on the maps (Map 99, p. 476).

Monsoons. There are certain parts of the earth where the prevailing surface wind direction is reversed between summer and winter. Winds that flow in opposite directions at different times of the year are called *monsoons.* This is derived from an Arabic word, *mausim*, meaning season, and was first applied by the Arabs to the seasonal winds of the Arabian Sea. The traditional explanation of such seasonal shifts of wind direction involves the differential heating of land and water. It has long been taught that during summers when the land is hotter than the ocean, the wind is on-shore; and during winters when the land is colder than the ocean, the wind is off-shore. It is now known that this explanation is much too simple, and, in fact, that monsoons occur in different parts of the world for different reasons.

The classical monsoon region of the world is in Asia south of the Himalaya Mountains, and involves the whole of the Indian Ocean north of the equator and as far as the eastern margin of Africa. This is the so-called Indian Monsoon. It is now believed that the alternation of wind direction in this region is related to the shifts of the subtropical jet stream. All over the world this jet stream moves northward in summer and southward in winter in the Northern Hemisphere. But nowhere else does the course of this jet stream shift so much as it does in South Asia. In winter the jet stream moves all the way to the south of the Himalayas, and in summer it moves back again north of the Highlands of Tibet. In winter, when the jet stream is south of the Himalayas, the piling up of air to its right and the associated rise of pressure results in surface winds from the northeast, similar to the northeast winds of the southern part of the North Atlantic Oceanic whirl. These winds sweep across southern India from the northeast, across the Indian Ocean as far as Africa, and across the equator as far as northern Madagascar. In June, however, this jet stream suddenly breaks up and reforms north of the Highlands of Tibet. At this time the southwest winds of the equatorial westerlies sweep over the North Indian Ocean, across India, and reach the southern side of the Himalaya Mountains.

To the east of the Indian monsoon is another system of winds known as the Malayan monsoon. Here the alternation between winds from the south in the Northern Hemisphere summer and winds from the north in

*Zones of latitude may be described as follows: from the equator to latitude 30° in both hemispheres may be called the *low latitudes;* from 30° to 60° in both hemispheres are the *middle latitudes*, which may be further subdivided into lower middle latitudes and higher middle latitudes; from 60° to the poles in both hemispheres are the *high latitudes.*

the Northern Hemisphere winter affects all the territory between northern Australia and Manchuria. There are only small departures from the general south-north or north-south winds. During the northern summer, air moves from the southeast out of Australia, crosses Indonesia from the southeast and east, crosses Malaya and the mainland of southeast Asia from the southwest, sweeps into South China from the south. During the northern winter air moves from the north across South China, from the northeast across southeast Asia, from the northwest and west across Indonesia, and into northern Australia from the northwest.

The monsoon of East Asia is quite different. Out of Siberia and across Japan in winter come frequent and strong polar outbursts. Although these alternate with winds from other directions during the passage of cyclonic storms, the average wind direction is from the northwest. In summer the oceanic whirl predominates. The southeast winds sweep across Japan and toward the Asian mainland. Although there are occasional interruptions by winds from other directions, the summer average wind is from the southeast. Some meteorologists describe this as a pseudo-monsoon.

Although the monsoons of eastern and southeastern Asia are more complicated than those of North America, a similar pseudo-monsoon can be observed at similar latitudes. The average wind direction of summer in the southeastern United States is from the southeast: the average wind direction of winter is from the northwest. The similarity of the seasonal march of temperature and rainfall at similar latitudes in eastern Asia and eastern North America is striking, although in January the Asian temperatures are some 10° lower than those of North America.

Rainfall. The systems of surface winds are related to the world pattern of rainfall (Plate 12, p. 568). In general the largest annual averages of rainfall are found in parts of the world where different wind systems converge. The interrupted belt of heavy rains in the equatorial regions is related to the convergence of the oceanic whirls along the equator. In the middle latitudes the areas of heavy rains (including snow and other forms of precipitation) are related to the zones of maximum impact between the polar outbursts and the oceanic whirls. Where air masses belonging to different systems converge, a large amount of air is forced to rise. The rising air cools and the water vapor in it condenses. This process forms clouds and rainfall.

The two climatic stations in the world where the highest annual rainfalls have been observed are not in zones of convergence. The world's record is held by a station on the northeast slopes of the island of Kauai, the northernmost of the Hawaiian Islands. Here an average of 476 inches is reported, with a fairly even distribution in all months of the year. The northeast winds on the southern side of the North Pacific oceanic whirl rise on the windward slopes of a mountain. Rainfall produced in this way is known as *orographic* rain.

The second highest average annual rainfall in the world has been recorded at Cherrapunji, a station on the south-facing slopes of the Assam Hills north of Calcutta. During the summer on-shore monsoon the air is forced to rise; it brings incredible amounts of rain. The average rainfall for July at this place is 109 inches. But December, during the time of the off-shore monsoon, averages only 0.2 inches (see the climatic data in Appendix F, pp. 533–541).

Heavy rains in the low latitudes and the lower middle latitudes along the continental east coasts are also produced by occasional violent storms known as tropical cyclones. These storms rotate counterclockwise in the Northern Hemisphere and clockwise in the Southern Hemisphere. They are more than 100 miles across, and there are wind speeds of more than 75 miles per hour. Such storms originate over warm ocean water more than ten degrees from the equator, near the zones of convergence of the oceanic whirls. They move westward in the same course as the oceanic whirl, curving northward near the western sides of the oceans, where they frequently cause damage on the southeastern margins of the continents in the lower middle latitudes (see Appendix B, p. 475). They are known as hurricanes in the North Atlantic and the Caribbean, and also in the eastern Pacific off Mexico; they are known as typhoons in the western Pacific; cyclones over the Bay of Bengal; and willy-willies off Australia. They are most frequent in late summer. In the Bay of Bengal there are about thirteen a year; there are about twenty a year in the western Pacific; there are about three a year that reach northeast Australia.

These storms bring such enormous downpours of rain that in the regions they visit frequently there are always high averages of rainfall in the late summer months. The northward projections of the belt of more than 80 inches into the Bay of Bengal, and across the Philippines to southern Japan are produced by these tropical cyclones. The world's record for rain during a 24-hour period is held by a station near Manila (Baguio, 48 inches).

Climatic Regions. The patterns of temperature, rainfall, and wind direction, together with other climatic elements, combine to form the climatic regions of the world. It should be noted that the traditional divison of the world into temperate, torrid, and frigid zones is unacceptable to geographers; for, in spite of its simplicity, it obscures more important climatic relationships than it reveals. The world's highest and the world's lowest temperatures at low altitudes occur in the so-called temperate zone; the only truly temperate climates in the world occur over the tropical oceans in the so-called torrid zone. Because of these, and of other facts to be noted later, the use of these terms has been dropped.

The system of climatic regions presented in this book is one which was devised by a German geographer, Wladimir Köppen. It is a system based on quantitative definitions, and as such can be applied to any part of the earth where climatic data are available. The definitions and the methods of using the classification are presented in Appendix B; the map of the world's climatic regions is on Plate 11; representative climatic data on which the map is partly based are in Appendix F.

For those who do not wish to make use of the Köppen system as a quantitative classification of climate, the following description of the characteristics of each of the major climates shown on Plate 11 is presented.

Af-Afi	Tropical rainy climate with no cool season, with little range of temperature, and with no dry season or only a short dry season
Am-Ami	
Aw-Awi	Tropical climate with no cool season, with little range of temperature, and with a distinct rainy season and a distinct dry season
BSh	Hot, semiarid climate
BSk-BSk'	Cool, semiarid climate
BWh	Hot, arid climate
BWk-BWk'	Cool, arid climate
Cwbi-Cfbi	High altitude, low latitude climate
Cwa-Cwb	Mid-latitude climate with mild, dry winters and rainy summers
Csa	Mid-latitude climate with mild, rainy winters, and hot, dry summers
Csb	Mid-latitude climate with mild, rainy winters, and cool, dry summers
Cfa	Mid-latitude continental and east coast climate with mild winters and hot summers, and with no dry season
Cfb	Mid-latitude marine climate with mild winters and cool summers, and with no dry season
Cfc	Mid-latitude marine climate with mild winters and short, cool summers, and with no dry season
Dfa	Mid-latitude continental climate with severe winters and hot summers, and with no dry season
Dfb	Mid-latitude continental climate with severe winters and cool summers, and with no dry season
Dfc	Mid-latitude continental climate with severe winters and short, cool summers, and with no dry season
Dwa, Dwb, Dwc	Same as Dfa, Dfb, and Dfc, but with very dry winters
Dfd, Dwd	Same as above, but with extreme low winter temperatures
E	High latitude or high altitude climate with no summers

THE PATTERN OF WATER

The oceans constitute the greatest reservoirs of water on the earth. We have already discussed the relations of the prevailing surface winds and the pattern of average annual rainfall. The air picks up moisture from the oceans by evaporation, and the moving masses of air carry this moisture onto the land in the form of water vapor or clouds. The water vapor is condensed into liquid form as a result of lowering the temperature. The chief way in which air temperature is lowered is by making the air rise. The decrease of pressure with increasing altitude results in a drop of temperature and the formation of the little droplets of water that make up clouds. Water falls from the clouds in the form of rain when the droplets get big enough to fall through the updraft of air (as explained in Appendix B, pp. 467–470). If temperatures are below freezing the water falls as snow, hail, or sleet.

When rain falls on the surface of the land, it will follow one of several courses. Unless the water is frozen in the form of snow or ice some of it will run off over the surface in sheets or rivulets, eventually to be gathered together in rivers. Or some of the water that reaches the surface may be evaporated again. And some of the water sinks into the soil, percolating through the soil particles down into the mantle of broken rock fragments below the soil, and into the cracks in the underlying bedrock. At varying distances below the surface is the zone of saturation. The top of this zone is called the *ground-water table*. Ground water seeps slowly downhill until it comes out at low areas in the surface to form rivers or lakes, maintaining the flow of rivers even when there is no surface run-off. Unless the water is evaporated again, the rivers eventually return to the oceans. This circulation of moisture, partly visible, and partly invisible, is known as the *hydrologic cycle* (Appendix D, pp. 519–520).

Only the water that is in the soil available to the roots of plants is effective in supporting vegetation. Any conditions that increase run-off or evaporation decrease the effectiveness of rainfall. Or any conditions that permit the water to sink too rapidly through the soil also reduce the effectiveness of the precipitation. The water that does remain in the soil is drawn into the roots of plants and passes up through the stem and branches to the leaves. From the leaves water in the form of water vapor is transpired to the atmosphere. The combined loss of moisture from the ground to the atmosphere by evaporation and transpiration is known as *evapotranspiration*. It is possible to estimate the total amount of water under specified conditions of soil moisture, temperature, and plant cover that would be lost by evapotranspiration. Where the potential loss of water is greater than the amount received and stored the result is a condition of moisture deficiency.   Then the moisture in the soil and in the ground water decreases and the ground water table sinks.   When more moisture is supplied by rainfall than is lost by evapotranspiration the result is an increase of soil moisture and a rise of the ground-water table.   Since the ground-water table governs the surface of lakes and the flow of permanent streams, these surface water bodies are closely influenced by the balance of moisture.

THE PATTERNS OF VEGETATION AND SOIL

The arrangement of vegetation and soil on the earth is related not only to climate and water, but also to the pattern of surface features.   The broader global patterns of vegetation correspond in a general way with those of climate, and consequently they reveal a certain basic regularity. But, like the climate, these regular patterns are modified by the irregular arrangement of surface features.   The so-called *edaphic* factor in the arrangement of vegetation pertains not only to the relief of the surface but also to the nature of the soil material.*

Soil is produced by the interaction of physical and chemical processes operating on inorganic rock fragments with the organic material supplied by plants and animals.   Insofar as soil reflects the characteristics of the underlying rock—the *parent material*—its distribution over the earth is irregular, corresponding to the irregular patterns of surface features and rocks of the earth's crust (the *lithosphere*).   But where the soils reflect the characteristics of the vegetation cover, the pattern of arrangement is regular.   Actual soils reveal, perhaps to a greater extent than any other natural feature, the interplay of the principles of regularity and irregularity.

The major categories of zonal soils are shown on Map 70 (soils of the western part of the Soviet Union) and Map 62 (soils of the United States). The soil-forming processes and the global categories of soil are described on pp. 284–289.

THE GROUPS OF REGIONS

The habitats of the world are defined in terms of the interaction of these various processes, including those of physics, chemistry, and biology, as modified through unplanned human action.   There are nine major categories of habitat regions.   Each is a recurring areal association of surface features, climate, water, vegetation, and soil.   A recurring association is one that is found in essentially similar form in different parts of the earth.

*The major categories of vegetation are shown on Plate 10, p. 564. They are described briefly in Appendix E, pp. 527–529.

The first eight groups of regions are defined in terms of associations of climate, water, vegetation, and soil, and therefore these groups develop a regular pattern over the earth—a pattern that is generalized in Figure 12 (p. 424). Because the arrangement of these eight groups is regular, it is possible to predict the kind of habitat that will be found in any particular part of the earth if one knows the latitude and whether the place is on the western side, the interior, or the eastern side of a continent. The ninth group, on the other hand, includes the high mountains of the world, and is, therefore, irregular in its arrangement with reference to the poles and the latitudes. The first eight groups are subdivided irregularly by the arrangement of surface features other than high mountains. And the ninth group is subdivided regularly by the vertical arrangement of climate and vegetation. The nine groups are outlined in Tables 1 through 3.

TABLE I. Habitats

GROUPS OF HABITAT REGIONS	CLIMATE AND WATER		VEGETATION	SOIL
I. The Dry Lands	BW	Water deficient at all seasons	Desert	Sierozem
II. The Tropical Forest Lands	Af, Am, Aw	Water adequate at all seasons, or deficient during a dry season	Rainforest and Seasonal Forest	Laterites
III. The Tropical Woodlands and Savannas	Aw, Bsh	Water deficient during the dry season	Woodlands and savannas, parklands	Laterites
IV. The Mediterranean Woodlands	Csa, Csb, BShs	Water deficient during a dry season	Evergreen woodlands	Mostly immature soils
V. The Mid-Latitude Mixed Forest Lands	Cfa, Cfb, Dfa, Dfb	Water adequate at all seasons	Seasonal forests	Podsols, Brown Forest Soils, Red and Yellow Forest Soils
VI. The Mid-Latitude Grasslands	Cfa, Dfa, BSk	Water deficient during a dry season, or adequate at all seasons	Grasslands, parklands	Black Prairie Soil, Chernozem, Chestnut-Brown Soil, Brown Soil
VII. The Boreal Forest Lands	Dfc, Dfd, Dw	Water adequate at all seasons, or deficient during a dry season	Seasonal forests, woodlands	Podsols
VIII. The Polar Lands	E	Water deficient during the cold season, or deficient at all seasons	Tundra, Polar desert	Tundra Soils
IX. The Mountain Lands	—	—	—	—

TABLE 2. Percentage of Land Area in the Nine Groups

	NORTH AMERICA	SOUTH AMERICA	AFRICA	EUROPE	ASIA	AUSTRALIA NEW ZEALAND PHILIPPINES EAST INDIES	ANTARCTICA	WORLD
I	9	8	34	1	24	13	—	18
II	3	39	9	—	11	8	—	10
III	1	31	51	—	3	32	—	17
IV	1	(T)[a]	1	6	(T)	10	—	1
V	15	2	(T)	37	5	9	—	7
VI	11	7	2	19	12	22	—	9
VII	20	—	—	21	18	—	—	10
VIII	24	—	—	5	7	—	100	16
IX	16	13	3	11	20	6	—	12

[a](T) indicates less than one half of one per cent.

TABLE 3. Percentage of World Population by Groups
and Continents about 1963

	NORTH AMERICA	SOUTH AMERICA	AFRICA	EUROPE	ASIA	AUSTRALIA NEW ZEALAND PHILIPPINES EAST INDIES	WORLD
I	3	3	12	—	8	—	6
II	7	47	19	—	38	14	28
III	1	2	42	—	1	1	5
IV	7	5	11	16	0	6	5
V	53	2	1	74	42	75	42
VI	11	16	5	3	7	3	7
VII	0	—	—	1	0	—	(T)[a]
VIII	0	—	—	(T)	0	—	(T)
IX	18	25	10	6	4	1	7

[a](T) indicates less than one half of one per cent.

INTRODUCTION

Culture

THE NINE GROUPS of regions that make up the human habitats have a significance independent of the part they play as natural surroundings of man. In the fields of physical geography, including biogeography, they may be studied as examples of the interaction of physical and biotic processes leading to the differentiation of the surface of the earth into *ecosystems* —that is, areas within which there are associations of interacting natural features. When man enters the scene, either as a user of earth resources or as a creator or modifier of ecosystems, the resulting divisions of the surface of the earth may be described as habitats. The nine groups of habitat regions are defined for the purpose of clarifying the changing significance of the habitat to man.

The significance to man of the physical and biotic features of the habitat is a function of the attitudes, objectives, and technical skills of man himself. Attitudes, objectives, and technical skills are traits that form parts of the traditional way of living. Each human group is distinguished by differences in these traditional forms of behavior. Each group has its own peculiar set of beliefs, its own institutions, its customs, its familiar foods, its consecrated system of moral values, and its language in which these things are recorded and communicated. The tendency is to resist change. The aggregate of all these customary forms of thought, communication, and action which characterize a group of people is what may be described as a *culture*.

RACE AND CULTURE

A clear distinction must be made between race and culture. Race is a biological matter. Racial characteristics are hereditary, passed on from parents to their children.   Culture, however, is learned.   Young people learn from contact with parents and other children to adopt the accepted ways of behavior of the social group.   By a process of education such things as language, religious beliefs, or technical skills are passed on from generation to generation.   An individual is born into a race; but he learns to live in accordance with the ways of a culture.   In nonscientific writings race and culture are not always clearly distinguished.

To define a race is not a simple matter.   The popular distinction of races on the basis of skin color is not accepted by the anthropologists.   Skin color is only one of a number of hereditary physical traits.   There are also such traits as stature; head form; hair color, texture, and form; eye color and shape; and nose shape.   These are not necessarily associated with skin color.   There are actually no "pure" races.

The anthropologist, Carleton S. Coon, defines five chief races as follows: 1. *Australoids*, including the Australian natives, the Melanesians, and the Negritos who are scattered from the Philippines to the Andaman Islands and mainland India; 2. *Mongoloids*, found today in eastern Asia, Polynesia, and among the descendants of the native Indians of the Americas; 3. *Caucasoids,* including the Europeans and people all over the earth of European ancestry, the people of North Africa and Southwest Asia, the people of India, and the Ainus of Japan; 4. *Capoids*, the Bushmen and Hottentots who were living in the southern part of Africa when the Europeans first came upon them; and 5. *Congoids* (or *Negroids*) the people of the Congo Basin, including the Negroes and Pygmies of African origin.*

The world is full of misinformation about racial inheritance.   History records many examples of the attempt by self-conscious human groups or societies to explain assumed pre-eminence on the basis of racial superiority. The great Christian principle that all men are brothers has never been widely accepted, even among Christians.   The fact that this principle expresses what scientists are step by step proving to be a fundamental truth does not alter the fact that belief in racial purity and superiority is a very common cultural attitude.

Culture is not hereditary.   The individual learns to behave as he is taught by those around him.   He learns the technical skills of his group; he learns how to make use of the familiar tools; he learns to accept the framework of the social, political and economic institutions; he learns to think in terms of the religious beliefs of the group, and to express himself through the accepted art forms.   And, above all, he learns to communicate, even to think, in terms of a particular language.   These are all parts of a culture, or a way of living.   Because a culture is passed on by a learning process, its traits tend to be preserved with little change.   Cultural stability and uniformity are much more common than revolutionary change.

*Carleton S. Coon, *The Origin of Races* (New York, 1962).

PREHISTORIC CULTURE DEVELOPMENT

The genus *homo* has existed on the earth for something like two million years. The earliest men appeared in a tropical zone extending from central Africa to southeast Asia. For hundreds of thousands of years the primitive tribes occupied this zone, depending for a living on hunting, fishing, and collecting the seeds and fruits of wild plants. Although knowledge of fire was gained very early, these people could not rekindle their fires easily. Very early, too, the tribes of primitive men were joined by the dog.

The only surviving species of genus *homo* is *homo sapiens*, from which all of mankind is descended. This species, according to the anthropologists, appeared some 50,000 years ago in the same tropical zone that had been the habitat of man for a long time. Man was still a hunter, fisher, and collector; his tools were few; his numbers rather strictly limited by the availability of wild game and edible plants. But unlike any other living creatures, man had the capacity to communicate by language in which abstract ideas or mental images could be represented by word sounds. Because of language man could retain the memory of past experiences. He could learn from experience, and pass on his knowledge to others. This culture period is known as the *Paleolithic*.

As Paleolithic man increased in numbers the tribes of hunters and fishers began to spread out from the center of origin. In the search for better hunting grounds some pushed westward into Europe, some went southward in Africa, some migrated along the land bridge which at that time led to Australia and the islands of Melanesia. Others went northeastward in Asia crossing the peninsula that connected Asia with North America. They fanned out over North America and went on southeastward to the southernmost part of South America. This spread of man over the earth took place before there was any knowledge of agriculture, or any domestic animals other than the dog.

During the 50,000 years since the appearance of *homo sapiens* there have been three periods of radical culture change, when the relationships of man to his habitats were fundamentally altered. The first of these was the agricultural revolution, which began about 8000 B.C. The first farmers were living in the highland country that borders the valley of the Tigris-Euphrates and the Persian Gulf on the northeast. Here several native plants were cultivated: wheat, barley, peas, lentils, and vetch. And two native wild animals were domesticated: sheep and goats. When men began to cultivate crops instead of collecting the seeds of wild plants, a different kind of habitat was necessary: the farmers began to move down from the highlands and through the valleys onto the vast, alluvial plains that we now call Mesopotamia. Here they added another crop—the date palm. And they made three basic inventions: the wheel, the plow, and the loom.

There were other parts of the world where farming was developed independently. In Southeast Asia the farmers were the first to raise taro, yams, sugar cane, bananas, and rice. They also domesticated pigs and chickens. Also in southern and central Asia, horses and camels were domesticated, and the ass was domesticated in Ethiopia. Quite separately the people who had migrated into the Americas first planted several crops: maize, potatoes, manioc, tobacco, squash, and cacao. The only domestic animals in the Americas were llamas in the Andes, guinea pigs in Colombia, and turkeys in North America. However, most of the so-called Indians of the Americas had no domestic animals other than the dog, knew nothing of the wheel or the true arch, and nothing of the art of writing. Yet in Peru they invented every known method of weaving textiles. The anthropologists describe the cultures that include knowledge of crops and animals as *Neolithic*.

Neolithic peoples, wherever they appeared, were stronger and better able to provide themselves with food than the Paleolithic peoples. The latter were pushed out of the places that were suited to agriculture or grazing, and survived only where the climate and surface were unsuited for farming: Tasmania, southern Africa, the southernmost part of South America, and small isolated spots in mountainous areas or in the Polar Regions. As the new way of living was brought to an area previously occupied by hunters and fishers there was conflict and turmoil. But in the long run the farmers and herders were the winners.

CULTURE DEVELOPMENT IN HISTORIC TIMES

The next great revolution in human living took place at the dawn of written history. At six widely scattered parts of the earth, groups of men established the first "civilizations" based on law and government. The first two of these appeared about 4000 B.C. One was in Mesopotamia, where Sumeria and Babylonia were situated; the other was in the Nile Valley of Egypt. Along both of these alluvial lowlands there were small village communities of farming people, each self-sufficient. Each family worked to provide its own food, or the food of the village community. There was no surplus, but only annual variations between what was barely enough and what was not enough to prevent famine. In these valleys farmers had to irrigate their crops; but since there was no common control of water, the villages downstream were at the mercy of those higher up. The formulation of codes of water laws and the organization of a government to administer the law were a revolutionary step forward.

For the first time the villages could raise more food than could be consumed locally. The surplus could be sold or exchanged for the products of another place. And for the first time a new class of city people could be supported—people who did not have to spend all their time just providing their own food. These city people could become merchants, or priests, or government administrators. For the first time part of mankind, even if a small part, was free to devote its attention to the study of the stars and the observation of the earth, and to speculate about the meaning of what it saw.

Early civilizations based on law and government appeared in four other parts of the world. The Indus civilization developed in the valley of the Indus River in what is today Pakistan. Chinese civilization had its beginnings in the valley of the Wei River, a tributary of the Hwang (Yellow River). In Yucatán and Guatemala the Maya civilization appeared. And in the mountains of Peru the Andean civilization developed.

This revolutionary change in the way of living also made possible a very great increase in the population. The poorer, more primitive people outside the civilized areas were attracted by the new luxury. Their prosperous, well-fed neighbors seemed fat and lazy to the hungry nomadic warriors. Repeatedly there were conquests; but always the conquerors were absorbed by the conquered, adopting their ways and discarding their own. Such is the story of the conquests of Babylonia by the Assyrians, of the conquests of China by the people from Manchuria and Mongolia, of the conquests of the Maya by the Toltecs, and of the conquests of the Toltecs by the Aztecs. Even Egypt, surrounded by deserts, was subject to invasion. Only the Empire of the Incas was so isolated that no outsiders ever could challenge its armies until the arrival of the Spaniards.

For thousands of years after the rise of these early civilizations the world saw no fundamental change in culture. There were the same methods of transporting things from place to place, the same dependence for power on human or animal muscles, on wind, or on falling water. There were the same agricultural methods, the same basic skills used in manufacturing things by hand. There was the same division of mankind into the well-to-do minority of city people, and the great majority of farm workers on whose incessant labor the whole system was based. Most of the people had no time to lift their eyes from the land. Only a minority had the leisure to enjoy luxury, or to devote themselves to scholarship, or religion, or art.

For most of this time the various cultures of the world remained distinct. If a Marco Polo traveled to China and came back to Europe with reports of the burning of black rocks, the people at home refused to believe him. In terms of economy, or the way of making a living, the Oriental cultures from India to China were built around the cultivation of rice, and the American cultures were built around maize. The Mediterranean cultures of Greece and Rome were based on wheat and barley, and these grains, along with rye and oats, became the basis of living north of the Alps. Cattle and domestic animals were used throughout Europe, Africa, and Asia. Not until the great age of exploration that started in the fifteenth century did the Europeans make contact with all the other peoples of the earth. Often the contact meant destruction for the simpler peoples. But it also meant that such American crops as maize, potatoes, and manioc were spread over the parts of the world suitable for them; and that to America were brought wheat, barley, rye, oats, rice, coffee, sugar cane, citrus fruits, grapes, and many other things. To America also came the Old World's domestic animals.

The culture of the people of Europe, at that time, was developed largely from Greek and Roman sources. What we may call Occidental, or Western, culture, as it had developed by the end of the sixteenth century, was essentially an "illiterate agriculturism." With the traditional farm techniques widely in use, yields per acre were small (wheat, for instance, gave only from six to ten bushels to the acre); and each community was entirely dependent on the food products of its immediate vicinity. It was a system of local self-sufficiency, of economic independence for small areas. Because transportation overland was slow and costly, only luxury goods of high value could be brought from distant places, and such goods were of interest only to a small minority of well-to-do people. Local crop failure meant famine, even if supplies were abundant in some neighboring area perhaps less than a hundred miles away. Only where sailing ships could bring bulky products to seaports could commerce reach out to the foods and raw materials of many distant places. Especially in England, and around the continental shores of the North Sea, commercial towns made their appearance early, and to these places came not only the goods but also the ideas of many people all around the world's oceans. Basically it was a society dominated by the land-owning aristocracy. Associated with the aristocracy were the officers of the army, the priests of the church, the higher civilian officers of the government, perhaps a few of the more lucky artists and scholars. But the majority were illiterate, ill-fed, ill-clad, and without rights or powers with respect to decisions of political policy. The land was divided into vast private estates. The many, whose endless toil supported the whole system, were clustered about the great castles, or within the walled towns where soldiers could give protection.

All of this is now in process of change. Another of the great revolutions of culture history is taking place, and we live in the midst of the turmoil, confusion, and conflict which inevitably accompany such change. Actually there are two revolutions in human living which are going on at about the same time, but not always in the same areas. These are the *Industrial Revolution* and the *Democratic Revolution*.

THE INDUSTRIAL REVOLUTION

January 5, 1769, is a date of profound importance, for on that day James Watt patented his first successful steam engine. This was the first important use of controlled inanimate power. In 1785 a steam engine was first used to run the machinery of a textile mill at Popplewick, near Nottingham in England. Early in the nineteenth century a steam engine was used to pull cars on a railroad; but it was not until 1825 that the first passenger railroad began operation—between Stockton and Darlington in England. The first steamship crossed the Atlantic in 1819.

This was just the beginning. The change from human and animal muscles, wind, and falling water to controlled inanimate power appeared first in Great Britain. It then spread to the countries of Western Europe, and rapidly to the English-speaking countries of other continents. Once the basic techniques of experimental science and engineering had been mastered, new control over the forces of the physical earth came at a faster and faster rate, until now we have taken the first steps toward the use of controlled nuclear power. All the mechanical aspects of life have been changed, and where these changes have occurred man is no longer a lifter and mover. Inanimate power applied to manufacturing industry has so immeasurably increased man's capacity to produce useful things from earth resources that it has now become mechanically possible for all people to live in greater material comfort than was possible for kings in centuries past. Inanimate power applied to agriculture has rendered time-honored farm techniques obsolete, and has transformed lands once rated as poor into lands of high potential productivity. Transportation has been so completely changed that now, for the first time in human history, it is possible to transport vast quantities of foods and other materials from one part of the earth to another. The capacity of man to produce and to move his products about has been increasing at a more and more rapid rate for about a century and a half.

The Industrial Revolution has brought with it numerous changes in the relation of people to the land. For the first time in history the presence of coal underground became a significant factor in the location of people. With power furnished by steam engines, large industrial establishments could produce not only the essentials of life but also what were once the luxuries, in much greater quantities and at much lower cost per unit than had ever been possible before. Quickly the luxuries came into such common use that these new items became necessities. The traditional prestige of the owners of the land was challenged by the new economic and political power of the owners of capital; that is, of the tools or machines with which people worked.

The new system raised the general level and security of living. Not that everyone could be free from wants. In fact, one of the peculiar traits of the new way of living is the continued expenditure of effort to increase the wants, and so the frustrations, of the people. But, compared with the way of living in the pre-industrial society, the variety and certainty of the foods, the quality of the clothing, and the adequacy of shelter were all raised to an unprecedented level while the hours of labor were decreased.

The unprecedented scale on which goods were exchanged in the new system gave significance to locations where routes of travel converge. Here cities grew. Great cities—that is, cities of more than a million inhabitants —made their appearance for the first time in history. London passed a million in 1802; Paris about 1850; New York about 1870; Vienna in 1878; Berlin in 1880; Tokyo, Chicago, and Philadelphia about 1890; Calcutta in 1900; Buenos Aires about 1906. In 1965 there were well over one hundred great cities in the world.

The use of controlled inanimate power made these cities possible. Prior to the use of such power so many people in such a small area could not have been supplied with food. But with the development of railroads and ocean ships, an urban population was able to devote itself to commerce, manufacturing, and arts and sciences, or to serving other people; and such non-food-producing people could be supplied with food from distant sources of supply so scattered that local crop failure had little effect. The urban people can produce so much beyond their own needs that they have plenty to exchange with those who supply them with things they lack. But never before the present time has there been such a demand for the raw materials of the earth. The mining of ores and fuels, the cutting of forests, and the exploitation of all resources have proceeded on a scale never before imagined.

The new industrial society by its essential nature was global in its scope, international in its needs. Local self-sufficiency had to be abandoned for world-wide economic interdependence. Society had the possibility of building with all the varied resources of the earth; but in so doing, society became vulnerable to any natural or human disturbance of the steady flow of traffic along the new lines of transportation. The old economic, social, political, or military forms became insufficient because the new society could accept no limitations but the globe itself.

The industrial society had its origins around the shore of the North Sea in Europe. In Britain, northern France, and parts of neighboring countries, the Industrial Revolution introduced the new way of living early in the nineteenth century. The change in this area can now be studied only in the history books. But the transformation did not stop there. The attitudes, objectives, and technical skills of the industrial society were quickly adopted and further developed in Anglo-America and Australia-New Zealand. The culture change pushed against opposition into the western part of Germany, the northern part of Italy, and the northeast corner of Spain. The new skills have been enthusiastically adopted by the Soviet Union and Japan. Today the conflict and turmoil introduced by this revolution are in process of transforming Latin America. Even the most remote parts of the world are feeling the effects of what is now called "economic development," and the "under-developed" countries of the world are demanding assistance in a world-wide attack on pre-industrial poverty. The immediate effect is to make the contrasts between rich and poor countries greater than ever before.

THE DEMOCRATIC REVOLUTION

Meanwhile another revolutionary change in human living has been going on. The Democratic Revolution consists essentially of a revolt against special privilege, and expresses the demand that each individual be treated with dignity and in accordance with law. The revolt is directed against inherited power, and against power or privilege granted on the basis of social status, race, or creed. The beginnings of the Democratic Revolution were also made around the shores of the North Sea—in Great Britain, in the Netherlands, and in France.

There are five basic principles in the Democratic Revolution. First is the right of every individual to equal treatment before the law. Second, the individual has the right to protection from the arbitrary acts of those in authority. Third is the right of self-conscious groups of people to select their own form of government, and the right of the individual members of the group to be represented where laws are made or taxes levied. The right to select representatives and to record opinion on issues of policy by secret ballot is fourth; and fifth is the right to free access to knowledge and to the free discussion of the issues of public policy. Government is not something forcibly imposed by a minority; rather it is to be based on majority opinion—the 51 per cent principle, as opposed to the veto principle. In the long history of mankind there has been no more profound change in the status of the individual. This is the most revolutionary idea to appear in many thousands of years.

THE INDUSTRIAL SOCIETY, THE PRE-INDUSTRIAL SOCIETY, AND THE SOVIET SOCIETY

As a result of the twin revolutions now going on, Occidental culture has been sharply divided, and all the other cultures of the world have been modified in one way or another.

Where the Industrial Revolution and the Democratic Revolution have both gone on rapidly, the culture has been most profoundly affected. In

Great Britain, after bitter civil warfare, the new principles became firmly established, even though set in the traditional framework of a titled aristocracy. In France, the French Revolution eliminated the landed aristocracy. Both revolutions have gone forward rapidly in the Scandinavian countries, and in Belgium and the Netherlands. But the revolutionary changes touched only western Germany, only northern Italy, only a corner of Spain, only the Bohemian part of Czechoslovakia. Elsewhere both revolutions moved rapidly in the English-speaking world. At the present time both are moving into Latin America. The ideas of the Democratic Revolution are sweeping Africa and Asia.

Naturally these changes are resisted by those who benefit from the old order. It is difficult to resist the tremendous economic productivity and military power brought by the Industrial Revolution; and, in fact, the new technology is being eagerly learned throughout the world. But the Democratic Revolution meets strong reaction in those places where the power of the ruling groups was great. Fascism can be described as an attempt to adopt the new technology but at the same time to deny the principles of democracy. Communism starts with an attack on privilege, even to the forceful liquidation of the landowning class. But it proceeds to set up a new and equally rigid class structure, with power and privilege going to members of one political party. In these terms the communist countries represent a reaction against the most profound revolutionary movement of our time.

Occidental culture, therefore, has been divided into three chief parts. The *industrial society* is that part in which the twin revolutions have gone forward most rapidly—today incomparably the most prosperous and powerful part of the world, and the part in which the individual has the greatest freedom. The *pre-industrial society* is that part in which the traditional forms of economy and privilege remain. And the *soviet society* is that part currently dominated by the Communist Party.

These changes have had a tremendous impact on the other cultures of the world—the non-Occidental cultures. The world's simpler cultures have been all but wiped out during the past few centuries as a result of contacts with Occidentals. Consider the case of a hunting people, where the number of hunters is in delicate balance with the supply of game animals. Into such a community the Occidental trader comes to establish a trading post. He sells firearms, among other items, in exchange for furs. But firearms quickly upset the balance of hunters and game, and very soon, because of lack of food, the hunters are forced to abandon the land they once occupied. The new technology has resulted in an exhaustion of the resource base. Around the trading post, or around a mission station, the poverty-stricken remnants of the hunting people are clustered, an easy prey to the white man's diseases against which they had developed no previous immunity.

Contact of the Occidentals with the more complex cultures of the Orient has also brought changes of enormous significance. All the countries from India and Indonesia to China and Japan are in various ways making use of the new industrial productivity. They have accepted enough democracy, also, so that they demand equality of treatment in international affairs, and an end to their former status as colonies, subservient to European powers. Today communism and democracy, in this densely populated area, are locked in a struggle for the control of men's minds.

THE INDUSTRIAL SOCIETY AND POPULATION

One of the far-reaching results of the growth of the industrial society has been the increase of population. Before the beginning of the nineteenth century the population of Europe, for example, was increasing slowly from about 100,000,000 in 1650 to about 140,000,000 in 1750, to about 187,000,000 in 1800. Birth rates were high, but so were death rates. Deaths, especially of children, were due to lack of hygiene, to poor nutrition, and to poverty. Famines and epidemics prevented any very rapid increase of the population. But during the eighteenth and nineteenth centuries population suddenly expanded: cities burst from inside the ancient walls that had long protected them; forests were cleared and new farms established farther and farther from the market centers. By 1900 there were 400,000,000 people in Europe and by the middle of the century there were nearly 600,000,000 people.

Not only did population grow in Europe, but from that continent came one of the greatest migrations of history. More than 50,000,000 people left Europe in the century after 1846. Most of them poured into the United States, but large numbers also went to Argentina and Brazil in South America, to Canada, Australia, and New Zealand, and to many other places. Between 1775 and 1950 the population of the United States increased from 2,500,000 to over 150,000,000—a growth which has no equal in all history.

The growth of population with industrialization is a common phenomenon. The industrial way of living brings better food supplies, less danger of local famines, larger economic opportunity, an increase of literacy and education, and better hygiene and sanitation. The result is a drop in the mortality rate, especially among children—a drop that began slowly in the early nineteenth century and continues at an increasingly rapid rate. Birth rates at first remain high, but after a lag they too begin to decline at a more and more rapid rate. The net result is a period of very rapid population increase, followed by a decline in the rate of growth, and finally the achievement of a nearly static population again. The whole cycle has been passed through in parts of Western Europe. It is just beginning in the Soviet Union, however; and what will happen following the industrialization of China, India, and Java remains a major issue not only in the economic problems of the world but also in the problems of political reorganization.

The period of expanding population was an extraordinarily prosperous one in the Western world, especially in those overseas countries where Europeans were able to move out into new first-class lands, as in the United States. As cities grew and markets for food products were constantly increasing, pioneer settlers moved onto new land from which the very scanty native population had been all but completely removed. Railroads were extended to provide cheap access to markets. As new settlements appeared, as new railroads were built, as new towns were established, and as population as a whole continued to grow, there was a steadily increasing market for the manufactured products of the cities. Steady expansion—interrupted, to be sure, by panics and depressions, but nevertheless always going on to new heights—was the basic characteristic of the nineteenth century capitalist society. And in both country and city the increase of population and the spread of settlement brought about a great increase in land values—the so-called "unearned increment" of the economists. This increase of land value is the basis not only of many large fortunes but also of a vast number of small ones.

Between the two world wars, especially in the period of the depression, people were forced to take a new look at the industrial society. With no new empty pioneer land suitable for farm colonization, and in the face of rapid population increase, questions were raised about the capacity of the earth to support many more people. But while the economic institutions were shaken, the scientists and engineers continued their research studies and proceeded to the development of new machines and new techniques to support the increasing population.

Since World War II the revolution in agriculture in the United States has been spectacular. A farm worker in the years from 1935 to 1939 could produce enough food to feed himself and ten others. In the 1960's, however, he could feed himself and nearly thirty others. The great problem of the future is to apply the new technology and especially to spread its use to areas now economically underdeveloped. This involves readjustments in many other aspects of our culture.

Under all the confusion and uncertainty of this extraordinary period of human history in which we are privileged to live there is the fundamental fact that no human society can long survive that fails to establish workable connections with the resources of the land. Even our highly productive technical skills will not insure survival if we squander the essential raw materials of the earth without thought of their replacement. Many of the simpler cultures have been more successful in the establishment of permanently workable connections with the land they occupy. In the United States we have used forests, minerals, and soils at rates which, if continued, cannot fail to bring us to disaster. Even the much publicized "substitutes" developed during World War II by the chemical industries require the use of raw materials from the earth.

Whether the resources of the earth are sufficient to maintain a permanent industrial society in which all the world's people might participate is a question. There are some who insist that if earth resources are used in accordance with the best techniques, there is "enough and to spare,"* and that only the wasteful methods dictated by the division of the earth into sovereign states, each desiring self-sufficiency, or by the nineteenth-century system of exploitation for private gain, or by the wars on the scale of those in the modern era, can destroy resources so fast that man may again be faced by basic lacks. On the other hand, there are others who quote the enormous figures of production which would be necessary if all the world's people were raised to what is commonly described as a minimum standard. To provide all the world's people with such a standard would, according to a United Nations committee, require increases of production of the following order: cereals, 50 per cent; meat, 90 per cent; milk and other dairy products, 125 per cent; vegetable oils, 125 per cent; and fruits and vegetables, 300 per cent.† The question is whether our capitalist economy or any other system could manage to develop and maintain such vast increases in food production at sufficiently low cost. The answer is not clear.

Before these problems of social science can be studied profitably, it is essential to examine the present distribution of people in the world and their relations with the resources of the land. For what befalls mankind in the centuries ahead will, in part, flow from the present; and, similarly, to understand the present it is necessary to go back to origins and trace developments. The present pattern of people is obviously not a static thing; it is a stage in a process of which the two basic elements are the human culture and the land.

HABITAT AND CULTURE

In the chapters that follow we shall examine the characteristics of each of the nine groups of habitat regions. These characteristics result from the interplay of surface features, climate, water, vegetation, and soil.

*Kirtley F. Mather, *Enough and to Spare* (New York, 1944).

†Quoted in Guy Irving Burch and Elmer Pendell, *Population Roads to Peace or War* (Washington, D. C., 1945) p. 30.

Then in each region we shall examine the record of man's experience with the problems of making a living from earth resources. The changing significance of the habitat with changes in the culture is the central theme, the variations of which run as a connecting thread through the whole book. In the final chapter we shall bring together some of the concepts concerning population and resources in an attempt to see more clearly what kind of data are needed to estimate the population capacity of different parts of the earth.

At the back of the book there are seven appendices, each dealing topically in condensed outline form with one of the systematic aspects of geography. There are lists of books and articles at the end of each appendix, and in Appendix G the references are arranged for each of the groups of regions.

GROUP I

The Dry Lands

WATER AND SUNLIGHT are the basic needs of life. In the dry lands of the earth there is abundant sunlight, but the supply of water is small. Over vast areas life forms can gain a foothold only by persistent struggle against drought, or through ability to endure long periods without water and to carry on the life processes hurriedly and vigorously during those rare periods when water is available. In those spots in the dry lands where water is present a most amazing exuberance of life exists.

Man too concentrates his activities on these wet spots. His problem is constantly to maintain or enlarge his supplies of water. Yet for all his efforts an almost negligible proportion of the deserts has proved permanently habitable. The rich green of the oasis vegetation and the teeming activity of its numerous inhabitants are set in striking contrast against a background of barren solitudes. Beyond the sharp line which separates the land of life from the land of death one enters another world, a strange and unnatural one for those who are familiar with the abundance of growing things where rainfall is adequate. Here the land needs only water to make it bloom, but, lacking only water, it has remained a wilderness.

The Habitat

DESERT CLIMATE AND DESERT VEGETATION

The basic fact concerning the regions of Group I is that they are deficient in moisture. Much more water would evaporate during the average year than is supplied by the rainfall. In most deserts rains come only at infrequent and irregular intervals, many years elapsing between showers. When rain does fall, it comes in the form of cloudbursts, tremendously heavy downpours sometimes accompanied by hail and lasting several hours or even several days. Damage by floods, strange as it may seem, is a characteristic occurrence in deserts; for the heavy rains are all the more destructive because of the lack of well-defined stream channels, the sparsity of vegetation, the hard-packed soil, and the character of the buildings and other human works that are not made to withstand much water.

Very few parts of the world are truly rainless, although portions of the

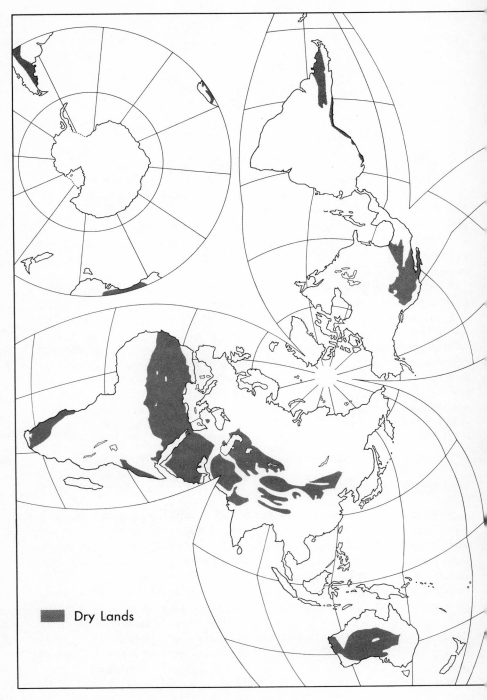

Dry Lands

Map 3.

Libyan Desert and of the Atacama Desert approach this condition. In all deserts the hills and mountains receive more rain than the flatter lands. Over some of the higher ranges clouds may hang most of the time, supporting a little green pasturage in the cloud zone throughout the year; but even here the rule of desert rainfall is irregularity and uncertainty.

Temperatures in the dry lands vary considerably according to the latitude. In the poleward portions of the deserts, especially in the Northern Hemisphere, the winters are very cold. At lower latitudes, however, are found the highest air temperatures ever recorded at the face of the earth. Death Valley, in California, formerly held the record with a temperature of 134.1° recorded on July 10, 1913.* But on September 13, 1922 an even higher temperature was recorded at Azizia in Libya, about twenty-five miles south of Tripoli, 136.4°. These are shade temperatures in the free air. The temperature at the surface of the ground in the sunlight may be as high as 170°. In all the world's deserts, excepting those at higher latitudes or along coasts bathed by cold ocean water, summer temperatures over 110° are regularly experienced (Map 4). The world's largest area of great heat includes the Sahara and the Arabian Deserts. The most unpleasant climate, in terms of high temperature combined with high humidity, is in an area of Group I, along the shores of the Red Sea.

The desert night, on the other hand, generally brings a rapid drop of the temperature. Especially on elevated plateaus the surface of the earth cools rapidly under the clear night sky, and great diurnal ranges of temperature are the result. In fact, the desert holds the world's record for this also; in the Saharan oasis of In-Salah in Algeria, the temperature ranged from 26° to 126° within twenty-four hours.

Desert Vegetation. These climatic conditions are reflected in the landscape by a characteristic type of vegetation cover. Contrary to popular impression, very few parts of the deserts are entirely barren. Such bare places do occur, but they are rare. Even the great sandy deserts have a scattering of drought-resistant shrubs in the hollows between the dunes, and where water seepage brings moisture near the surface the result is a profusion of plants. The typical desert scene includes a cover of low shrubs and grasses, which, at least after a rain, gives the landscape a distinctly greenish tinge.

The vegetation that can exist under these extreme conditions of drought and high evaporation must be especially adapted to them. This is accomplished in various ways. The annuals evade the drought by lying dormant during the long dry period, springing into bloom and rapidly completing

* Climatic data throughout this book are given in Fahrenheit degrees and in inches, unless otherwise specifically stated. Official air temperatures are always taken in a shelter which provides shade but does not shut out the wind.

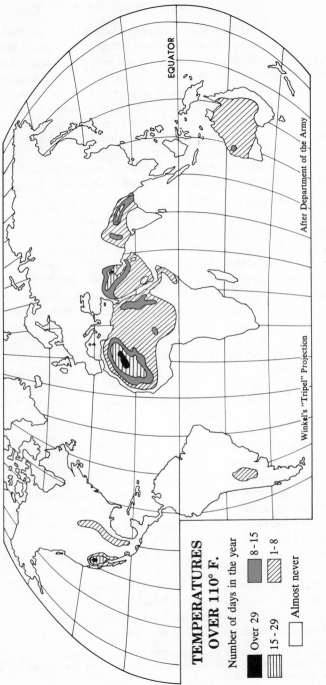

TEMPERATURES OVER 110° F.

Number of days in the year

- Over 29
- 15 - 29
- 8 - 15
- 1 - 8
- Almost never

EQUATOR

Winkel's "Tripel" Projection

After Department of the Army

Map 4. Areas with temperatures over 110° F.

Desert vegetation in Death Valley (Center, from Cushing).

the life cycle during the rare intervals when water is available. Then there are the perennials which endure the drought, quickly sending forth leaves and stems during the periods of rain, but remaining brown and apparently dead as long as no moisture reaches them. There are also the succulent plants, such as the cacti; these resist the drought by storing water inside their roots and stems, protecting themselves from evaporation by thick bark, by narrow, hairy, or waxy leaves, or by a complete absence of leaves. Such plants are protected also from the attacks of thirsty animals by an armament of thorns.

Desert plants usually grow some distance apart and have a remarkable development of the root system—both laterally, to catch the infrequent rains, and vertically, to tap the deep-lying supply of water. Because of the short growing season those plants which are especially attractive to insects, the carriers of the fertilizing pollen, have an advantage of survival. Hence among the most striking peculiarities of desert vegetation are the brilliant coloring and penetrating odor of the flowers.

Plants that are adapted in these various ways to dry conditions are called *xerophytes,* or xerophytic plants. A scattered cover of xerophytic shrubs with bare ground between the plants is the characteristic natural vegetation of the regions of Group I. In fact, the lack of a complete cover of vegetation is the feature which distinguishes the regions of this group from those of neighboring groups.

Vegetation and Rainfall Effectiveness.   The various plant associations included in the general term "desert" occur in areas which are deficient in moisture.   But moisture deficiency is not solely a matter of low rainfall. Deserts cannot be defined as having less than, say, 10 inches of rain a year, because there are a number of things that combine to determine the effectiveness of rainfall in terms of plants.

When rain falls on the ground, part of it is evaporated again, part runs off over the surface, and part sinks into the soil.   Only the part that sinks into the soil can be effective in the support of vegetation, and if the percolation downward through a porous soil goes on too rapidly even this water may go beyond the reach of the plants.   The presence of only scattered xerophytic shrubs, therefore, may be the result of low rainfall, rapid evaporation, rapid drainage, too-rapid downward percolation, or a combination of these.   The rate of evaporation is much greater at higher temperatures than at lower ones, and it increases also with lower humidity and with higher wind velocities.   And there are still other elements affecting evaporation.   The amount of water that remains on the surface to be evaporated after a rain depends on the degree of slope, on the nature of the soil, and, to a certain extent, on the nature of the cover of vegetation.   It also depends on the rate at which the rain falls, for much more water is soaked up by the soil in a long-continued drizzle than in one of the violent cloudbursts so typical of the deserts.

Desert vegetation, a visible result of moisture deficiency, is the product of all these numerous factors, some *climatic* (resulting from the average state of the atmosphere), and some *edaphic* (resulting from the character of the soil and surface).   In general, the broad outlines of the desert regions are the result of climatic conditions, whereas the details observed in particular localities are the result of edaphic conditions.

Two examples from the United States will make clearer the effect of differences of temperature and rainfall in determining moisture effectiveness. Denver, Colorado, is located east of the Rocky Mountains in an area once covered by short grass.   It is outside the dry-land region, with a climate that is described as semiarid rather than arid (BS) according to the climatic system used in this book.   See Appendix B, pp. 480–485.   Denver's average annual rainfall is 14 inches, which comes chiefly in summer and is therefore less effective than if it came when temperatures were lower. Denver's average temperature is about 50°.   Under these circumstances the amount of rain necessary to support a continuous grass cover is about 10 inches.

El Paso, Texas, is located in a part of North America where the climate is arid (BW), and where typical dry-land vegetation is to be found with bare ground between the plants. El Paso's average annual rainfall is just under 10 inches, and, like the rainfall at Denver, it comes chiefly in summer. The average annual temperature is about 63°. Experience indicates that at such temperatures more than 12 inches of rain are necessary for the support of grass vegetation.

Man as an Agent of Change.   All these natural conditions and processes, however, have been changed by the presence of man. Man as an agent of change has been especially effective on the dry-land margins where he upset the delicate balance of natural forces by clearing the vegetation cover. Around almost every desert there are areas known to have been covered with a continuous grass sod which once supported a variety of wild grazing animals. The clearing of the grass cover permitted a more rapid runoff of water over the surface, and therefore a decrease in the proportion of water that could sink into the soil. The more rapid run-off caused soil erosion, the formation of deep gullies where formerly the land sloped gently, and the accumulation of gravel and other porous deposits where once the soil was fine enough in texture to hold the water where the roots could reach it. These changes, introduced by human action, have had the effect of extending the area of desert vegetation into areas that once were grass-covered. Some scholars believe that a very large proportion of the areas at present covered by only scattered xerophytic shrubs are actually the result of unplanned human action.

The World Distribution of the Dry Lands.   An examination of the maps (Map 3, p. 42, and Plate 10, p. 564) will show that the regions of Group I are regularly placed on the earth. Dry land regions can be found on the western sides of all the continents, both north and south of the equator, in the zone between 20° and 30°. Each continent, to be sure, differs somewhat in the exact latitude of the boundaries of Group I. The dry lands along the west coast of South America, for example, extend as far as 4° S.; but in North America they do not reach 20° N. These differences result from differences in the surface features, the shapes of the coast, the mountains, and other related features that modify the strict regularity of the climatic patterns. The dry lands also extend inland from the western sides of the continents, bending poleward in each hemisphere. In the continental interiors of the Northern Hemisphere the dry lands extend as far as 45° N., or even 50° N. in China. In the Southern Hemisphere, where only South America extends far into the middle latitudes, the dry lands reach the east coast south of 40° S.

There are five great areas of dry land in the world. These are listed below, with the regional names of the various parts:

1. North African-Southwest and Central Asian
   Sahara (including Libyan Desert); Arabian Desert: Persian Desert; Thar; Turkestan; Tarim; Gobi
2. North American
   Northern Mexico, New Mexico, West Texas; Sonora, Baja California, Southern California; Mojave; Great Basin; Snake River; Wyoming Basin
3. South American
   Coastal Desert of Peru; Atacama; Western Argentina; Patagonia
4. South African
   Namib; Kalahari
5. Australian
   Great Sandy Desert; Great Victoria Desert

The general regularity of the global pattern of dry lands is a reflection of the regular arrangement of certain climatic and water features. Plate 10 (pp. 564–565) shows that parts of the west coasts of all the continents are bathed by cold ocean water. The water is especially cold between latitudes 35° and 15° in each hemisphere. In the Southern Hemisphere off the west coasts of South America and Africa the cold ocean currents extend almost as far as the equator (the Peru Current off the west coast of South America; the Benguela Current off the west coast of Africa). A comparison of the map of ocean currents with the map of the dry lands (Map 3, p. 42) shows that the position of the deserts on the western sides of the continents corresponds with the presence of cold water off shore. Furthermore, where the cold water extends farthest toward the equator, the dry lands also extend farthest in that direction. The presence of dry lands along the east coast of South America in Patagonia is also associated with a wide expanse of cold water in this part of the South Atlantic Ocean (Falkland Island Current). On the other hand the dry lands along the Red Sea and in Somalia are bordered by warm water.

The reason for this association of cold ocean water and low rainfall has to do with the stability of the air. Cold air is heavy and stays close to the ground. When air that has been chilled by passing over cold water moves against a mountain front, as it does along the coast of Peru, the air rises sluggishly. It may be further cooled enough to produce a cloud, but it is a stratus, or sheet-like cloud, from which little or no rain falls. On the other hand, when air is heated at the surface of the earth, the colder air aloft being heavier tends to sink and push the warmer air up. Under such conditions—with warm air below and colder air above—the air is said to be unstable. The rising air is cooled adiabatically (as a result of expansion), and so produces puffy cumulus clouds and rain.* The lack of rain along

*The principles of meteorology, and the methods of classifying climates are discussed in Appendix B, pp. 465–488. The adiabatic cooling of air is treated on page 467.

the Red Sea and in Somalia can be understood by looking at the maps of wind direction (insets on Plate 12, pp. 568–569).

In the Northern Hemisphere the continental interiors are dry for still another reason. Both the eastern and western sides of the continents in the middle latitudes have on-shore winds, at least for part of the year. These on-shore winds are moving around the oceanic whirls, and when the polar outbursts meet the oceanic air the result is storminess and much rain or snow. But air masses circulating around the oceanic whirls, being continuously deflected to the right, reach the continental interiors only rarely. In North America the dry lands cannot extend so far toward the east as they do in Asia because of the movement of moist maritime air from the Gulf of Mexico up the Mississippi Valley, and the lack of such air moving across the Himalayas.

SURFACE FEATURES AND DRAINAGE

These great desert areas, however, are by no means uniform in character. The concept of a desert as a vast expanse of shifting sand is incorrect, for actually only a relatively small proportion of the dry-land area is of this sort. A much larger proportion is composed of rocky plateaus channeled by dry watercourses, or of basins surrounded by barren mountains.

Desert Landforms.* To a person used to the forms of hills and valleys in rainy regions the deserts are strikingly different. In the first place, because of the scanty covering of vegetation, even the minor irregularities of form are revealed—especially, late in the day, when the shadows make the relief stand out boldly. One notices, too, the prevailing absence of permanent streams, although in some deserts the surface is scored by numerous dry watercourses. Perhaps the most striking peculiarity, however, is the accumulation of rock waste, the flood of debris which masks the base of every hill and cliff and which fills the valleys and basins. In the rainy lands, with permanently flowing streams, the waste material is gradually carried away; but in the deserts, outside of the immediate valleys of the few streams which do flow through to the sea, the only agent that can carry off the loosened rock waste is the wind. Only the finer particles can be picked up in this way. In the rainy lands on the lee sides of the great deserts, accumulations of fine dust, known as *loess,* tell something of the extent of wind erosion.

Basin and Range Deserts. From the point of view of the larger surface features, three chief kinds of deserts may be recognized. These are basin and range deserts, hamadas, and ergs.

* For a discussion of the forms and origins of the various kinds of surface features, see Appendix C, pp. 489–516.

The first desert type, known as the basin and range desert, is characterized by scattered ranges of barren hills or low mountains separated by more or less extensive basins or bolsons.*   In this kind of country most of the rain falls on the highlands.   Because of the steep slopes and the violent nature of the showers, a very large part of the rainfall runs off over the surface, rapidly eroding deep V-shaped ravines and gullies.   Although the desert rains may be infrequent, and many years may elapse between showers, most of the work of sculpturing the mountain ranges is accomplished by the violent rains and resulting floods.   When the flood waters emerge from the mountains and enter the bolson, their rate of flow is suddenly checked. Much of the load of sand and gravel picked up in the mountains is deposited in the form of alluvial fans which spread out in front of each valley mouth along the margins of the bolson.   During a cloudburst, and for a short time after, water may actually cross the alluvial fans and reach the center of the bolson, there forming a temporary shallow lake.   But the rapid evaporation speedily removes the water from such a lake, leaving in its bed an accumulation of dazzling white salt.   In some of the larger bolsons enough water may enter to support a shallow salt lake permanently, like Great Salt Lake in Utah; but more commonly the lakes in the bolsons are temporary, known technically as *playa* lakes, their beds marked most of the time by salt accumulations left over from the repeated evaporation of water.

There are, then, three chief divisions of the surface of basin and range deserts.   There are the mountain ranges with their steep, rocky slopes; there are the alluvial fans smoothing the angles between bordering mountains and bolson bottoms; and, in the lowest part of the basin, there is the playa, either a shallow salt lake with fluctuating shores or simply a flat salt plain over which at rare intervals the flood waters may form a lake.   It is the alluvial fans of such regions that offer the best sites for human settlement; for by irrigating the fans with water from the mountain streams and permitting it to drain off easily to the playa, rich oases may be formed.

Hamada Deserts.   The second of the major types of dry land surface features is described as a hamada.   This is an Arabic word, adopted in Anglicized form to refer to rocky plateaus.†   It is by far the commonest of the types of surface found in the regions of Group I.

Although the surface of the hamada is covered with a mantle of angular rock fragments, this mantle is not very thick and does not obscure the underlying rock.   The character and position of the geologic formations are

---

* From the Spanish word *bolson,* meaning "pocket."
†The terms used to describe desert surfaces are mostly borrowed either from the Arabic (hamada, erg, wadi, etc.) or from the Spanish (bolson, playa, mesa, cuesta, arroyo, etc.). The English language is notably poor in words to describe the surface features of deserts.

therefore of primary importance in determining the landforms of the hamada. Especially varied are the forms which appear in areas of stratified
rocks where the strata are of varying degrees of resistance to weathering
and erosion. The weaker formations are quickly excavated, leaving the
stronger rocks standing out in bold relief as *mesas* or *cuestas*.*

Many hamadas are shaped as broad, flattish domes. Erosion by streams
or wind may strip off the layers of sedimentary strata from the higher parts
of the dome, leaving a core of massive crystalline rocks exposed in the center. In desert areas many of the crystalline rocks disintegrate more easily
than sedimentary strata, so that the rocks in the center of the structural dome may be worn away to form a surface basin. A few types of crystalline rocks, however, especially recent igneous rocks, may stand out
boldly. Around the crystalline center a series of infacing cuestas correspond to the outcrops of resistant strata. This is a common geologic structure not only in the dry lands but also in the rainy parts of the earth. In
rainy lands, however, the details of surface formed are distinctly different
from those produced on the same kind of structures in dry lands.

A distinction must be made between two quite different kinds of hamadas. Some of the rocky plateaus are surmounted by higher elevations. In
some cases steep-sided pinnacles of crumbling rock rise so abruptly from
the rocky platforms on which they stand that, viewed from a distance, they
resemble islands rising from the sea. Because of this the Germans have
given them the descriptive name *inselberg* (plural *inselberge*) meaning "island mountain." In other cases the rocky platforms are surmounted by
highlands, or even by high mountains that tower above the desert surfaces.
When hamadas are surmounted by groups or ranges of peaks these higher
elevations force the air currents to rise and bring rainfall. Draining the water from the highlands out over the hamadas are numerous valleys, most
of which remain dry at the surface except after cloudbursts in the mountains. Such dry desert valleys are called *wadis* (or *arroyos* in southwestern
United States). Excavated in the course of time by the recurring floods,
the wadis remain most of the time quite dry at the surface. The wadi is
characteristically steep-sided, often cliffed, with a flat, gravel-filled bottom. When rain does fall in the mountains, torrents of water fill the wadis from wall to wall; but as the floods subside the load of loose rock fragments or gravel and sand carried along by the water is dropped in the wadi
bottom. Where the hamadas are surmounted by highlands they are usually cut by radiating systems of wadis.

The second type of hamada is found where there are no surmounting
highlands. The hamada surface stretches unbroken by wadis for mile after
monotonous mile to the horizon.

* Described in Appendix C, pp. 499–501.

An erg landscape in the Sahara (Ewing Galloway).

Erg Deserts.   The third of the major kinds of desert surfaces is the *erg*, or sandy desert, where the sand has been piled up by the wind into great dunes.   Ergs often fill the depressions in hamada deserts.   This kind of surface is, actually, much less common than either the hamada or the basin and range.   The largest area of erg in the world is the southern part of the Arabian Desert.

Water in the Deserts.   The most important physical condition in the desert from the point of view of life is the occurrence of water.   Knowledge of the places where fresh water may be found is of vital concern to desert dwellers, and habitability is in almost direct proportion to the amount of water which can be made available.   There is a supply of ground water in most deserts, just as in humid lands, but the water table lies at a much greater depth below the surface.   Therefore the places where the water table can be reached by ordinary surface wells are few and far between.

In the basin and range deserts, even where no permanent surface stream reaches the bolson from the neighboring ranges, water is usually to be found in the gravel fill of each mountain valley.   As soon as the water reaches the alluvial fan it sinks deep into the porous material and is difficult to reach with wells. The playa is of no value as a source of water; for even where moisture is abundant enough to support a more or less permanent playa lake, the evaporation renders the lake salty. Fresh water is usually not available even on the lower fan slopes. The best place to dig a well in such deserts is at the apex of an alluvial fan, near the mouth of a mountain ravine.

Water in the hamadas is most commonly to be found in the gravel fill of the dry valleys. Ordinary wells in the wadi bottoms are usually able to reach a fairly dependable supply, and if floods are not too frequent an almost continuous string of oases may become established along these dry stream-courses. Hamadas which are crossed by numerous wadis, such as the plateaus lying south of the Atlas Mountains in the western Sahara, may support a relatively large population. On the other hand, hamadas which are cut by few wadis, such as the Libyan hamada, west of the Nile, are among the least habitable portions of the deserts.

The water supply in an erg depends on the number of wadis draining into it. Where these are numerous, as on the southern slopes of the Atlas Mountains in western Sahara, the erg basins act as huge reservoirs, and the porous sands protect the water from evaporation and so from becoming salty. The hollows between the dune ridges are closest to the water table, and here a considerable growth of desert shrubs may reveal the

Rio Puerco, New Mexico, northwest of Albuquerque (photo by J. G. Widdison).

Irrigation ditch along the Nile, Egypt (C. Frank).

presence of moisture not far below the surface.* But where the ergs are poorly supplied with water, generally because few wadis drain into them, the zone of saturation may lie so far below the surface that it cannot be reached even in the deepest depressions. Very dry areas, whether in ergs or hamadas, in which no forms of life can gain a foothold are known in the Sahara as *tanezroufts*.

In addition to the ordinary surface well, there is another important method of reaching water in the deserts. This is by means of an artesian well tapping a deep-lying source of water. Artesian springs may occur naturally, in some cases as the result of a crack, or fissure, in the bedrock. Not a few of the oases of the Sahara are dependent on such a natural source of water. During the last century many artesian wells have been made artificially, either creating an entirely new wet spot in the desert or

*See the classic description of two Saharan oases, one occupying the hollows between the dune ridges of an erg, the other occupying the wadis of a hamada, in *Human Geography*, by J. Brunhes, Abridged Edition by M. Jean-Brunhes Delamarre and Pierre Deffontaines [translation by E. F. Row (London, 1952)] pp. 177–186.

supplementing the ground water of an earlier oasis. Artesian wells are dependent on the existence of a certain geologic structure, and they may occur, where this structure is found, in hamadas or ergs or even, in some cases, in basin and range deserts (see p. 521).

Another important source of water in the dry lands is provided by the so-called *exotic* streams. The deserts as a whole are characterized by a lack of native surface streams rising within the areas of arid climate. There are numerous cases, however, where streams rise in rainy areas elsewhere and maintain a flow across the dry lands. Such streams may be illustrated by the Nile in Egypt, the Colorado in the western United States, the Indus in Pakistan, the Loa in Chile, and many others. These exotic rivers have the peculiar character of decreasing in volume downstream and of lacking tributaries. Owing to the progressive loss of volume, they are constantly dropping a part of their load of mud, silt, and sand, which they are no longer able to carry, so that the river is split by sand bars into a number of distributaries, or separate channels. Such rivers are said to have *braided channels*. On entering a dry-land region, rivers tend to spread out in broad areas of shallow lakes or marshes and in some cases fail to continue across the desert, the water being evaporated so rapidly that surface flow cannot be maintained. A comparison of the Niger, the Chari, and the Nile shows how these streams have spread out on reaching the desert margin.

Soils in the Desert.   The mantle of loose rock fragments, known as *regolith*, that develops all over the earth where the lithosphere and the atmosphere are in contact, is largely the result of physical disintegration of the bedrock in the dry lands. The great differences of temperature between day and night cause the exposed rock to crack and split. When a rock, such as a granite, is composed of minerals of different colors, each mineral expands or contracts at a different rate. The dark minerals absorb heat faster and also cool faster at night. Such rocks quickly crumble into a coarse sand or gravel.

Soils are formed in regolith by processes that require the presence of both water and plants. It is the mixture of organic materials and inorganic rock fragments, and the removal of soluble minerals from the upper soil layers by downward percolating water that combine to produce a soil. These processes will be more fully discussed later. It is sufficient to note here that over large areas of the dry lands the regolith has no soil developed on its surface. On the margins of the dry lands, however, where there is enough percolating water to moisten the upper layers of the regolith at more or less regular intervals, and where there is a greater than average concentration of xerophytic plants, a dry type of soil is formed; it is known as a *sierozem*. This soil is gray in color at the surface, and becomes lighter in the subsoil.   Mixed with the inorganic matter in the subsoil, a few inches below the surface, is a concentration of salts, mostly calcium and magnesium salts.   The salts were dissolved by the percolating water and redeposited in the subsoil where the water evaporates.   Such soils, rich in calcium, are potentially very productive when water can be applied to them.

A major problem in the irrigation of dry lands, however, develops when the water is not drained away fast enough.   If irrigation water is evaporated or transpired through plants it must leave its burden of salts behind. As long as the salts it carries are chiefly calcium salts, similar to those already present in a sierozem, there is no trouble.   But when sodium salts accumulate too rapidly, a layer of slimy and impervious alkali is formed. Where drainage is not adequate to flush out the excess sodium salts, this alkali may render a desert soil completely sterile.

Surface and Drainage Features in the Deserts.   The various surface and drainage features give variety to the different desert areas of the world. The actual distribution of these basic conditions is shown on the accompanying maps (Plates 1–5, 13).   These maps show that the Sahara and Arabia are mostly composed of hamada and erg surfaces, with only a few isolated mountain ranges.   The deserts of Iran, on the other hand, are of the basin and range type.   The Thar Desert of India is composed of hamada and erg.   The various deserts in inner Asia are built on a huge scale.   They might well be considered as bolsons of continental proportions, with the Aral Sea or the Lob Nor as playas; but in addition to the usual features of bolsons, there are extensive areas of rocky plateau and erg.   The Australian desert is composed of hamada and erg, whereas the desert of southern Africa is mostly hamada.   The deserts of North and South America are mostly basin and range, but with a few rocky plateaus, such as the Colorado Plateau in the United States or the Patagonian Plateau in southern Argentina.

All the desert areas except Australia are crossed by exotic rivers. Not all of them, however, are like the Nile, the Niger, the Tigris-Euphrates, or the Indus.   The Colorado, except in its lower course, is deeply trenched in a canyon, as are also the Loa and the Orange.   Although the Amu Darya and the Syr Darya do not flow out to the sea, along their courses they are much like exotic streams.

The Occupance*

Only a small proportion of the world's population is found in the regions of Group I. Although deserts, as defined in this book, occupy about 18 per cent of the land surface of the earth, only about 6 per cent of mankind lives in them. Water and sunlight, as we have said, are the basic needs of life: in the hot deserts there is an abundance of sunshine, and when these deserts can be supplied with water, plants grow luxuriantly. The long story of man's occupance of the dry lands is involved with the continued struggle to increase the supplies of water. In the modern world, if the water problem could be solved, a considerable increase of population in some of these regions might be expected. But the water problem remains far from solved.

Although the regions of Group I as a whole are occupied by only a small proportion of mankind, in certain places where an abundance of water is available there are very dense concentrations of people. Furthermore, some of these concentrations have been gaining rapidly in population during the present century. In the Nile Valley, for example, there is a population density of more than 1800 people per square mile. One of the parts of the United States that grew most rapidly in population between 1950 and 1960 is the dry land area between Los Angeles and San Diego.

Over the course of time the dry lands have been occupied in a variety of ways. At the dawn of written history in North Africa-Southwest Asia, the wet spots in the deserts were already occupied in proportion to the amount of water available. Changes in the technology of water control and in the political control of the users of water have been reflected in increases or decreases of population at the wet spots. The deep drilling of wells has made possible the appearance of entirely new concentrations of people. And where resources needed by the modern industrial world have been discovered, no expense has been spared to provide the necessary water. It is clear that if the economic and political conditions require it, the engineering skills exist to make any desert habitable—even the tanezroufts.

To illustrate the ways in which the significance to man of the features of

---

* The term *occupance* is an obsolete word revived and adopted in geography to indicate the process of occupying or living in an area and the transformations of the original landscape which result. A distinction is made between *occupance* and *occupation*. *Occupation* refers specifically to the economic activities of a people, that is, to their mode of gaining a living from an area or in an area. *Occupance* refers not only to these economic activities but also to other activities only indirectly or not at all related to the economic life, such as the construction of buildings, roads, etc. The term *occupance* (occupancy) was first suggested by R. S. Platt and D. S. Whittlesey.

the dry-land habitats changes with changes in the attitudes, objectives, and technical skills of man himself, we shall examine the sequences of settlement in certain specific dry-land regions. We identify the periods of occupance during which the ways of living of the people remain essentially unchanged. In each such period we note the areal relations of the occupance with the critical features of the habitat. In other words, we recreate past geographies. From period to period we follow the changes in the areal relations of the occupance of the habitat. Such a succession of man–habitat relations is known as *sequent occupance*.

Eight examples of desert regions are selected for studies of sequent occupance in the regions of Group I. These are: 1. Arabia; 2. the Nile Valley; 3. Western Sahara; 4. Turkestan; 5. The Atacama; 6. The Orange River Valley; 7. The Great Basin of the United States; and 8. The Imperial Valley.

ARABIA

Arabia is the vast thinly-peopled desert area between the Red Sea and the Persian Gulf (Map 5). The desert surface is made up of hamada and erg. The great Rub' al Khali in southern Arabia is a vast accumulation of shifting sands 750 miles long by 400 miles wide almost entirely empty of human inhabitants. The greater part of Arabia is formed as a block of massive crystalline rocks partly covered on the east by layers of sandstone and limestone. The block is tilted toward the east, and in the higher western part, known as the Hejaz, the covering of sedimentary rocks has been removed by erosion. The edges of the sedimentary strata form cuestas facing toward the Hejaz. The western edge of Arabia drops abruptly to the Red Sea. But toward the east the hamada surface slopes gradually to the alluvial lowland of Mesopotamia and the Persian Gulf. Arabia has no exotic river, no permanent surface water in streams.

There are three distinct periods in the sequent occupance of Arabia. The earliest extended over many thousands of years during which the traits of Arabic culture were developed. The second period began with the preaching of Muhammad in the early part of the seventh century A.D. The third period began with the drilling of the first oil well in the Persian Gulf region in 1908.

The Period of Early Settlement.   The events that led to the first settlements in Arabia are lost in antiquity. As a habitat for people dependent on hunting, fishing, and collecting, Arabia could have had little to offer. Even if a somewhat greater rainfall ten thousand years ago may have supported a scanty vegetation, areas nearby were better supplied with game and seed plants. But at some time two developments in the technology of

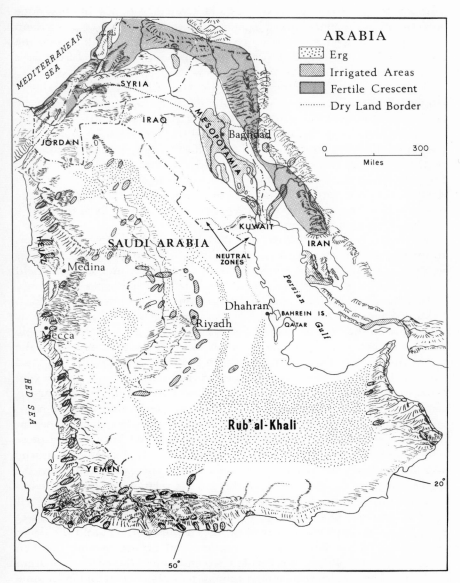

ARABIA

- ⠿ Erg
- ⫽ Irrigated Areas
- ▓ Fertile Crescent
- ⋯ Dry Land Border

0 ————————— 300

Miles

MEDITERRANEAN SEA

SYRIA

IRAQ

JORDAN

Baghdad

MESOPOTAMIA

SAUDI ARABIA

KUWAIT

NEUTRAL ZONES

IRAN

HEJAZ

Medina

Dhahran

Riyadh

BAHREIN IS.

QATAR

Persian Gulf

Mecca

RED SEA

Rub' al-Khali

YEMEN

20°

50°

Map 5. Arabia.

people living on the borders of Arabia made the desert itself habitable. One was the use of the date palm as a cultivated crop, possibly first done successfully in the highlands of Yemen.   The other was the domestication of the single-humped camel, a native of Arabia.   The date palms made the small oases habitable, and the camel made it possible to travel from oasis to oasis.

By the beginning of written history the Arabian desert was already occupied.   The earliest accounts tell of the sharpest of contrasts between the rich green of the oases where water could be provided, and the monotonous reddish-brown of the arid lands beyond the last irrigation ditch.   The people of the oases lived in relative comfort.   They were well-fed, contented, and pleasure-loving.   The desert men, on the other hand, were lean, hungry, accustomed to hardships, accustomed to obey their leader, and devout and uncompromising in religion.   They looked with scorn at the oasis dwellers, but after they conquered an oasis and had lived there for a while they took on the characteristics they had once disliked.

The desert people of Arabia were partly nomadic.   People who are entirely nomadic have no permanent attachment to any place.   Their wealth is in the form of herds of domestic animals, and all household goods must be transported from place to place on the backs of animals. These nomads set up their tents and form temporary camps near good pastures.   When they hear of a distant rain they quickly fold up their tents and move to the new pastures.   Such a life is not permanently possible within the dry lands, and the nomadic way of living is found on the grassy margins around the dry lands, in the regions of Group VI.   And even in these places nomadism was developed only by those people who made use of camels, horses, sheep, and goats.   But from the grassy margins of Arabia, the nomadic peoples could cross the desert from oasis to oasis. And because of their superior mobility, and their military form of organization, they could take control of the oases and collect rent from those who stayed to farm them.   Therefore, it was usually the desert man who was the landlord, the group leader, or sheikh.   The oasis dweller was the farmer, the tenant.   As a result of this kind of relationship between semi-nomadic owner and sedentary farmer, no central focus of settlement developed in Arabia.   There were only scattered oases occupying the small wet spots between the dense cluster of people in Mesopotamia and the dense populations of the Nile Valley.   Traders and armies moving between these two places followed the Fertile Crescent around the northern margin of Arabia where there was enough rainfall to support grass and even some crops.   In all the centuries of empire-building and conquest in this part of the world, Arabia remained unconquered—largely because of its scattered and unfocused pattern of people.

The Period of Muslim Expansion. Arab culture gained a focus in both the religious and the geographic sense as a result of the work of the great religious leader, Muhammad. During the early part of the seventh century, A.D., Muhammad was preaching in the oasis town of Mecca. His disciples wrote down the substance of his teaching in the holy book of the Muslims, the Koran. Muhammad laid down rules not only for religious practice, but also for the proper conduct of a business or of public administration. His teaching extended to personal hygiene and cleanliness, and to the avoidance of certain foods, such as pork, which could spoil quickly in a hot climate. But, more than anything else, Muhammad instilled an aggressive faith in his followers that caused them to set forth on a wave of conquest for the objective of increasing the number of believers in the one God, Allah. The culture change that took place was chiefly in the attitudes and objectives of those who embraced the religion of Islam.*

The begining of the period of Muslim expansion is usually set A.D. 622. In that year, on July 16, Muhammad left Mecca and took up residence in Medina where he assumed political leadership. The very next year, in 623, the Arabs started out from the Arabian homeland to spread the faith. First they invaded the Fertile Crescent and Mesopotamia. In 641 they conquered Persia (now Iran), and in 642 they assumed political control of Egypt. Muslim expansion moved rapidly both westward and eastward. By 732 they had gained control over the whole of the Sahara, and had crossed the Strait of Gibraltar into Europe. In that same year they were defeated at the Battle of Tours in France and pushed back to the Iberian Peninsula, south of the Pyrenees. They were not finally forced to leave Spain until 1492 in the Battle of Granada. At the same time they were extending their rule eastward to India, to Indonesia and the Philippines (Map 6).

The center of the Muslim world was established on the margins of Arabia. For a while it was in Damascus, but after 750 the Muslims made Baghdad their major center. In the ninth century, in fact, Baghdad became the intellectual center of a large part of the world.

Although the Muslims established their rule over a vast extent of territory they did not try to set up a single unified empire. In days when the fastest means of overland travel was by camel, it would have been impossible to keep a close administrative control of so vast an area. The Caliph in Baghdad was the religious leader of the Muslim world, and he was the supreme authority in economic and political matters as well. But the several parts of the Muslim world were mostly ruled as separate units.

The map (Map 6) shows that the Muslims occupied a strategic position in the world of that time. There was a highly profitable trade going on

*Believers in the religion of Islam are known as Muslims.

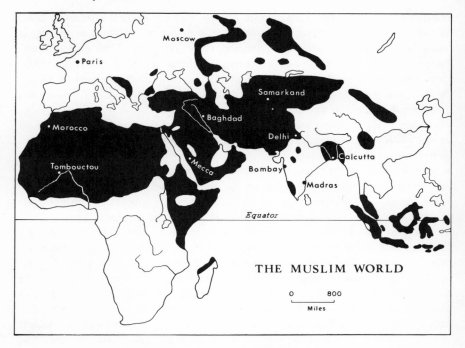

Map 6. Extent of Muslim World.

between Europe and southeastern Asia. The Europeans provided a growing market for the silks, spices, gems, and other exotic products from Asia.
In the year 810 Charlemagne granted to Venezia (Venice) the right
to carry on trade with Europe. The Venetians sailed their ships to the
Egyptian port of Alexandria, where they made contact with the Arabs.
The Arabs maintained strict control of the passages across the belt of
deserts that separates Europe from the Indian Ocean.

There were several routes across the belt of deserts. The Red Sea route,
now so important, was little used before the invention of steamships. The
prevailing north winds and the presence of coral reefs along both
shores made it diffcult and dangerous for sailing ships to tack. Ships
could be rowed northward as far as the Egyptian port of Quseir, and
then sailed back again with the wind behind them. But the overland caravan routes carried most of the trade. There were two chief
routes. One went to Baghdad following the Fertile Crescent around
the northern margin of Arabia from the Mediterranean ports. The other
extended from a port near Aden parallel to the Red Sea through the
Hejaz, through Mecca and Medina, and on into either Palestine or Egypt.

The Europeans made various efforts to break the Arab monopoly. Led by Prince Henry the Navigator, the Portuguese were the first to find a sea route to the Indian Ocean around southern Africa (Vasco da Gama in 1498). But the overland caravan routes remained in some use until the completion of the Suez Canal in 1869. Only after the invention of steamships, which could sail northward against the wind, did the Red Sea become a major strategic route.

Within Arabia life was little affected by the political conflicts and changes. Each nomadic tribe and each oasis community were under the rule of a local chieftain or sheikh. The great majority of the people of Arabia were farmers, toiling incessantly on the oasis lands to produce for the landlords. The farmers were seldom far from hunger, and high death rates kept the population in strict proportion to the amount of available water. Most of the sheikhs lived only a little better than their subjects, although those whose domains bordered the Persian Gulf carried on a profitable trade in pearls. The most important oasis town was Mecca, and the sheikh who controlled the Hejaz held a kind of authority over all the others.

Among the sheikhs there was constant warfare as each sought to establish his rule over the others. The chieftains in control of the oases of the Hejaz were in the best position to collect tribute from the others, but they were constantly challenged by those who hoped to overthrow this power.

Ibn Saud, a shiekh who ruled over some oasis communities near the Persian Gulf, gained control over a wide area in eastern Arabia when he captured the oasis town of Riyadh in 1902. By 1910 he had most of eastern Arabia securely under control. After World War I he led his forces westward and in 1924–1925 he captured the oases of the Hejaz. The United Kingdom of Saudi Arabia was proclaimed in 1932. In bringing all the local rulers under one king, Ibn Saud was continuing a process of conquest that had started in A.D. 622.

The Oil Period. The drilling of an oil well marked the end of the period of Muslim expansion in Arabia, and the beginning of a new period of sequent occupance. The first producing oil well in the Persian Gulf region was drilled in 1908 in Iran. The presence of oil in this part of the world had been known for thousands of years, and appears in many references in the Bible. Aladdin's Lamp, we may assume was supplied with oil from this region. But the world demand for oil was not great until the development of motor vehicles and diesel engines. Even as late as 1948 the Persian Gulf region was supplying only 5 per cent of the world's oil: by 1958 it was supplying 23 per cent. The first oil wells in Saudi Arabia were drilled in the Damman field in 1936. Large quantities of oil were found in the little sheikhdom of Kuwait that remained independent of the king of Saudi Arabia. In 1961 it was estimated that the Persan Gulf region as a whole held over 60 per cent of all the oil reserves of the world. Of this huge reserve, Kuwait* had the larger part, followed by Saudi Arabia.

The revenues from oil are beginning to produce major changes in Arabia. First the king has become enormously wealthy, and the sheikhs under his rule have shared in the new wealth, although to a lesser degree. Wealth for the king has meant first of all that the army could be well paid and would remain entirely loyal. The army, equipped with modern weapons, can keep the widely scattered communities of Arabia under control —although some of the sheikhs along the more remote coasts have been able to maintain their independence. Wealth has meant that irrigation works can be improved, and perhaps some new areas irrigated. Impressive new public buildings can be constructed, and schools can be provided. Oil has reoriented the economic and political life toward the Persian Gulf. Although Mecca remains the religious center of the Muslim world, Riyadh has now become the capital and largest oasis settlement. Riyadh is connected with the Persian Gulf port of Damman by a railroad. There is a striking difference to be seen in the old town of Riyadh, and the new city.

For the great majority of the people of Saudi Arabia the new wealth from oil has not yet made much difference. Most of the people are still farmers, still poor and illiterate. Some have found jobs with the oil companies, and as they return to their villages the existance of a new way of life will become more widely known. Health measures will decrease the death rates; schools will decrease the illiteracy; revolutionary new ideas about national sovereignty, new hatred of foreigners, new demands for equality of treatment will begin to spread. The victims will be those who have held positions of power and prestige—the sheikhs, the army officers, and the foreigners.

THE NILE VALLEY

The Nile is the world's longest river, 4150 miles in length. Its headwaters in equatorial Africa drain into Lake Victoria. The main stream drains from Lake Victoria into Lake Albert, descending from a plateau. It then drains northward from Lake Albert, and when the river reaches the margins of the arid lands it spreads out into a vast area of marsh, from which half of its volume is lost by evaporation. But then the main stream is powerfully reenforced by two tributaries—the Blue Nile and the Atbara

---

* When the discovery of oil in Kuwait made the precise demarcation of boundaries necessary, agreement between Kuwait and Saudi Arabia and Kuwait and Iraq could not be reached. Two neutral zones were established, from which the oil revenues are shared between the neighbors. The neutral zones were established in 1922. Kuwait became an independent state in 1961.

—which drain the Highlands of Ethiopia. Below Khartoum in Sudan the river enters a narrow V-shaped channel, descending from 1217 feet above sea level at Khartoum to 282 feet at Aswan. In this stretch of the river there are six cataracts, the first of which (numbering from downstream) is just above Aswan. From Aswan to the head of the delta at Cairo there is a ribbon of alluvial land a little less than 600 miles in length, and never more than 12 miles wide. North of Cairo the delta extends some 100 miles to the Mediterranean Sea, spreading out to a width of 150 miles east and west.

The regular rise and fall of the Nile in Egypt long governed the rhythm of life for the farmers who were dependent on water for irrigation. Before the completion of the Aswan Dam in 1902, the lower river started suddenly to rise each year in mid-May reaching the highest flood stage in September. Between the middle of July and early September more than half of the annual volume of water used to pass down the river. After September the water dropped, reaching its lowest stage in April and early May. During the flood stage about two-thirds of the water in the Nile comes from the heavy summer rains of Ethiopia through the Blue Nile and the Atbara. But during the low water stage 83 per cent comes from the main stream.

The Period of Basin Irrigation. The Nile has provided the support for a relatively dense population along its valley for many thousands of years. Anthropologists think that the Neolithic farmers began raising crops along the Nile about 4500 B.C. The Early Civilization in Egypt began about 3000 B.C. For something like six thousand years the ribbon of floodplain across the Sahara was used in about the same way to support population. The technique was to depend on the annual rise and fall of the river. Short canals guided the flood waters onto the fields. The fields were divided into compartments or basins by low dikes running from the river banks to the valley bluff which marks the edge of the floodplain. Into these basins the muddy flood water was guided. Then when the river started to fall after September, the water drained out again through the canals, and in the well-soaked, dark-colored mud the farmers planted wheat that gave abundant harvests before the next flood season.

As the historian, Herodotus, wrote, "Egypt is the gift of the Nile." Without the annual flood, people could not live in such numbers in the desert. The continued harvesting of wheat year after year on the same land with no deterioration of the yields could never have been achieved without the annual layer of fresh mud brought by the water. Furthermore, the drainage of the basins was so complete during the drop of the river level that Egypt never had to face a problem of alkali accumulation. The floods were not always of the same height: when the floods were less than normal there was starvation and many people died; and when the floods were higher than normal, more people could be fed.

During all these thousands of years the density of population in Egypt probably did not change very much. At a very early date the number of people dependent on the irrigated wheat reached a close adjustment to the annual wheat yield. The periodic starvation when floods were less than normal would be balanced in subsequent years of higher water when the population soon increased again. There were also periods of conflict when the administration of water laws broke down. Again there was starvation and a decrease of population. But with a birthrate, then as now, of between 40 and 50 per thousand, the restoration of order was followed by a rapid increase of population to the limits of the food supply. The first census ever taken in Egypt was in 1882, when 6,804,000 people were counted. The irrigable area at that time was 13,500 square miles, which had not changed much in many thousands of years. The average density of 500 people per square mile was about the same density that existed at the time of Christ.

The population of Egypt was sharply divided into two classes. There were the very few who owned the land and formed an exclusive society around the king. And there were the tenant farmers who worked on the land—illiterate, ill-fed, ill-housed, and long accustomed to performing the same endless tasks with the same hopeless future of more endless tasks to be performed. The rural Egyptian is known as a *fellah* (plural *fellahin*). For the fellahin life had not changed for thousands of years.

The British Period.   There is another important peculiarity that distinguishes Egypt from many other oasis communities supported by exotic rivers in the regions of Group I. The Nile Valley is more protected than are most other exotic valleys. To the west is the Libyan hamada which, because it is so monotonously level over vast distances, has few wadis and only a few miniature oases where the geologic structure permits water to rise to the surface in natural springs. The Libyan hamada is very thinly inhabited and difficult to cross. On the other side is the Red Sea that separates Egypt from Arabia. The Nile Valley was protected along its whole length, but it was vulnerable at either end. There were times when the Ethiopian kings controlled Egypt from upstream. In 663 B.C. the Assyrians invaded and took control of the delta, and soon thereafter brought the whole of the Nile Valley as far south as the first cataract under their control. But foreign control made its impact on Egypt only at the ends of the valley: the fellahin continued to work in their traditional ways almost untouched by outside ideas or contacts.

The French and the British began to find an interest in strategically placed Egypt when steamships made the Red Sea a potential route of commerce. With the completion of the Suez Canal in 1869, this route became an essential link in Britain's "life-line of empire." The British wanted to be certain that there was a friendly government in Egypt. In the latter part of the nineteenth century the British began to extend technical assistance to Egypt, and to seek ways to increase the prosperity of the politically powerful groups. Technical assistance introduced fundamental changes into Egypt that quite completely reoriented the traditional relations of people to the land. The changes included an attack on health and poor hygiene, a vast engineering program to control the Nile water, and a change from subsistence to commercial agriculture. Egypt entered a new stage of sequent occupance.

The Aswan Dam was completed in 1902. It was built at the first cataract just upstream from Aswan. In 1912 the dam was made higher; and again in 1933 its height was increased. The reservoir behind the dam backed up the water for 230 miles.

With the construction of the Aswan Dam the old traditional basin irrigation had to be given up in favor of *perrennial irrigation*. The annual floods no longer reach the lower river, since the flood water—and the silt —are captured and held in the reservoir. Water is taken out of the reservoir in irrigation canals, from which ditches guide the water at any time of the year onto the individual fields. Although the valley bluffs bordering the Nile floodplain effectively restrict the expansion of the irrigated area along most of the valley, some expansion was possible in the Fayum Basin and the delta (Map 7). The irrigable area was increased by 200 square miles. More important, it was now possible to have three crop seasons each year instead of only one.

The British introduced a variety of new crops. First of all, the owners were shown the advantage of having a crop for sale. The crop for which Egypt became famous is the valuable long-staple Egyptian cotton, which found a ready market in the textile factories of Great Britain. From February to May is the planting season for cotton—and also maize, rice, sugar cane, millet, peanuts, sesame, and vegetables. In July rice and millet are sown. In November wheat, barley, flax, and vegetables are sown. The chief food crop has become maize, and corn bread challenges the traditional wheat bread in the Egyptian diet.

Meanwhile, however, other changes were taking place. The medical program resulted in a sharp drop in the death rate, while the birth rate remained unchanged. The net rate of increase took a sudden jump. In 1907 the population had passed 11,000,000. The census of 1947 counted over 19,000,000; and that of 1960 counted 26,059,000. In 1962 the population was estimated at 27,000,000. The population density in the Nile

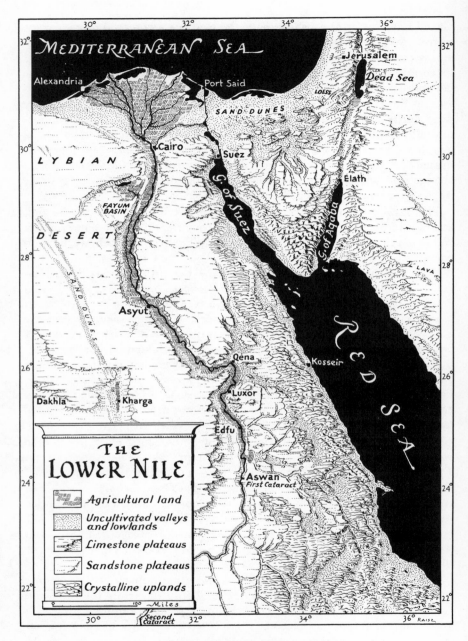

Map 7. *The lower Nile and adjacent territory.*

Valley averages more than 1800 people per square mile, and there are parts of the valley where the rural population has a density of more than 3000 per square mile—a density exceeded only in parts of rural China.

Another result of the change to perennial irrigation has been the progressive deterioration of the soil. No longer supplied with fresh mud each year, the hard-worked land now had to be fertilized artificially. After 1902, Egypt became a major purchaser of Chilean nitrate. To reduce the cost of importing fertilizer the Egyptians tried another technique. The Egyptian rural landscape now includes numerous pigeon towers, where the droppings can be collected. These droppings, rich in the elements needed to keep the land productive, are now used as fertilizer, supplementing the imported nitrate.

But in spite of these efforts to increase and regularize the flow of water, and to provide a greater variety of crops, the supply of food per capita decreased. In 1952, the average fellah was eating less and living more poorly than he was before the British period. The population was increasing so much faster than the food supply that Egypt seemed headed for disaster.

The Period of Independence. A third period of sequent occupance began in 1952 when the Egyptians declared their independence of all foreign control. They also overthrew the king and substituted a military dictatorship for the monarchy. They seized the Suez Canal, hoping to derive from its tolls the much-needed income to be used in building manufacturing industries.

There are several parts to the program of economic development undertaken by the new government. First is the construction of a new High Dam with Soviet financial and technical assistance. The new dam will be just above Aswan, and will back up the largest man-made lake in the world. This new reservoir will make it possible to enlarge the irrigated land area by almost a third. At the dam, electricity will be generated to provide power for the industries. The electricity will also be used to extract nitrogen from the air and so to end Egypt's dependence on imported nitrate for fertilizer. In Cairo and other cities, new manufacturing plants are being built to provide jobs for people who cannot be supported in rural areas.

Yet some simple arithmetic shows that all these efforts will fall far short of providing even the minimum essentials for the predictable population of a few decades hence. The still-rising net rate of population increase means that the increase of the agricultural area cannot possibly supply the needed food, and that the jobs in factories cannot be provided fast enough to meet the increasing numbers of people seeking work. Egypt offers the horrible spectacle of a nation suffocating under its own population.

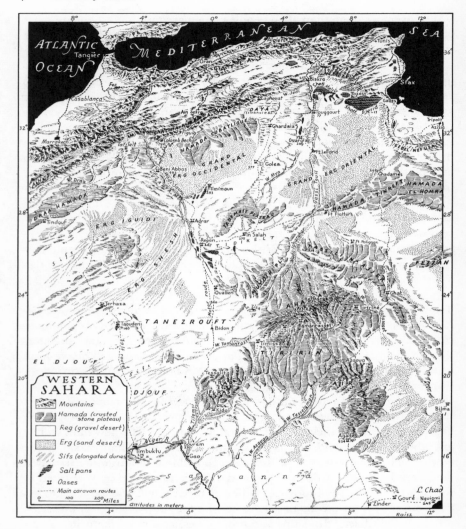

Map 8. The western Sahara.

THE WESTERN SAHARA

The Western Sahara has also a long record of human settlement, although nowhere are there population densities comparable to that of the Nile Valley. Between the high Atlas Mountains in the north and the woodland savannas of the Niger Valley in the south, there is a country made up mostly of hamada and erg desert, surmounted in the Ahaggar by the towering peaks of a group of high mountains. From these mountains wadis extend across the hamadas in all directions (Map 8).

The Sahara has not always been arid. During the period when the great ice caps were covering much of northern Europe and northern North America, the northern part of Africa received enough rainfall to support regularly flowing streams and a complete cover of vegetation—probably a woodland savanna. The present wadis were filled with water, and a people seeking animals to hunt could find support throughout the area that is so desolate today. The climatic change that brought about the melting of the ice caps farther north also brought a decrease of the rainfall in northern Africa. When this happened the rivers dried up, leaving the wadis to mark their former courses. The Romans found dwarf elephants along the Mediterranean shore, separated by impassable deserts from their natural habitat south of the Sahara. And in the water holes of the Ahaggar there were dwarf crocodiles.

The Period of Oasis Farming. It has not yet been possible to reconstruct the pattern of settlement during the period of adequate rainfall in the Western Sahara. But the earliest records of contacts of the Phoenician traders and the Greeks with the Sahara include accounts of Negroid farmers living around the scattered places where water was available. At Ghadames and Ghat (near the eastern margin of Map 8) there were natural springs where fresh water bubbled up to the surface. There were a very few spots, too, where ground water in the wadis was near the surface. In all such places there were clusters of Negroid people raising millet for their own subsistence. In each isolated oasis the number of people was closely adjusted to the amount of water available. The large area to the west of the Ahaggar known as the Tanezrouft, is the very dry uninhabited land that gave its name to all similar empty places where even plants cannot gain a foothold.

The Muslim Period. The second period of sequent occupance in the Western Sahara began with the invasion and conquest of the desert by the Muslim peoples. When the Arabs spread into Egypt in A.D. 642 they brought with them two important skills: the cultivation of the date palm, and the use of the camel. To the west of the Nile, occupying the grassland margin along the Mediterranean shore that extends westward to Morocco, were a pastoral people with sheep known as the Berbers. These nomads were quickly converted to the faith of Islam, and, armed with date palms and camels, they too started out to conquer parts of the world that were not yet Muslim. Pushed on by the Arabs behind them, the Berbers fanned out over the Sahara. Between Arabs and Berbers there was no feeling of brotherhood; the Arabs were stronger and better organized, and they caused the Berbers to flee to the most remote and isolated spots wherever grass could be found for their sheep. In the Western Sahara, Berber tribes survived in the high Atlas Mountains and in the mountains of the Ahaggar. They also occupied certain of the oases, enslaving the Negroid farmers, and waging constant warfare with the Arabs.

The Arabs overran all of the Western Sahara, and by the eighth century they were in complete control. Arabs pushed southward into the Sudan, and northward across Gibraltar into Europe. In the Western Sahara they took control of the oases, introducing the date palm to make the oases much more productive than they had been before. Ordinary wells sunk in the gravel floors of the wadis made it possible to irrigate date palms all along the wadi bottoms. The Arabs, as in Arabia, became the landlords; the cultivation of the crops was left to the Negroid peoples. The Arabs would appear at harvest time to collect the rent. They also established caravan routes across the Sahara, over which they brought gold, ivory, ostrich feathers, and Negro slaves for sale in the ports of the Mediterranean. The Berbers regularly raided the caravans, extracting toll for safe passage from their enemies, the Arab merchants.

The European Period. The third period of sequent occupance in the Western Sahara began after 1830 when the French started the invasion and conquest of the great desert. There was a long period of warfare with the desert tribesmen, but in the end the Europeans were victorious. The resistance to conquest was most stubborn from the Berbers, and in Algeria they were all but wiped out. Most of those who survived in the more accessible places learned to adjust to the French way of living—becoming garage mechanics, hotelkeepers, or perhaps chauffeurs on the bus route from Algiers to Gao on the Niger River. Some moved into the Algerian cities where they continued to act as a restless and rebellious group, resentful of any authority. In Morocco, which the French entered in 1911, one third of the whole population still uses the Berber language.

Meanwhile the Arabs became farmers and merchants. With French technical assistance, the Arabs increased the production of date palms, now producing not for their own food supply only, but also for export. An almost continuous ribbon of date palms followed the course of the Wadi Saura for some 750 miles from the southern base of the Atlas Mountains to the oasis of In-Salah. Date culture was extended, too, along the wadis radiating from the Ahaggar, such as the Igharghar, which leads northward, the Tamanrasset, which leads westward, the Tafasaset, which leads eastward, and the Tesselaman, which leads southward. These changes represented an extension of the wet spots, but no radical change in their pattern; they also meant a considerable increase in the density of population. In addition, the use of well-drilling machinery created entirely new oases by tapping the deep-lying artesian water. Whereas the sedentary oasis farmers of the first period were able to dig wells as much as 150 feet deep at Ghardaia, for example, in the hamada west of Touggourt, the Europeans could bore wells the depths of which are measured in thousands of feet. To be sure, the increased use of the underground sources of water resulted in a decrease of the supply, threatening the whole pattern of settlement in this region. For a time, however, more area could be irrigated and more people could be supported in the desert. The Europeans also substituted a commercial economy, based on the export of a surplus product and the import of goods from outside the region, for a subsistence economy, in which the people were entirely dependent on the products of their own locality.

The Period of Independence. Still another stage in the occupance of the Western Sahara began after World War II when Algeria, Morocco, and Tunisia became independent. The demand for an end to the colonial system that had been imposed by French military forces was a part of a world-wide reaction against all forms of colonialism. Countries that never had any sense of nationality demanded status as independent states, and at the same time economic and technical assistance. In 1956 French and Spanish Morocco, and the international settlement at Tangier, were brought together in an independent Morocco. Tunisia was also granted independence in that year. After a major effort to hold Algeria as a part of France, in 1962 that country was also granted independence.

Actual settlement by the French in Algeria was limited to the coastal fringe that lies outside of the dry land region. In Algeria as a whole, 89 per cent of the inhabitants were Muslim, and in the dry land area south of the Atlas Mountains almost all the people were Muslim. The Berbers especially were unwilling to maintain any ties with France; but when Algeria became independent the Berbers continued to rebel against the new authorities.

Meanwhile, another major change has taken place in the Sahara. In 1957 large supplies of both oil and gas were found, and for the first time the French could look forward to being free from dependence on Persian Gulf oil, and on the continued movement of oil tankers through Suez. Pipelines were built to carry gas to the Algerian city of Oran, where a petrochemical industry was being established with French aid. Oil pipelines were built to reach Mediterranean ports in Algeria and also Tunisia. Wherever oil was found, the supplies of water to maintain the oilfield workers and keep the well drills operating were provided at whatever cost. Even tanezroufts become habitable if the engineering costs of piping in water can be supported.

The old way of living in the desert is now gone, or is at least restricted

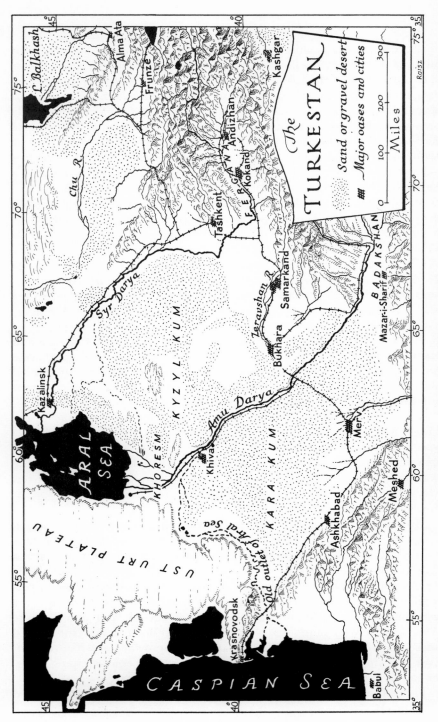

Map 9. The southern portion of the Aral depression.

to the most remote spots. The Western Sahara is now crossed by paved motor highways, supplied with service stations, and by motor vehicles including regular passenger bus service. Airlines provide even faster access to distant places. Pipelines move the oil and gas, and the water. Farming in the better lands is becoming mechanized, and more and more of the former desert dwellers are seeking employment in the growing cities.

THE OASES OF CENTRAL ASIA

Another great dry land area is located in Central Asia to the east of the Caspian Sea (Map 9). This vast depression, with the Aral Sea in its lowest area, was for thousands of years very thinly inhabited. The Kyzyl Kum and the Kara Kum are vast areas of sand and gravel, only occasionally wet enough to support poor grazing for sheep. But on the alluvial fans sloping out from the high mountains on the border of China, and along the courses of the two rivers—the Syr Darya and the Amu Darya—there have been oases for thousands of years.

Before the nineteenth century with its steamships and railroads, some of the oasis towns of Central Asia were famous as trading centers where caravan routes came together. One very ancient route leads from Mesopotamia and Persia to the oasis towns of Merv, Bukhara, Samarkand, Tashkent, and Kokand. From these places the caravans traveled on eastward around the margins of the Tarim Basin (Map 10), and on into eastern

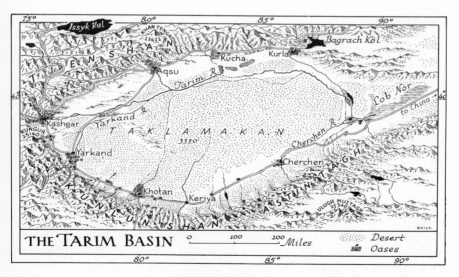

Map 10. The Tarim Basin.

China.   The early centers of Chinese culture in the Wei Ho Valley and the lower Yellow River were connected with the Mediterranean by this route.   A place such as Samarkand was a major stop on this ancient route.

The oases of Central Asia, in the area known generally as the Turkestan, are now part of the Soviet Union.   Bukhara, Samarkand, Kokand, and Tashkent are in the Uzbek Soviet Socialist Republic, a Muslim state included within the Soviet Union.   The Soviet engineers have provided for a large increase in the supply of water for irrigation in this area, enlarging not only the area in crops, but also the cities which serve these areas.   The oases of this region are now used to provide the greater part of the Soviet supply of cotton.   Cotton textile factories in Tashkent are supplied from nearby farms.   Electric power generated nearby provides the necessary power.   Samarkand is a city of monuments—the half ruined structures built when the Mongol leader Tamerlane made Samarkand his capital (1370–1405).   But today there are no longer any caravans of camels: Samarkand has its new apartment buildings to house the industrial workers, its factories, its airfield, and its richly productive farms in the surrounding countryside.

In China to the east of the Turkestan is the Tarim Basin (Map 10).   Here is a vast depression many hundreds of miles across, and lying at a much higher elevation than that of the Turkestan.   The center of the Tarim Basin is occupied by an erg (the great Taklamakan), which is uninhabited. The waters draining from the bordering mountains are gathered in the Tarim River and brought to the salty depression of the Lob Nor.   But where the rivers emerge from the mountains, near the apexes of the alluvial fans, an abundant supply of water is available, and here the oases are located. From Kashgar and Yarkand the old caravan routes run eastward either along the northern edge of the basin or along the southern edge, passing from oasis to oasis.   Along these routes, which eventually reach the populous eastern part of China, two-humped camels are still used to carry a small current of trade in highly valuable products.   People are permanently settled only in the isolated wet spots.   This is a part of the thinly-peopled dry-land area that separates the Soviet Union from China.

THE ATACAMA

There are many other deserts of the world.   The great Gobi of Mongolia, like the Tarim, is cold and wind-swept as well as arid.   There are hot deserts, such as those of Australia, where isolated settlements are scattered many days' overland journey apart and where the few isolated settlers raise sheep for a meager living.

In Northern Chile there is the Atacama Desert, important because of

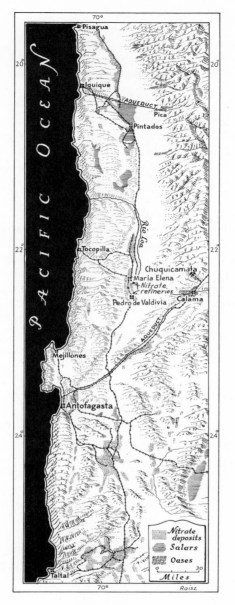

Map 11. The Atacama.

the lesson it offers in the permanency of desert settlement. This desert (Map 11) lies between the Pacific Ocean and the very high western cordillera of the Andes on the border of Chile and Bolivia. The land rises abruptly from the sea to an elevation of more than 3000 feet. But inland from this abrupt rise there is a long structural valley of gentle slopes extending parallel to the mountain front.   Along the west-facing front of the Andes very small valleys emerge onto alluvial fans that stretch out westward as much as forty miles into the desert.   But since the mountains are also dry, only those streams that rise in the snow fields above 20,000 feet in altitude carry water all the year round.   The others offer only enough water to support small oasis communities—some of only a few hundred people.   The only exotic river is the Río Loa, which emerges from the mountains near Calama, but shortly thereafter enters a deep gorge cut through the coast range and into the floor of the structural valley.

The Early Period.   Human settlement in this region goes back thousands of years before the Inca rulers who lived in the mountains to the north established a route of communications through the Atacama to Middle Chile.   The communications were maintained by runners who went from oasis to oasis along the mountain front.   Each little oasis was built at the very apex of an alluvial fan, sheltered even within the mountain valleys. With water supplies very small, the best place to dig a well is exactly where the fan begins to emerge from the mouth of the valley.   Farther out on the fan slope, the water is too far below the surface.   Only where the rivers carry much water, as in the Turkestan, can the oases extend well down the fan slopes.

The European Period.   When the Spaniards came to the Atacama, the north-south line of communications was abandoned and east-west roads were built to the coastal ports.   As a result Calama, a relatively large oasis supported by the water of the exotic Loa, became an important Spanish settlement.

During the nineteenth century two important minerals were found in the Atacama.   These were copper and nitrate.   Big mining establishments were built, railroads were built to connect them with ports along the coast, and thousands of workers were brought into the region.   In such a desert all the fuel, all the building materials, even all the food had to be brought in from outside to supply the mining camps and the ports.   In some cases pipelines, such as the one from Pica to Iquique, were built into the mountains to bring water to the mines.   But in many cases water was actually brought in by steamer and distributed to the mining towns by tank car. Only such valuable products as copper or nitrate could pay the high cost of such expensive settlement.

And then the mines had to curtail their production or shut down entirely.   Copper was too abundant on the world markets, and nitrate was being produced from the air by a manufacturing process.   Workers by the thousands had to leave the Atacama since they could no longer be

An open-pit copper mine at Chuquicamata, Chile.

supported there. Today production of both copper and nitrate continues at a reduced rate; but the time will come, and in the not distant future, when the supplies of these minerals are exhausted, and what then? The ports will be abandoned, since there will be no commerce to pay to keep the aqueducts in order or to import supplies. Only Calama and the ports that serve it will remain active. But the Indian farmers along the western front of the Andes, long forgotten by the busy world of industry and commerce, will continue to occupy their little oases. They alone have formed a permanently workable connection with the land.

THE ORANGE RIVER

European settlement in the dry lands is not necessarily temporary, although the unregulated exploitation of resources for quick profit, which is an Occidental trait, makes continued settlement impossible in many places. In the Orange River region of South Africa (Map 12) we have an example of apparently successful settlement by European farmers based on irrigation. Much of South Africa is arid or semiarid, and the Orange River, like the Nile, rises in a rainy mountain region and flows as a dwindling exotic stream across country which becomes drier and drier.

In the larger sense, most of South Africa is a plateau standing 4000 to

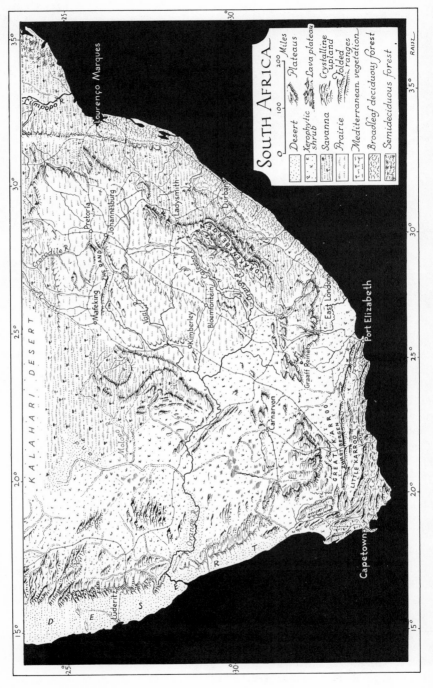

Map 12. South Africa.

6000 feet above the sea. The watershed between the Atlantic and Indian oceans is in a high and mountainous escarpment edge known as the Drakensbergen, which overlooks the coastal region around Durban. Many short swift rivers run to the Indian Ocean, whereas the Orange and its principal tributary, the Vaal, take the westward drainage from the Drakensbergen to the Atlantic over a course of 1640 miles. The eastern two thirds of this distance is through areas that receive an annual rainfall of from two to fifteen inches, with temperatures that permit a growing season throughout the year. Here the natural vegetation changes toward the west from a semiarid grassland to a true desert with only scattered desert succulents and almost no grass. Upstream, above the junction of the Orange and the Vaal, rainfall is more adequate, and cultivation of the land is possible without irrigation or with supplementary irrigation. Even in this humid area the rainfall is erratic in seasonal distribution and in amount. The Orange River system is unlike the Nile in that its waters come from only one catchment area. Thus the irregular rainfall at the source is translated into non-periodic occurrences of high and low water in the valley lower down. In the dry-land section, the Orange may be a raging torrent at one time and a series of stagnant pools at another, a condition which makes irrigation difficult. Another difficulty is the narrow trench-like character of the valley. There are only a few places where alluvial land can be reached by canals and feeders and also be protected against floodwaters. And, finally, the dams and canals used to control the waters are quickly filled with silt because of the heavy burden of sediment carried by the Orange River.

Because of these difficulties only particular places are suitable for irrigation projects. One such area is the middle course of the Orange, where the valley is open and broad, with alluvial terraces, and the river itself is a braid of several channels enclosing low-lying silt and sand islands. Occasional narrows where hard rock structures are intersected by the stream provide sites for storage and diversion dams. Only a half century ago this middle course, where the rainfall is less than 10 inches a year, was occupied almost solely by pastoral Hottentot peoples who had been driven to the water by prolonged droughts. They made only primitive attempts to divert water to their gardens. The first farming project by white men in this desert was undertaken in 1894 at Upington, which is located where the northwest-southeast railroad crosses the river. At that place Boers (South Africans of Dutch-Huguenot ancestry) settled and developed the land under the auspices of the Dutch Reformed Church. The church and individuals sponsored other small but independent irrigation projects until, in 1929, the government built the Buchuberg Dam, some 100 miles above Upington, to act as a reservoir for all the improved land as far as the Aughrabies Falls, about 75 miles below Upington. Thus in the short span of one

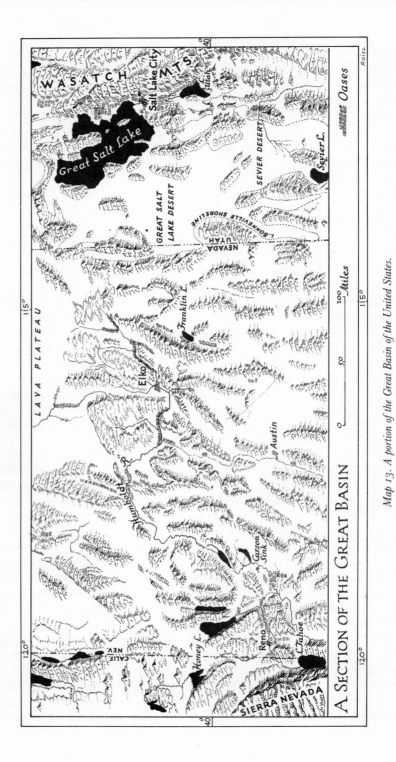

Map 13. *A portion of the Great Basin of the United States.*

generation an oasis has been created where formerly mankind had no permanent habitation. Today the oasis has a population of 35,000, including the town of Upington (20,249), which is supported by the intensive cultivation of some 70 square miles of irrigated land producing raisin grapes (sultanas), alfalfa, wheat, oranges, maize, and a little cotton.

The fight to win the land along this part of the Orange River has been successful; the fight to maintain the victory continues. The Buchuberg dam is silting rapidly, so that eventually other reservoirs (such as the Vaaldam, north of Kimberley, 700 miles away) must be used. There is always the danger of extreme drought, and the even greater risk of combined heavy floods on both the Orange and the Vaal, which might severely damage any irrigation works below their confluence.

THE GREAT BASIN

There are also deserts in the United States and Mexico. There is a large area of inland drainage between the Sierra Nevada on the west and the Wasatch Mountains on the east (Map 13). This is a portion of the Great Basin—a basin and range desert where flat-floored bolsons separate irregularly-placed desert ranges. Water from the high Sierra Nevada or the Wasatch Mountains is abundant and provides support for large oases; but from the desert ranges comes only a small supply of water, and here the oases are small and placed high on the fans. The Humboldt River, however, rises in the high ranges in the central part of the basin and provides water for irrigation at several places along its course. Carson City and Reno are surrounded by extensive irrigated lands. On the eastern side there is an almost continuous fringe of irrigated land on the alluvial fans of the Wasatch Mountains. The important cities are Salt Lake City, Ogden, and Provo, in Utah. The rivers from the Wasatch drain into Great Salt Lake, the fluctuating shores of which reflect the varying quantity of water supplied to it.

The sequence of settlement in the Great Basin is much simpler than that of the Sahara, or even the Atacama. The Indians of this part of America were a hunting people. The few who inhabited the Great Basin itself sought the wild game of the mountains and formed no permanent settlements in the bolsons. The first people of European origin to settle in the region were the Mormons, who, at Salt Lake City, established a farming community in a spot they hoped would be so remote that their persecutors would never reach them. In this hope they were disappointed, for the discovery of gold in California soon brought many travelers plodding westward across deserts and difficult mountain passes. The Mormons were caught up in the fabric of American settlement in the course of time and made a part of it. The isolated oases of the Great Basin were reached by

Salt Lake City, a modern oasis city (Wasatch Mountains in background)
(Salt Lake City Chamber of Commerce).

railroads. From a purely subsistence economy, the oasis communities adopted commercial crops which could be exchanged for the much-desired manufactured products of the eastern cities. Since these oases are too far north to permit such hot-desert specialties as cotton (which can be grown at Phoenix) and dates (which can be grown along the lower Colorado), the greater part of the irrigated lands in Utah and Nevada are used for growing summer feed crops to be fed to animals during the winter, and for such high-value but hardy crops as sugar beets and potatoes.

THE IMPERIAL VALLEY

One other example of the occupance of the regions of Group I is the Imperial Valley in southern California. This region has only a very brief record of successful settlement; but it is spectacular among desert oases because here man has at last learned how to control the formation of alkali.

The Imperial Valley was at one time the head of the Gulf of Lower California. The Colorado River entered the Gulf near its northern limit, and

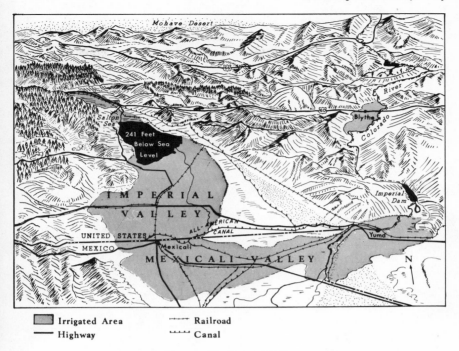

Map 14. The Imperial Valley.

the delta built by the river cut off the head of the Gulf. No longer connected with the ocean, the water quickly evaporated, leaving a depression with a very salty lake in its bottom—the Salton Sea. The surface of this lake is 273 feet below sea level (Map 14).

This depression was long feared as the hottest, driest, and most desolate desert of western North America, rivalled only by the famous Death Valley a little to the north. Travelers wanting to reach California from Yuma on the Colorado River, made a wide circle to the north to avoid the valley, and many of those who tried to cross it directly lost their lives. It is one of the world's hottest areas, with between 15 and 29 days over 110° in the average year, and with less than three inches of average annual rainfall.

Efforts to bring water to the valley began in the 1890's when an irrigation and land development company was formed. About 1900 water was brought to the valley from the Colorado River in a canal that passed through Mexican territory. The company changed the name from the California Desert to the Imperial Valley and started selling land. Now water is supplied in the All-American Canal in sufficient quantity to irrigate

A grove of date palms in southern California (Josef Muench).

about a million acres.   With plenty of water in the hot sun, crops grow luxuriantly, much as they do in the similarly situated Fayum of Egypt.

The land in the Imperial Valley became very valuable.   In this one area
it is possible to produce an abundance of vegetables, fruit, cotton, alfalfa
and other crops.   In January and February most of the country's supply
of lettuce, carrots, and cabbage comes from here.   Enough lettuce is produced to fill four 100-car freight trains each day.   As a result the land increased in value to between $1000 and $1500 an acre.

Across the Mexican border in the southern part of this same area, farmers have developed one of Mexico's largest areas of cotton production.
These two parts of the same valley, which are dependent on water from
the same river, have developed quite different kinds of land use because in
Mexico there is no such national market for high-value vegetables and fruits
as there is in the United States.

Then the usual problem of irrigated areas in hot deserts began to develop.
When the water was allowed to evaporate in the soil it dropped its load of
salt.   Little by little the calcium salts, which are good for crops, were replaced by the sodium salts which form the sterile alkali.   By 1920 some 50,-
000 acres had been abandoned, and the Imperial Valley seemed headed
in the same direction as many other irrigated lands in other parts of the
world's dry lands.   Several decades of study and experimentation, however,
provided the answer—drainage.   A thirty-million-dollar drainage system
has been constructed.   Tile pipes lie buried some six feet below the surface,
and the salts are flushed into these pipes and deposited in the Salton Sea.
Now some 300,000 acres have been tiled.

This way of handling the alkali problem, however, raises other problems.
The canal to the Imperial Valley takes off about 25 per cent of the total
volume of the Colorado River, which is three times as much as is allotted
to the cities of Los Angeles and San Diego.   And about 25 per cent of this
water is used to flush out the salts and carry them through the drainage
pipes to the Salton Sea.   The thirsty cities of southern California want more
water; and the cotton farmers south of the border also want more water.
The Hoover Dam on the Colorado provides a vast storage reservoir, but
even then there is not enough water to meet all these needs.

As in all the dry land regions, water is scarce, and there are many competing uses for it.   But in the Imperial Valley the engineers have found the
technical means of solving the alkali problem, and of making the dry land
oases continue to produce luxuriantly year after year.

Summary

The world's deserts have held different meaning for different people.
They have meant hardship and hunger; but where water could be provided,

they have meant luxury and comfort.   The deserts have been described as "difficult" habitats in which to make a living; yet there are parts of the world today where the dry lands are attracting throngs of new settlers.

The world's deserts have not been unproductive.   In the hot deserts, wherever irrigation is possible, the yields of crops have been high.   The crops include long-staple cotton, fruits (dates, oranges, lemons, grapefruit, limes), vegetables, grains, and alfalfa for cattle.   In the cool deserts the crops are more limited, but still valuable enough to make the cost of irrigation development worth while.   Here the crops include alfalfa (for the winter feeding of cattle), sugar beets, potatoes, and grains.

The problem of increasing the supply of water is not always easy.   Modern deep-drilling techniques can tap deep-lying underground water sources. But such water sources can be used too fast.   Wells near the oceans can be pumped out so fast that salt water seeps back into the ground water and ruins the wells.   There are interesting possibilities in processes for taking the salt out of sea water; already the oil-rich state of Kuwait gets all its water supply from a desalinization plant.   The island of Curaçao in the Caribbean is similarly supplied.   But desalinized sea water cannot be pumped very far inland under present economic conditions. Sea water could be very important for coastal cities, or for irrigated areas less than 50 miles from the ocean.

The alkali problem remains a threat in any irrigated area.   To be sure, in the Nile Valley natural conditions that kept alkali from forming existed before the building of the Aswan Dam.   But in Mesopotamia a very large area has already been ruined.   Irrigation on alluvial fans permits better drainage than on flat land, but even on the fans alkali can form if the water is allowed to evaporate.   In the Imperial Valley the engineering skill has been perfected for eliminating the alkali hazard—provided enough water is available, and the high costs are justified.

The Tropical Forest Lands

T HE TROPICAL FOREST LANDS of the earth also represent a distinctive kind of habitat. Although these regions can be contrasted in almost every way with the dry lands, they nevertheless serve to illustrate some of the same general principles of man-land relations that were discussed in the last chapter. Here again we find illustrations of how very similar habitats hold quite different meanings for people with contrasted attitudes, objectives, and technical skills. These different meanings can be discovered not only by following the sequent occupance in specific regions, but also by comparing the occupance in widely separated but physically similar parts of Group II. For farmers who cultivate the land with hoes, living in the tropical forests is one thing; for the skilled paddy-rice farmers of Southeast Asia, the tropical forests hold a quite different meaning. Europeans and Americans, moreover, have had to overcome strong preconceptions about these regions inherited from the writers of antiquity.

The regions of Group II differ from one another with respect to the density and pattern of population. The great area of tropical forest in the Amazon Basin is one of the world's largest areas of very scanty settlement. In contrast, Java is one of the more densely populated parts of the world, and smaller areas of very dense settlement are to be found in parts of the American tropics and in parts of India. The densely populated areas have so many people in them that the regions of Group II as a whole, which include about 10 per cent of the world's land area, are occupied by some 28 per cent of the world's population.

The Habitat

VEGETATION AND CLIMATE

A distinctive association of habitat features characterizes the regions of Group II. These are rainy lands—some very rainy with a superabundance of moisture, some seasonally rainy. There is enough water so that most surface streams are perennial. The cover of tropical forest, found here before human inhabitants cleared some of it away, reflects not only a plentiful supply of water, at least during a part of each year, but also an absence of cold weather. A lateritic soil, where mature soils can develop, results from the peculiar combination of physical and organic processes. The

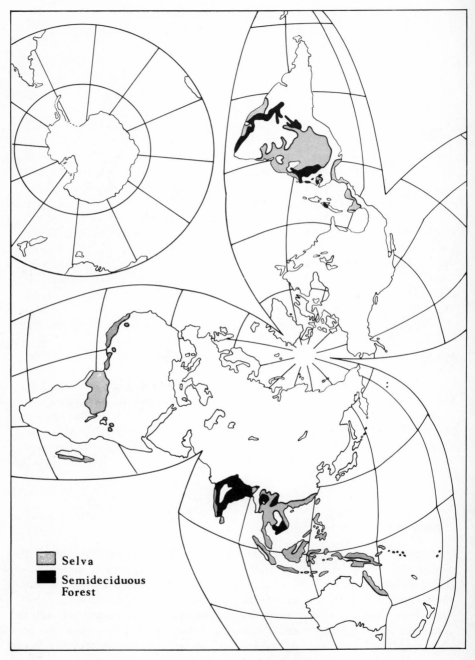

Map 15. The tropical forest lands.

surfaces of these regions are not classed as high mountain; they range from low mountains to plains. The landforms are produced under very different climatic conditions than those characteristic of the dry lands.

Forests, wherever they occur, are made up of trees that grow close enough together so that the foliage forms a complete cover over the ground. For this reason there are few low branches, and the trees are tall and straight-stemmed. The tropical forests are made up of species of trees that cannot survive low temperatures. There are two kinds of forests in this group: in very wet areas where there is no prolonged dry season there is a *tropical rain forest;* where there is a distinct dry season there is a *tropical semi-deciduous forest.*

The Tropical Rain Forest. The tropical rain forest, or *selva*, is the world's most vigorous vegetation growth. Unlike most of the forests familiar to mid-latitude people, the selva is composed of an extraordinary variety of species. In one square mile of the island of Trinidad, where a special study of the forest composition was made, nearly three thousand distinct species of trees and plants were identified. It is not unusual to find as many as eighty to a hundred different kinds of trees on a single acre. For the botanist such conditions offer a fascinating and almost inexhaustible field of study; but for the person who wishes to make commercial use of any

Tropical rain forest, Brazaville, Congo (Three Lions).

one kind of tree, this profuse variety is a major handicap, for the individual trees of any one species are usually widely scattered throughout the forest.

The tropical rain forest is an impressive sight for persons brought up in other parts of the world. The endless variety of vegetation forms defies detailed description. Within the selva one feels shut in, as in the crypt of a cathedral, for little light is able to reach the forest floor. The individual trees are tall and straight-stemmed, with only a plume of branches and foliage at the top. From the ground one sees only the massive perpendicular trunks that support the thick canopy of leaves overhead where the branches are interlaced in the relentless struggle for sunlight and life. In the gloom below there is little color and little underbrush; the space between the tree trunks is laced with a network of lianas, some as fine as hairs and others like great knotted ropes.

The remarkable rapidity of vegetation growth is best revealed when a clearing is made. Perhaps the clearing is an abandoned garden plot; perhaps it is the result of the fall of some giant tree which has crushed in its descent all the lesser trees within reach. Through the hole in the leafy covering the sunlight is able to reach the ground. In a very brief time an impenetrable tangle of plants fills the opening, thereby producing a true *jungle*. There is a period of fierce struggle to grow upward to the light, which is ended only when another forest giant has replaced the fallen one, and the fabric of the foliage is whole once more.

The rhythm of life in the selva is confused. Each individual plant goes through the life processes, producing leaves, flowers, fruits, and seeds in its own period. At all times of the year there are individual trees losing their leaves, or budding new leaves and flowers, or covered with ripened fruit, which, for a short time, attracts a multitude of birds. The forest is evergreen.*

The Tropical Semideciduous Forest.   Such a vegetation growth as the selva can be supported only by excessive amounts of moisture: where the moisture supply is less abundant, or where a dry season imposes at least a partial rhythm, a lighter forest which is semideciduous in character is the result. The semideciduous forest is composed of smaller trees than the selva. The canopy of foliage is not so thick that light is excluded from the forest floor. As a result, the semideciduous forest has a thicker underbrush than the selva and is not so easy to pass through. Yet even in the case of

*An evergreen tree is one which does not drop its leaves and stand with bare branches during any season of the year. It may drop one leaf at a time, or even all its leaves at one time, but each leaf is immediately replaced with a new sprout. A forest composed mostly of trees of this sort is described as evergreen. A deciduous tree is one which does lose all its leaves and which stands with bare branches during a season of the year. A forest composed partly of evergreen and partly of deciduous species is described as a semideciduous forest.

this type of forest the true jungle appears only when the land has been cleared. The jungle is a second growth, usually resulting from human action.

Another great difference between this and the rain forest is the existence of a seasonal rhythm. The dry season, which is more pronounced in these regions of lighter forest, imposes a period of rest on the vegetation, just as the winter season imposes a similar period on the forets of the middle latitudes. Many, although not all, of the trees lose their leaves, and the landscape takes on a brownish or grayish tinge. The beginning of the rainy season brings back the dark green of vigorous and thriving vegetation. The sprouting of new leaves, the budding, the flowering, and the ripening of fruit are synchronized.

The Wet Margin.   Where both the tropical rain forest and the tropical semideciduous forest border the ocean along low, shelving coasts, there has developed a peculiar vegetation type which has a number of unique characteristics. This is the mangrove forest—not distinguished from the other kinds of tropical forest on Map 15 because it occurs only in a fringe along the coast which is usually too narrow to show on these maps. True mangrove consists of only one kind of tree of the genus *Rhizophora*. On the shores of tidal swamps where the water is brackish, there is a dense tangle of evergreen trees which grow some 15 or 20 feet in height, with spreading bushy branches and numerous aerial roots. The bark is reddish in color and useful as an astringent; the leaves are oblong and glossy; the pale yellow flowers and conical berrylike fruit appear at all times of the year with no seasonal rhythm. New trees develop from seeds that germinate in the air and that are attached to the root system of the parent trees. The result is a tangle of bushy forest which is all but impenetrable. The mangrove fringe actually makes long stretches of tropical coasts approachable only with difficulty, especially for people with sailing vessels. Many of the ports in tropical lands were originally established where natural breaks in the mangrove permitted the entrance of ships to the higher ground behind. For persons equipped with modern machinery the clearing of mangrove offers no serious problem.

Native Animals of the Tropical Forests.   The native wild animals of the tropical forests differ considerably on the different continents. In the South American forests there is a notable paucity of large ground animals, although there are many different kinds of birds, monkeys, and snakes inhabiting the dense foliage far above the ground. Underneath, in the deep shadows, close observation reveals a multiutde of insects, such as ants and spiders. The termites, or white ants, are particularly destructive of any

A water buck at the margin of a stream in the tropical scrub forest in Uganda (photo by H. V. B. Kline, Jr.).

organic matter which chances to fall on the ground. Whole villages have been abandoned in the face of an invasion of ants.

In Africa the rain forests are occasionally penetrated by larger animals than those found in South America. There are elephants, buffalo, hippopotamus, okapi, bongo, and crocodile. But most of these animals are characteristically associated with the woodland savannas of Group III, and will be discussed in connection with those regions.

It is important to point out, however, that the insect life is especially varied in the tropical forest lands. In fact, human settlement in some of these regions seems more severely restricted by the presence of certain insects than by any supposed difficulties of the climate. Especially dangerous are the disease carrying mosquitoes, such as the anopheles mosquito of which some 35 species carry malaria and yellow fever. These mosquitoes are not restricted to the tropical forest regions, but because of the lack of economic development and modern health measures in these regions, the anopheles has remained common in these regions longer than elsewhere. In the period since the development of insecticides such as DDT, the anopheles mosquito and malaria have been greatly reduced.

Weather and Climate in the Tropical Forests. One of the parts of the world where weather and climate come close to meaning the same thing is in the wetter parts of the tropical forest regions. As these terms are properly defined, weather is the state of the atmosphere at any given time, whereas climate is the average of weather at a particular place and for a particular period. But in the tropical rain forest, at least, the day-to-day and month-to-month weather is so remarkably uniform that the two words seem to have almost the same meaning. The weather is so similar from day to day that the common small talk of mid-latitude peoples is difficult to carry on, and appointments are made in terms of the showers and alternating periods of sunshine.

These regions are characterized by monotonously high temperatures. The common belief that the equatorial regions are unbearably hot is quite incorrect. The highest temperatures in the world have been observed, as we have seen, in the deserts. Temperatures in summer in the lower middle latitudes (in the Mississippi Valley, or the Ganges Valley, or the Argentine Chaco) are much higher than any experienced in the low latitudes near the equator. At Belém, near the mouth of the Amazon, for example, the temperature has never reached 100°. The highest temperature recorded at a place farther up the Amazon was 96.3°. Yet between the average of the coldest and warmest months there is a range of only about 3°. It often has been said that "night is the winter of the tropics," for the diurnal range (between day and night) is actually greater than the annual range. At Belém the temperatures at night drop some 15° below those of the hottest part of the day. In such a climate the terms *summer* and *winter* are misleading, for there is really nothing that corresponds to our mid-latitude concept of winter. The average annual temperatures are between 70° and 80°—few are higher than that. Only rarely are very high temperatures experienced, and rarely do the temperatures drop below 60°. At Belém the average highest and lowest temperatures of the year are 91.4° and 68.0°, respectively.

The *heat equator* is the line connecting the places of the world which have the highest average annual temperatures. It passes along the northern coast of South America and along the Guinea Coast of Africa—lying some five to ten degrees north of the geographic equator in these continents. It runs south of the geographic equator only in northern Australia.

Temperatures such as are recorded in the rainy tropics would be quite comfortable were it not for the rains and the humidity. In the tropical rain forests the humidity is especially high. Even though the year in all but a few parts of the tropics is divided into a rainy season and a dry season (instead of summer and winter), the dry season in the selva is actually only a season of less rain. On a characteritic day the sun rises in a clear sky. Fog is sometimes hanging in the low valleys but this speedily rises in curling wisps of vapor as the land is heated by the sun's rays. Soon puffy cumulus clouds appear and before long cover a large part of the sky. A light shower may occur, often as early as eight or nine o'clock in the morning. This is followed by a period of brilliant sunshine and then by another shower. Showers and sunshine alternate in this way throughout the day, the former becoming more severe and of longer duration as the day progresses. About four in the afternoon a very heavy shower occurs—a deluge of rain accompanied by little wind. The storm, at first torrential, later settles down to a steady rain which continues into the evening. It is a characteritic remembrance of the rainy tropics: the beat of rain on an iron roof, the monotonous splash as the water runs off onto the ground, and the sticky wetness that penetrates everything and leaves one soaked with perspiration. Well into the night the rain gradually ceases and is succeeded by a deep silence, relieved only by the dripping of water from the soaking foliage and by the hum of the dreaded mosquito. Without the cooling winds of an exposed coast the tropical rainy lands may become quite uncomfortable.

But there are many parts of the tropical forest lands where the climate is not at all like this. Especially on the east coasts of the continents and islands, strong easterly winds increase the evaporation and in part compensate for high humidity. Where the graceful coconut palms toss their heads in the steady, strong breeze from the water and where the buildings are open to the moving air, life can be untroubled by the stimulating effect of variable weather such as is experienced in the middle latitudes. Here, in a veritable paradise, men may relax if they know how to do so.

The paradise is a dangerous one, however. It is a fact that where the human body is not subject to the necessity for making adjustments to frequent changes in temperature and humidity, it eventually loses the capacity for such adjustment. The "chills" which are described as dangerous for health in almost all handbooks on tropical living can result from a drop of only a few degrees in temperature. Long residence in the extremely monotonous climates of parts of the low latitudes can, apparently, produce bad physiological effects on the human system. It is the monotony, rather than the high temperature, which is bad; and it is equally bad for people of all races.

Wartime studies of the effect of high temperature and high humidity on the human system have demonstrated that there are certain maximum combinations of heat and humidity beyond which the human body cannot survive. Heatstroke and death can result where the air is saturated with moisture and where the temperature reaches only $85°$. Where the air contains 70 per cent of all the moisture it can carry (in other words, where the relative humidity is 70 per cent) the danger point is reached when the temperature is $95°$. These combinations of heat and humidity are actually experienced occasionally in nature, but no place on earth has average conditions of this sort. The fact is, too, that the places where high heat and high humidity occur together most often are generally not in the rainy tropics.　The part of the world in which human life is most difficult in terms of these weather elements is along the shores of the Red Sea, in a region which receives very scanty rainfall.

Distribution of the Tropical Forest Lands.　The general arrangement of the tropical forest lands in the world can be described quite simply (Map 15).　They occupy a belt somewhat less than 20° wide on either side of the equator and extend poleward along the eastern sides of the continents to the margins of the low latitudes.　Even more than in the case of the dry lands, this general position is modified in detail on each of the continents.　As a result of the disposition of the land masses, however, there are three chief areas of occurrence: in the Americas, in Africa, and in Asia-Australia.

The largest single area of selva in the world is in the Amazon Basin and parts of the Guianas (Plate 10).　The westward extension of this forest is limited by the Andes, and only a narrow fringe of selva is found along the Pacific Ocean in Ecuador and Colombia.　On the east coast of South America the selva is found as far south as latitude 25° S.; and a semideciduous forest extends somewhat farther south in the Paraná Valley of eastern Paraguay.　Most of the eastern margin of the Brazilian Highlands was once covered with semideciduous forest.　North of the equator the wetter east-facing sides of the Antilles were once covered with semideciduous forest.　The island of Trinidad was almost wholly covered with selva.　The lowlands along the eastern side of Central America and Mexico, as far north as Tampico (about 22° N.), were covered with selva and semideciduous forest.

In Africa selvas and semideciduous forest occupy parts of the Congo Basin and parts of the south-facing Guinea Coast.　The Congo forests are not so luxuriant as those of the Amazon Basin, nor are they so extensive.　The east coast of Africa, on the other hand, has no tropical forest in the latitudes where such forests normally occur.　Here the irregularity resulting from the arrangement of surface features prevails over the regularity of climate.

Selvas and semideciduous forests occur in many small areas in southern and southeastern Asia, northeastern Australia, and many of the islands of the Pacific.　Very dense selva once covered the rainy area at the head of the Bay of Bengal.　Semideciduous forests occupied the Ganges Valley and a large part of southern India.　In the narrow valley lowlands and deltas of Southeast Asia there were many small areas of dense forest, interspersed with woodlands either where rainfall is lighter, or where man has intervened.

The distribution of these types of tropical forests is related to the pattern of rainfall effectiveness.   Where the rainfall is heavy throughout the year there is a rain forest.   A rain forest is also found where there is a brief dry season, provided enough rain comes during the rainy part of the year so that the soil does not dry out during the dry season.   Table II (Appendix B) defines this boundary for the Köppen system of classification.   The climates that support rain forests are Af or Am.   On the other hand, where the conditions of rainfall and other factors permit the soil to dry out during one season of the year, semideciduous forests occur; and, as the dry period is longer and drier, these become poorer and more like woodlands.   On the dry margin, under natural conditions, the semideciduous forests merge into woodlands.

SURFACE FEATURES

The surface features of the humid lands of the world are quite different from those of the dry lands.   There are, to be sure, the same kinds of geologic structures and rocks in both; but the manner in which the rock structures have been sculptured by the processes of erosion in the rainy lands is very different from that in the dry lands.   Under rainy tropical conditions, where there is a dense cover of forest vegetation, the rock surfaces are usually decomposed to great depths by chemical action.   The mantle of loose earth that covers the solid rock is molded into rounded forms quite different from the angular forms of the deserts.   Rivers find their ways to the ocean and carry with them large quantities of alluvium.   Where structural basins occur which in the dry lands might form bolsons, they are filled with water.   The rift depressions of East Africa (Plate 3), which are filled with fresh-water lakes, are very similar in geologic structure to such dryland rifts as Death Valley in California or the Dead Sea depression of Palestine.

Surface Configuration.   The larger surface features that stand out when we examine continental maps—and are comparable to such features as hamadas, ergs, or basin and range in the dry lands—are four in number: plains, plateaus, hilly uplands, and low mountains.   The high mountains, which in some places closely border the regions of this group, are included in Group IX.

The words used to describe these four major surface features are all common in nontechnical language.   The words used by geographers to describe the surface features of the dry lands are strange to most people who speak English, but every such person thinks he knows what is meant by the words plain, plateau, hill, or mountain.   Yet the actual use of these words in naming the features of the land suggests that in the popular vocabulary there is no very careful definition of them.   The Turtle Mountains of North Dakota, for example, are only a few hundred feet high above the plain upon which they stand; they are really a part of the plain, but the local people call them mountains. If they are to be called mountains, then the Berkshire Hills of Massachusetts would certainly have to be renamed. To use these words in a more exact geographic sense, we must define them more carefully than does the dictionary; but in so doing we must be prepared to find that features popularly called mountains are really plains, that features called plateaus are really hills, or that features called hills are really plateaus. We must be ready to distinguish between proper names and the more or less technical geographic terms which describe them.

These four categories of surface features may be given somewhat more accurate definition as follows. A *plain* is an area of low relief,* generally less than five hundred feet. It is low-lying with reference to bordering areas, and is usually, but not in every case, low in altitude. A *plateau* stands distinctly above bordering areas, at least on one side; and it has a large part of its total surface at or near the summit level. Its local relief may be very great in cases where it is cut by canyons; or it may have as small a local relief as a plain, from which it differs in such a case only because of its position with reference to bordering areas. A *hilly upland* has more than five hundred feet of local relief and has a relatively small proportion of its surface at or near the summit level. *Low mountains* have more than a thousand feet of local relief, and, like hilly lands, have a relatively small proportion of the surface near the summit level. High mountains, which are given further definition in the chapter dealing with Group IX, generally have a local relief in excess of three thousand feet.

These distinctions between the major surface features of rainy lands are, of course, arbitrary, and in many places are difficult to apply. An area which fulfills the definition of a plateau on one side may resemble a plain on the other side; or a hilly upland may seem conspicuous enough to be called a mountain from one viewpoint. The name actually applied is more or less a matter of custom. For example, the Congo Basin might be classified as a plateau because it drops steeply toward the sea; or as a plain because it is almost entirely surrounded by higher land and because its local relief is less than five hundred feet. As a matter of fact, it is generally described as a plain.

*The relief of an area is the difference in elevation between the highest and lowest points. Relief is different from altitude, which is usually measured from mean sea level. There may be surfaces of very slight local relief standing at very high altitudes—for example, the Plateau of Tibet; or there may be very steep slopes and great differences of local relief within an area which lies below sea level—as on the slopes of Death Valley. Local relief may be defined as difference of elevation within any selected area of restricted size. See V. C. Finch, G. T. Trewartha, A. H. Robinson, and E. H. Hammond, *Elements of Geography, Physical and Cultural* (New York, 1957), pp. 213–216, 265–355.

A hilly upland with tropical woodland in the rainy season—Northeast Brazil (photo by the author).

Distribution of Surface Features. The surface configuration of the several areas of Group II is presented on Plates 1–5, 13. The two great plains regions in this group are found in the Amazon Basin of South America and in the Congo Basin of Africa (Maps 16 and 17). However, although these two regions resemble each other in their relatively low relief, they are otherwise quite different. The Amazon drains a region of low altitude. The main stream is navigable for ocean ships for more than 2000 miles inland, almost to the base of the Andes. The Congo, on the other hand, drains a plain that lies over a thousand feet above sea level. The whole continent of Africa, in fact, may be thought of as a huge plateau with steeply scarped sides. The Congo descends over this escarpment in a series of falls and rapids. It is navigable for river steamers above the falls, but ocean ships can do no more than enter its mouth. Elsewhere throughout the regions of Group II small coastal or river lowlands exist, but none are on the scale of the Amazon and the Congo.

The plateaus, hilly uplands, and low mountains of this group are most extensive in Africa and South America. The East African Plateau follows

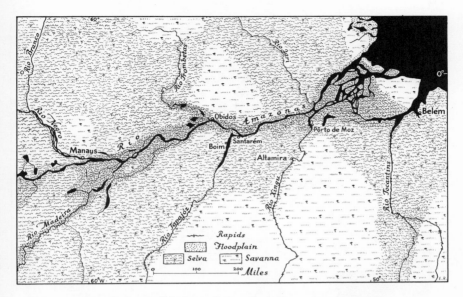

Map 16. A part of the lower Amazon Basin (vegetation after Denis).

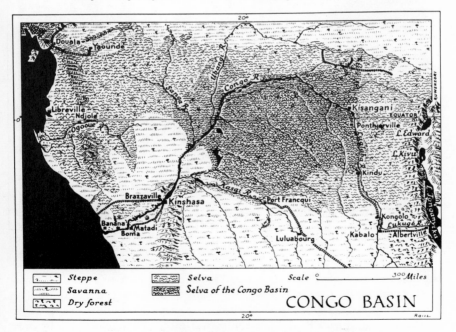

Map 17. Surface configuration and vegetation cover of the Congo Basin and adjoining areas (vegetation after Schantz and Marbut).

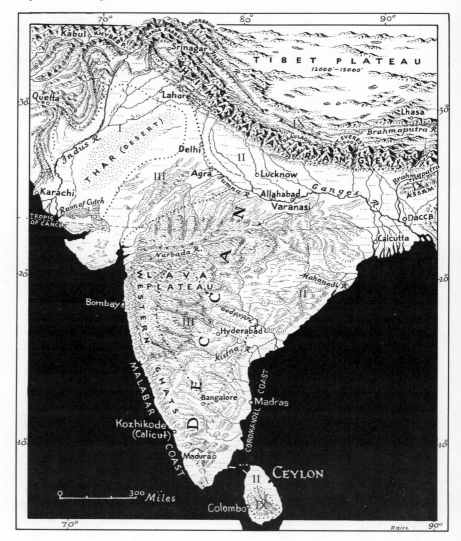

Map 18.

the eastern coast of Africa southward from Ethiopia, leaving only narrow patches of coastal lowlands along the water. In a few places the plateau is surmounted by mountains or broken by great rift valleys. The high-lands of Guiana and Brazil are somewhat more complicated. They are composed of a mixture of hilly upland, plateau, and low mountains.

Map 19.

From northeastern Brazil far to the south, the highland faces the coast with
a steep escarpment which rises between two and three thousand feet above
sea level. The peninsular part of India is also composed of a mixture of
plateaus, hilly uplands, and low mountains, and there is even a small area
of high mountains along the southwest side (Map 18). South of Bombay

the narrow fringe of coastal plain is known as the Malabar Coast. Northern Australia and parts of New Guinea and Borneo are also hilly.

Most parts of the Asian tropics, however, are made up of great river lowlands set in the midst of ranges of high or low mountains. There are extensive plains formed by the alluvial deposits along the lower courses of the Ganges-Brahmaputra, the Irrawaddy, the Chao Phraya, and the Mekong (Map 19). There are relatively wide plains along the northern sides of Sumatra and Java and in southern Borneo. But elsewhere there are only narrow delta plains that have formed where the rivers come down from the mountains. Similar conditions exist in Central America, in the Antilles, and in the islands of the southwest Pacific.

LANDFORMS, DRAINAGE, AND SOILS

The landform details developed by the processes of erosion under a forest cover where rainfall is abundant at least during one season also differ from the details of dry-land landscapes. Wherever there is land standing above the sea, rivers are doing the work of wearing it down, by carrying the loose rock particles downhill and eventually to the lowlands or into the sea. Under a dense forest cover, however, fairly steep slopes can remain protected from rapid erosion by the tangle of roots. When such slopes are cleared by man the results are often disastrous, for, with the protection of the forest removed, deep gullies speedily develop unless special measures, such as terracing, are taken to guard against this kind of destruction. When the streams descending from mountains or uplands reach the plains they begin to deposit silt and gravel, building alluvial plains and deltas. The rivers usually wind back and forth, or meander, across the plains, only in time of high water spilling out of their channels and inundating large areas. The land across which a river meanders and which is subject to flooding at high water is called the *floodplain*. It is sharply set off from the rest of the plain, which is not subject to flooding, by steep valley bluffs. Along the lower Amazon (Map 16) the floodplain is some fifty or sixty miles wide, and the valley bluffs which border it stand some two hundred feet above the river (see Appendix C, p. 495). Only on the floodplains or in lagoons along low coasts are there extensive swampy areas. The evaporation is too rapid to permit the presence of standing water at the surface for any long period of time except when it is actually raining.

In the wet parts of the world a certain proportion of the water that falls on the surface sinks into the ground. We have seen that in the dry lands only a small part of the rainfall actually gets into the soil where it is effective in the support of plants. In regions that are frozen for part of the year, the amount of water sinking into the ground is reduced. But in the rainy tropics the ground is never frozen; water sinks into it whenever rain falls. This percolating water is one of the factors which determines the character of the soil.

Water descending through the loose rock fragments that mantle the surface changes the soil in two ways, physically and chemically. In the first place (the physical change) it carries down with it the smaller soil particles. The upper layer of the soil becomes coarser and coarser; and the fine particles are deposited in a layer at some distance below the surface, eventually becoming a hardpan of clay. This process is called *eluviation*. The longer it goes on the poorer the surface soil becomes for shallow-rooted crops.

The second change produced by percolating water is a chemical one. The minerals which can be dissolved in the water are, little by little, carried away in solution, leaving in the upper soil layers only the relatively insoluble minerals, the ones least valuable for plant food. Like any chemical process, solution goes on more rapidly at higher temperatures than at lower temperatures. This process is called *leaching*, and, as in the case of eluviation, the longer it goes on the poorer the soil becomes. In the rainy tropics the minerals least apt to be dissolved are the iron and aluminum compounds. On level land which is not subject to flooding and so to the deposition of new alluvial material, the soil which develops is a yellowish or reddish sandy material known as a *latosol*. Outside the floodplains, other level lands of these regions normally have soils of low fertility for shallow-rooted crops. That tropical soils are fertile is one of the common misconceptions about the low latitudes.

There is a third soil-forming process that contributes also to the characteristic infertility of tropical soils. This is called *humus accumulation*. Organic matter falling on the forest floor is rapidly attacked by bacteria and decomposed. In cooler and less rainy regions bacterial action is slow, and a layer of dark-colored or black humus is found under the fallen leaves. But in the rainy tropics temperatures are high and bacterial action is very rapid. Humus can accumulate only in a very thin layer and in certain spots. When the forest is cleared the humus is quickly destroyed. This is another element of infertility in these soils in terms of the common food plants.

The Occupance

The conquest of these tropical lands by man is far from complete. In a few parts of the world the original landscape has been permanently and radically transformed by human settlement, but in each case this has been accomplished only by large numbers of settlers. Where such settlement has been made the population today is very dense—as in the Oriental rice lands. But the forest does not yield easily to small numbers of pioneers, nor to the more or less temporary activities of Occidental plantation owners. Certain people of simple farming culture have occupied parts of the tropical forest lands with moderate density, but the clearings they make are constantly threatened by the closely crowding cover of vegetation and are usually not permanent. Large areas of Group II are occupied by less than one person per square mile.

In these tropical regions, as in the dry lands previously described, the culture determines the way in which people occupy the territory. Besides the Occidental culture, which has in relatively recent times extended its influence into the different parts of this group, there is a considerable variety of "native" cultures. The word "native" is used here to describe non-Occidental cultures, although this use is admittedly somewhat loose, since many of the so-called native cultures were imposed by conquest upon still earlier native peoples, who themselves no doubt entered the region originally from outside. These cultures occupied the tropical forest lands before the advent of the Europeans and Americans and range from quite simple, primitive types to the advanced and highly elaborate types of India and Java. Since, unlike the deserts, very few parts of these regions are uninhabitable, the various cultures have a wider freedom to develop patterns of occupance peculiar to themselves. Although in the dry lands all cultures alike are tied to the sources of water, in the tropical forest lands some peoples concentrate permanently on the hot and well-watered alluvial plains, others concentrate on the cooler highlands not too remote from access to the outer world, and still others move about from place to place so that the arrangement of their settlement at any one time is a temporary and fluid one.

OCCUPANCE BY MIGRATORY FARMERS

There are many resources in the tropical forest regions on which a primitive people with few and simple wants can support themselves. Edible fruits and nuts are available for those who know how to find them. The rivers abound in fish and turtles, and many of the primitive tribes make regular seasonal migrations to the fishing places.* Sea-fishing is of great importance among those who occupy islands or coastal lands. Many of the rain forests are poor in edible land animals, so that hunting is generally limited to the search for a few kinds of birds and monkeys. The lighter forests, however, especially those of Africa, have a more varied animal life, as we have seen. Some of the primitive tribes of the Congo, such

*J. Brunhes, study of the "Fang Tribes" of Africa, in *Human Geography*, Abridged Edition by M. Jean-Brunhes Delamarre and Pierre Deffontaines [(translation by E. F. Row) London, 1952], pp. 152–156.

A clearing planted with rice in the semideciduous forest—Central Brazil (photo by the author).

as the Pygmies, were at one time specialized hunters, carrying on no agriculture, but attaching themselves to the outskirts of agricultural settlements and exchanging meat for agricultural products.

In most of these regions the hunting, fishing, and collecting are supplemented by crop cultivation. Imagine, however, the difficulties standing in the way of a people whose culture includes the use of only a few implements! The removal of the large trees of the forest is a task which requires more effort than the results make worth while. In the Amazon forest the clearings for agriculture are made by removing and burning only the smaller trees. Crops are planted among the charred trunks in the partial shade of the forest giants, which are not touched. Such haphazard agriculture is a purely temporary affair; the confusion of weeds that soon springs up among the crops makes it easier to clear a new area elsewhere than to attempt a more permanent cultivation. Crops are harvested from a jungle, and the tribe moves on. This is known as *migratory agriculture.*

Other native peoples, however, practice a more elaborate form of migratory agriculture. With the aid of better tools the forest is entirely cleared, except for a few species of trees which bear edible fruits or nuts and are too valuable to be destroyed. In the first year after clearing, these native gardens support an extraordinary wealth of plants. Towering overhead are the fruit or nut trees left over from the forest. Below, the tallest planted crop is the banana. Below this is a haphazard confusion of manioc shrubs,* maize, sugar cane, dry-field rice, peanuts, and tobacco.   Finally on the ground are such crops as yams, beans, eggplants, tomatoes, and many others of our common vegetables.   Although these gardens are inefficient and unsystematic in appearance, more actual food per acre is probably produced in them than in gardens planted by any other agricultural method.

Such productivity, however, cannot be maintained.   In a year or so, after the crops of maize, rice, and vegetables are harvested, the bananas and manioc become so thick that no other crops can survive.   The manioc continues productive for as long as four or five years, after which the bushes are cleared away and the bananas and fruit trees alone occupy the land.   The banana plants overrun the clearing, intertwined with creepers, vines, and a profusion of other plants.   Gradually the former garden takes on the aspect of a jungle.   The clearing of new land presents fewer difficulties than the removal of this second growth.

As long as migratory agriculture can be practiced over a wide extent of territory by a relatively small number of people, the essential infertility of the soil may not become important, for only virgin soils are used.   In areas of somewhat denser population, however, the decline of crop yields may become serious.   When all the territory in the neighborhood of a village has

---

*Manioc is a root crop that continues to yield for a number of years after it is first planted.   From it is derived what we know as tapioca.   This crop is also called mandioca or cassava.

Manioc, maize, and peanuts growing together in an African shamba, or garden, in Mengo District, Uganda (photo by H. V. B. Kline, Jr.).

been worked over and abandoned, either the village itself has to be moved to a new site or else previously worked land must be cleared for a second time. The abandonment of the village is a simple matter, for the houses are of light construction and are built of readily available materials. But the repeated use of the land for the production of such heavy crop loads rapidly exhausts the small amount of natural fertility in the soil. Not only are the yields much diminished, but on the abandoned clearings the coarse savanna grasses begin to come in to the exclusion of the other vegetation types which can no longer be supported. For a people armed only with the hoe, the removal of grass is even more difficult than the removal of the forest. Eventually the community is faced with starvation and may break up into several streams of migration, as the Mayas of Yucatan are thought to have done. The abandoned clearings now form open grassy patches in the midst of the forest. To this kind of economy the Germans give the expressive term *raubwirtschaft,* or robber economy, because it makes use of the resources available in nature in such a way as to destroy them.

THE OCCUPANCE OF THE RICE LANDS

The cultivation of rice is one of the distinguishing traits of several Oriental cultures. The first cultivation of rice was probably carried out on hilly land outside of the river floodplains in Burma and Thailand. In those countries today there are hundreds of varieties of rice, each especially suited to particular combinations of slope, soil, and drainage. Later the technique of controlling the water of river valleys and growing paddy rice on the floodplains was perfected. The different cultures of South Asia, Southeast Asia, and East Asia are all built around the cultivation of rice; for not only does this crop furnish a very large part of the food supply, but the labor of producing it takes up a large part of the working hours of the Oriental peoples, and customs associated with rice are found in the religious ceremonies and in the idiomatic phrases of the language.*

The requirements of paddy or wet-field rice are quite different from those of any other cereal crop. In the first place, most of the varieties of rice require a hot growing season. Since most of them also require that the fields be inundated during at least a part of the period of growth, an abundant supply of moisture must be available, either from large rivers or from a very heavy rainfall. Rice is ideally suited, then, to the monsoon type of climate, because of the very heavy rains which come during the summer months. But within the monsoon regions not all soils and surfaces are equally suited to this form of cultivation. Some places are too far from a supply of water for flooding the paddies; some soils are too porous.

*In Chinese, for instance, the general word for food (*fan*) is also used specifically for cooked rice.

Transplanting rice seedlings in a Japanese paddy field (Tiers, from Monkmeyer).

The best places for rice are the floodplains of the larger rivers, where there is a fertile alluvial soil and an abundant supply of water.

The relatively small amount of first-class rice land, where the most favorable conditions of climate, surface, and soil are combined, leads to the intensive utilization of these places. The land is divided into small field units, generally not more than a quarter of an acre in size. A very great amount of labor is applied to the rice crop; for after the land is plowed and smoothed, in some places with the aid of domesticated buffaloes, the remainder of the planting, cultivation, fertilization of the soil, and harvesting of the crop is done by the energy of human muscles. Dense populations are required for the production of rice by these methods and are in turn supported by its production. In parts of India and Java a population of nearly two thousand people per square mile is reported.

Perhaps under no other agricultural system is the surface of the earth so completely transformed as in the rice lands. No remnant of the original cover of vegetation is left. With certain exceptions the people live in compact villages, almost hidden by a dense growth of planted vegetation. Palms, banana plants, tall, feathery clumps of bamboo, and here and there the towering bulk of a kapok, or silk-cotton tree, or one of the several kinds of tropical fruit trees, such as the mango or the breadfruit—all these nearly conceal the houses of the villages. Somewhat raised above the general level of the rice paddies, these villages resemble heavily forested islands, especially during the season of the year when the rice fields are brown with bare mud or concealed beneath the flood waters. Roads lead from the villages into the surrounding country, over which the workers pour out in the early morning and return at night, leaving the countryside quite uninhabited.

Outside these nucleated settlements the rice paddies are almost uninterrupted. Here the surface of the earth itself has been remodeled. Each individual field is leveled and surrounded by a dike. In order to insure drainage, each one of the paddies must lie at a different elevation from its neighbor. Whatever may have been the original landforms, man has

Rice-field patterns in the plain of the Hwang Ho (Fritz Henle, from Monkmeyer).

Rice terraces in the densely populated island of Java (Philip Grendreau).

sculptured the surface for his own needs, neglecting no small bit of this very valuable land. Most spectacular of all is the terracing of hilly areas, where contour-like platforms outline the shape of ridges and valleys. In parts of Java, rice terraces have been built on slopes of as much as $45°$.

Thus a new landscape is created—a landscape which changes its color and its character with the swing of the seasons. While the fields are being plowed the scene is brown and desolate, dotted here and there with the verdant islands, on which lie the hidden villages, or with the few patches of vivid yellow-green where young rice plants have been started and are waiting to be transplanted. Then the paddies are inundated, and, wading knee-deep in water, the workers set out the young plants. These quickly take root, and in the course of a week or so the pale color of standing water is replaced by the rich green of the growing crop. Myriads of water birds feed on the paddies and on the insects which breed in them, and the nights vibrate with the voices of millions of frogs. As the grain begins to ripen, the color changes again—now to a golden yellow. The water is drained away, and carefully, so as not to lose a bit of the precious crop, the rice is harvested. Again the brownish fields, thick with the stubble of rice straw, await the plowing and the repetition of the cycle. There is nothing left to suggest the tropical forest, over which man with such difficulty establishes his conquest.

Other crops also are grown in the monsoon regions. In some cases a dry-season grain such as wheat or millet, or perhaps sugar cane, is planted on the dry rice paddies. But there are great areas entirely unsuited to rice, either because of low rainfall and consequently inadequate supplies of water or because of porous soil, which allows the irrigation water to seep away too rapidly. Even in Java and India only a relatively small proportion of the country is first-class rice land and supports the dense populations previously mentioned. Of necessity, settlement spreads to the poorer, non-rice-producing areas. Here other subsistence crops form the basis of the occupance: millets of various kinds or a combination of the food crops previously described for the other regions of this group, such as maize, manioc, upland (or dry-field) rice, peanuts, and bananas and other tropical fruits.

Europeans in Southeast Asia. The Europeans brought major changes in the ways of living to the people in the tropical forest regions of Southeast Asia (Map 19). The Portuguese arrived first, establishing a naval base at Malacca in 1511, and gaining title to the port of Macao (across the bay from Hong Kong) in 1557. But the Portuguese were not numerous enough to hold all this vast extent of territory. In 1565 the Spaniards began to occupy the Philippines, coming to them from across the Pacific Ocean from the Mexican port of Acapulco. The Netherlands gained control of the Netherlands East Indies (now Indonesia) which they administered from their capital city at Batavia (now Djakarta). The British were able to push out the competing European powers and establish their rule over India and Burma, and also to claim the scantily inhabited Malay Peninsula. In 1824 they began the construction of their great naval base and commercial port of Singapore on a previously almost unoccupied island. The French took control of Indochina (now Laos, Cambodia, and the Vietnams). Only Thailand, in the zone between the British and French territories, remained independent.

The Europeans brought about a considerable change in the population of Southeast Asia. Although few Europeans ever settled in these countries, they did encourage the immigration of both Indians and Chinese. Today in Burma, Indians form the largest minority group; and elsewhere the Chinese make up the largest minority—except in Singapore where the Chinese are in the majority. Finding the Malay people on the Malay Peninsula unwilling to change their ways of living to work for the colonial powers, the British brought in Chinese, Indian, and Javanese workers. The Chinese became the leading retail merchants and bankers.

Southeast Asia had for a long time supplied goods for sale in Europe. The expense of transportation in the centuries before the invention of the steam engine was so great that only goods of high value per unit of weight could be exported. The trade was in silks, spices, perfumes, and tin. But the Europeans of the nineteenth century undertook to increase the production of bulk goods, such as sugar and rice.   Using the river floodplains for paddy rice was not new, but before the period of European colonization the rice was consumed mostly by the people who raised it.   The Europeans built commercial cities, and built the transportation lines to supply the cities with food.   And they also developed certain new areas, not previously used for rice, as surplus rice-producing regions.

There were three new commercial rice areas developed in Southeast Asia.   One was the delta of the Irrawaddy River near Rangoon in Burma. The British, with Indian workers, cleared the mangrove, built dikes to control the floods, roads and railroads to transport the product, and ports suitable for ocean-going ships.   The British also developed the surplus rice production of Thailand, again making use of the previously almost unoccupied delta of the Chao Phraya, downstream from Bangkok.   The French did the same thing on the delta of the Mekong, south of Saigon.   These three areas became the leading suppliers of rice to India and Japan.

The Europeans also developed other plantations for producing export products.   The British (and Chinese) in Malaya and the Dutch in Sumatra developed rubber plantations, with trees grown from plants brought from Brazil.   This area became the supplier of more than 90 per cent of the world's natural rubber.   The Dutch made Java second only to Cuba in the production of sugar.   In all these cases there were only a very few managers and technicians from Europe, and business men who lived in the cities to carry on the trading activities.   The working force was made up chiefly of Javanese and Chinese, or Indians in Burma.

The Europeans also introduced health measures and programs of medical care.   Especially in the twentieth century the death rate from so-called tropical diseases was greatly reduced.   The tropical diseases, such as malaria, were really not limited to the tropics: but during the nineteenth and twentieth centuries when health measures in the economically advanced countries of the middle latitudes had reduced or eliminated these diseases, they were still widespread in the less developed tropical regions.   The medical profession came to describe them as tropical diseases—thereby contributing to the prevailing idea that the tropics were generally unhealthful places because of the climate.   The European health measures resulted in population explosions in already densely populated places like Java.   In 1815 Java had a population of about 4,500,000, concentrated chiefly on the productive volcanic soils of the northern coastal plain around Djakarta.   By 1900 the population had increased to 28,400,000, and by 1945 it had reached 50,000,000.   The census of 1961 counted 63,000,000.   With a continued high birth rate Java had reached a condition similar to that of Egypt, making economic development virtually impossible.   The newly in-

dependent government of Indonesia turned the former commercial plantation land over to intensive food production, chiefly rice and maize; it also
attempted—without much success—to move some of the Javanese into the
thinly populated parts of the country, such as Sumatra and Borneo.

The Rice Lands of India and Pakistan. Another major area in the tropical forest regions where rice is the chief food crop is in India and East Pakistan (Maps 18 and 20). Rice has been grown on those areas suitable for
the development of paddies for thousands of years, since the idea of cultivating this crop was introduced from Southeast Asia. As elsewhere in this
part of the world, the period of European colonization brought fundamental changes in long-established ways of living, in some cases breaking up
the traditional patterns without replacing them with a more productive system. Now, since World War II, independent India faces a problem of population growth in relation to the developed resources of the habitat that is
similar to the problems faced by Egypt and Java.

Rice has provided the basic support for the population for thousands of
years wherever the land is suitable for the development of paddies. Dense
population and rice production are found in the Ganges-Brahmaputra
Valley and Delta, and in the narrow belt along both the eastern and western coastlands of the Indian Peninsula. During all the periods of sequent
occupance since the rice plant and the skills necessary for cultivating it were
imported from Southeast Asia, the pattern of population and the methods
of producing food have changed but little. Although the European period
has been marked by the introduction of commercial agriculture in
some places, the population dependent on rice was too dense and too
closely attached to the land to permit such widespread changes of land use
as took place in either Egypt or Java.

The alluvial plain of the Ganges-Brahmaputra Rivers has many features
typical of such plains in other rainy parts of the earth, but is built on a huge
scale. It is some thousand miles long and 200 miles wide. The rivers that
drain from the glaciers and snowfields of the high Himalayas and are
swollen by the torrential monsoon rains of summer are collected by
the Ganges and the Brahmaputra and drained into the Bay of Bengal
across one of the world's largest deltas. The rivers carry great quantities
of rock fragments eroded from the mountains and deposited as alluvium
on the plain to the south. The alluvium varies in texture from coarse gravel
or sand to fine silt or clay. The rivers wind across the plain in great loop-
ing meanders, but in times of flood the water spreads far beyond the river
channel, inundating wide areas. Then when the water recedes the rivers
often follow new courses. Sometimes whole meanders are cut off leaving
crescent-shaped lakes where once the river ran. Old channels may be

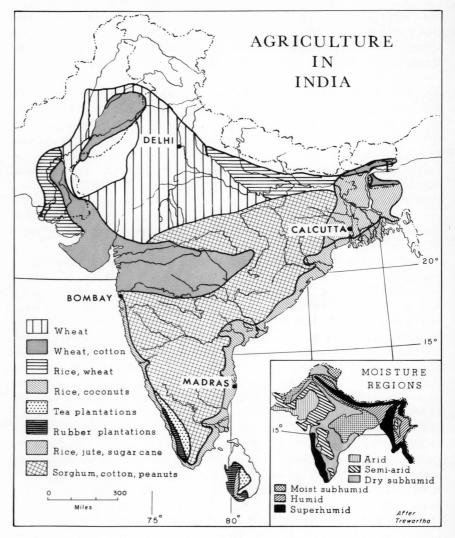

Map 20.

marked by curving belts of gravel, sand, or clay.   When the rivers follow
one course for a long time, so much alluvium is dropped on the river bottom and along its banks that the channel is built up higher than the rest
of the floodplain.   The rivers come to flow along the highest parts of the

floodplain, held in by so-called natural levees (see Appendix C, p. 495). When the channels are built up too high, the river seeks a lower route to the sea and the old channels are abandoned.

For a dense population of farmers dependent on the alluvial plain for its yield of food, the rivers are a constant threat—something to be worshipped, and bribed not to show too violent an anger. On the floodplain only the villages, protected by dikes, are permanently fixed. Each year a new pattern of rice paddies must be built, for only the silt and clay can retain water long enough. The belts of sand and gravel are too porous. They can be used for wheat or for other dry crops, but not for the water-loving rice. And only rice yields enough food per acre to support the very dense population of farmers. The production of rice is reduced by too much water, or not enough water; it is threatened not only by the unpredictable behavior of the river, but also by the irregularities of the amount of rain brought by the summer monsoon. The dense population of farmers remains always not far from the margins of hunger.

The conditions of life are a little better along the coastlands on either side of the Indian Peninsula. On the east the narrow zone of coastal plain extends all the way from the delta of the Ganges-Brahmaputra to the southern tip. This is the Coromandel Coast. It is crossed by several rivers, such as the Mahanadi and the Godovari, draining from the hilly upland of the Deccan. But these rivers are not so violent as those draining from the high mountains, and along their lower courses they deposit mostly silt and clay. On the western side of the peninsula is the Malabar Coast, extending from the southern tip almost as far as Bombay. Here the coastland is from five to seventy-five miles wide, and abundantly supplied with water during the summer rains (see the inset on Map 20). Both of these coastal lowlands are excellently suited for the production of rice, and they have been densely populated since the earliest historical records.

Elsewhere in India, within the area once occupied by the tropical forests, conditions are not suited to the production of rice. Either the land is too hilly, or it is deficient in moisture. The farmers in these poorer areas grow wheat, millet, or one of several varieties of sorghum—all of which yield much less food per acre and therefore support a much smaller population.

The pattern of isolated rural villages has been a feature of the Indian rice lands for thousands of years, and was only indirectly touched in the period of British colonial administration. As late as 1941 there were 450,000 villages in India of less than 500 inhabitants each. The average village consisted of about a hundred mud huts strung along a narrow, unpaved lane suitable only for people on foot (Map 21). Since the movement of wheeled vehicles from village to village was almost impossible because of lack of roads, each small rural community had to be essentially self-sufficient. If crops

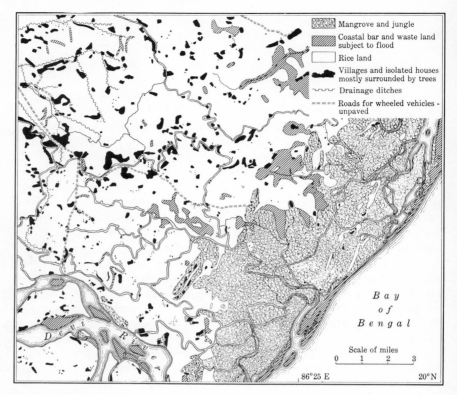

May 21. Riceland topography* on the delta of the Mahanadi. The roads for wheeled vehicles lead to the northwest to the city of Cuttack, about thirty miles away. Within this area most of the local communications are by footpath. (From Bihar and Orissa sheets of the British Survey of India, 1928, 1929.)

failed in any one village, the resulting famine could not be relieved even if there were an abundance of food only a few miles away.   Now all this is in the rapid process of change as new roads are built for motor trucks.   The Indian economy is being modernized step by step.

---

* Unfortunately the general misuse of the word "topography" has caused the loss of its original meaning.   In many writings the word is now used to refer only to the landforms or the character of the surface features.   In this book, however, its original meaning will be retained.   It will refer to details which comprise the landscape of a small area—the landforms and also all the other features occurring together on the earth's surface—as on a topographic map.   A topographic study refers to the study of a small area.   In this sense topography, chorography, and geography form a series of increasing generalization.   Chorography refers to studies of larger regions; geography, to a study of the world or of its larger parts.

Modernization procedes slowly, however, because of the rigid caste structure which was built into the traditional Hindu culture. Castes are being broken down but have not yet been eliminated. Each caste was dedicated to a particular product or a particular service. At the top were the elite, the Brahmins, who made up the dominant minorities in rural areas. There were also castes devoted to the trades, such as shoemaking, or the making of wrought iron objects, or to the home weaving of textiles. And at the bottom were the "untouchables" who performed only the most menial tasks, for whom even separate wells were dug so that other castes would not be contaminated. The process of culture change includes an attack on these ancient traditions.

The British Period. The first Europeans to reach this part of the world were the Portuguese. In 1510 they captured one of the best harbors on the west coast at Goa. The Portuguese held Goa until they were forced out in 1961. The Dutch and the French also established footholds on the Indian coast, each seeking to get a share of the profitable Indian trade with Europe. But the British gained control of the port of access to the wealthiest part of India—the Ganges Valley. Calcutta was the key to the British success. The French and Dutch turned their attention elsewhere.

There were two phases in the British period. From 1600 to 1784 the British monopoly of the India trade left the way of life in India itself essentially untouched. Contacts with India were left entirely to the East India Company. The company maintained a police force, which cut down the amount of warfare between rival princes. The company provided a wider market for certain high value products than had ever existed before, and so brought wealth to some of the already wealthy people who controlled the supply of these products. The India trade consisted largely of high-quality steel and iron goods, and fine textiles.

After 1784 the second phase of the British occupance began. The East India Company was gradually reduced in its powers until it was finally eliminated in 1858. The administration of India was taken over step by step by the Colonial Office of the British government. The greater part of India was directly administered by the British; but there were also some 600 native states, ranging in size from one that was only 15 acres, to Hyderabad which included 82,313 square miles. These princely estates were semi-independent, but were not permitted to maintain armies or carry on relations with foreign governments.

The second phase of British occupance was marked by several fundamental changes. It was British policy to develop the export of raw materials from India and the import of British manufactured goods. The raw materials included some minerals, but also certain commercial agricultural products. On the productive volcanic soils of the Deccan east of Bombay (labeled Lava Plateau on Map 18) the British extended the planting of cotton, along with wheat.   Bombay prospered from the export of cotton, and in Bombay some cotton textile factories were established to produce coarse cotton cloth for sale throughout southeast and south Asia.   On the parts of the delta of the Ganges-Brahmaputra east of Calcutta that are so deeply flooded at high water stage that they cannot be used for rice paddies, the British encouraged the planting of jute, a fiber crop that requires vast amounts of water.   On the parts of the delta that can be used for rice, two harvests can be taken each year, and no fertilizer is needed.   The jute is grown on previously unoccupied delta land.   The British also built textile factories in Calcutta to manufacture jute fabrics (such as burlap bags sent to Brazil for the shipment of coffee, or Cuba for the shipment of sugar, or Chile for the shipment of nitrate).   Bombay and Calcutta grew into large cities of more than a million people each.

Meanwhile the import of British manufactured goods undermined the traditional household industries.   British cotton textiles could be sold well below the prices charged for the native cotton cloth.   Only in the most isolated villages could the household weavers continue their traditional activity: over most of India there are many castes left without employment, and the members were forced to become farmers, or migrate to the cities. In the census of 1961 Calcutta had 4,500,000 people; Bombay had 4,400,000 people.   There are also several other big cities in which a way of life derived from Europe has replaced the traditional Indian ways.   There is even a large-scale steel industry based on local sources of coal, iron, and manganese developed by Indian capital and located in the margins of the hilly country west of Calcutta.

The majority of Indians are still living in isolated rural villages, largely unaffected by the changes introduced by the British.   The kind of agriculture they carry on is notably inefficient.   The yield per acre of rice in India is only twenty-four bushels, compared with fifty bushels in China and seventy-one bushels in Japan.   Yields of wheat per acre are less than half those of the United States.   There are several reasons for this condition. There are still crop failures resulting from the shifts of the great rivers, the destructive force of floods, or from floods that are lower than average because of a failure of the monsoons.   But also the Indian farmer is reluctant to change the techniques of farming that have been handed down from parents to children for hundreds of generations.   Before the period of British rule there was enough idle land so that farmers could shift their crops from time to time, leaving worn-out soils to regain fertility in a period of fallow. But now there are too many people to permit any of the good land to remain idle.   In the middle part of the Ganges Valley rice is now grown in summer and wheat in winter on the same fields.   Even on the alluvial plain fertilizer is needed to maintain the productivity of the soil.   And although India has more cattle than any other country in the world, the animal manure is not available for fertilizer.   Animal dung is the only fuel available for cooking.   Long ago every stick of wood that might be used for fuel was used up.   Dried dung is burned and none of the manure can be used to fertilize the fields.

Furthermore, the orthodox Hindus will not eat meat because their religion prohibits the taking of life.   Even fish are not eaten.   The vast numbers of cattle are used as draft animals, or for wool or leather.   Many are not used at all, but are permitted to find what feed they can on land that is too dry for crops.   The technology exists for bringing about a great increase in the production of food; but religious taboos, followed for thousands of years, defy the forces of change.

Independence.   In 1947 India and Pakistan were separated and each was granted independence.   Pakistan is a Muslim state and India remains predominantly Hindu.   But there are still many Hindus within Pakistan and many Muslims in India.   Unfortunately, the new international boundaries in many cases cut across the established patterns of trade.   One of the most difficult problems has been created in East Pakistan, which is the almost solidly Muslim Ganges-Brahmaputra Delta region.   Calcutta, which remains in India, is cut off from the source of its jute supply. The Indians are trying to increase the growing of jute around Calcutta and the Pakistani are building jute textile factories within their territory.   The territory included in Pakistan used to grow a large part of the wheat and rice consumed in the big cities, but the Indians do not want to remain dependent on food sources in another country.

As elsewhere in the world, the periods of European colonial administration were marked by a sudden explosion of the population.   Medical care and sanitary measures reduced deaths by disease and extended the life expectancy.   In 1966 there were only a little less than 500,000,000 Indians and the rate of population increase, due chiefly to the drop in the death rate, was about eight million each year, or twenty thousand each day.   In spite of an elaborate program of economic development including the building of new manufacturing industries, it seems almost impossible to create new jobs fast enough just to meet the increase of people seeking jobs. There is not much doubt that the Indian peasant today has a poorer house, poorer clothing, and less to eat than he had before the arrival of the Europeans in the sixteenth century.

Tropical Plantations.   There is a long list of agricultural products that cannot be grown in the middle latitudes because of climate, but which have become essential for the needs of the economically well-developed countries of the Occidental world.   Some of these are food crops; others are used in the manufacture of many kinds of goods used by Occidental peoples.   Among the food products are sugar cane, coffee, cacao, chicle, vanilla, spices (such as pepper, cloves, cinnamon, and ginger), and many tropical fruits (including bananas, coconuts, pineapples, avocados, and mangoes).   Rubber is of major importance among the industrial products, although the increasing use of synthetic rubber is gradually reducing the demand for the natural product.   Other such items include Manila hemp, sisal, gums, and insecticides.   Even tropical cabinet woods are becoming increasingly popular as their special qualities are appreciated and utilized.

Sugar cane, starting in the sixteenth century, became a highly profitable tropical plantation product.   The production of sugar cane with Negro slave labor started in Brazil, and brought great wealth to the planters of the Northeast.   It was carried by the Dutch into the Antilles and the Guianas.   The production of sugar cane provided the support for the British in Jamaica and Barbados, and the French in Haiti.   After slavery came to an end (between 1834 in the British colonies and 1888 in Brazil), sugar cane was grown with wage workers.   There was a time when Cuba was the world's chief source of sugar.   Now improvements in the efficiency of beet sugar production make it possible for this mid-latitude (mostly Group I) product to compete with tropical cane sugar without subsidy or tariff protection.   Beets actually improve the soils used to grow them, whereas tropical land cleared of its cover of forest and used to grow sugar cane deteriorates rapidly. Many former cane lands are now eroded and

Tapping a rubber tree on a Malayan Plantation (United States Rubber Company).

abandoned, with much accompanying poverty among the people who were once employed in producing the sugar.

Generally the tropical plantations are speculative and temporary. In the plantation system all of the land is used for just one crop, and that crop is grown for export. Much agricultural and engineering skill is needed to keep the land productive; and usually an abundant supply of low-cost labor is also required. Plantations may be abandoned as a result of the spread of plant diseases, the destruction of the soil, or changes in the markets.

OCCUPANCE BY OCCIDENTAL CULTURES

In some cases the tropical plantations involve few workers of European or American origin. As we have seen, this is the case throughout Southeast Asia. But some plantations, and some general farming in the regions of Group II, have been based on the actual settlement in these regions by Occidental people. An outstanding example of the occupance of tropical forest regions by Occidentals is offered by a review of the historical geography of Brazil.

The Case of Brazil. The experience of the Brazilians with the problems of agricultural settlement in the tropical forests goes back to the early years of the sixteenth century. The first period involved little actual settlement by Occidentals because most of the work was done by imported Negro slaves. This was the period of sugar cane plantations (1532 to 1700). Sugar cane plantations were carved out of the tropical semideciduous forest lands of the Northeast (Plate 10, p. 564, and Map 22). As a result, by 1700, almost all of these forests had been cleared in this part of Brazil (Map 23). Between 1700 and 1800 the Brazilians were seeking wealth through the mining of gold that had been discovered in the highlands to the north of Rio de Janeiro. The mining communities were supplied with food, chiefly meat, rice, beans, and maize, grown in the nearby areas of tropical semideciduous forest. By 1700 almost all the forest north of Rio de Janeiro had been cleared. Then came the period of speculative coffee development, chiefly in the state of São Paulo. Again the best crop land was found in the area covered by semideciduous forest. The coffee period came to an end in 1930, and although Brazil is still the world's chief coffee producer, it is no longer an exclusive interest. By 1930 a large part of the tropical forest lands of São Paulo had been cleared. During this same time cacao plantations were laid out in the state of Bahia just south of Salvador; and German, Polish, and Italian colonists had been settled in the southern part of Brazil, resulting in the clearing of the forest in that region. By 1930 there were only a few areas where the tropical semideciduous

Map 22. The natural vegetation of Brazil (reproduced by permission of the American Geographical Society of New York).

forests remained essentially untouched. Between 1930 and 1950 most of these last remaining forest areas were cleared. Agricultural settlement, by 1950, had almost reached the limits of this kind of forest.

Since the middle of the nineteenth century, most of the forest clearing in Brazil has been done by tenant farmers, not slaves. On any one piece of once-forested land the sequence of events runs more or less as follows. A large landowner comes into possession of an extensive area of forest. The landowner is traditionally interested in cattle, and much less interested in the hard labor of clearing the forest and planting crops. He welcomes the tenant farmer or share cropper, who stakes out a part of the forest and starts clearing it. The farmer cuts all but the larger trees and awaits the end of the dry season to burn the tangle of branches and withered foliage.

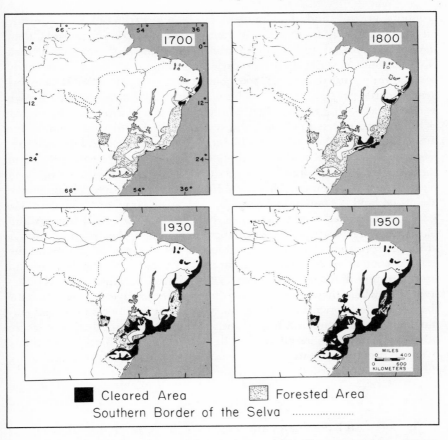

Map 23. The clearing of the tropical semideciduous forest in Brazil, 1700–1950 (reproduced by permission of the American Geographical Society of New York).

After the burn, he plants crops in between the charred stumps and half-burned trunks. On soil from which the organic matter has not been entirely burned away, and which has been enriched by the wood ashes, he gets good yields of maize, rice, beans, or manioc. After a few years, usually not more than three, his yields begin to decrease and he plants grass in the clearing and moves away. The landowner then has pasture for his cattle. But he takes no care of the pasture, and gradually second-growth vegetation of scrubby trees invades it, the grass is choked out or overgrazed, and the field is again abandoned to the forest. Then if the forest can remain on the land for at least fifty years, the soil is rebuilt and is again suitable for the growth of crops. The process of clearing, burning, cropping, grazing, and abandonment can be repeated. But if the pressure on the land is so great that a sufficient period of rest is not possible, then the soil becomes less and less productive. There are large parts of the area of Brazil once covered with tropical semideciduous forest that are today covered only with poor grass, too poor even to support more than a few head of cattle per square mile. This wasteful agricultural system—known as *land rotation*— has made a very considerable part of Brazil unproductive.

Since 1950 efforts to change the system of agriculture have had some limited success. The traditional hoe agriculture, applied to hilly country, has been so obviously destructive that even illiterate people can understand the need for change. But for people without capital, occupying any one piece of land only temporarily, there has been no incentive to improve the use of the land. Then after World War II a few large landowners in São Paulo state applied a new system to their lands. They used tractors and plows, they terraced their lands along the contours, they planted certain kinds of crops that could be plowed under before ripening to rebuild the organic content of the soil. The lands so treated, even lands that had been seriously damaged by wrong farm practices, became highly productive. But where there were once 800 tenant farmers living miserably, now there was employment only for about 300: the remainder had to find employment in the cities and towns, with manufacturing industries or where other kinds of jobs were offered. The new agriculture has spread widely over the progressive state of São Paulo, but the rest of Brazil is still using the traditional, destructive farm methods.

Summary

The forest still dominates the landscape in most of the areas of this group. The high temperatures and the absence of a winter, the rank vegetation which springs up with such rapidity in every open space, and the teeming exuberance of all forms of life have conspired to create in the minds of middle-latitude visitors the impression of easy living in the midst of an abundance of resources. But this impression is actually far from the truth. The prevailing poverty of the soils is not reflected in the vegetation cover; for the heavy leaching and eluviation and the lack of humus are brought about by those same conditions of the climate which produce the forest, namely, high temperature and humidity. Easy living is possible if wants are few. But the real conquest of the forest for the permanent establishment of human settlement has been accomplished only where great numbers of people have been willing to live lives of unremitting and persistent toil. The way of the pioneer is indeed hard; for those things which can be accomplished by great numbers of patient workers do not yield easily to the isolated frontiersman.

People with different cultural heritages face the problems of living in these regions in quite different ways. For the primitive forest dwellers, with simple culture and few wants or ambitions, life is not at all difficult. These people do not attempt the conquest of the forest, but rather are content to accept such living as the untamed selva provides. Until white men came to develop new wants and to spread new diseases, distress or poverty was probably little known. This kind of human occupance, however, develops no fixed patterns of distribution and leaves few traces of its existence on the land.

People with a somewhat more elaborate cultural heritage, on the other hand, have been unwilling to accept the primitive existence afforded by the forest and have sought to establish themselves more permanently on the land. During the course of history a number of such groups of people have actually been able to gain a temporary dominance over the forest. Clearings have been made over a considerable area, and by some variant of the native garden type of occupance a large agricultural productivity has been developed. But this type of conquest is no more permanent than the primitive one. The soils have not withstood continuous agricultural utilization, but have gradually deteriorated until the decreasing food supply could no longer support the increasing population. The ruins of ancient civilizations, such as those of Central America and of Cambodia, are now overgrown with a dense jungle cover, all but obliterated by the victorious forest.

The massed human hordes of the rice cultures have succeeded in making their conquest permanent. By completely transforming the original scene they have left no trace of the forest, and by persistent labor they leave no opportunity for its return. The crop around which they have built their way of living yields enough sustenance to support as many as five hundred people per square mile. But only relatively few square miles possess just those qualifications of climate, surface, and soil which permit rice cultivation. On these suitable areas, therefore, the population is concentrated densely, and the use of the land is intensive. Where European colonial administration has resulted in a population explosion, the rice-land population can no longer be supported from the area it occupies, and the poverty of the people becomes more and more severe.

Actual settlement by Occidental people develops another series of problems. First it has been necessary for Europeans and Americans to get over the attitude toward the rainy tropics that dates back to the writings of Aristotle. It was difficult to demonstrate that people of European origin could live and work in the low latitudes as well as people native to these regions. Now the demonstration has been made—that colored people are no better able to work in the rainy tropics than are people of any other race. That European workers could actually perform the work of producing sugar cane in the low latitudes was demonstrated by the experience of the British in Queensland, Australia.

Nevertheless, there are many parts of the tropical forest regions where the speculative agricultural system has resulted in the destruction of the land. Tropical rainy soils are especially subject to damage by erosion when the forest cover is cleared, or when special soil conservation measures are not adopted. The new agricultural technology can be applied to tropical lands with excellent results, but this will require a fundamental change in attitude. It will also require a decrease in the number of farmers, and an increase in the number of employment opportunities in pursuits other than farming.

Within the regions of Group II, most of the agricultural development has been in the areas once covered with semideciduous forest. The tropical rain forest, or selva, has been successfully occupied only in a few places, and chiefly by rice-growing peoples. The vast basin of the Amazon, the world's largest area of tropical rain forest, is very thinly occupied. An effort to develop plantations of rubber in this area was successful from the technical standpoint; but the effort failed because there are not enough people in the whole Amazon Basin to do the necessary work; and Brazil is not likely to permit the importation of any large numbers of people who would be willing to do such work. When, at some future time, the pressure of the world's population on the food supply is such that every possible technique of food production must be put into operation, the Amazon may be occupied. This region possesses one great unused natural resource: a superabundance of water. The Amazon carries a greater volume of water than any other river in the world, collected from a drainage area almost as large as the continental United States without Alaska. The fresh, mud-laden water pushes out into the ocean for two hundred miles beyond the river mouth. If food is someday grown in artificial basins in which the one basic resource is water, the Amazon Basin might then become one of the world's most productive regions.

The Tropical Woodlands and Savannas

SEASONAL CHANGE is the theme that characterizes the tropical woodlands and savannas. This is not change from a hot season to a cold season, as in parts of the middle latitudes; rather it is change from a season of moisture abundance to a season of moisture deficiency. It is not appropriate to refer to the seasons of Group III as summer and winter. Where these words are used to refer to the dry season and the rainy season, respectively, as they are in some regions, the real conditions are only obscured. In the dry season the landscape turns to a monotonous brown: the scrub trees stand with bare branches, and the tall savanna grass becomes brittle and crumbles. The smaller tributary streams dry up entirely, and even the main rivers lose so much volume that they deposit much of their load of sand and gravel in the channels. This is the season, almost everywhere in this group, when the inhabitants cause fires in the dry grass and leaves, and the fires rage out of control over wide areas. When the rains begin the trees suddenly cover themselves with new leaves, and new shoots of green grass appear on the blackened ground. The rivers are suddenly filled again and the clogged channels cannot carry off all the water. As a result there are widespread floods. The alternation of parched aridity, when drinkable water is difficult to find, and heavy floods, when the water spreads out in sheets over the land, produces sharp seasonal contrast.

These regions occupy a characteristic position on the world framework of climate intermediate between the tropical forests and the dry lands. Yet the large area occupied by these regions seems to be chiefly a result of human action. It is in this intermediate zone that man's fires spread most easily. In the wetter areas fires cannot get a good start; in the drier areas there is not enough organic matter to maintain a fire unless fuel is gathered from a wide area. But in between, the forest litter is highly inflammable at the end of the dry season, and the dead grass burns furiously. The young trees are killed by fire, but the grass comes up even more luxuriantly after a burn. Fire, started by man, is the basic cause of the existence of these habitats.

The tropical woodlands and savannas cover 17 per cent of the world's land areas, and are occupied by 5 per cent of the world's population.

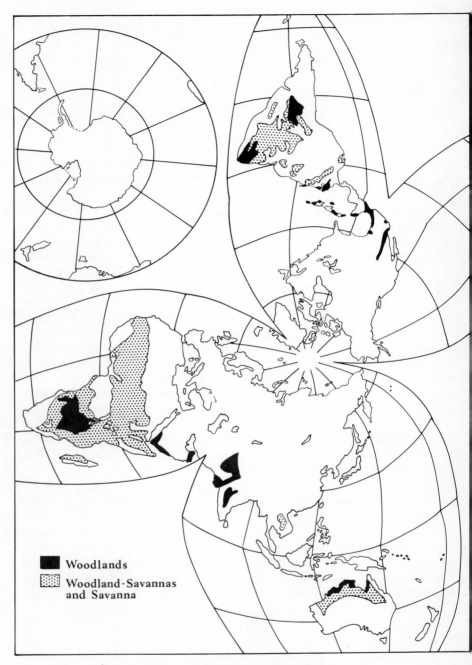

Map 24. *Tropical woodlands and savannas.*

Woodlands

Woodlands

Woodland-Savannas
and Savanna

The Habitat

VEGETATION AND ANIMAL LIFE

In the regions of Group III there are three major subdivisions of the vegetation cover. There are some areas where there is no grass at all, and where the land is covered with a scrub woodland; there are also relatively small areas where there are no trees and the land is covered with grass; and there are large areas in which grass and trees are variously intermingled.

The Tropical Scrub Woodlands. The tropical scrub woodlands are made up of trees standing far enough apart so that the crown of foliage fails to form a complete cover over the ground. Where the foliage cover is complete, as in the regions of Group II, the individual trees are straight and have few or no branches except near the top: but in woodlands, where the canopy of foliage is broken, the tree trunks are gnarled and there are branches all the way to the ground. The trees of a tropical woodland are deciduous, dropping all their leaves in the dry season. In many places, moreover, the trees are protected by thorns, and may form thickets very difficult to penetrate. The transition from trees to low brush is gradual.

The evidence is clear that such woodlands and brushlands were formely more widespread. Probably a large part of the present dry lands were once covered with scrub woodland and brush. In Argentina, where the cover of thorny brush is still widespread along the dry eastern piedmont of the Andes north of 40° S, this kind of vegetation is described as *monte*. Where the monte brush is sparse enough to leave bare ground between the plants, the area is classified as a part of Group I; where the brush is thicker and is mixed with trees it forms the scrub woodland of the Chaco. In Northeast Brazil is an area once covered with thorny, scrubby deciduous trees, known to the Brazilians as *caatinga*. Similar scrub woodlands are found in Central America and Mexico, extending along the Gulf coast as far north as Monterrey. There are large areas of scrub woodland in Africa, Angola, Zambia, Rhodesia, and also in India in the dry parts of the Deccan. Scrub woodland also forms a fringe along the northern coast of Australia.

Woodland Savannas. Most of the area of Group III is covered with woodland savanna, made up of various mixtures of grass and scrubby, deciduous trees. These parts of Group III are generally wetter than the parts occupied by scrub woodland, and most students of vegetation believe

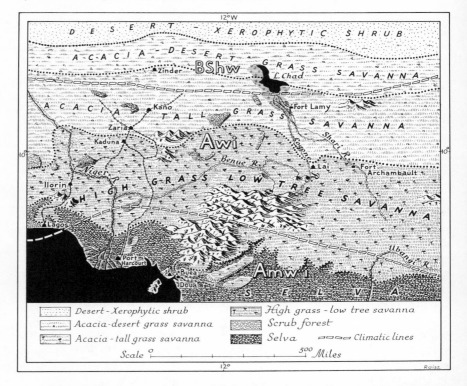

Map 25. The savannas of the central Sudan (vegetation after Shantz and Marbut).

that they have been created from former tropical forest regions by human action.   The major areas of occurrence are in Africa, where woodland savannas cover a large part of the low latitudes, and in the interior of Brazil.

Homer L. Shantz, in a classical study of the vegetation of Africa, recognized three kinds of woodland savanna in the zone of transition between the selva of the Congo and the xerophytic shrub of the Sahara (Map 25).*
In the south, bordering the selva, is the "high grass—low tree savanna," composed of grasses which, at maturity, reach heights of ten or twelve feet, mixed with a fairly close scattering of low trees, together with numerous patches of thicket.   The grasses are coarse and do not form sod because each plant stands individually.   Farther north, in the direction of decreasing rainfall, this formation gives way to the "acacia–tall grass savanna,"

*H. L. Shantz and C. F. Marbut, "The Vegetation and Soils of Africa," American Geographical Society, Research Series no. 13, (New York, 1923).

composed of grasses growing from three to five feet in height and associated with scattered, flat-topped acacias which stand somewhat farther apart than the low trees of the southernmost zone. Still farther north, where annual potential evapotranspiration exceeds the rainfall, is the "acacia–desert grass savanna" where the stunted trees stand far apart and the short desert grasses cover most of the surface.

A large part of the interior of Brazil is made up of various mixtures of woodland and savanna. Where scrubby trees cover most of the ground, the vegetation is described as *cerradão* (a Portuguese word for which there is no simple literal translation). The most common and widespread woodland savanna, where trees usually cover between 30 and 50 per cent of the surface, is known as *campo cerrado* (literally, closed grassland, because trees close in the horizon). Where the surface is mostly covered with grass, but there are a few low scattered trees, the Brazilians use the term *campo sujo* (literally, dirty grassland). And there are some areas where the trees are entirely absent, which the Brazilians call *campo limpo* (literally, clean grassland).

Similar combinations of grass and scrubby trees are found elsewhere in the world (Map 24). A large part of the Orinoco Llanos is a woodland savanna, and there are patches of this kind of habitat throughout Middle America and the north coast of South America. There is an area of woodland savanna in Thailand and Laos and a smaller one in Burma. Woodland savanna borders the woodlands of northern Australia.

Savannas. There are a few places in the world where pure grass savannas occur. Some of these, like the campo limpo of interior Brazil, seem to have been produced by excessive burning and grazing. Where savannas are found in the midst of the tropical forests, as in parts of the Amazon Basin, they are clearly the result of human action. But there are also some examples of pure savannas where neither burning nor grazing seem to explain their origin. These are the edaphic savannas, where the absence of trees is a reflection of the nature of the soil and water. Where the land is seasonally inundated to a sufficient depth, there are wet savannas, and these are quite different from the dry savannas. Wet savannas are extensive in places along the Orinoco, and in the northeastern part of Bolivia.

Galeria Forests. Another distinguishing characteristic of the regions of Group III is the existence of ribbons of dense tropical forest along most of the streams. Where the streams are small the tall trees form a complete arch so that the streams seem to flow through tunnels. Such forests are

Map 26. Forest and savanna in the planalto central of Brazil (from Preston E. James, Latin America, *3rd edition, 1959, The Odyssey Press, p. 531. Reproduced by permission).*

described as *galerias* (from the Italian word meaning tunnel). Where the streams are so wide that the trees cannot cover them, the galerias form forest fringes on either bank.

These galeria forests are too narrow to be shown to scale on the world

Wilde beeste Sevengeti (Donald Paterson).

vegetation map (Plate 10, pp. 564–565).   The actual complexity of the patterns of woodland savanna and forest is shown on the enlargement of a part of interior Brazil around the new capital of Brasília (Map 26).

Animals of the Woodland Savannas.   The woodland savannas of Africa are unique among the regions of Group III in the number and variety of native wild animals. A major problem in animal geography is to find an explanation for the fact that so many different kinds of animals occupy this distinctive habitat which itself must have been created by human action.   There are many different kinds of plant-eating animals, each dependent on a different part of the habitat.   The giraffe reaches to the tops of the trees for food.   The eland feeds high on the trees, but below the giraffe.   Elephants knock over the trees to feed on the roots while the wart hog digs for the roots of herbs.   The impala browse on the lower shrubs.   The zebra, the wildebeest, the antelope, the waterbuck, and the buffalo are grazing animals, but each selects somewhat different plants on which to feed.   In the rivers and marshy spots are the hippopotamus and crocodile.   And preying on the various herbivora there are carnivora that form a vital part of the natural balance because they keep the numbers of the plant-eaters from increasing beyond the limits of their food supply.

Raymond F. Dasmann points out that the wild game could provide a much larger supply of meat under these conditions than can be provided from such domestic animals as cattle. The cattle feed selectively on a few kinds of plants, and soon have the effect of destroying a part of the habitat without touching the rest of it. Some sixteen different species of wild game animals make the best possible use of the variety of trees, shrubs, and grasses without destroying their food supply. But all over Africa the lions are hunted, the elephants are hunted, the various game animals are in one way or another destroyed, until now only a few individuals of some species remain in the game preserves. The destructive effect of cattle and of man's efforts to clear away the wild plants results in a decline in the total capacity of the habitat to produce food. Curiously it is chiefly in the places infested with the tsetse fly that the natural habitat still retains its capacity to support a numerous animal population. This fly which breeds in wild brush, spreads a fatal disease among cattle and infects the human population with sleeping sickness. Modern methods of eradicating the tsetse fly will soon open these last areas to settlement and destruction by man.*

*Raymond F. Dasmann, *The Last Horizon* (New York, 1963).

Zebras in Ngorongora Crater, Tanzania (George Holton).

THE CLIMATE

In the Köppen system of climatic classification the types most commonly associated with woodlands and savannas are Aw and BShw (see the definitions in Appendix B, p. 480). These symbols indicate that cold weather occurs rarely if ever, and that there is a season of moisture deficiency and a season when more moisture is available. In the BS climates the rainy season does not bring enough moisture to compensate for the dry period of the year, so that on the average for the year the climate is semi-arid.

In the central part of Brazil, where the woodland savannas occur in areas of Aw climate, the average annual rainfall is generally over 40 inches. At Goiás, a little to the west of the area shown on Map 26, there is an average of 66 inches a year. But most of this rain is concentrated in the rainy season from October through April. In the dry season from May through September, no month receives as much as 2 inches, and two or more months may pass with no rain at all. With temperatures averaging more than 72° in every month the evaporation is high. Each month from December through March averages more than ten inches.

In the Orinoco Llanos of Venezuela, which lie north of the equator, the dry season is at the opposite time of the year. From mid-December until April there is very little rain; but the rains are heavy from May through November.

A similar seasonal distribution of rainfall is found in the other regions of this group. In the area shown on Map 25 the rains are heavy from May to September, but December, January, and February are usually completely dry. In Rhodesia, on the other hand, the dry period lasts from April to October. In northern Australia the season of little rain lasts from May through September.

There are parts of these regions, similar to parts of the tropical forest regions, which have two maxima and two minima of rainfall each year. In Uganda and Kenya, for example, there is a rainy season from March to June, and another between October and early December. This double maximum of rainfall is found in areas near the equator extending from the Guinea Coast across the northern Congo to the highlands of East Africa.

SURFACE FEATURES, DRAINAGE, AND SOILS

Plains and plateaus are the surface features most commonly found in the regions of Group III. There are some hilly uplands but almost no low mountain areas. Low mountains, and to a certain extent hilly uplands receive more rain than nearby plains or plateaus, and where there is enough rain the seasonal droughts are neither so long nor so dry, and forests can survive. Furthermore, fires can sweep unobstructed across level surfaces, whether plains or plateaus, whereas they do not spread so easily across deeply cut valleys or into hilly uplands. The maps (Plates 1–5, 13, pp. 553–571) show the arrangement of these surface features.

There is an important contrast between the drainage of plains and that of plateaus. On plains the river floodplains are wide and flat, and during the rainy season large areas are flooded. Vast floods are characteristic of the Orinoco Llanos, the Upper Niger, and the Chari which drains into Lake Chad. Few rivers cross the woodland savannas of northern Australia, but if they did this also would be an area of extensive floods. In plateaus, on the other hand, the rivers flow in narrow valleys cut into the plateau surface. The floods of the rainy season are confined to the narrow valley bottoms.

On flat surfaces that are not flooded annually, the soils in the course of time are deeply leached of their soluble materials. On the plateau surfaces in Brazil, for example, a laterite has developed which is among the world's poorest soils for shallow-rooted crops. The surface horizons are coarse in texture, and contain little organic matter. The minerals are those that are least soluble. Underneath is a hard-pan of iron limonite, cemented like a solid rock stratum, so that to break it up it is necessary to use dynamite. This plateau surface in Brazil, on which the woodland savanna—mostly campo cerrado—is found, is understood to be a very ancient level, reduced by erosion to a remarkably even plain and then lifted by geologic movements of the earth's crust to its present elevation of nearly 4000 feet above sea level. This surface has been exposed to the action of percolating rain water during millions of years: it is one of the oldest surfaces on the earth. Therefore it has soils that are low in potential productivity (see Map 22, p. 126).

THE POSITION OF GROUP III

The regions of Group III occupy a position in the generalized regular pattern of habitats that lies between the tropical forests and the dry lands. Yet woodland savannas occur in rainy climates that normally support forests, and there are forests in places throughout the areas of Aw climate. Without the interference of man, even in the areas of marked seasonal rainfall deficiency, the woodland savannas would be few.

Most students of vegetation think that at one time the forests covered a large part of what is now woodland or savanna. On the dry margins of the forest there were probably woodlands, grading into xerophytic brush as the climates became more arid. Human action by primitive man involved the use of fire—used at a very early time for the purpose of aiding in the hunt for game animals. Fires once started in places where enough inflammable material lay on the ground would spread out of control. Semideciduous forests, with dense undergrowth, will burn fiercely at the end of the dry season, generating enough heat to kill all the young trees. In the course of time, repeated burning has the effect of pushing back the edge of the forest, and of replacing the forest with a savanna in which only scattered, fire-resistant trees can gain a foothold. The fires also make the boundary between forest and savanna sharper than it was before human intervention by favoring the growth of grass at the expense of trees. There are many places, today, where one can pass from dense forest to open grassland within a few yards—a feature that is clearly not related to the pattern of climates.

Human action, then, has been largely responsible for creating the woodland savannas within regions where prolonged seasonal drought permitted the development of such vegetation. Man's activities have continued to support the existence of these regions and to keep the forests from recapturing the lost areas. Cattle and goats feeding selectively on the savannas can also keep young tree seedlings from making a start. Once the forests are removed, there is little to hold the water of the rainy season from running off in torrents over the surface, carrying off the surface layers of the soil in sheets, or digging steep-sided gullies. The debris of rock fragments eroded from the higher surfaces is spread out over the floodplains as sheets of sand or gravel. During low water periods all this material is dropped in the river channels, so that the channel is split into numerous smaller channels. A river overburdened with its heavy load forms a braided channel among the sand banks. When the floods come on again at the beginning of the rainy season the channels are clogged with debris and the water spills out over the surface of the floodplain. Such an alternation of floods and droughts is characteristic of drainage basins from which the forests have been removed.

The Occupance

The tropical woodlands and savannas are for the most part very thinly populated. Not only is the proportion of the total population of the world living in Group III very small (5 per cent), but also there are no areas of dense rural population, and few cities. Yet there are a large number of the new African states that are wholly or in part dependent on just this kind of a habitat. To be sure there are modern technologies that can be applied to almost any kind of land, where the poorest soils can be made highly productive. But the new agricultural technology is costly, requiring a high capital investment. Most of the new states have neither capital nor technical skill, and are therefore closely tied to the natural productivity of the land.   And in most cases the use of fire to clear away dead leaves and grass, and the use of cattle and goats to graze on the unimproved ranges leads only to a continued impoverishment of the land base.   The problem of making use of these habitats constitutes a major challenge in the modern world both in the African states and in the Brazilian backlands.

It is instructive, therefore, to review the experience of man in attempting the settlement of various parts of Group III.   We shall look at the record of sequent occupance in four places: 1. in Rhodesia; 2. in northern Nigeria; 3. in the Orinoco Llanos; and 4. in the *Planalto Central*—the Central Plateau of Brazil.

RHODESIA

The occupance of the high plateau of south central Africa involves many events that recur throughout the world in the settlement of Group III, and also many that are peculiar to the area of impact between Africans and Europeans.   This is the part of Africa that is drained by the Zambezi River, and was once known as Zambezia.   We are concerned especially with the area now included in Zambia (formerly Northern Rhodesia)* and Rhodesia (formerly Southern Rhodesia, Map 27).

The Habitat.   The area included in the Rhodesias is made up of wide expanses of gently rolling surface, surmounted here and there by mesa-like hills capped with bare rock.   The Zambezi River collects the water from a large area south of the Congo Basin, some of it from the tsetse fly-infested Okavango Swamp of northern Bechuanaland.   The Zambezi plunges over the famous Victoria Falls, 400 feet in height, located near the town of Livingstone on the border between Zambia and Rhodesia.   Downstream the river flows through a deep gorge cut below the general upland surface.   The altitude of this upland surface near the river is less than 3000 feet, but the surface rises to the north and the south to about 4000 feet, and in the eastern part of Rhodesia it is more than 8000 feet above sea level.

The climatic conditions are characteristic of the regions of Group III. In the higher areas throughout most of this part of Africa the climate is described by the symbol Aw (Appendix B, p. 486), but toward the southwest of Rhodesia, on the border of Bechuanaland, the climate is a BShw.   At Bulawayo, for example, the average annual rainfall is 23.4 inches, most of it coming in a rainy season between November and March.   At Salisbury, on the other hand, the average annual rainfall is 33.4 inches, most of it coming between October and April.   Temperatures at both Bulawayo and Salisbury—both of which are more than 4000 feet above sea level—are cool,

* When Northern Rhodesia became independent in 1964 it officially adopted the name, Zambia.   At that same time Southern Rhodesia became Rhodesia.

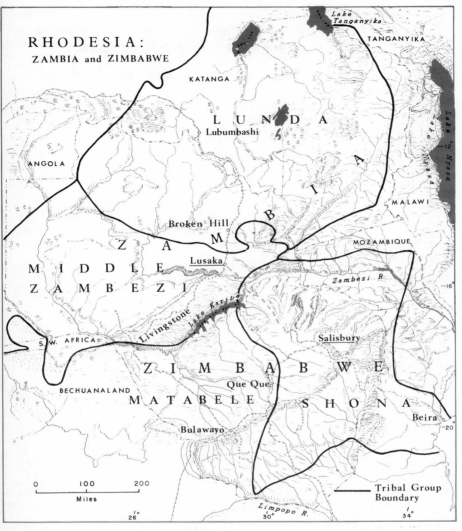

Map 27.

averaging in the 50's during the dry season, and in the low 70's just before the beginning of the rainy season. Only in the lower areas near the Zambezi River are temperatures sometimes in the high 80's during the day. In the higher areas the temperatures may be uncomfortably cool, and on winter nights (June, July, and August) there are occasional frosts.

No one knows what kind of vegetation covered this area before it was modified by the earliest human inhabitants. Perhaps it was a scrub woodland, similar to what the Brazilians describe as *cerradão*. But the early use of fire changed the vegetation to a woodland savanna, or a mixture of woodland areas and open grassy savannas with scattered trees.

Sequent Occupance before the British Settlement.   Before the arrival of the British settlers in 1890 there had been at least four periods of sequent occupance.   It is possible that creatures of the genus *homo* were present in this area nearly two million years ago, since one of the earliest known skulls of man, dated some 1,700,000 years ago, has been found in nearby Tanganyika.   But the earliest inhabitants of whom there is a certain record were the Bushmen.   These were nomadic hunters and collectors who were attracted to those places where the wild game was plentiful.   They were probably the earliest users of fire to aid in the hunt.   A relatively small population created the characteristic habitat of this group of regions—the mixture of woodland and savanna.   But the hunters lived in close harmony with the supply of game and were able to survive without destroying their resource base.

The Bushmen were pushed out of the Rhodesias as a result of an invasion of agricultural people from the north.   The invaders were Negro Bantus of many different tribes and groups of tribes.   Two chief groups settled in the Rhodesias—the Shona tribes south of the Zambezi River and the Lunda tribes north of it.   Today there are six tribes of the Shona group in Rhodesia and the northern part of Mozambique; and there are thirteen tribes of the Bemba group in Zambia and bordering parts of the Republic of the Congo.   These tribes originally brought with them Kafir corn and several varieties of sorghum and millet, as well as vegetables.   In modern times, however, the chief crops are of American origin: maize, manioc, beans, and sweet potatoes.

The agricultural people were scattered thinly over the whole area of the Rhodesias.   They lived in small hamlets and practiced a kind of shifting cultivation.   The wild vegetation was cleared from an area near the settlement and crops were planted.   But after a few years the decline of yields from the lateritic soils made it necessary to move to new areas.   The old farms were permitted to grow up again in brush.   The population was sufficiently scattered so that a considerable period of soil regeneration could be allowed before the wild vegetation would be cleared again and the cycle repeated.

Among the tribes there was constant warfare.   Sometimes a powerful ruler was able to extend his control over a large area.   From the late seventeenth century until the nineteenth century the king of the Luba tribe in what is today the Katanga District of the Congo controlled most of Central Africa to within three hundred miles of the Atlantic.   He controlled most of the Lunda group north of the Zambezi. Warfare, as well as periodic famines resulting from less than normal rainfall, kept the total population from increasing beyond the capacity of the land to give support.

The third period of sequent occupance was ushered in when a new group of Bantu tribes invaded the Rhodesias from what is today Tanzania and Malawi.* These now make up the Middle Zambezi group (Map 27). The whole group, including twelve separate tribes, brought with them cattle. They pushed aside the agricultural tribes and settled in the southern part of Zambia and in bordering parts of Bechuanaland. But cattle cannot thrive in the territory these people invaded. All over this part of Africa at elevations below 3000 feet wherever the wild brush is permitted to remain on the land the tsetse fly can breed. Most of the tribes of the Middle Zambezi group, therefore, turned to agriculture and to hunting, fishing, and gathering. In the tribes that occupy better land, cattle are still of major importance, but not as a supply of food. The cattle are, rather, a symbol of wealth, a source of prestige. Where cattle are to be pastured there must be grass; and in this part of the world grass is the result of fire.

The final period of sequent occupance before the arrival of the British began in 1837 and 1838 with invasions of the Rhodesias from the Kalahari Desert. Tribes from South Africa established their rule over the whole southwestern part of Zambia, the area today known as Barotseland. To be sure, the conquerors were pushed out in 1864, but the Lozi tribe assumed authority over Barotseland. A divinely appointed king ruled with the support of a hereditary aristocracy. Wealth among the Lozis as well as the tribes they control remains in the form of cattle.

At the same time the Matabele invaded Rhodesia, in 1838 gaining control over the southwestern part of that state. The agricultural tribes were subject to continued attack, and so they grouped themselves together in villages or *kraals* consisting of thatched cone-cylinder huts with walls of clay daubed on a frame of sticks. The kraals are frequently located on the tops of the hills for purposes of defence. The Matabele, meanwhile, introduced a quite different way of living, including a social system with many classes under a hereditary king. The Matabele, alone among all the tribes of the Rhodesias, included slaves captured in raids on their neighbors.

As a result of all these conquests and invasions the Rhodesias were occupied by a variety of tribes, each with a distinctive economy, different customs, different house-types, even different languages. All of the tribes depended on agriculture, but some of them maintained pastures for their cattle. All the tribes included such other domestic animals as goats and chickens. And before the arrival of the British all of them had adopted such American crops as maize and manioc. Continued warfare, however,

* When Nyasaland became independent in 1964, it officially adopted the name, Malawi.

kept the total population from increasing beyond the limits of the food supply.

The British Period.   The complex picture of tribal warfare and of diversity from tribe to tribe was enormously complicated by the arrival of the British settlers.   In 1890 a group of 187 British under the leadership of Cecil Rhodes arrived at the site of Salisbury after a four-month journey with ox-carts from Kimberley.   The British settlers were accompanied by 150 Africans.   On a high part of the plateau, at an elevation of 4800 feet above sea level, where insect pests were at a minimum, the British laid out their new city.   Almost at once they were involved in warfare with the Matabele and the Shona, but the superior arms of the Europeans soon brought the tribes under control.   In 1893 the Matabele were vanquished, and the British founded another settlement on the site formerly occupied by the Matabele king.   The next year the settlement was moved to a new site nearby.   The new settlement was called Bulawayo.

Other British settlers moved northward from South Africa into the Rhodesias after the construction of railroads.   In 1897 the first railroad was built from Johannesburg to Bulawayo; and in 1899 it was extended through Salisbury and down from the highlands to the Indian Ocean at the Portuguese port of Beira.   In 1904 a bridge was completed across the Zambezi River at Livingstone, just below the Victoria Falls.   Then the rails were laid northward across what was then Northern Rhodesia, finally reaching Elisa-

A railroad swatch cut through the "bush" in Southern Rhodesia.   The large rectangular clearing is a European farm.   (From R. U. Light, Focus on Africa, American Geographical Society.)

bethville (now Lubumbashi) in the former Belgian Congo in 1910. Later, rail lines were built to connect Elisabethville with navigable water on the Congo River, and westward across Angola to the port of Lobito on the Atlantic Ocean. By 1931 the Rhodesias had rail connections to both oceans, southward to South Africa and northward to the Congo.

The British came in part as farmers, in part as city people. The British farms were mostly laid out close to the railroads which were built, so far as possible, along the stream divides on the highest parts of the plateau. The British occupied the higher lands, leaving the country below 4000 feet to the Africans. But most of the British concentrated in Salisbury, Bulawayo, and other cities.

To the British settlers all Africans looked alike. There were no anthropologists to identify the different tribes and to describe the fundamental differences in culture among the tribes. There were no geographers to identify the tribal areas and to describe the different ways people in different tribes derived a living from the resource base. The British colonists divided the area of south-central Africa into new political units; but the boundaries they established had no relationship to the complex pattern of tribal areas. Map 27 shows that the political areas defined by the Europeans included numerous African tribal areas, and that many tribes were cut in two by the colonial borders. These boundaries remain basic geographic factors in the modern Rhodesias—as well as elsewhere in Africa.

The present division of this part of Africa into Rhodesia and Zambia is a result of numerous changes in the administration of the Rhodesian settlements. In 1923 the British settlers were offered a chance to join the Union of South Africa. They rejected the offer, preferring to set up Southern Rhodesia as a self-governing colony. Northern Rhodesia, Nyasaland, and Bechuanaland remained British protectorates. In 1953, when the British government was attempting to move these three territories forward to independence as fast as possible, the Federation of Rhodesia and Nyasaland was created. But the forces of disintegration among these states were too strong, and the people of these three areas could not agree on a formula that would permit them to work together under a single government. In 1964, Northern Rhodesia became the independent Zambia, and Nyasaland became the independent Malawi.

In 1962 it was estimated that the Federation of Rhodesia and Nyasaland had a population of about 8,800,000. Southern Rhodesia had about 3,800,000, with a core of Europeans numbering about 223,000. Northern Rhodesia had about 2,500,000 and only 76,000 Europeans. Nyasaland, with about the same total population as Northern Rhodesia, had only about 9300 Europeans. In Zambia and Malawi the political control of the new states was clearly in the hands of the Africans; but in the former

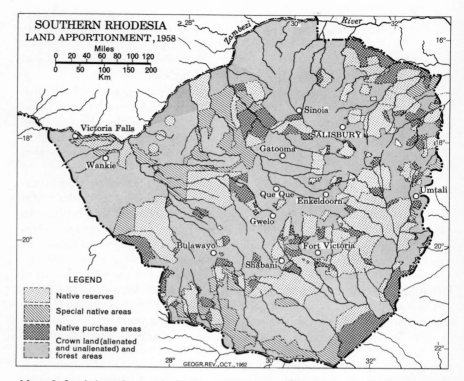

Map 28. Land Apportionment in Southern Rhodesia, 1958 (from Barry N. Floyd, "Land Apportionment in Southern Rhodesia," Geographical Review, 52:566–582, 1962. Reproduced by permission of the American Geographical Society).

Southern Rhodesia the minority of people of British origin were still seeking a formula for maintaining their political control, and the majority of Africans still live on reservations (Map 28), and are paid wages that are much lower than those paid to Europeans for the same work.

Rhodesia is far better off than the other two parts of the former Federation in terms of economic development. The largest deposit of good quality bituminous coal in tropical Africa is located along the railroad between Bulawayo and Salisbury. At Que Que there is also a deposit of high-grade iron ore. A large, modern steel industry has been developed at this place. There are also mines of chromium, cobalt, manganese, tungsten, and asbestos. Salisbury and Bulawayo have become major centers of manufacturing industry. In 1960 the famous Kariba Dam on the Zambezi River was completed, creating one of the world's largest man-made lakes (Map 27).

A very large supply of electric power was made available to serve both Rhodesia and Zambia.

Zambia includes an even larger assortment of metal ores. It shares with the Katanga District of the Congo one of the world's richest mineralized zones—including the ores of copper, lead, zinc, iron, cobalt, manganese, and uranium.

The Africans in the Rhodesias are only beginning to be concerned with mining and industrial development. Among the Africans, even those who have gone to the mines and cities to seek a living, the chief loyalties are still to the tribes, and tribal customs are still supported. Cattle remain a prestige item, rather than a source of food. Food comes mostly from farming, yet of the total area of the two Rhodesias not over 29 per cent is classed as arable, and only 20 per cent is suited for intensive farming. More than three quarters of the area is suited only to produce forest, wildlife, or cattle. As long as cattle remain desirable in the eyes of the majority of the people, the forest is cleared and grass is encouraged by repeated burning. When the pressure for pasture becomes stronger even the grass may be destroyed. When the fires are lighted early in the dry season the grass itself is killed. Then only a useless brush survives. If the land is given complete protection, as in some of the game reserves, woodland soon replaces the grass, and eventually a semideciduous forest pushes out the woodland. But the African majorities are not yet convinced that the increase of the cattle population, and the ill-advised use of fire to create more pastures, can before long destroy the land base. Even the tsetse fly plays a part: for where the tsetse fly is common, at lower elevations, cattle are few and wild game is abundant; but at higher elevations where cattle can thrive the land is being destroyed and wild game has all but disappeared.

In the modern period of independence the struggle for power involves much more than problems of race relations, or of political supremacy. It involves also the threatened destruction of the land base on which the population depends for its supply of food.

SEQUENT OCCUPANCE IN NORTHERN NIGERIA

The record of sequent occupance in Northern Nigeria is perhaps less complex than that of the Rhodesias, but it also includes sequences of events that are characteristic of all of Africa South of the Sahara. This is the region in which is developed the remarkable symbiotic relationship among the agricultural Hausa people and the pastoral Fulani who occupy the same area. The period of European colonial rule did not involve actual colonization by Europeans, but it did result in a change in the relation of people to the land. The increase of population, resulting from a decrease of local warfare and an improvement in public health, accompanied by an increase in the cattle, brings a threat to the continued productivity of the land, as in other parts of Africa.

The Habitat.   Northern Nigeria is in the belt of woodland savanna that lies south of the Sahara and west of Lake Chad (Map 25). The city of Kano is in the midst of the region we are considering. Vast nearly level plains extend westward from the lake toward the upper Niger River. But these plains are more than a thousand feet above sea level, and Kano itself is 1750 feet above sea level. Most of the northern part of Nigeria lies within the zone of Acacia—Tall Grass Savanna.

The climatic conditions at Kano are representative of this part of the woodland savannas. The average annual rainfall of about 32 inches comes almost entirely in a five-month rainy season from May to September. The month of August alone has an average of over 11 inches. At this time of the year the rivers overflow their banks and spread floods over wide areas. The vegetation grows luxuriantly and the air is filled with the hum of insects. But from October to April there is an average total of only one inch, and between November and February no rain falls at all. At this time the vegetation turns brown and the scrub trees drop their leaves. The rivers dry up, leaving only a string of stagnant pools along the sand-choked channels. Temperatures are high, for this is within the Saharan region where daytime temperatures of more than 110° are regularly recorded each year. The hottest month is April, just before the beginning of the rainy season; and the coolest month is August, during the very rainy period. But no month experiences long periods of cool weather. As a result the rate of evaporation is high, and the dry season is one of extreme moisture deficiency.

Periods of Sequent Occupance.   There were at least five chief periods in the sequent occupance of Northern Nigeria. Little is known about the earliest period. It is believed that this country west of Lake Chad was the original home of the Bushmen, the primitive hunters, fishers, and collectors who were pushed into the southern part of Africa by repeated invasions of Negroid peoples. These hunters probably had the same effect in Nigeria as they had much later in Rhodesia—their fires pushed back the edge of the forest and created the woodland savanna.

The second period began with the movement into what is now Northern Nigeria by the Hausa tribes. These were Negroid farmers who were pushed out of the oases of the central Sahara by the invasions of Berbers and Arabs (described on pages 71–72). The Hausas brought with them their subsistence agriculture based on the cultivation of millet and a variety of vegetables. Kano, the center of Hausa settlement, was founded in the ninth century after Christ, and soon gained importance as the southern terminus of one of the trans-Saharan caravan routes developed by the Arab traders. Hausa products went north, along with Hausas who were captured as slaves; and in return European goods became common around Kano. The Hausa tribes, who shared in this trading, developed a common language, using Arabic letters, and adopted the religion of Islam. In their language there is a considerable body of written history; and because there was a record of Hausa history, these people—long before the arrival of the Europeans—had developed a feeling of unity based on their common tradition. Although the Hausa tribes remained politically separate, the whole group had a stronger sense of national unity than did any other African group before the arrival of the Europeans.*

The third period of sequent occupance began shortly after 1400 with the arrival of the Fulani. These people were at one time living in the middle part of the Senegal Valley, near the Atlantic Ocean. Invaded and conquered by the Berbers, they intermarried with the newcomers, adopted the religion of Islam, and also the pastoral nomadism based on cattle, sheep, and goats. They, in turn, started out on a wave of conquest toward the south and east which reached the land of the Hausas in the fifteenth century. They brought the Hausa tribes together in one kingdom and ruled from their capital in Kano (rebuilt on the early site in the sixteenth century).

The symbiotic relationship developed between the Hausa farmers and the Fulani herders, which still persists, is an unusual example of cooperation between two different groups of people in the same area. Actually the two groups make use of different features of the habitat and so avoid competition. The Hausa farmers paid the Fulani herders to pasture their cattle on the farm lands because in this way the soil could be periodically enriched with animal manure. The two groups exchanged their products, and as a result both groups lived better. Kano grew in importance not only because of its connections across the Sahara, but also because its inhabitants developed the manufacture of a unique product—Morocco leather—made from glazed goatskins.

The fourth period of sequent occupance was the period of British rule. The British forces captured the walled city of Kano in 1903. Although they did include the whole of the Hausa territory within Nigeria, they also included hundreds of other tribes, some wholly within Nigeria, and some partly in Nigeria and partly in neighboring colonies. The Fulani herders, moreover, are spread over the whole territory extending westward from Nigeria and are now divided among numerous independent countries.

The British introduced a number of major changes during their administration of Nigeria. They forced the many different tribes to give up warfare

* George P. Murdock, *Africa: Its Peoples and Their Culture History* (New York, 1959), p. 137.

as a way of life, and they trained Nigerians to administer the parliamentary and legal institutions of a democratic country. They introduced new crops and new farm techniques. The Hausa farmers learned to grow peanuts and cotton for sale outside of their immediate territory, and Kano became a major manufacturing center for the production of peanut and cotton products, as well as the traditional leather goods. Kano now is a city of over 100,000. The British also introduced modern health measures and medical services, with the result that there has been a sudden upturn in the rate of population growth. When Nigeria became independent in 1960, it had a population of some 34,000,000. In Northern Nigeria there were about 5,000,000 Hausas and a little over 2,000,000 Fulani.

In the period since 1960 the independent Nigerians have struggled to establish a modern, viable state. The problem has been to find a body of common traditions and purposes that would lead hundreds of different peoples speaking hundreds of different languages to accept one government. Fortunately Nigeria included in its territory three major African groups—two in the southern part of the country, to balance the Hausa and Fulani in the north. Had the latter been included in a country with just one other major tribal group, the new state might soon have disintegrated.

Since independence, however, the old relationship of Hausa and Fulani has been strained. This is partly an indirect result of the increased pressure on the land to support a rapidly increasing population. More people in Northern Nigeria means an increasing need for foods. But increasing food production calls for modern techniques of agriculture, with machinery, chemical fertilizers, and new soil conditioners. And more people also means an increasing number of cattle. But as cattle herds increase and the pastures are grazed by more animals, the grass is destroyed and brush begins to come up in its place. Brush offers the breeding place for the tsetse fly, and the cattle are threatened. These complex, but related changes are gradually undermining the traditional symbiotic relationship developed in a time when life was simpler, and man's relation to this habitat was more direct.

THE ORINOCO LLANOS

Another of the regions included in Group III is the lowland bordering the Orinoco River in Venezuela—known as the Orinoco Llanos (Map 29). This is a vast plain 600 miles long by 200 miles wide, sloping gradually from the southern base of the Andes to the Orinoco River. Even at its highest part, the plain is only some 600 feet above sea level. The streams that cross it to join the Orinoco wind about in broad valleys with low gradients; and between the valleys low, flat-topped divides form the most conspicuous features of the landscape.

As in other parts of Group III, the year is divided into a rainy season and a dry season, and during these two contrasted seasons the Llanos undergoes an extraordinary transformation. The rains begin in April, and the wettest part of the year is between June and October. So heavy are the rains in this period that the rivers are unable to carry off all the water, and a large part of the country, especially near the Orinoco, is under water. In October the rains begin to decrease, and from January to March not a drop of water falls on the parched land. The vegetation turns brown, and the rivers dry up. Only the Orinoco itself continues to flow throughout the year. Temperatures are high, but not nearly so high as in Northern Nigeria. The highest temperatures come just before the period of heavy rains, in April and May. As in Nigeria this is a region of varied—and mostly unpleasant—insect life. Although mosquitoes during the rainy season make life miserable, in the Llanos there are no tsetse flies.

The native Indians of Venezuela found the Llanos almost uninhabitable. There were few native game animals to attract them, and they lacked the technical skill to drain or irrigate and to raise crops. They could occupy the lowlands only along the permanent streams where there were fish and turtles.

When cattle were first introduced into the Llanos by the Spaniards in 1548, the herders found only one natural advantage for cattle: in addition to the absence of anything like the deadly tsetse fly, the Llanos were occupied by no native carnivora to prey on the herds of domestic animals. But

Map 29. Northeastern Venezuela (from Preston E. James, Latin America, 3rd edition, 1959, The Odyssey Press, p. 68. Reproduced by permission).

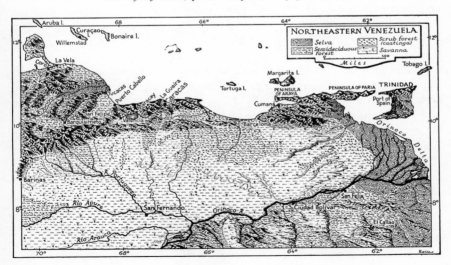

otherwise herding in this region was very difficult. During the rainy season the herds had to be driven back to the highest part of the region, or to the low mesa-like stream divides. Often the higher ground would be grazed bare, and the animals had to wade or swim through the flooded areas to reach another dry spot. Then as the flood waters receded, the young green shoots of new grass would appear in the wet places, and for a time the herds could find enough to eat. But in the dry season the grass turned brown, and much of it was so brittle and sharp that it would pierce the stomach of an animal unfortunate enough to have to eat it. Between the floods and droughts, and the insects, the cattle made such a poor living that they had to be fattened on special pastures before they could be marketed.

Nevertheless, within a century after the introduction of cattle to this region there were herds of wild cattle numbering perhaps 140,000 grazing on the plains. By 1812 the herds had been increased to 4,500,000 under the care of seminomadic cattlemen, or *Llaneros*. During the wars of independence, when the Llaneros were in demand as mounted troops, the size of the cattle herds decreased to about 256,000 in 1823. Since that time the number of cattle has gone up or down according to the political stability of the country, but the number was never higher than eight million. In spite of efforts to improve the quality of the breeds, by introducing zebu cattle from India, the animals from the Llanos could rarely be used to supply export products. The Llaneros continue to raise cattle, but without financial profit.

Agriculture was tried in the higher parts of the Llanos during the slave period. Some of the wild vegetation was cleared by hand, and the chief crop was indigo—a valuable dye that ceased to be of importance after the development of coal-tar dyes during the nineteenth century. After 1854, when slavery was abolished, the use of the Llanos for farming was abandoned.

The most recent period of sequent occupance in the Llanos started during the 1950's. Venezuela, we must remember, enjoys a large national income from the royalties on oil. Even during the dictatorship of Juan Vicente Gomes which ended in 1935, oil royalties were used to pay for new all-weather roads, most of which only reached the margins of the Llanos. But now good roads run along the southern piedmont of the Andes and cross the Llanos to Ciudad Bolívar. Just east of this old river port, Venezuela has built its new steel industry, based on nearby sources of iron ore to the south. In the large cities, such as Caracas and Valencia, there are numerous manufacturing industries, and now oil and gas pipelines connect the oilfields (at Maracaibo and in the easternmost part of the Llanos) with the industrial cities. But Venezuela for a long time has been dependent on imported foods. The freely elected government (since 1958) plans to make use of the income from oil to build up the national economy; and a part of the national plan includes the development of the Llanos.

In 1956 the first of the development projects in the Llanos was opened. An earth dam, nine miles long and 98 feet high, was built across one of the tributaries to the Orinoco and behind the dam a lake was formed. Downstream from the dam, along the floodplain of the river it is now possible to irrigate 272,000 acres, marked off into 550 new farms. Since that date some twenty additional irrigation projects have been completed, mostly along the Andean piedmont where streams emerge from the mountains. The projects include the irrigation of land that has always remained useless during the dry season, and the control of floods during the rainy season. The irrigated lands are used to raise alfalfa and other feed crops, together with food crops for the farmers. The cattle are no longer permitted to wander freely over the plains: rather they are kept in fenced pastures where breeding can be controlled, and where the animals can be fattened for market. The new insecticides and antibiotics control cattle and human diseases. For the first time since the arrival of the Spaniards the use of modern machine techniques, including highway transportation, have made the Llanos habitable. The government hopes that the region will make a substantial contribution to the national food supply.

THE PLANALTO CENTRAL OF BRAZIL

The fourth of the regions that illustrate the problems and conditions of settlement in the woodland savannas is the *Planalto Central* of Brazil. This is the high plateau country in the South American interior northwest of Rio de Janeiro, in the midst of which Brazil has built its new capital, Brasília (Map 30; see also Map 26). This country is not uninhabited, nor is it unexplored. South of the selvas of the Amazon (Plate 10, p. 564) the area shown as woodland savanna is thinly populated by widely scattered rural communities and isolated farms. Brazilian agricultural settlement, as we have seen (pp. 125–128), has largely been limited to the area once occupied by semideciduous forests. But now the forest land has been partially destroyed by four hundred years of shifting cultivation. The problem in Brazil is whether a great westward movement of pioneer farmers can enter the *campo cerrado* and transform these regions into productive farm lands. To understand the problem we should first examine the nature of the Brazilian backland and review man's experience with it.

The Habitat. The Planalto Central is the central part of Brazil's backlands in which three of Brazil's great rivers have their headwaters: the Rio Paraná which drains southward eventually to reach the Atlantic near

PLANALTO CENTRAL BRAZIL

0   50   100 MILES
0   50   100 KILOMETERS

Large forested areas (first class forest)
I   Mata da Corda
II   Triangulo Mineiro
III   Matto Grosso de Goias

············· Author's main routes in 1946-47

GEOGR. REVIEW, OCT. 1948

*May 30. Planalto Central of Brazil (from Geographical Review, **38**: 531, 1948).*

Buenos Aires; the Rio São Francisco, which flows for a thousand miles toward the north before it turns eastward to plunge over the Paulo Afonso Falls on the way to the ocean; and the Rio Tocantins, which flows northward to mix its waters with the Amazon near Belém.   The divides between the major rivers, and also the smaller ones between the tributary streams, are monotonously level.   The high-level surface stands between 3600 and 4200 feet above the sea.   This surface cuts across rocks of varying degrees of resistance to erosion, including some ancient crystalline rocks as well as more recent sandstone strata.   Students of landforms recognize here a very old erosion surface—one which has probably been exposed to the action of the weather for a very long period of geologic time, time measured in millions of years.   A very old soil has formed on this level surface: a laterite which is very porous and coarse textured at the surface, and has a layer of iron limonite, or *canga,* at varying distances below the surface.   This whole surface is so porous that water quickly percolates down to the water table, which is some 30 to 60 feet below the surface. Even during a heavy rain there is almost no surface run-off; and even during a long dry period springs that are fed by the ground water continue to flow.   It is this high-level surface that is covered by the *campo cerrado,* the mixture of scrubby woodland and tall savanna grasses (Map 26).

The headwaters of the rivers commonly occupy shallow semi-circular depressions, or *dales,* only slightly below the high-level surface.   In many places the canga forms a cliff a few feet high around the edges of the dales. The dales, like the higher surface, are covered by *campo cerrado.*

Below the dales, however, the rivers drop abruptly down into narrow and steep-sided valleys.   These are in process of being cut down and back into the high-level surface: but the headward cutting of the streams is not so rapid as might be expected because of the lack of surface runoff.   The deeply cut valleys are filled with semideciduous forest, or galerias.

The climatic conditions in this region have numerous similarities to those of the highlands of Rhodesia.   To be sure, the Planalto Central receives a much greater average annual rainfall—60 to 70 inches in Brazil. But the rain is concentrated, as it is in south-central Africa, in a rainy season that extends from October to April.   During the dry season there is almost no rain at all.   Temperatures average in the 70's, and are highest in September just before the beginning of the rainy season.   Frosts occur very rarely in this part of Brazil.

It is important, also, to note that the woodland savanna of Brazil is not occupied by a population of wild game animals comparable to those of Africa.   There are mosquitoes at lower elevations to spread malaria and yellow fever, but there are no tsetse flies.

The Sequent Occupance.   In this part of Brazil it is not yet clearly established whether the woodland savanna is a man-made feature, or whether it represents a vegetation type produced by natural processes.   The close areal correspondence of the *campo cerrado* with the high-level surface and its very ancient porous soil suggests that the woodland savanna is an edaphic one. It is clear that in places where there is a *campo limpo,* or a *campo sujo,* these have indeed been produced by the repeated use of fire. There are some students of this problem, however, who insist that the "natural vegetation" of the Planalto is a scrub woodland or *cerradão.*

This region was never densely settled by native peoples in any way similar to the pre-European settlement of Rhodesia. The Indian tribes, all speaking varieties of the Ge language, are thought to have migrated into the backlands from the forested regions farther east and north. If they were originally hunters, fishers, and collectors, they seem to have given up this kind of an economy and have turned to agriculture. Perhaps they had to make this change because of the lack of game animals. Their agriculture was restricted to the galeria forests in the river valleys. Did they, then, burn the high-level surface each year?

The second period of occupance began with the Portuguese explorers—the *bandeirante*—of the sixteenth and seventeenth centuries. These semimilitary expeditions, known as *bandeira,* went out from São Paulo to explore the backlands in the search for some form of wealth. Where mission stations had been established by the Jesuits, and Indians had been gathered together and taught the use of European crops, the bandeira carried the Indians away to be sold as slaves. But Indians were few, and they were quite unsatisfactory as workers. It was not long before there were no Indians left, except deep in the Amazon selvas, and very few there. The bandeirantes searched for gold. An expedition would reach a likely-looking spot, usually in a stream valley where it was thought the gravels might contain gold. Here they would establish a temporary camp. They would plant crops. But the chief effort was directed to the search for gold by digging up and washing the gravels. They finally did find gold in the stream gravels in the state of Minas Gerais, north of Rio de Janeiro, in 1698. Gold was discovered far to the west, at Cuiabá, 1719, and at Goiás in 1725. Diamonds were also discovered in the stream gravels of the São Francisco and its tributaries in 1729.

As a result of the bandeira and the search for gold there is no part of the vast Brazilian backland that has not been explored. The explorers, however, were not literate people, and they did not write books or draw maps. But they poked into every remote part of the backlands. There are many places, now grown up again with forest or woodland, where the valley bottoms are marked with small mounds—the evidence that once there had been a search for gold. Where gold was discovered, towns were established, and some still survive, even after all the gold was dug up. And there are many small communities with less than 500 inhabitants each, established in the midst of the backlands, perhaps 50 miles from the nearest neighboring settlement, where a bandeira stopped and for one reason or another never moved on again.

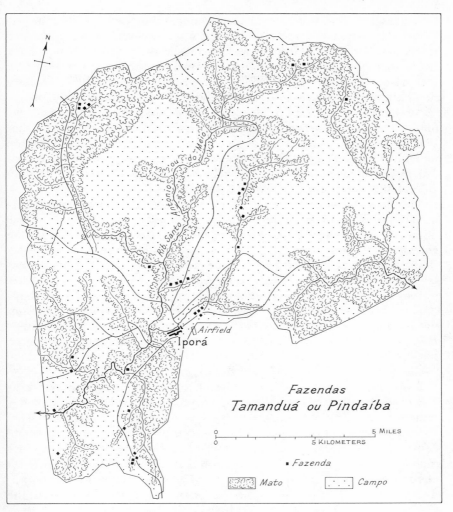

Map 31. Fazenda Tamandua (*Geographical Review*, **38**: *539, 1948*).

Before the end of the nineteenth century the whole of the backland south of the Amazon selvas was divided into vast private properties and used for the grazing of range cattle. The Fazenda Tamanduá (Map 31) is located near the old gold-mining town of Goiás, to which it sends cattle. The property includes the characteristic mixture of *campo cerrado* (campo) and galeria forest in the valleys (mata). There is a little village, Iporá, and even a landing strip for small aircraft. Isolated rural homes occupied by tenant farmers are scattered throughout the property in the forested areas. The system of forest clearing that was described in connection with the Group II regions of Brazil (pp. 126–128) is also practiced here. Each September the newly cleared forest is burned, and the fires are also set on the grassy areas for the purpose of improving the pasture. There is no doubt in this case that fire has extended the area covered by grass.

Attempts to plant crops on the *campo cerrado* lands have failed. So lacking are the deeply leached soils in the minerals essential for plant food that shallow-rooted crops fail to come up. So far, most of the efforts to develop agriculture in the backlands have been directed to the forested areas, and usually to the steep slopes of the valleys. Colonies of immigrants from Europe that were settled on *campo cerrado* land have not been successful.

This does not mean, however, that new technology may not make agriculture possible and profitable on the *campo cerrado*. The high-level surface offers a terrain suited to the use of machinery. As long as the hoe is the chief agricultural implement, the forested valleys offer the best opportunities. But if tractors and plows were adopted, the valleys would not be suited for such use. The porous soil would respond well—as other porous soils do—to fertilizer. For deeply rooted crops there is an abundant supply of ground water. The kind of settlement required would not involve tenant farmers, each working a small plot of land: rather the settlement must include especially skilled machine operators and managers, backed by a large capital investment. In terms of total population there would be a decrease of people per square mile, not an increase.

Brazil faces a serious question. Granted that modern agricultural technology could make the *campo cerrado* lands productive, would it bring better results—in the form of more food at less cost—to apply the new technology to former forested lands close to the big city markets, or to these remote backlands? The answer is not simple. Probably the staple food crops such as rice and maize would be produced at less cost in the Group II regions near the big cities: but the *campo cerrado* might well prove highly productive for such high-value crops as cotton or pineapples. In any case the whole pattern of settlement would have to be changed to include modern machine operations rather than scattered peasant farmers using their own muscles.

Summary

There is no kind of habitat that can be described as permanently uninhabitable. In every case there is a balance of costs and prices to be considered. Perhaps there is a strategic consideration that would make costly settlement worth while, or some other condition that would require a new evaluation of the significance of the resource base.

The experience of man with settlement in the regions of Group III cannot lead us to be optimistic about the use of these lands in the immediate future. Furthermore, these transitional areas—between forests and deserts —are especially vulnerable to damage by improper use. Maybe the improper use is burning too early, or not burning at all; maybe it is permitting the grazing of too many cattle; or maybe it is clearing the wild vegetation. Each area offers its own peculiar set of conditions and problems. There is one important lesson to be learned: that no attempt to occupy these lands should be made without careful study in advance. Detailed maps should be made of water balance, soil properties, slopes, and cover of wild plants, and for each category of these habitat features there should be a recommended form of use, based on actual experiment. The difficulty is that clear as this lesson is, it is being disregarded almost everywhere. In Africa it is much simpler and more exciting to overthrow a government, or to destroy non-African farms, than it is to undertake a program of resource inventory and agricultural experimentation. In Brazil there could scarcely have been a more imaginative and brilliant political project than the construction of a fabulous new capital city in the midst of the *campo cerrado*. And it is spectacular to cut new roads through empty country. But it is much more difficult to find the wise leadership that will insist on a careful survey of land quality in advance of settlement.

The Mediterranean Scrub Woodlands

A T A TIME when little of the world was known, and when Western
culture was beginning its development in the Mediterranean countries,* Aristotle set forth his famous classification of climates. With
the hot, dry Sahara to the south, and with the cool, rainy forest lands of
Europe to the north, it is little wonder that the Mediterranean world, with
its mild temperatures, its abundant sunshine, and its scanty but sufficient
supply of rain, should seem to him the most "temperate" of all lands. His
classification of the world he knew included three zones: a torrid zone, too
hot to be inhabited by civilized men; a frigid zone, too cold and stormy
for any but barbarians; and a temperate zone, the home of the Greek culture, the only habitable part of the world. It is a remarkable evidence of
the keenness of Greek thought that on *theoretical grounds alone* the existence
of a south temperate zone and a south frigid zone was postulated. This
classification is perfectly understandable in view of the knowledge the
Greeks possessed, although the application of these zones to the world as a
whole has been very misleading. It is to these "temperate" lands of Aristotle and their counterparts in other continents—for some cultures, perhaps, the pleasantest of the world's habitats—that we now turn our
attention.

In many ways the classification into zones developed by Aristotle points
out the salient peculiarity of the regions of this group. They are essentially
transitional; yet in the zone of transition are developed a number of striking characteristics that make them unique among the world's habitats.
Transitional in climate, most of the regions of this group lie closely hemmed in between high mountains and the sea. This transitional character
is further emphasized by the position of the Mediterranean Basin, on the
margins of which are the coasts of three continents—Europe, Asia, and
Africa.†

*The borders of the Mediterranean Sea make up the most extensive area of this group. The
use of the name "mediterranean" to refer to all the analogous regions throughout the world is
in accordance with common practice in other writings on regional geography. In this book Mediterranean will be written with a capital M when it refers to the lands about the Mediterranean
Sea, and with a small "m" when it refers to the group as a whole.
† Our concept of the separateness of Europe, Asia, and Africa is inherited from classical antiquity,
when the three sides of the Mediterranean stood out as sharply differentiated not only physically
but also in the very different cultures of the inhabitants. The modern notion of Eurasia—of
Europe as a peninsula of Asia—was developed only after the world map had been much more
completely filled out.

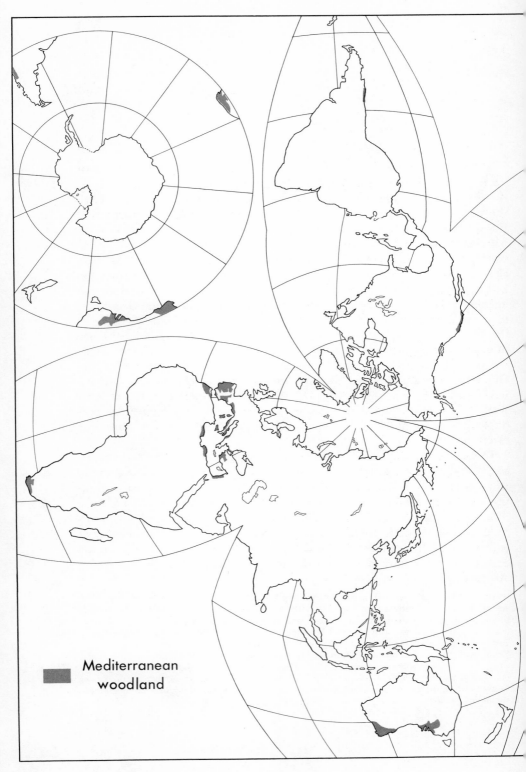

Mediterranean
woodland

Map 32.

The mixture of ideas coming from such widely separated parts of the earth gave to the new cultures developing in the Mediterranean Basin that vitality which arises only as a result of the compounding of diverse elements. During the many centuries of the classical period the Mediterranean peoples were drawing greatly contrasted culture traits from the ends of the known world, and from the clash of these varied ideas and modes of living the fundamentals of what is now broadly called "Western culture" were being worked out and established. History has given abundant proof of the fact that cultural growth takes place not in sheltered spots, but in places where the currents of travel converge—where all kinds of people come together. Sheltered and isolated places are more commonly regions of survival, where ancient and traditional ways of living are preserved. The evolution of a new culture out of the accumulation and digestion of diverse elements at a focal point in the world lines of circulation is perhaps best illustrated by this "cradle of Western civilization."

The major lines of travel no longer converge on the Mediterranean lands of the Old World. The present larger foci lie elsewhere. Many of the analogous regions in other continents, especially those of the Southern Hemisphere, are notably handicapped by their remote position in the economic world. But all the regions of this group share with the Mediterranean Basin the more permanent qualities of transition: those related to the climate and to the surface features.

For various reasons, then, the significance of the regions of Group IV in terms of human affairs, especially in the building of the Occidental culture, is much greater than the total area of these lands would suggest. Of all the world's land masses, only about 1 per cent has this peculiar type of climate and this unique type of vegetation. Yet on this relatively small area are found today about 6 per cent of the world's population.

The Habitat

CLIMATE AND VEGETATION

The unique character of the landscapes of this group rests fundamentally on the peculiarities of the climate. In the various parts of the world it is not unusual to find rainfall more or less evenly distributed throughout the year or to find places where there is a summer maximum of rainfall with a winter dry season. The outstanding peculiarity of the mediterranean climate is its winter rains and summer droughts. Lying generally on the west coasts of the continents poleward of the deserts, the regions of this group have a climate that is transitional between the semiarid climates and the cool, rainy climates of the higher middle latitudes, poleward of 40° (Plate 11). As one proceeds away from the deserts the amount of winter rain increases

and the length of the summer dry period decreases. The typical mediterranean climate is divided into a hot summer with brilliant sunshine and
clear blue skies, and a mild winter with irregular periods of rain.

The mediterranean summers resemble those of the deserts. Near the
arid boundary the summer drought may extend over a period of five or
six months, as in Israel; but on the poleward margins of the mediterranean
lands the drought may be reduced to only one month. Typically the
driest month receives no rain at all, but near the poleward margin a little
rain may fall even in summer. Day after day the sky remains cloudless.
The wind, which becomes quite strong near the water, picks up clouds of
dust from the dry earth. Most parts of the mediterranean lands become
very hot during these summer months; but near the open oceans, where
cool water bathes the coast, the summers are cool and, along the California
coast, foggy (Map 33*).

The mild winters, on the other hand, are quite different from the monotonously clear summers. The winter temperatures generally average
between 35° and 50° for the coldest month. If destructive frosts and
snows occur now and then, they are destructive more because of their
rarity than because of their severity. During this season the weather is
variable; there are spells of warm, muggy, rainy weather with cloudy skies,
followed by cool and brilliantly clear periods.

Cold Air Masses. These varying spells of weather result from the passage
of typical middle-latitude storms. We have already noted the characteristic monotony of low-latitude weather. The middle latitudes, in contrast,
are variable in weather; so much so that the traditional term "the temperate zone" is highly misleading and has been dropped from the vocabulary
of modern geography. If we recall the discussion of the major wind systems (pp. 11–16), we remember that over the eastern parts of the ocean
basins about 30° N. and S. are found the centers of great whirls of air of
planetary proportions. The equatorward half of each whirl is marked by
air moving from the east, the northeast, or the southeast. The prevailing
wind direction in the poleward part of each whirl is from the west, the
northwest, or the southwest. The oceanic whirl sweeps over the margin of
the neighboring continent, and, unless mountains interfere, penetrates inland as far as is permitted by the deflective effect of the earth's rotation.

---

*On Map 33, the climates are shown by lines and letter symbols. These are the symbols of
the Köppen system, which are explained in Appendix B. Qualitative descriptions for each of
the types of climate shown on this map are:

    B   = Arid or semiarid climates
    Csa = Mediterranean climate with mild, rainy winters and hot, dry summers
    Csb = Mediterranean climate with mild, rainy winters and cool, dry summers
    Csbn = Mediterranean marine climate with mild, rainy winters and cool, dry
             summers with frequent fogs
    D   = Mountain climates with cold, snowy winters

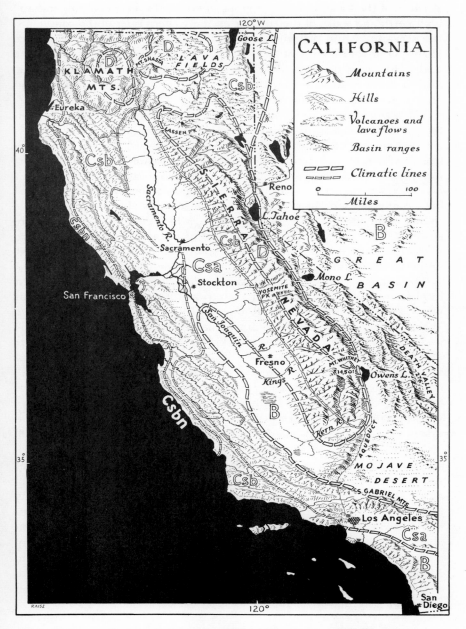

*Map 33. Surface and climates of California (climates after R. J. Russell).**

Because of the location of the regions of Group IV between 30° and 40° both north and south of the equator on the western sides of the continents, the prevailing wind directions are northwest and north in the Northern Hemisphere, and southwest and south in the Southern Hemisphere (Plate 12).   The strong north winds which sweep across Greece, the Aegean Sea, and the eastern Mediterranean were so well known to the ancients that they were given the name *Etesian Winds.*

The regions of Group IV are within range of the polar outbursts in winter.   Cold air masses, originating, as we have seen, over the ice or snow-covered surfaces of higher latitudes move equatorward burrowing into the stream of oceanic air circulating as part of the oceanic whirl.   During the summers, when the cold air masses are neither so cold nor so strong as they are in winter, the western sides of the continents equatorward of about 40° are usually beyond their reach.   Weather remains clear, and with little change from day to day.   But in winter, when the cold air masses are stronger, they push equatorward at least as far as 30° along the western sides of the continents.   The cold fronts bring winter rains to these areas, and occasionally bring freezing temperatures.

The winds associated with a passing cold air mass have all been given local names in the Mediterranean countries of Europe.   When the cold air pours southward through the Rhône Valley, it is known as the *mistral.*   When it pours over the mountainous border between the Danube Basin and the Adriatic Sea (Map 46), it is known as the *bora.*   Because it drops rapidly over the coast of Yugoslavia, it is warmed adiabatically*—the bora is a very dry wind that desiccates the crops and picks up clouds of dust.

When a cold air mass pushes into the stream of the oceanic whirl it sets up eddies along its front.   In the Northern Hemisphere these secondary whirls rotate in a counterclockwise direction, and in the Southern Hemisphere they rotate clockwise.   Meteorologists describe such a whirling storm on the front of a cold air mass as a *cyclone.*†

During the passage of one of these secondary whirls in the Mediterranean Basin, the winds come from various directions.   Normally, as the cold air mass moves southward, the cyclone advances toward the east.   At any one place, the coming of a cold air mass is first heralded by an interruption of the prevailing north or northwest winds.   The winds are at first variable, and then come strongly from the south and southeast.   The warm, dust-laden air from the Sahara is called the *sirocco.*   Crossing the warm Mediterranean Sea, this air picks up large quantities of moisture.   North of the Mediterranean, as the cold front approaches, cloudiness increases

* For a discussion of such meteorological processes see Appendix B.
† Note that there is a distinction between the popular use of the word "cyclone" to refer to a very violent storm, such as a hurricane or tornado, and the technical use, which includes under the term "cyclone" all whirling storms.   When the word "cyclone" is used without modification, it refers to these general storms characteristic of the middle latitudes.

and usually there is rain. Where the air contains much dust the first showers are apt to contain large amounts of mud. Then, with a sudden shift of the wind to the north or northwest, the skies become clear, and bracing, cool air replaces the depressing air of the cyclone. Such a succession of weather types is experienced several times during the winter. Similar weather types are experienced in all the other regions of mediterranean climate of the world.

Rainfall occurs as the cold front sweeps on toward lower latitudes. It is widespread throughout these regions, but in any case is heavier in mountains and hilly lands than on level lands. Wherever air is forced to rise, it is cooled; and eventually, if it rises far enough, the moisture in the air is condensed to form cloud and rain. In the dry lands, we may recall, rains come frequently to the mountains. In the mediterranean lands the higher mountains are almost always cloud-capped. Because the prevailing winds are from the west, the western slopes of mountains and hilly uplands receive more rain than the eastern slopes. One result is an abundant supply of water for irrigation purposes in all the mediterranean regions of the world where there are bordering mountains.

The Mediterranean Woodland and Brush. These climatic conditions support a scrub woodland of unique character. The mediterranean vegetation may be described in technical terms as a broadleaf, evergreen, sclerophyll, scrub woodland. Although in the different continents different species and even different genera compose the woodland, the appearance of the vegetation, resulting from its adaptation to the peculiarities of climate, is strikingly similar in all the regions of Group IV. The broadleaf, evergreen woodlands of southern Europe, for example, are composed mostly of various kinds of oaks (of the family *Fagaceae* and chiefly of the genus *Quercus*), whereas the similar forests of Australia belong to the *Myrtle* family, which is of the genus *Eucalyptus*.

In all these forests, however, certain common characteristics appear. The winters are not cold enough, or the summer droughts long enough, to enforce a period of rest, and as a result there is no season when the leaves drop from the trees and growth ceases. The sprouting of new leaves and the accumulation of reserves take place in the fall at the beginning of the rainy season, and the flowering and reproduction take place in the spring at the end of the rainy season. In this way the mediterranean vegetation differs from the selva, which is also evergreen but which has no seasonal rhythm. Furthermore, the seasonal rhythm of the mediterranean woodland is of quite a different nature from that of the tropical woodlands, or of the woodlands of other parts of the middle latitudes.

In numerous ways this mediterranean woodland adapts itself to the summer droughts. The individual trees are widely spaced so that each may draw supplies of water from a large area of ground.   Between the larger trees there is a heavy growth of underbrush.   On all the plants deep tap-roots and a wide development of the surface root are characteristic.   The woody and fibrous parts of the plants are emphasized, and the foliage is relatively light.   The evaporation from the plants is diminished by a thick bark (notably in the case of the cork oak, *Quercus suber*) and by the nature of the leaves, which are small, thick, and stiff, with hard, leathery, and shiny surfaces.*   Very commonly spines and thorns are developed, as in the case of other typically xerophytic vegetation types.

There are many parts of the regions of Group IV where the original cover of woodland has been radically altered, probably by human action.   Almost all of the woodlands of the Mediterranean Basin are gone, and so also are some of the stands of forest in the mountains bordering the region.   The original vegetation of California has also been greatly changed.   At present there are large areas of this group covered by a thick, low growth of bushes and shrubs, known in Europe as *maquis*, and

* This characteristic leaf form is described by the botanists as *sclerophyll*.

Cutting the bark from a cork oak in Portugal (Casa de Portugal).

Wind-bent scrub pines on the Italian coast north of Livorno (Burton Holmes from Ewing Galloway).

in the western United States as *chaparral*. Such a growth is composed mostly of the plants which make up the undergrowth of the scrub woodland: of dwarf or scrub oak, chestnut, and various kinds of myrtle and laurel. A cover of this sort is almost worthless, for goats are the only animals that can feed on the bark and leaves, and the growth is too thick to permit the existence of grasses.

The maquis or chaparral is the result of fire. Whether fire is kindled by lightning or not is still debated by some students; but it is certain that most fires in the brush have been started by man. The early inhabitants of both the Mediterranean lands of southern Europe and also of California were accustomed to kindle fires to flush out the game. But fires were also started to create grass pastures for grazing animals, usually sheep. Grass can get a start in these regions when the brush is burned, and sheep can keep the brush from returning unless they are introduced in such numbers that the grass is killed off. Goats are so utterly destructive that they only make the return of the brush more rapid.

A curious problem of resource management has developed in parts of California. The fires raging out of control through the brush can be very destructive, especially when they sweep into the suburban areas around the cities. But when an attempt is made to keep the fires from starting, the brush grows thicker and thicker, and accumulates a deeper and deeper layer of leaves and twigs underneath. During the dry summers this litter becomes highly inflammable. A fire once started spreads rapidly as the brush seems almost to explode. As a result the brush fires are more destructive than they were when smaller fires were set each year. Furthermore when a large fire has completely burned the cover, the torrential winter rains that follow produce mud flows and floods. The soil may be swept completely away, leaving only the bare rock exposed at the surface, while the bordering valleys are filled with mud and sand.

Bordering Vegetation Types.   Most parts of this group are closely hemmed in by high mountains and deserts. Closely associated with the mediterranean vegetation, therefore, are types which really belong in the mountain lands or the dry lands. While the broadleaf sclerophyll forest invades the lower slopes of many of the bordering mountains, the higher, or wetter, slopes in many places support dense stands of coniferous forest. The pine and cedar forests of the mountains bordering the Mediterranean Sea were widespread in ancient times (for example, the cedars of Lebanon).

Barley (in foreground) and oats (already harvested) in the Santa Inez Valley of California. On the hills in the background are remnants of the broadleaf evergreen scrub forest (Josef Muench).

There are similar pine forests in the other mediterranean regions; and in the fog belt of the California coast, mostly north of San Francisco, are the stately groves of redwoods.

Grass is not common in these regions. Grassy areas of small extent do occur in the cloud zones high in the bordering mountains, or in marshy lagoons along the coast. But for the most part where grass is now found it is the result of human action. The grass which is so familiar a part of the California landscape when it turns yellow in the dry season is made up of European species, first imported by the Spaniards.

Distribution of the Regions of Group IV. The mediterranean woodland and brush, and the peculiar climate they reflect, are found characteristically on the west coasts of the continents between about 30° and 40° N. and S. There are five such locations in the world. The largest area borders the Mediterranean Sea, extending from Portugal and North Africa in the west, eastward to the eastern margin of the Mediterranean, and northward to include parts of the shore of the Black Sea such as the southern side of the Crimean Peninsula, which is known as the "Soviet Riviera" (Plate 11, p. 566). In North America the area included in this group lies between Los Angeles and the southern part of Oregon. In Middle Chile it lies between Coquimbo on the southern margin of the dry lands, and Concepción on the northern margin of the rainy forested region of the south. There is a small area of this group in South Africa around Capetown. The fifth locality is in Australia, where it is divided into a western area around Perth and an eastern area in the neighborhood of Adelaide.

SURFACE FEATURES AND DRAINAGE

Few are the landscapes of this group that do not include either the mountains or the sea as a background. The mediterranean vegetation covers the immediate coast and the lower foothills of mountains which, in many places, rise directly from the water. Among the mountains there are numerous small and isolated valley lowlands and delta plains where the rivers empty into the sea. The surface features of Greece illustrate this complex pattern of lowlands closely hemmed in by mountains (Map 34), and clarify the background of the growth of the many independent city-states of ancient Hellas, each based chiefly on its own physically distinct area of lowland. Most of the lands around the Mediterranean Basin are of this sort: small, isolated valleys or delta plains bordered by hills and backed by high mountain ranges. No really extensive areas of lowland exist.

Compared with the complex arrangement of plains and mountains around the Mediterranean Sea, the surface features of the other parts of Group IV seem relatively simple. In both North and South America

Map 34. Greece.

(Plates 1 and 2, pp. 553–554), ranges of high mountains lie parallel to the coast, and the lowlands and hilly belts are longitudinal. In California, west of the Sierra Nevada, lies the broad Central Valley, drained mostly by the San Joaquin and Sacramento rivers (Map 33). In the southern part of this depression lies the basin of Tulare Lake—a dry-land bolson with its playa. Between the central lowland and the Pacific there are several ranges of hills separated by narrow longitudinal valleys. Because of the trend of hills and lowlands in this region, which differs slightly from the trend of the coast, some of the longitudinal valleys open out to the sea—for example, the Salinas Valley. The entrance of the sea through the Golden Gate into the San Francisco and San Pablo bays partly drowns the lower parts of a number of these valleys. Toward the north the central lowland of California is terminated by the mountains of southern Oregon, which extend westward to join the Klamath Mountains along the coast.

In Chile (Map 35), there is a central valley, crossed at right angles by the rivers coming from the east, and separated by projecting ridges of the Andes into more or less distinct basins. Between this longitudinal valley and the ocean is a coastal hilly belt. North of Santiago the longitudinal valley is pinched out by the spurs of the Andes, which reach westward to the coast. The southern part of the central valley, south of the Río Bío-Bío, is heavily forested and is included in Group V.

Only in South Africa and Australia are the bordering ranges of high mountains lacking (Maps 12 and 36). Even here there are prominent escarpments, as in South Africa or in southwest Australia, or ranges of hills, as the Flinders Range north of Adelaide.

Relationships with the Mountains. The intimate connections between these plains and the mountains close by are many. In the first place, the relatively heavy rains in the highlands feed numerous torrential streams. Even where the climate is deficient in moisture the mountain piedmonts are supplied with such an abundance of water from the streams that a continuous band of irrigated land can be supported. Then, again, these vigorous, youthful streams in the mountains accomplish a great deal of erosion. The gravels and sands which they bring down with them to the lowlands are piled up in huge alluvial fans along the piedmonts. Where the streams descend directly into the sea extensive delta plains are formed (Map 37). So great is the amount of load brought down by the rivers that the delta plains grow with remarkable rapidity. In the Mediterranean Basin, delta growth is aided by a tideless sea; many towns which are known historically to have been situated on the ocean are now located many miles inland. Owing to the concentration of the rain during the winter season, the regimen of these streams shows a maximum in that sea-

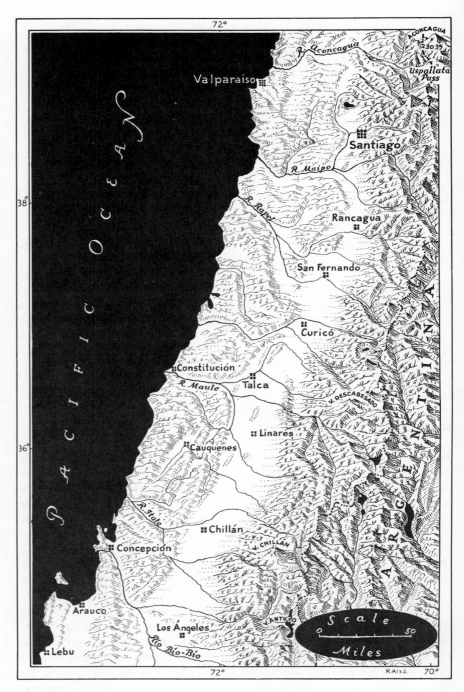

Map 35. Middle Chile.

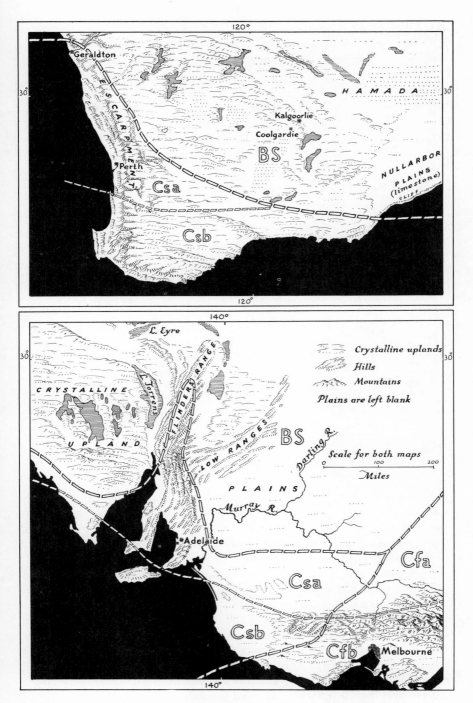

Map 36. Surface and climates in southwest Australia (top) and in the Adelaide region (bottom).

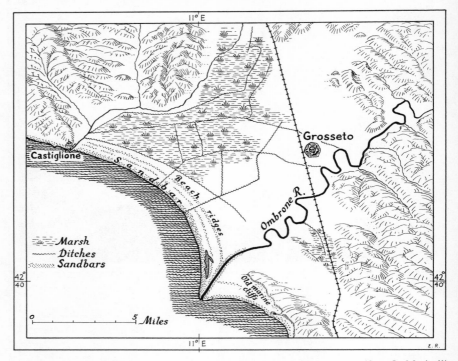

*Map 37. A portion of the Maremma coast of Tuscany—a bar and lagoon coast (from O. Marinelli,
Atlante de Tipi Geografici, Firenze, 1922).*

son, whereas the summer is a period of low water. However, where the
streams rise high enough in the mountains to reach the snow fields,
the maximum flow comes during the melting period in the spring and
early summer, and considerable water is available in the rivers well
on into the dry season.

The removal of the forests from the mountains has in many areas seriously changed this regimen. Forests have the effect of retarding the run-
off during a rain and also of delaying the melting of winter snows. The
vegetation cover therefore makes the flow of the streams more uniform.
The removal of the forests causes severe floods during the winter and
spring, and during the summer these floods are followed by droughts,
when the streams may become entirely dry. The original forest cover of
most of the regions bordering the Mediterranean Sea has been very largely
cut off, and this has seriously affected the habitability of the lowlands.

A Karst landscape in Yugoslavia (Ewing Galloway).

The Karst Lands. The presence of a large amount of soluble limestone in the regions bordering the Mediterranean Sea results in the widespread development of *karst* landforms. The opening of caverns underground and the resulting disappearance of the streams from the surface create a landscape of more arid appearance than the climatic conditions alone would warrant. Many of the plateaus and hilly uplands are of little value except for poor grazing for sheep and goats. The most habitable spots in such areas are to be found in the bottoms of the larger sinks, or *uvalas*, or on the narrow delta plains along the coast. The prevalence of karst landscapes in the countries of the Mediterranean Basin distinguishes these areas from the analogous regions elsewhere.

Map 38. Italy.

Relationships with the Sea; Types of Shores.   Since all the various regions of this group are on the continental margins, the character of their shores is a matter of great significance.   The northeastern part of the Mediterranean Sea, with its many harbors and its clusters of islands, provided an

ideal setting for the early development of the art of navigation. The difficulties of overland connection were more than compensated by the ease of
sea travel. Without the contacts by water the spread of the various cultural influences from one shore to another around the Mediterranean
Basin would have been very difficult.

Parts of the borders of the Mediterranean Sea are shorelines of submergence; that is, they are embayed by a lowering of the land with reference to
the water. However, the results of submergence are somewhat different
when there are mountain chains with axes parallel to the shore and when
there are chains with axes at right angles to the shore. In the first case a
number of elongated offshore islands are formed, but there are few projecting promontories and few deep embayments. An example of this type
is the eastern side of the Adriatic Sea—the Dalmatian coast (Map 38). On
the other hand, if the mountain axes are at right angles to the shore, long
fingerlike ridges project seaward, with strings of partly submerged summits
beyond them. Between these ridges there are deep embayments leading
well inland and providing fine harbors. The Aegean Sea is bordered
by coasts of this sort, of which southern Greece provides an outstanding
example (Map 34).

Most of the shores of the Mediterranean, however, are not indented. In
some cases, as on the Rif coast of northwestern Africa or the Riviera of
France and Italy, the mountains rise precipitously from the water's edge;
but in other cases the shore is low, as in much of western Italy. Most
of these various shorelines are shorelines of emergence, modified by the
action of waves and currents.

The borders of the mediterranean regions of other continents are mostly
emergent. The western coast of the United States from Puget Sound southward has no large harbors except for the one magnificent example produced
by local submergence at San Francisco. The mediterranean coast of Chile
is entirely lacking in harbors; even at Valparaiso, the chief port, the
shipping must be provided with artificial protection behind a breakwater.
Though there are several broad embayments near Adelaide, in Australia,
the shores of these embayments are straight and offer only a few harbors.
Also because of the large tidal range on the open oceans, these analogous
mediterranean regions do not have so many delta plains along their coasts
as do the lands bordering the Mediterranean Sea.

The Occupance

Man's experience in occupying these distinctive habitats has been long
and varied. At least by 3000 B.C. the lands bordering the Mediterranean
Sea were occupied by people who lived by farming and stock-raising.
These were the "Temperate" lands of the Greeks, the lands that Aristotle

said were favored above all others for human settlement.   A distinctive kind of occupance was developed, based on a unique combination of crops and animals.   During classical antiquity, which included the Greek and Roman civilizations from about 1000 B.C. to the fifth century A.D., a harmonious balance was developed between the qualities of the land and man's use of it.   But thereafter the record is one of gradual destruction of the land base and of gradual increase of poverty among the people.

The regions of this group are peculiarly vulnerable to erosion and the destruction of the land base when the cover of wild vegetation is removed too completely.   Under natural conditions the heavy winter rains are caught and held by the layer of organic material that covers the surface under a woodland or forest.   But when there is nothing to hold back the run-off during a winter rain, the result is disastrous.   Over the centuries the lands around the Mediterranean Sea have been seriously damaged. In the other parts of the world where there are similar habitats, some of the same mistakes have been repeated.   In all these regions, in recent times, the application of programs of resource conservation and reconstruction and the development of new forms of occupance are repairing some of the damage, but are perhaps now creating new problems.

To illustrate man's experience with these regions we shall review the record of occupance in four places: 1. in the Mediterranean countries of Southern Europe; 2. in Israel; 3. in California; and 4. in Middle Chile.

SOUTHERN EUROPE

The regions that border the Mediterranean Sea have been occupied by relatively advanced and complex cultures for long periods of time.   The Mediterranean Basin has been described as the "cradle of Occidental culture."   Here many of the traditional attitudes and objectives that characterize the Occidental ways of living originated.   In these regions the distinctive "mediterranean agriculture" was developed—an association of a unique combination of crops and animals in a unique habitat. Although each part of Southern Europe has its own varied record of sequent occupance, in very general terms the relations of man to the habitat throughout the Mediterranean Basin have gone through two periods and are now entering a third.   The classical period, which came to an end in the fifth century A.D., saw the development of mediterranean agriculture in harmonious adjustment to the habitat.   The period of decline, extending from the fifth to the twentieth centuries, saw the gradual destruction of the land base through gradual increase of population and the continued use of the same traditional techniques of farming and stock-raising.   The modern period after World War II, is witnessing the application of new technology,

Hill slopes terraced for orchards near Castelamare, Italy (Sawders, from Cushing).

new concepts of land use and tenure, and a new kind of economic development.

Land Use in the Classical Period. The agriculture that was developed during the classical period was based on a unique combination of crops, most of which were first cultivated in Southwest Asia not far away. The basic food grains were wheat and barley. The tree crops included olives and figs which were native members of the wild vegetation, and also orchards of peaches, plums, almonds, and citrus fruits such as oranges and lemons. From vineyards came the grapes to make wine. And there was a considerable variety of vegetables and flowers. Although all these crops are produced in areas outside of Group IV, this combination was peculiar to this group alone.

Each of these crops occupied a somewhat different part of the habitat. The barley was planted on flat or gently sloping land where the soil was porous and dry. Because such a large part of the lowlands around the Mediterranean are made up of land of this sort, barley was, and still is, a major crop. Wheat, which is less tolerant of dry conditions than barley, was grown on the better soils. The orchards of peaches, plums, almonds, and citrus fruits also require a supply of moisture during the dry summers, and must either be irrigated, or placed where the ground-water table is not too far below the surface.   The figs and olives, on the other hand, can be grown almost anywhere, and can survive on the thinnest soils and steepest slopes.   The vineyards were commonly placed on the south-facing hillsides where the abundant sunshine would make the grapes sweet. In drier areas the vines were planted in pits and allowed to lie on the ground to cut down evaporation; but in wetter areas they were strung on trellises or festooned in the trees.   The vegetables and flowers, which were always grown during the dry summers, had to be irrigated and were there-fore restricted to the floodplains or alluvial fans where soil was not too porous.   In many places wheat was grown during the winter on land that was to be irrigated during the summer, or was interplanted among the fruit trees.

The farmers learned how to conserve moisture where rainfall was low and evaporation high.   A field that was later to be planted with barley or wheat was carefully plowed, and then smoothed with a harrow.   The har-row was used frequently during the winter to break up the surface layer of soil and make it powdery.   This had the effect of sealing in the mois-ture from the occasional rains and keeping it from rising to the surface again and evaporating.   After a whole winter during which the field was kept bare soaking up moisture, it would be ready for a grain crop during the fol-lowing winter.   This is essentially what is known as *dry farming*, a technique now used in other semiarid parts of the world.

The classical period of occupance also saw the introduction of domestic

One of the many fine vineyards in the Mediterranean Basin (Fenno Jacobs, from Three Lions).

animals—cattle, sheep, and goats.   There was very little land, however, suited for the grazing of cattle.   Exceptional were the wet marshes in lagoons along low coasts, or the marshy spots in the centers of the limestone sinks and uvalas (see Appendix C, pp. 510–515).   In these very few wet places, which would stay wet all summer, there were herds of dairy cattle. But generally cattle were few.   Sheep were much more numerous, and provided both meat and wool.   Everywhere in these regions the sheep were driven into the neighboring high mountains during the summer to graze on meadows high above the tree line or on pastures created by the clearing of the mountain forests.   In winter the herds of sheep were driven down again to be fed on lowland pastures moistened by the winter rains. This seasonal movement of herders with sheep or cattle between lowlands and highlands, which is now to be found in many other regions of the earth, is known as *transhumance*.   It was practiced throughout the Mediterranean borders during the classical period.

The Period of Decline.   There had been some destructive clearing of the mountain forests during the classical period.   There was a steady demand for timber for ship-building, and to form the roof beams of houses.   The earliest known document specifying a commercial transaction described a shipment of cedar logs from what is now Lebanon bound for Egypt.   Classical writers describe forests in many places: the cedar forests of Lebanon; the pine forests of southern Italy; forests of oak and other species in parts of Greece, in Sicily, in Corsica, and in southeastern Spain.   But even by the fifth century B.C., Plato describes Attica, around Athens, as a land denuded of trees with the rock ribs of the hills standing out "like the skeleton of a sick man."   This was a land once covered with woodland.   But near the larger cities there was so great a demand for timber and for pasture that here, even in classical times, the cover of vegetation was removed. There was a similar destruction of the forest around Rome.   Yet, for the most part, the countries of the Mediterranean Basin were still well covered with forest and woodland when the period of Roman rule came to an end. Furthermore, during the period of barbarian invasions many previously cleared farm lands were abandoned, and the woodland grew back again.

Thereafter there was a slow increase in the area cleared for crops and pasture.   The large landowners in medieval Italy encouraged tenants to clear the wild vegetation and plant crops or pasture animals.   Where transhumance was practiced woodlands were cleared, often by burning, and kept from growing back again and so reducing the area of pasture.   The largest herds of sheep involved in transhumance were in Spain, moving back and forth from the summer pastures in high mountains to the winter pastures on the plateau, or Meseta.   It is believed that Spain was at one time completely covered with woodland and forest; but for many centuries now the Meseta has been entirely treeless.   The demand for timber to build ships for the fleets of Genoa and Venice left many once forested areas denuded.

It is the grazing of goats, however, that marks the ultimate stage in the destruction of the land.   As population increases, the rate of land destruction is accelerated.   Slopes that are too steep are cleared for crops; pastures in the hills are overgrazed until the grass is destroyed.   Step by step the brush, known as maquis, takes over the pasture.   When the maquis covers the land only goats can feed on it.   The goats eat the last remaining patches of grass and then survive on the bark and leaves which sheep could not eat.   Milk and meat from goats provides support for many rural communities, and as the population increases in these communities there is no way of getting more food except to increase the number of goats.   Eventually the goats destroy even the maquis.

Tourists do not usually understand what they are seeing when they visit the famous attractions of these Mediterranean countries.   They see ruins of ancient buildings, the marble temples on promontories erected by sailors to keep the weather gods in a good mood, the pieces of old roads, with ruts worn by the wheels of chariots.   But the bare hillsides, gleaming white where the limestone is exposed at the surface, only seem picturesque against the deep blue of the summer sky.   How can one imagine that once these barren hills were clothed with woodlands and forests?   How can one appreciate that these lands that yield such a poor living to the peasants of today once supported the thriving civilizations of Greece and Rome?

The Modern Period.   A new period of sequent occupance has now started.   The governments of the countries of Southern Europe, with technical assistance from the Food and Agriculture Organization of the United Nations and with outside financial aid, are applying programs of resource conservation and reconstruction.

There are five parts to the program for rebuilding the rural economy. First the watersheds and steeper hillsides are to be reforested, and this requires the reduction or elimination of goats.   The size of the sheep herds is to be cut down, and where possible sheep are to be replaced by cattle. Cattle are less destructive than sheep in the high mountains during the summer, but when they are driven to the lowlands for the winter they must be provided with feed.   To grow feed there must be an increase in the irrigated areas.   The second part of the program, therefore, is the construction of dams and reservoirs in the mountains and the building of irrigation systems wherever land suitable for irrigation is available.   The crop yields on the land where cattle are pastured during the winter are considerably increased through the use of manure as fertilizer.   The third part of the program involves the reconstruction of some of the old drainage systems to make certain wet lands habitable and productive again, as many of them were in classical times. In the wet lands mosquitoes breed and spread malaria. Drainage, therefore, not only increases the area available for food and feed crops, but also improves the health situation. The fourth part of the program consists of the introduction of new crops, such as maize, and new techniques of farming including the use of machinery, insecticides, and other new developments.

The fifth part of the program is a revision of the pattern of land ownership. Large privately-owned estates that are not as productive as they might be are divided into smaller properties and sold to selected peasants. But the lands thus made available are not nearly enough to take care of all the people who have been living as tenants or wage workers and who would like to gain possession of a piece of farm land. Another aspect of land redistribution is the regrouping of fragmented properties. Many farmers today find themselves owning miniature pieces of farmland in widely scattered localities—the result of many generations of inheritance. Spectacular success has been achieved in some places by regrouping these properties so that the land belonging to one farmer will be all in one piece.

But all these parts of the program would not solve the problem of poverty and unemployment. Everywhere in the world where economic development programs are being applied to agriculture it is found that there must be a reduction of the number of people employed in farming. There is simply not enough good land available in these countries to provide a farm for every person who in the past has been employed in agriculture. Furthermore, the use of modern farm technology increases the productivity per farmer and reduces the number of jobs in farming. Jobs, therefore, must be provided in urban industries or service occupations. To accomplish this essential part of any program of development, a large inflow of new capital is needed. Electric power must be generated and transmitted. Roads must be built. And after the factories have been set up, housing must be provided for people who are to be employed in them. The development of urban industries, therefore, is an essential feature of the attack on poverty.

Furthermore, no program of economic development can be successful unless there is also a reduction in the rate of population growth. Emigration has never been a permanent solution. As long as the number of people seeking jobs increases faster than new jobs can be provided, a successful attack on the problem of poverty cannot be achieved.

ISRAEL

A review of man's experience in living in these regions of winter rain and summer drought must include a study of Israel. This small Jewish state, formed in 1948 in spite of the protests of the Arab neighbors, provides a demontration of how modern technology can make a worn-out and desolate land productive again.

Israel is located along the eastern side of the Mediterranean Sea, on the margin between land once covered with woodland and land covered with only scattered xerophytic shrub. Along the Mediterranean coast there is a plain extending for 120 miles from Haifa to the Gaza Strip (Map 39). Inland the surface rises into a hilly upland, with a maximum elevation of about 2500 feet around Jerusalem. East of Jerusalem the surface drops steeply into the rift valley of the Dead Sea. This is a northward continuation of the structural depression occupied by the Red Sea and its arm, the Gulf of Aqaba. The depression continues northward parallel to the Mediterranean coast into Lebanon and Syria. The Jordan River brings water southward from the high mountains of Lebanon, through Lake Tiberias,* and on into the Dead Sea, 1292 feet below sea level, from which the water escapes only by evaporation.

The rainfall decreases toward the south. In northern Israel and along the coastal plain there is an abundant winter rainfall. At Tel Aviv the average for the year is 21.5 inches. As much as 40 inches is received in the high country northwest of Lake Tiberias. But at Beersheba in the south the average is only 8.5 inches, which places it just about on the border of the arid lands (the border between BShs and BWhs). Elath, on the Gulf of Aqaba, has an average of only 1.2 inches.

The hilly country west of the Jordan Valley and the Dead Sea was at one time characterized by "green pastures and still water." This was the Land of Canaan, into which Moses led the Hebrews. This is the "holy land" and Jerusalem is the holy city of three faiths: Christian, Jewish, and Muslim. For thirteen centuries from 636 to 1917 this was Muslim country. Arabic-speaking Muslims farmed the coastal plain, and tended sheep and goats in the hilly uplands. Little by little over the centuries the sheep, with the help of man, eliminated the woodland in favor of grassy pastures; then they destroyed the grass by over-grazing and the brush came in; then the goats destroyed the brush. No longer were there still waters, for the winter rains poured down the slopes in torrents carrying away the soil and leaving only bare rock. By 1917 the uplands were treeless, barren, and almost uninhabited. They looked like desert—and they were desert, a man-made desert where once there were trees and grass and places to lie down in the shade.

In 1917, during World War I, the British army took Palestine (as this area was called) from Turkey, an ally of Germany. The British recommended that Palestine should become a national home for the Jewish

*Lake Tiberias was formerly known as the Sea of Galilee. The Israeli call it Lake Kenneret.

Map 39. Israel.

people. Jews from various parts of the world did come to Palestine, building a new city, Tel Aviv, in the midst of the Jewish settlements on the coastal plain. After Hitler came to power in Germany there was a large increase in the number of Jewish refugees seeking security in Palestine. By 1940 the population of Palestine was nearly 1,500,000. Of these, 60 per cent were Muslim, and 31 per cent were Jewish. In 1948 the British withdrew from Palestine. Jordan and Israel became independent, but the boundary lines shown on Map 39 have never been accepted. The Arab states still do not recognize Israel.

Meanwhile, enormous changes have taken place in the occupance of this area since 1948. In the first place there has been a rapid increase of population, as some 100,000 new immigrants have been arriving each year. The census of 1961 counted a total population of 2,183,332, of which 88 per cent was Jewish. In 1948 it was necessary to import 80 per cent of the food supply; but by 1963 it was only necessary to import 20 per cent. Furthermore, the national economy was growing fast enough to absorb something like 70,000 new immigrants each year. How has all this been done?

The building of a modern commercial agriculture has been a major feature of the program of economic development. The cultivated area of Israel was increased 150 per cent between 1948 and 1963. This was done by draining some of the wet lands in the upper Jordan Valley, and by increasing the area under irrigation. But it was also done by extending the crop lands toward the dry margin around Beersheba. In this part of the country there is a covering of fine, powdery loess which is ideally adapted to growing grain by dry farming techniques. Some 75,000 acres of orange orchards have been developed along the coastal plain south of Tel Aviv, and oranges have become a major export product. A considerable expansion of orange planting is planned. Other new crops include cotton, sugar beets, potatoes, peanuts, tobacco, vegetables, and flowers. The hilly lands have been transformed by eliminating the sheep and goats, planting forests on the watersheds, and olives and grapes on the slopes. Dairy cattle have also been introduced.

A major problem is to find ways to increase the water supply. Wells in the coastal plain and in the plain that extends inland from Haifa have made a large expansion of the irrigated area possible. But so rapidly has water been pumped from these wells that around Tel Aviv and Haifa the surface of the ground water has been lowered below sea level, and salt water has started to seep inland. The Israeli are much interested in programs of research and development to find a method of converting sea water to fresh water at sufficiently low cost. A major engineering project involves the use of water from Lake Tiberias to irrigate the dry country beyond Beersheba. Underground pumps lift water from the lake; it then passes through the range of hills southeast of Haifa in a tunnel four miles long, and then southward along the coastal plain in a pipeline. This use of water from Lake Tiberias has brought protests from Jordan which claims a right to the use of Jordan River water lower down.

This program for increasing the production of crops and dairy would not, of itself, solve the problem of economic development. No large numbers of people can be employed in agriculture. Actually about 95 per cent of the population is concentrated on the coastal plain, mostly living in cities. It has been difficult to build new housing fast enough to accommodate the annual flow of immigrants; but the number of jobs has been increasing faster than the population. There are a variety of manufacturing industries, including a steel plant located near Haifa. Most of the factories produce consumer goods, and most of them make use of imported raw materials. The leading export of Israel by value—making up about a third of the value of all exports—is cut diamonds. The stones are imported from South Africa, and Israel profits from "value added by manufacture."

All of these developments require capital. Until 1965 Israel received reparations from West Germany; after 1965 it was necessary to attract a large flow of new capital from other sources, chiefly from the United States.

Given the financial backing, the Israeli possess the technical skills and the administrative organization to build a strong economy. They have demonstrated the important point that although the closest possible adjustment of the occupance to the details of the habitat is necessary there is no land so poor or so badly damaged that it cannot be made to support a workable economy.

CALIFORNIA

The sequent occupance of the part of California included in this group does not involve so long a period of time as does that of Southern Europe or of Israel. The native Indians of California were hunters and fishers, who may have started fires to assist in the hunting of deer. They had only one grain crop, maize; and maize does poorly in a mediterranean climate unless it can be irrigated. As a result some of the poorest Indians in North America were in this part of California.

The first European penetration of California came in the late eighteenth century. The first pioneers were the missionaries who established mission stations along the route from the centers of Spanish settlement in Mexico northward along the Pacific coast as far as San Francisco (Map 33). At the missions the scanty Indian population was gathered together, taught

Christianity, and instructed in the methods of agriculture. The crops introduced were those already well known to the Spaniards: wheat, barley, figs, olives, and the vine. Cattle were also introduced, and the Indians were taught to care for domestic animals. With the establishment of Mexico's independence and the removal of the mission system during the first quarter of the nineteenth century, the practice of agriculture in California declined. The land was given in large tracts to colonists from Mexico, but the only use to which it could be put with profit was cattle-ranching; the chief products were hides, tallow, and salt beef. When the gold rush began shortly after the whole area was annexed by the United States, the incoming flood of new settlers could not find enough local supplies of food to maintain themselves.

The period since the middle of the last century has been marked by a series of forms of land use, each motivated by the search for speculative profits. Each speculative development was applied to a different part of the land, and, once established, has been continued even after speculative profits could no longer be made. Between 1860 and 1870 wheat farming was started on large areas, chiefly in the Central Valley and mostly unirrigated. Between 1870 and 1880 there was a big development of sheepherding with wool as the commercial product. Between 1880 and 1890 vast areas were laid out for fruit orchards and vineyards. The decade 1890–1900 saw the beginnings of the use of California's pasture lands for dairy cattle. More recently many small localities have come to specialize in the production of certain vegetables to be sold not only in the cities of the west coast, but also in the east.

As these developments appeared one after the other, there was a steady increase in the use of water for summer irrigation. At first the winter runoff was permitted to escape through the rivers to the sea. But now it is widely recognized that a more efficient use of water is needed: that there must be dams and reservoirs to store the winter rain, and a coordinated system of canals to spread this water over the lowland farms in the summer. The Central Valley project, now in process of development, will greatly increase the supply of water for use in summer, and will add both new areas of summer crops and a greater volume of production of such crops from older areas.

The present agricultural localizations in California are notably distinct. Where conditions of climate, soil, or water supply are especially favorable for a certain crop, the result—in an economy of relatively unrestricted trade and low-cost transportation—is a concentration of production in the best-suited areas. Today citrus groves cover the irrigated alluvial fans around the border of the Los Angeles lowland. Vineyards are found along the alluvial fans of the Sierra Nevada from Fresno northward, and in valleys of the coastal region north of San Francisco. From the Santa Clara

Valley, south of San Francisco Bay, comes a large part of the world's supply of prunes. Almost all the lima beans of the United States are grown without irrigation in the belt of light fogs along the coast (this is to the south of the area noted on Map 33 as having almost continuous summer fogs, Csbn). In addition to these localizations, there are areas devoted to barley, which has now greatly surpassed wheat in this region; to rice, chiefly in the lower part of the Central Valley between Sacramento and Stockton; to lettuce in the Salinas Valley; and to sugar beets and cotton.

In California there is no such problem of overpopulation as complicates the process of settlement in parts of the Old World. The rural population of California is densest in the lowland east of Los Angeles. Here the figure is between 75 and 100 per square mile. Over most of the Central Valley, except for the section between Stockton and Sacramento, the density is less than 25 per square mile. In the San Francisco Bay region it is between 25 and 50 per square mile. Los Angeles and San Francisco are among the large commercial and industrial cities of the United States. Especially in the cities around San Francisco Bay there has been a considerable development of manufacturing industry, and this part of the United States is now among the fastest growing regions of the country.

Harvesting spinach in the Salinas Valley of California (Josef Muench).

Citrus groves bordering the Los Angeles lowland (Sawders, from Cushing).

MIDDLE CHILE

In many ways the part of Chile between Valparaiso and Concepción is remarkably similar to California (Map 35). The arrangement of the surface features recalls the essential lineaments of its North American counterpart. But Middle Chile has had a very different kind of occupance. There the land was divided early in the colonial period into vast private estates, and this form of land tenure persists to the present time. Furthermore, Chile has never had access to a large market in which it could dispose of surplus agricultural production in exchange for other things. As a result there are fewer agricultural localizations in Chile than in California. The chief use of the land is for pasture, or for the raising of feed crops such as alfalfa. The chief food grain is wheat. There are also considerable acreages of vineyards, olives, and other mediterranean fruits. But much the same combination of crops is repeated on each estate. The better lands of the valley bottom are used for alfalfa and the poorer lands for wheat—a reflexion of the predominant interest of the Chilean landowners in stock-raising; vineyards are on the slopes of the alluvial fans on wetter hillsides; the bordering hills and mountains are mostly used only for summer pasture. The density of rural population in this part of Middle Chile is generally higher than that of comparable parts of California. In the vicinity of Santiago there are over 400 people per square mile. Poverty among the people who do the agricultural work is widespread.

The city of San Francisco, with Golden Gate in the background (Spence Air Photos).

Summary

The regions of Group IV occupy only a small part of the earth, but where they occur they are distinctive in climate and in certain problems of settlement. They are found on the western sides of the continents, roughly between latitudes 30° and 40° in both hemispheres. Because of the distinctive climate with its mild, rainy winters and its dry summers, there is a considerable amount of similarity in the cover of wild vegetation. Wherever Europeans have occupied these regions they have brought the particular combinations of crops and animals described as mediterranean. But the mediterranean scrub woodland is a vegetation type that is peculiarly vulnerable to destructive change by human action. The woodlands are easily burned, and after a burn the presence of sheep can be effective in preventing a return of the trees. But over-grazing by sheep can destroy the grass, after which the land is invaded by a low brush which can support only goats. These animals can even destroy the brush, leaving the surface bare and subject to rapid erosion. Where the inhabitants are dependent on the traditional forms of mediterranean agriculture, the result has been increasing poverty.

The new technology of agriculture can rescue these lands, even after they have been seriously damaged. But to apply the new technology successfully there must be a series of related changes. Facilities for transportation must be provided to ship products at low cost to markets. The traditional system of land tenure must be revised to give a farmer a sufficiently large area on which to support a family. Steep hillsides must be replanted with trees, or terraced to stop erosion. Drainage and irrigation works must be built. And changes in the rural areas must be matched with the growth of urban industries and service occupations in the cities. It may well be in the future that the use of water for irrigation may prove too costly, and that the scarce supplies of water will be devoted wholly to use in cities and industries.

The regions of this group are included in the belt of latitude that Aristotle called the "Temperate Zone." In the part of the world known to the Greek geographers there was a zone running east and west with relatively temperate climate—never so hot as in the dry lands to the south; never so cold as in the regions of Group V north of the Alps. The Greeks had no reason to doubt that this temperate zone extended all the way around the earth at these latitudes. But now that the world is better known, it is clear that this most delightful of climates—from the point of view of human comfort—is actually restricted to the western continental margins, and that the great east-west extension of these regions in Southern Europe and Southwest Asia is due to the presence of the Mediterranean Sea and the Black Sea at just these latitudes.

The Mid-Latitude Mixed Forest Lands

T HE MID-LATITUDE MIXED FOREST LANDS make up only 7 per cent of the land area of the earth, yet they are occupied by about 42 per cent of the world's population. This notable concentration of people in the regions of Group V raises some important questions concerning the basic geographic concept of man–land relations. Careful study of specific areas makes it clear that the arrangement of population on the land is never random. Can we, then, identify some characteristic of these habitats that makes them peculiarly favorable for human settlement? Has population always been concentrated in these regions? Can it be demonstrated that people concentrate in these regions in different parts of the world for the same reasons? Are the present concentrations a result of processes no longer operating? How can the presence of so large a proportion of mankind in these regions be explained?

The causes of the distribution of people have been debated since man first became conscious of his place in the world. The writers of ancient Greece first presented the argument for climatic control: that the torrid lands to the south of the temperate Mediterranean were too hot for civilized man, and that the frigid lands to the north were too cold. Since that time the centers of culture development and population have shifted north of the Alps into regions that the Greeks thought were fit only for barbarians, and the climatic argument has been suitably revised. There is a widespread popular opinion that people who live in a climate such as that of Western Europe, or the Northeastern United States, or Japan, have better health and energy than people who live under other conditions. There is even some body of scholarly writing to support this claim. But the validity of the argument is somewhat shaken by the fact that people who support this idea live in just this kind of climate. Actual controlled experimentation with human beings exposed to different combinations of climatic elements, with different kinds of clothing and shelter, points to the conclusion that with suitable protection from the environment, there is no part of the earth in which man cannot live and prosper.

In problems of this kind experience tells us to be skeptical of simple answers. The actual arrangement of people on the earth is a result of complex processes, some of which were imporant in the past but are not important today. We have learned to expect that the significance to

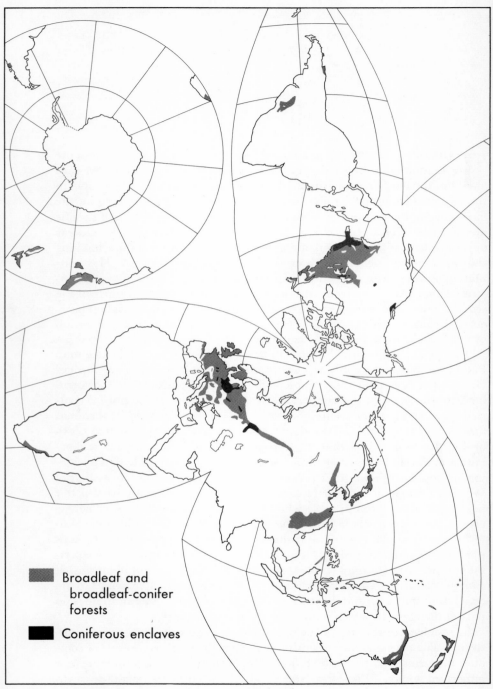

Broadleaf and
broadleaf-conifer
forests

Coniferous enclaves

Map 40.

man of the features of the earth's habitats will change with differences in the attitudes, objectives, and technical skills of man himself. To clarify the difficulties of finding answers to the questions posed above we shall first examine the physical and biotic characteristics of the regions of Group V, and then we shall review the record of occupance in certain representative areas.

The Habitat

The regions of Group V are found in certain regular positions on the global pattern of habitats (see the generalized habitat patterns, Figure 12, p. 424). In the Northern Hemisphere regions of this group are found on both the western and the eastern sides of the continents. On the western side they are found between 40° and 60° along the coast; on the eastern side they are between 25° and 45°. The regions of Group V extend inland toward the dry interiors of the continents, but the actual inland extension differs in each continent because of the irregularities of the surface features. From the western side the regions of Group V extend farther eastward in Europe than in North America because of the arrangement of high mountains. From the eastern side they extend westward much farther in North America than in Asia—again due to the arrangement of mountains and the configuration of the coasts.

Group V regions also occur in the Southern Hemisphere. They form a rim of forest from the southern end of the generalized continent, reaching latitude 40° on the western side, and about 25° on the eastern side. The actual areas included in Group V in the Southern Hemisphere differ from this generalized pattern because of the irregularities of surface features and coasts.

CLIMATE AND VEGETATION

These habitats occur within a certain range of climatic conditions. There is a winter cold season when plant growth ceases, and there is enough rain in summer to support a forest vegetation. Within these broad limits, however, there is a considerable range of climatic difference. Before discussing these differences in terms of specific climatic types, we shall review some of the basic climatic patterns discussed in the first chapter of this book (pp. 10–18).

Some Basic Climatic Patterns. The distribution of air temperature at the surface of the earth is determined in general by latitude, and by the character and arrangement of land and water. If the earth's surface were entirely covered by water there would be a simple arrangement of temperature by latitude, with the highest temperature along the equator, shifting north and south with the seasonal position of the vertical sun.   But on the actual surface of the earth the simple pattern of temperature by latitude is altered by the difference in heating and cooling capacity of land and water.   At the same latitude, the air over a land mass heats up faster when the sun is high, and cools off faster when the sun is low.   We have distinguished, therefore, between continental climates and marine climates: the continental climates at the same latitude are hotter in summer and cooler in winter than the marine climates.

This contrast is reflected in the arrangement of temperatures.   Any winter isotherm, drawn to connect points of equal temperature, must bend toward the equator as it crosses a land mass; and any summer isotherm must bend toward the pole.   In the Köppen system of climatic classification used in this book (see p. 18, and Appendix B, pp. 478–487), two isotherms are of special importance as they cross the continents through the middle latitudes. These are the isotherm for the average temperature of the coldest month of 26.6° (-3°C.); and the isotherm for the average temperature of the warmest month of 71.6° (22°C.).   The general position of these isotherms as they cross the land and water bodies provides the basic structure of the climatic pattern.

To illustrate this pattern let us suppose that there is a land mass of continental proportions that extends from about 70° N. to a little less than 60° S. (Figure 1).   This land mass is smooth in outline.   It is widest in the north and tapers to the south.   This figure generalizes the shapes of the actual continents, which have the greatest east-west extension between latitudes 60° and 70° N., and which become narrower toward the south. Except for Antarctica, the actual continent that reaches farthest to the south is South America—to about 56° S.   This generalized continental outline omits the irregularities of specific coastlines, and it omits the specific pattern of high mountains which distinguishes one continent from another. The general regularity of climatic features can be demonstrated by plotting their average position on this figure—recognizing that each continent presents its own particular distortion of the basic regular pattern.

The average position of these two isotherms in each hemisphere is plotted on this figure.   The isotherm of 26.6° for the coldest month reaches the west coast of the generalized continent at about latitude 65°N. On the map of world climates (Plate 11, p. 566) it can be seen that this isotherm (which marks the distinction between C and D climates) reaches the coast of Alaska at about latitude 60°N., and reaches the coast of Norway at about latitude 70°N.   The average position is shown on the generalized continent.   The isotherm then bends equatorward to about latitude 35° N. in the continental interior, and reaches the east coast a little

Generalized Global Pattern of Summer and Winter Isotherms

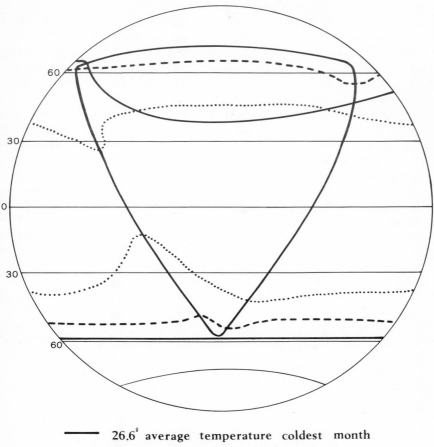

——— 26.6° average temperature coldest month

– – – 50° average temperature warmest month

········ 71.6° average temperature warmest month

Figure 1.

north of latitude 40°N. In the Southern Hemisphere this isotherm runs almost parallel to latitude 60°S.

The summer isotherm of 71.6° for the warmest month bends far toward the equator along the continental west coasts. This is the latitude where especially cold ocean water bathes the shore (p. 48). On the land the isotherm bends sharply poleward again, and then continues to bend poleward but less sharply as it crosses the land mass toward the east coast. In the Northern Hemisphere this isotherm reaches about latitude 45° in the continental interior, and touches the east coast at about the same place where the winter isotherm of 26.6° touches it. In the Southern Hemisphere, the summer isotherm also bends toward the equator along the west coast, but it does not bend poleward as far as it does in the Northern Hemisphere because the narrow extension of land at these latitudes does not permit the development of such hot summers.

The position of these isotherms in the Northern Hemisphere reflects still another control of climate—the prevailing surface winds (pp. 13–16). The western sides of the continents poleward of 30° receive the prevailing westerly winds circulating around the northern half of the oceanic whirls. The eastern sides of the continents, on the other hand, receive onshore winds from the south and southwest on the northwestern sector of the oceanic whirl. The result is a general movement of air from west to east in the middle latitudes. The moderating effect of open water is felt farther inland on the western sides of the continents than on the eastern sides. The greatest ranges of temperature between summer and winter occur east of the centers of the land masses, and east-coast climates are generally more continental than those on the west coasts at the same latitude. This is brought out strikingly by a comparison of the latitude of the big urban centers of Europe and eastern North America. Due west of London, on the eastern coast of North America, lies sparsely populated Labrador. Such northern European cities as Oslo, Stockholm, Helsingfors (Helsinki), and Leningrad lie in the same latitude as southern Greenland or the northern part of Hudson Bay. In North America, New York and Sitka both have about the same January mean temperature, 30° and 31°, respectively; but the warmest month in Sitka is 55°, and in New York it is 73°.

The pattern of rainfall in the regions of Group V is a result of the interplay of climatic elements. These are regions of interaction between the poleward parts of the oceanic whirls, and the equatorward-moving cold air masses produced by the polar outbursts. Along the advancing cold fronts there are cyclonic storms, heavy rain or snow, and generally variable weather. Actually the world's stormiest areas are found where warm ocean water is relatively close to the centers of cold air accumulation. The stormiest part of the world is in the higher middle latitudes of the Southern Hemisphere, surrounding the Antarctic Continent. Great storminess is also experienced over the North Atlantic Drift where it passes south and southeast of Greenland; and over the Kuro Siwo where it passes close to the cold Bering Sea and northeast Siberia. Storminess and weather variability, however, extend beyond these maximum zones: the continental

Cloud formations along a cold front (Photo by E. H. Hanlon).

coasts both on the west and on the east are very stormy in higher middle
latitudes. In winter the cold air masses push equatorward of 40° on the
west coasts, and much farther toward the equator on the east coasts, where
there are warm ocean currents. The cold air masses that reach western
North America come largely from Siberia, the Arctic Ocean, and Alaska;
in western Europe, cold air masses come not only from Greenland but also
from the continental interior to the northeast. In eastern North America,
cold air pours southward from the Arctic Ocean and from Greenland
across Canada and the United States. In eastern Asia the very cold area
of northeast Siberia is a source of so many polar outbursts that, latitude
for latitude, as compared with eastern North America, the winter temperatures of Asia are some ten to fifteen degrees lower. The basic cause of
the difference is the relative size of Asia and of North America. The temperatures of winter in the continental interior of Asia are much lower than
those in the interior of North America.

The Climates of Group V. There are three major kinds of climate in the
regions of Group V. They are the Humid Marine Climate (Cfb, Cfc), the
Humid Continental Mild-Winter Climate (Cfa, Cwa), and the Humid
Continental Severe-Winter Climate (Dfa, Dfb, Dwa, Dwb).

The Humid Marine Climate occurs chiefly on the continental west coasts,
and on islands of the higher middle latitudes. These coasts and islands are
bathed by warm ocean water, and the prevailing westerly winds bring an
abundance of moisture to the land. The westerlies are frequently inter-

rupted by cyclonic storms. As a result, the winters are mild, cloudy, and rainy, and the summers are cool and a little less rainy. Rain comes in the form of frequent drizzles, rather than torrential storms. On the immediate coast, the average annual rainfall is heavy. Farther back from the coast, however, the annual rainfall decreases, even to less than 30 inches (London 24 inches; Paris 22 inches); but in the absence of any very high temperatures there is so little evaporation that even this relatively small amount is highly effective and supports a luxuriant plant growth. The extreme of this kind of climate is found on oceanic islands or exposed coasts near the poleward limits (as in Iceland, the Aleutian Islands, and South Chile). The climatic type extends across the oceans of higher middle latitudes, and in the Northern Hemisphere touches the east coast in two places: in northern Japan and in Cape Cod.

The Humid Continental Mild-Winter Climate occurs on the eastern sides of the continents in lower middle latitudes, and in a few little spots in southern and eastern Europe west of the grasslands (such as the Po Valley of Italy). It is characterized by mild winters, with occasional freezing weather and falls of snow of short duration. The summers are very hot and humid—considerably hotter than the weather encountered in most parts of the rainy tropics. Compared with the marine climate, there is a much greater range of temperature between summer and winter; there is much less cloudiness, especially in winter; the rainfall maximum comes in summer rather than in winter; and the rain comes in the form of torrential downpours rather than drizzles. On the eastern sides of the continents in the Northern Hemisphere (in China and southeastern United States) the climatic conditions are almost identical latitude for latitude, except that the winters in China are much colder, for the reasons explained above. The average monthly rainfall at Charleston, South Carolina, and at Shanghai, China, is almost exactly the same, with a maximum amount in June and July and a minimum in December and January. At both places the prevailing winds shift from offshore in winter to onshore in summer. Shanghai is 12° colder in January, but in July the temperatures of the two places are almost the same. Clearly, then, to describe the climate of this part of China as a "monsoon" climate is correct only if the climate of eastern United States is also described in this way. Both regions have a Humid Continental Mild-Winter Climate, and both are in the area of the statistical monsoons.

The Humid Continental Severe-Winter Climate occurs on both sides of the dry interior in the Northern Hemisphere, north of the mild-winter climate. The difference between the two is that in the areas of severe winters there is a snow blanket that remains on the ground for weeks at a time. The line between mild winters and severe winters in Köppen's classification of climates is the isotherm of 26.6° average temperature for the coldest month (the distinction between D climates and C climates on Plate 11, p. 566). This line appears in the eastern United States just north of Boston, bends southward in the Appalachians, but returns northward again to pass north of Cleveland, and then runs through the middle of the Corn Belt westward into Kansas. In eastern Asia the line passes through northern Japan, crosses Korea, where it corresponds closely to the line between North Korea and South Korea, and passes to the north of the Yangtze Valley of China. In Europe, on the other hand, this same line runs north and south through Poland, separating the area of mild winters to the west from the area of severe winters to the east. In the southernmost parts of this severe-winter climate summers are hot, as they are in the Corn Belt, in North China and Manchuria, and in a few spots in eastern Europe. Elsewhere, however, summers are cool, as they are in the United States north of the cities of Boston, Detroit, Chicago, and Minneapolis; and as they are in both the eastern and western parts of the Soviet Union.

In the absence of any wide expanses of land in the higher middle latitudes of the Southern Hemisphere, there are no severe-winter climates.

The Vegetation Types. These climatic conditions are reflected in the vegetation pattern by a cover of seasonal forest. Unlike the seasonal forests of the low latitudes, here the deciduous trees drop their leaves in winter. In this group there are numerous forest associations: some are composed only of species of deciduous broadleaf trees, such as the oak-hickory forests of much of the Central Plains of the United States; some are composed only of coniferous trees, such as the pine forests of Poland, or the southern longleaf pines of the southeastern United States; and some are a mixture of broadleaf trees and conifers. In many places the stands of pure conifers are associated with areas of porous sandy soil. There are some students of vegetation who insist that the coniferous forests are the result of burning. In the southeastern part of the United States the southern pines survive fire whereas the broadleaf trees are killed.

On the equatorward side of these regions where Group V borders Group II, the differences in the forest are not sharply contrasted. Gradually the species that cannot survive frost drop out. But there is a considerable overlap, since pines occur as far equatorward in North America as Nicaragua, and palms are found as far poleward as North Carolina.

On the poleward side of these regions in the Northern Hemisphere, there is a relatively sharp line of demarcation. The Boreal or northern forests occur where there are severe winters and only short cool summers (Dfc), and here spruce, fir, and larch are the more widespread conifers, and aspen, birch, beech, maple, and willow become the chief broadleaf species.

Toward the continental interiors, on the dry side of Group V, the mid-latitude mixed forests are usually bordered by grasslands. As in the case of the tropical savannas, these grasslands seem to have been produced by the fires of prehistoric man. Where fires are controlled in modern times, the forest returns to the prairie lands, and even the semiarid steppes are covered by scrubby woodland. Fingers of galeria forest extend along the valleys far out into the grassy regions.

SURFACE FEATURES

A discussion of these generalized patterns of forest distribution gives us a basic understanding of the factors or controls which produce the major lineaments of the face of the earth. But it is also true that each continent, each area of mid-latitude mixed forest, can be identified because of its own unique arrangement of surface features. The particular patterns developed on each continent and in each major natural region result from the configuration of the surface and the trend of the coasts. No generalized pattern of surface features can be shown on the generalized continent because, as we pointed out in the introduction to this book, the relief features

An ungrazed oak-hickory forest in the United States (United States Forest Service).

of the earth are not regularly arranged with reference to the equator and the poles.

The regions of Group V, then, are all different in the arrangement of their surface features. Of all these regions, however, the ones located in Europe are the most intricate in pattern (Plate 4 and Map 46, p. 233). With a much indented coast line, and with many mountain ranges and enclosed basin plains or uplands, this continent is composed of a large number of distinct natural regions more or less isolated from one another. The largest area of low relief is in the east, extending from the Black Sea to the Arctic. Only in its central part is it included in Group V. Toward the west this plain narrows down like a funnel, constricted on the north by the Baltic Sea and on the south by the mountains and uplands of central Europe. The end of the funnel is on the shore of the North Sea. Here the natural lines of circulation come to a sharp focus; for not only is this the apex of the plain just mentioned, but also it is easily reached from the south through a series of basins and river valleys. Just south of the Plain of Flanders lies the Paris Basin, united by low passes to the Aquitaine Basin and to the Mediterranean through the Saône-Rhône Valley. The Rhine, also, leads to the North Sea. Even in the British Isles the largest lowland area, on which London is situated, faces the North Sea. In this portion of Europe, therefore, is one of the world's greatest foci of natural lines of travel, as guided by the configuration of the surface.

In contrast to Europe, eastern North America is built on a pattern of relative simplicity (Plate 1 and Map 52, p. 258). Its plains are extensive and continuous instead of being broken into numerous isolated units. The various parts of the Appalachian-Ozark system of hilly uplands and low mountains, extending southwestward from New England, are arranged in simple linear fashion, separating the coastal plains of the east and south from the central plains of the interior. The Mississippi Valley, south of the mouth of the Ohio, is one of the world's major river floodplains. Aside from the several natural foci of routes of travel in the interior of eastern North America, the natural outlets across the barrier of highlands are three in number. Perhaps the most obvious route from the interior plains is down the Mississippi to the Gulf of Mexico. Another natural outlet is provided by the St. Lawrence. For historical reasons, however, a third natural highway has been of greater importance than either of the other two: the Hudson-Mohawk route, by which an easy passage of the Appalachian system is made (with a climb of only four hundred and forty-five feet). This pass contributes an important part of the focus of natural lines of travel on the site of New York City.

Very different from either Europe or eastern North America are the Asian borderlands (Plate 13 and Map 41, p. 220). Here the areas of lowland are relatively small, being restricted by many ranges of hills and mountains to the alluvial valleys of the great rivers.   Furthermore, the regions of Group V are limited to the continental margins by the lofty mountains and desert plateaus of the interior.   In China the two mighty rivers, the Yangtze Kiang and the Hwang Ho,* have formed the largest areas of lowland, south and north of the Shantung peninsula.   Loess, carried by the wind from the deserts of the interior, has been added to the river alluvium to build the Hwang Plain.   Smaller valleys, such as the Si Plain of South China, the Chengtu Plain of the interior, or the river plains of southern Manchuria, are found in scattered positions, isolated by the highlands.   The southern side of Korea consists of narrow valley lowlands separated by transverse belts of hills descending from the backbone of high mountains along the east coast.   The islands off the coast of Asia, such as

* In the language of North China the word *ho* means "river"; in the language of South China *kiang* means "river."   It is incorrect to speak of the "Hwang Ho River."

Most of Japan is composed of hills and low mountains, with narrow valley lowlands (Horace Bristol, from Black Star).

A hilly upland in the Appalachian region (Ewing Galloway).

western Taiwan (Formosa), and most of Japan are included in Group V. Japan is crossed by a zone of high mountains, the Japanese Alps, which cut across Honshu from the west coast to the southeast coast between Tokyo and Nagoya (Map 72, p. 323). The rest of Japan is composed of low mountains and ranges of hills, enclosing small interior basins, and with numerous narrow strips of coastal plain or delta plain.

The other parts of the world where regions of Group V occur are all much smaller. In all of them the lowlands are closely hemmed in by mountains or hilly uplands. In western North America most of the land bordering the Pacific is mountainous (Plate 1). A long, narrow lowland, large enough to be distinguished from the bordering mountains, extends from Eugene, Oregon, to Puget Sound. In Oregon, south of Portland, it is known as the Willamette Valley; in Washington it is called the Puget Sound Lowland. The lowland crosses the border into Canada, where it provides the site for the port of Vancouver in British Columbia. To the north, however, the steep mountain slopes descend directly to the sea, leaving only a few narrow delta plains too small to appear on the maps. In addition to providing for the port of Vancouver, Puget Sound offers fine protected harbors for Seattle and Tacoma.

In the Southern Hemisphere the surface features of the regions of Group V, like the climates and the types of natural vegetation, show a close similarity to those of western North America. The Central Valley already described in mediterranean Middle Chile, extends southward, like the Puget Sound Lowland, to the beginning of the embayed section at Puerto Montt. In South Brazil the mid-latitude mixed forest region is found in the states of Paraná, Santa Catarina, and Rio Grande do Sul, and in the eastern part of Paraguay (Plate 2). This whole region consists of hilly upland and plateau, which faces toward the Atlantic with a steep escarpment some 3000 feet in elevation. On the border of Brazil and Paraguay the upland is cut by the deep canyon of the Paraná River, and tributaries to the Paraná which rise near the crest of the escarpment flow westward in valleys that become deeper and deeper. The Iguaçu River descends over great falls into the deep valley of the Paraná. In South Africa there is a small coastal strip which belongs in the regions of Group V (Plate 3 and Map 40, p. 204). It lies at the base of the escarpment capped by the Drakensbergen and extends from Port Elizabeth to and somewhat beyond Durban. Southeastern Australia is composed of small, isolated coastal lowlands, backed by hills and low mountains—not unlike the Appalachians in degree of relief (Plate 5 and Map 36). Isolated plains are occupied by Brisbane, Sydney, Melbourne, and Hobart. In New Zealand, too, the lowlands are small and isolated, backed by dissected plateaus and rugged mountains.

DRAINAGE AND SOILS

Most of these regions of Group V are well-watered, but droughts occur as a result of variations of rainfall, just as in the tropical forest lands. That these droughts result in famines, especially in the densely crowded agricultural lands of Asia, is a measure of the pressure of the population on the limits of subsistence rather than of the severity of the droughts. Similarly, the problem of providing a good water supply for the modern industrial and commercial great cities is a serious one and may even limit the size of these cities as it does in the dry lands. But compared with other parts of the world, the lands in this group have an abundant water supply.

Floods are perhaps more of a menace than droughts. In the monsoon lands every summer is a period of high water; but every few years more rain falls than usual, and as a result there are disastrous floods along the lower valleys. In the other parts of the group, floods occur during periods of excessive rainfall, especially if the rains come when the ground is frozen so that the water cannot sink into the soil. Spring floods associated with the melting of snow are common in the colder northern portions. The rivers are usually able to take care of the floodwaters, provided the tributaries do not all rise at once. The Mississippi floods of 1927, for example, were caused by the coincidence of several flood crests on the tributary streams.

A flood along the Connecticut River between Vermont and New Hampshire. Observe the natural levee in the making (Fairchild Aerial Surveys).

The removal of forests from the headwaters of tributary streams is an important cause of floods. As in the tropics, the runoff is much increased by the clearing of the land; and in the hilly areas of the middle latitudes, where snow may accumulate to considerable depth in a winter storm, the lack of a forest cover permits rapid melting to take place. The result is that the deforested slopes no longer act as reservoirs to hold back the water and maintain a more even flow, and therefore serious floods alternate with protracted periods of low water. An outstanding example of this is found in China. For more than four thousand years floods and droughts have punctuated its history as a result of the almost complete removal of the forest cover. Similar disasters have accompanied the removal of headwater forests in other parts of the world.

Soils.   Many of the same processes of soil development which operate in the tropical forest lands are active also in the middle latitudes, but with certain significant differences.   Leaching and eluviation take place wherever rain water is percolating through a soil to the ground-water table.   But all chemical processes in the middle latitudes go on more slowly than in the low latitudes, owing to the lower temperatures and less extreme humidity.   Humus accumulation, too, is possible in the middle latitudes; for the slower decay of organic litter on the forest floor results in the collection of a black mold, which, mixed with the soil layers, imparts a brownish color.

Three mature soil types are recognized in the regions of Group V.   The red and yellow lateritic soils of Group II extend poleward into the warmer parts of the mixed forest lands, and are known here as *yellow forest soils* Figure 2, C).   Farther poleward, however, humus accumulation is sufficiently rapid so that the soil color is darkened.   With the aid of earthworms the organic matter is mixed with the upper soil layers to form the *brown forest soils* (Figure 2, B).   On the northern borders of Group V and extending into Group VII lie the *podsols*.   In the profiles of the podsol the absence of earthworms is indicated by the concentration of the humus at the surface and the light, ashy color of the soil below (Figure 2, A).   The depth of these profiles decreases as the length of the frozen preiod of winter increases.   None of these soils may be described as fertile.

Mature soils, however, with their distinct horizons, develop only on flattish surfaces where the regolith has remained undisturbed for a long period of time.   Of much greater fertility are the immature soils, which have not suffered leaching and eluviation, although where these occur in hilly country the steepness of the slopes may make their agricultural use difficult.   As elsewhere in the world, the alluvial deposits of river floodplains provide the most fertile lands.

The Occupance

Studies of sequent occupance in the regions of Group V bring to light many varieties of human experience with these habitats.   Some regions, such as those of East Asia, have been occupied by man for such a long period of time that the original habitat has been profoundly altered. Western Europe has also been considerably altered by human action, but not so much as East Asia.   In eastern North America the course of settlement by people of European origin is much shorter.   Even shorter are the records of settlement in the other regions of this group: in western North America, in southern Brazil, southern Chile, parts of South Africa, and in parts of Australia.

We shall illustrate the settlement of these regions by looking at the

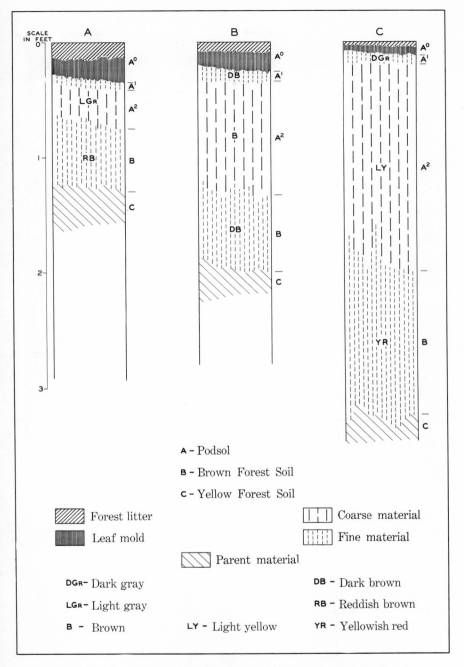

SCALE
IN FEET

A — Podsol

B — Brown Forest Soil

C — Yellow Forest Soil

Forest litter

Leaf mold

Parent material

Coarse material

Fine material

DGR— Dark gray

LGR— Light gray

B — Brown

LY — Light yellow

DB — Dark brown

RB — Reddish brown

YR — Yellowish red

Figure 2. Generalized mature soil profiles developed under forests (after Jenny).

Map 41. Eastern China.

record in three regions—in the eastern part of mainland China; in Western Europe; and in eastern North America.

EASTERN CHINA

There are parts of China where the record of continuous human occupance is longer than anywhere else on earth. The forest was cleared from the valleys of the Hwang Ho and of the Yangtze Kiang so long ago that the precise outlines of the area it once occupied can no longer be reconstructed (Plate 10, p. 564). Even the soils in these areas of dense agricultural settlement have been worked and reworked for so many thousands of years that they are essentially man-made.   The Chinese were so successful in forming a workable connection with the land that the Chinese culture persisted almost unchanged for a very long period of time.   And no country has been invaded and conquered more often than China, and has more often assimilated the conquerors to preserve the traditional culture unchanged (Map 41).

In the twentieth century, however, the massive, persistent culture of the Chinese has undergone revolutionary change.   The population density and the increasing rate of population growth, resulting in part from contacts with Europeans, had increased the amount of Chinese poverty beyond the point of endurance.   The Japanese invasion of World War II tore millions of peasants loose from their ancestral lands.   When the communists promised a program of reform they were given wide popular support. The program they undertook was aimed at changing China from an agricultural country to one based on modern manufacturing industry.

The Pattern of Population.   The pattern of population can be viewed at several different degrees of generalization.   On a very small-scale map, such as the map of Eurasia (Plate 7, p. 560), the concentration of people in the eastern part of China stands out clearly.   A large part of the huge national territory has a very thin population.   *China proper* is the region with more than 26 people per square mile.   This is the area in which most of China's 700 million people (almost one fourth of all mankind) are concentrated.

If we look more closely at China on a population map made on a somewhat larger scale, we can see the pattern of population in greater detail (Map 42).   A comparison of the population map with the map of surface features (Map 41) shows that the delta plains and river valleys of China proper are densely occupied, whereas, even within the general area of concentrated settlement, the hilly areas are only thinly inhabited. Especially high densities can be observed on the delta of the Yangtze Kiang, on the Plain of North China (the alluvial plain of the Hwang Ho), and in the Szechwan Basin of the interior.   High densities can also be seen in little patches along the coast south of the Yangtze, and in the narrow valleys of the hilly southeast.

We can look even more closely at China's pattern of population on a map showing topographic detail.   On such a map, even within the areas that show a very dense population on the other maps, there are marked differences between places where people actually live and work and places where there are few people.   On Map 42 there is an area of very great population density on the coastal plain along the western side of Taiwan.   Map 43 shows an enlargement of a part of Taiwan along the border between the

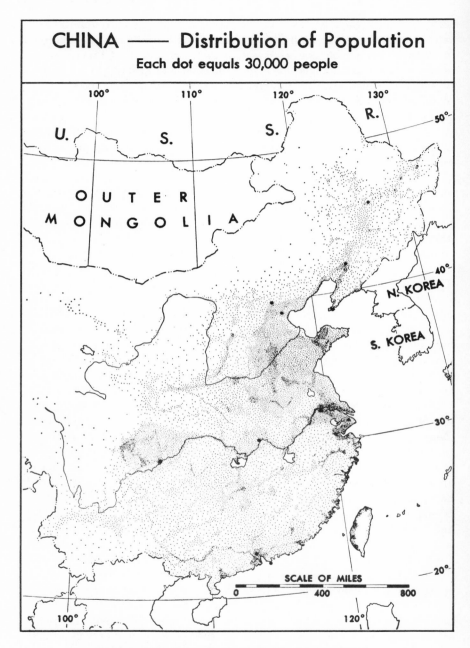

CHINA —— Distribution of Population
Each dot equals 30,000 people

Map 42. (From George B. Cressey, Land of the 500 Million,
McGraw-Hill Book Company, Inc., 1955.)

densely populated plain and the much more thinly populated mountains. On the plain most of the land is used to grow paddy rice, and these paddies remain almost empty at night. The people live in the numerous compact villages from which they emerge only in the daylight.

The density of population in the crowded parts of China proper is very high. The world's greatest concentration of rural people is on the Yangtze delta, where there are some 4000 people per square mile. Densities of more than 1000 per square mile are to be found in all the darker patches on the map of China (Map 42). Yet there are such large areas of very little population even in the eastern part of China that the overall average of China proper is only 350 people per square mile. The overall average for the total national territory (205 people per square mile) is a meaningless figure because so large a part of the area has no people at all. Within China proper nearly 90 per cent of the people are squeezed together on only 27 per cent of the area.

Map 43. Topography of a part of western Taiwan.

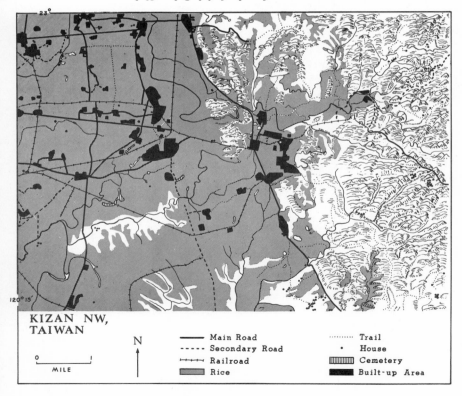

KIZAN NW, TAIWAN

N

0 _____ 1
MILE

——— Main Road
- - - - Secondary Road
+–+–+ Railroad
▨ Rice

·········· Trail
· House
▥ Cemetery
▰ Built-up Area

Before World War II only a small proportion of the Chinese population lived in cities. Not more than 6 or 7 per cent lived in cities of over 100,000, and only 12 per cent lived in cities of over 10,000. Some 75 per cent of the Chinese people lived in small rural villages or in isolated rural farm homes.

Chinese Agriculture. The reason for the concentration of people on relatively small areas and for the existence of large empty areas even in China proper is to be found in a study of the traditional Chinese agriculture. Since a man with a spade and a hoe cannot take care of much more than an acre of land in the time required by the passage of the seasons, he must concentrate his work only on the most productive places if he is to support his family. On such small farms the yield of crops in hilly areas of thin soil or in semiarid areas would not be enough. In the Occidental world farmers cultivate poorer lands, supporting themselves on larger areas by using machinery; but in China, as population approached the limits of the food supply, the farmers worked to produce more per acre. Irrigation is very laborious, requiring a large part of the farmers' time, but it results in very large production per unit of area.

During the thousands of years that the Chinese farmers faced this problem they devised one of the world's most productive agricultural systems. The yields of nearly all the crops of China were above world averages. The yield of rice was second only to that produced by the Japanese farmers, and about twice that of the rice farmers of India. There were plenty of people to do the work. The one major objective of the Chinese peasants was to increase even further the production per acre; not, as in the Occidental world, to increase the production per worker.

The continued increase of population, especially in the last century, placed a heavy burden on the land. Before World War II the average per capita area of farm land in China proper was about half an acre. Farm sizes, too, were small. In North China, where rainfall is not always plentiful, the average size of farms was five acres; on the crowded Yangtze delta it was only a little more than an acre. In the South, where the hot, humid climate supports a very productive agriculture, the farms averaged less than an acre. But in China proper there are only about 275 million acres of arable land, and this was not enough to provide all the Chinese with farms. There were millions who had no land.

Under these circumstances anything that interrupts the farm work or reduces yields can mean starvation for great numbers of people. Warfare brings starvation; droughts, when the onshore winds of summer fail to bring as much moisture as usual, bring starvation; floods, when there is too much rain or when the Hwang Ho, meandering on its flat alluvial plain, slips out of its channel to seek a new route to the sea—these disasters also bring starvation. For thousands of years the population of China has been held in check by recurring famines when thousands or even millions of people starved to death.

Agricultural Regions. Three different agricultural regions developed within China proper: the South China rice region, the North China wheat region, and the Yangtze Valley rice and wheat region (Maps 44 and 45). Rice produces more food per acre than any other grain, and consequently wherever it can be grown well it gets first choice of the land. In China, rice does better than wheat as far as the 30-inch average annual rainfall line. This line runs approximately along the Shantung peninsula and toward the projecting fingers of the Tsing Ling Mountains. Where the average anual rainfall is under 30 inches, wheat is more productive than rice. Thus rice is the dominant crop in South China, and in the Group II regions of the far south two harvests yearly can be taken from the same land. In North China, wheat is the dominant crop. It is planted in the spring, and there is only one harvest in late summer or early fall. In the Yangtze Valley, in between, rice is grown during the hot, wet summers, and wheat on the same fields during the mild winters.

In addition to these two dominant crops, certain other farm products are grown, usually on land that is not suited either to rice or wheat. In the tropical south, sugar cane is a minor crop. Cotton and maize are grown in the Yangtze Valley. On the Yangtze delta both cotton and silk are produced. Mulberry trees, on the leaves of which the silkworms are fed, are planted in rows along the dikes between the rice paddies. In the hilly country between Shanghai and Canton there are tea plantations. In North China a giant millet known as kaoliang is associated with wheat.

Ancient China. These basic patterns of population and agriculture had made their appearance thousands of years ago. By the end of the Han Dynasty (206 B.C. to A.D. 220) the political area of China was approximately what it is today. Although population was much smaller, the agricultural area was only a little less than that of the present. The distinction between North China and South China had long been recognized. In the long history of China first one and the other came to dominate the political life. Nanking (which means "southern capital") was used as the capital of China at times. Peking (which means "northern capital") was the capital of China at other periods when North China and Manchuria were dominant. On April 23, 1953, Peking celebrated the eight hundredth anniversary of its first adoption as capital of all China.

The two divisions of China might have wasted their resources in a bitter struggle for supremacy. Instead they became complementary, each making its distinctive contribution to the national economy. Commerce be-

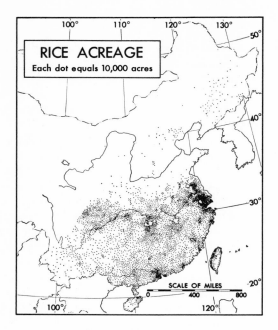

Map 44. Rice in China. *

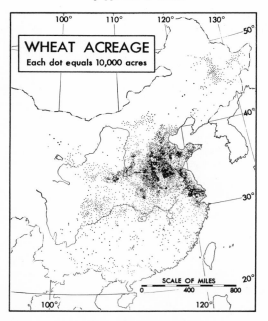

Map 45. Wheat in China. *

* Adapted by permission from William Van Royen, Atlas of the World's Resources, *Vol. I: The Agricultural Resources of the World, Prentice-Hall, Inc., 1954.*

tween the two parts was well developed. Goods were carried by boats along the rivers and the coast, and along the Grand Canal which tied the Hwang and the Yangtze together. Where there were no rivers, goods were carried by human porters. Chinese economic life faced inland, and the most important cities were places such as Hankow and Chengtu, Nanking and Peking, or Canton.

Nevertheless, long before the arrival of the Europeans, Chinese merchants carried on a considerable amount of trade with distant places. There was an important exchange of goods between China and India, and Chinese merchants were a familiar sight throughout Southeast Asia. Trade was carried on with the great market towns of Turkestan and Persia by means of camel caravans which plodded across the deserts of Inner Asia. Over this route Marco Polo traveled to China in the thirteenth century, returning by sea after many years at the court of the Chinese emperor.

European Contacts. Direct contacts with the countries of Western Europe began in the sixteenth century with the arrival of the Portuguese. The old Portuguese port of Macao, located across the mouth of Canton Bay from Hong Kong, is a relic of that period. The Portuguese name, Formosa, is still used for the island that the Japanese called Taiwan. After the Portuguese came the Spaniards, the Dutch, the French, the British, and the Germans, all seeking a share in the profitable trade with China.

In the nineteenth century Great Britain gained control of a strategic place just east of the entrance to the Canton River. In 1842 Britain seized Hong Kong Island, and in the war of 1858–1860 took the peninsula of Kowloon on the mainland opposite. In 1898 the Chinese government agreed to lease an area of some 390 square miles inland from Hong Kong. This colony and leased territory, which has now an urban population of more than a million, still remains in British hands. It has long served as the main commercial contact between Britain and South China, and, like Singapore, was a major fortress before the days of air power.

Other concessions were granted by the Chinese to the European traders. In Shanghai and other port cities certain districts were set off in which Europeans could reside under their own laws. Because of the importance of the China trade, the port cities grew to be much larger than the old commercial centers of the interior. Shanghai became the largest city of China; Tientsin was established to serve the old capital of Peking. To reach the interior the Europeans built railroads (Map 48, pp. 242–243) and established steamboat lines on the rivers.

The Japanese Invasion. All the commercial and missionary activities of the Europeans only touched the surface of Chinese life. The population, which was about 70 million in 1650, increased to 140 million by 1740, and

Looking toward the mainland (Kowloon) from "The Peak" on the island of Hong Kong. The city of Victoria is in the foreground (photo by China Mail).

at a more and more rapid rate thereafter. Population pressure on a land base that was already used to capacity frustrated every effort to do something about poverty and famine.

In the late nineteenth century, Japan began to awaken from its long period of isolation from the rest of the world, and to embark on a program of expansion. In 1894–1895 the Japanese went to war with China and were successful in taking Korea and Formosa (which they called Taiwan). In the war with Russia in 1904–1905 they received certain rights in Manchuria that placed that part of China under Japanese economic domination. In 1931 Japan established Manchukuo as a separate state, and proceeded to build up the heavy industries and to develop the mineral resources of that area. In 1937 the Japanese invaded China proper and in 1941 forced the Chinese government to take refuge in Szechwan. Millions of Chinese peasants were torn loose from the land, either to serve in the army or to avoid the floods along the Hwang Ho when the dikes were broken as a defense against the invaders. When Japan was defeated in 1945 and withdrew from China, the country was in chaos. A bitter civil war developed between the Nationalist Republic of China which had survived the Japanese occupation, and the People's Republic of China which was communist. The communists established their government at Peking in 1949, and in 1950 the Nationalist government fled to the island of Taiwan.

Communist China. The Central People's Government has adopted a program that strikes at the roots of the traditional Chinese culture. The Five-Year Plan of 1953–1957 and the Constitution of 1954 show clearly that the communist objective is to make China once again the major power in the Oriental world by building up a large industrial capacity as quickly as possible. In spite of the fact that 80 per cent of the communist support comes from the peasants, the government has no intention of making the welfare of these rural people its primary concern.* Political dominance within China has again been shifted to North China and Manchuria, and away from South China.

Nevertheless one essential of the communist program is agrarian reform. In 1952 the farm population of China was grouped into five classes: landlords, rich peasants, middle peasants, poor peasants, and landless laborers. The land was taken from the first two classes, who probably owned about 60 to 70 per cent of the agricultural area, and was given to the last two classes, who make up a vast majority of the rural population. The liquidation of the landlords and the rich peasants was carried on with popular acclaim and ruthless brutality. Yet the fact remains that there are some 500 million rural people and only 275 million acres of farm land.

*See the chapters by Charles A. Fisher in W. G. East and A. E. Moodie (editors), *The Changing World* (New York, 1956).

The communist program calls for a complete break with previous forms of occupance. The family is no longer the basic unit of settlement, and the farming people have been deprived of their traditional attachment to particular pieces of land. All private property is eliminated, and the scattered farm dwellings have been removed to clear the way for the development of large fields. The people have been brought together in farm communes where they are housed in barracks and fed in communal kitchens.

Many technical changes were introduced. Fertilizer was spread over wide areas by digging out the compost pits that were once a common feature of the rural landscape. Even chimneys have been taken apart to secure wood ashes. The numerous cemeteries that once dotted the landscape were demolished to make room for more crops. A large dam at Sanmen Gorge* will control the floods of the Hwang Ho, and will make possible an extension of irrigation to areas now out of reach of water. Electricity will also be generated at the dam, which is scheduled for completion in 1967.

The major effort of the communist government is to build manufacturing industries, especially heavy steel industry. In this program China has one great advantage—it is more amply supplied with the basic raw materials for industry than any other Oriental country. China has large deposits of high-grade coal and iron. China is already the world's leading producer of tungsten and antimony, and within the national territory there are large supplies of tin, copper, and salt. The new industrial development is to be scattered in seven major economic regions. Each region will have a basic steel industry to support the development of other forms of manufacture. This decentralization of industry will be costly, because it loses the advantages of large-scale operations. However, according to the communist planners, it has the advantage of providing for a more uniform development of the country.

China's Prospect.   Under whatever political regime, China is still faced with a major population problem. The birth rate is one of the highest in the world, averaging between 45 and 50 per 1000. For centuries this high birthrate has been almost balanced by a very high death rate. When medical aid was brought to China by the missionaries, and when the level of living was raised, at least in the port cities, the death rate was lowered. The result was a population explosion. It is estimated that by 1975 the population will have increased to more than 800 million. At first the communist government took the stand that there was no population problem, only a problem of economic development. But by 1958 there were signs

*Located about 60 miles downstream from the junction of the Wei Ho and the Hwang Ho (Map 41).

A crowded street in Shanghai (Black Star).

that the government had at last accepted the need to develop some kind of a birth control program.

What is likely to happen to China? The Chinese themselves, accustomed to think in terms of a long history of civilized living, are more willing to wait for the outcome of the present communist conquest than are the impatient Westerners. During more than forty centuries China has been conquered many times, but it has always absorbed its conquerors and digested their foreign ideas. The violence of the period after 1950, the "liquidation" of the landlords, is only an incident in the long history of these people. As one Chinese is reported to have said: "After all, things were much worse during the Han Dynasty." It would be difficult for an Occidental, especially a communist, to understand how anyone could hold such a resigned view of the great sweep of history.

There is another aspect of the question that worries the Occidental world. Under a ruthless communist leadership, inspired by purposes unfriendly to the Western nations, an industrialized China with new military strength and with an overwhelming desire for more space for its vast population, could become the world's major military problem. The question then would be to what extent the basic ideas and attitudes of the traditional Chinese culture may have survived the revolutionary change in the economy.

WESTERN EUROPE

Both of the great revolutions of the contemporary world originated in Western Europe during the second half of the eighteenth century. The changes in the attitudes, objectives, and technical skills that have been produced by the Industrial Revolution and the Democratic Revolution have profoundly affected the significance of the resource base. Studies of sequent occupance in Western Europe, therefore, throw light on the problems and conditions throughout the Occidental world.

The Background of Settlement in Europe. Europe is not really a continent at all, except in name. An examination of the globe shows that the great land mass of Eurasia is formed like an isosceles triangle, with its base at the east coast of Asia and its apex in Western Europe. No barrier of any sort separates Europe from Asia; in the course of many centuries people have migrated back and forth from the great central heartland of Asia to the various peripheral areas, of which Europe is one.

There is an important difference, however, between the broader eastern part of Europe where it adjoins Asia, and the narrower, western part. West of a line drawn from Leningrad to Trieste most parts of the land are easily accessible to people with ships (Map 46). There are three reasons

Map 46. Western Europe.

for this.   In the first place, the land itself is tapering so that no part of the continental interior is far from the ocean.   In addition, the coast line of this part of Europe is deeply indented and has many excellent harbors. And, most important, this part of Europe is crossed by a series of navigable rivers.   The Seine-Saône-Rhône system provides a fine route of travel and communication which was of special significance to a people otherwise dependent on transportation overland by horse and wagon.   From the Saône, the Gap of Belfort between the Vosges and the Jura gives access to the Rhine, which, in turn, is navigable to the North Sea.   The Elbe and the Oder, together with other smaller rivers, connect the North Sea and the Baltic with the heart of western Europe.   In contrast, eastern Europe is much less accessible for people with ships, except for the Danube, which leads to the Black Sea.

This difference was of importance to the people who settled in the forested regions north of the Alps.   In the days when overland travel and transportation was dependent on pack animals or horse-drawn vehicles, places located on navigable rivers or near the ocean enjoyed great advantages over places isolated from water transportation.

The People of Europe.   Europe was thinly populated north of the Alps when the Romans pushed their conquest across Gaul and into Britain. The Celtic tribes who came very early to the forests near the apex of the great Eurasian triangle were pushed on by later migrants. Today the parts of Europe which are predominantly Celtic are the westernmost islands and peninsulas (Map 47).   About 2000 B.C. the Germanic tribes were in southern Scandinavia and on the plains between the Rhine and the Oder. Seeking better crop land where summers were warmer, they pushed southward into what is now France, and into the middle valley of the Rhine, and into the upper valley of the Danube.   Wherever the soils were easy to drain and to cultivate with simple tools they established settlements and planted crops; but between the settlements were large areas of untouched forest, pictured in German mythology as the dwelling places of gods and demons.   To the east were the land-minded Slavs, a pastoral people but recently come from the grassy steppes of the Eurasian interior.   They established fixed villages wherever lands could be cleared for pasture. Many of these early villages are marked today by large cities, identified as Slavic in origin by the endings *-in* or *-zig* (such as Berlin or Leipzig).

The Romans brought language and many social and political ideas to western Europe.   When Roman power collapsed, people in the area west of the Rhine continued to speak a Latin language, but the Germanic language persisted east of the Rhine.   English was enriched from both sources. The relation of people to the land, both among the Latin people and the Germanic people, was based on the feudal concepts of the Romans.   Feu-

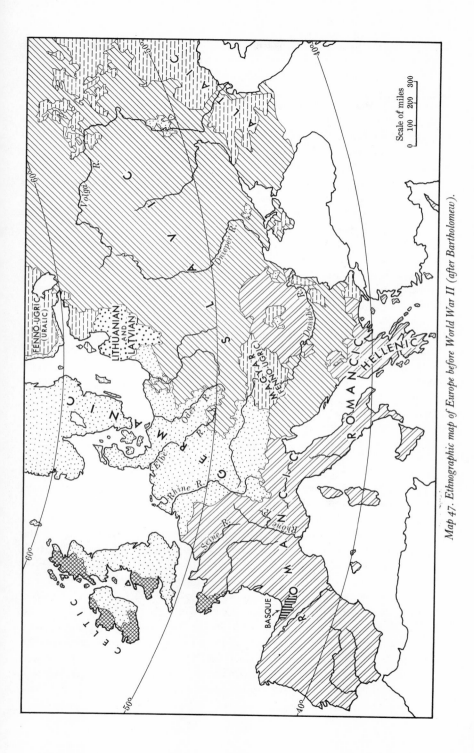

Map 47. Ethnographic map of Europe before World War II (after Bartholomew).

dalism was the basic and widespread way of living in Europe before the rise of the industrial society, and to this day it characterizes the pre-industrial society wherever it is found.

Medieval Europe.   Medieval Europe was still not densely populated. There were areas of concentrated settlement, but between them were large expanses of uncut virgin forest, mostly uninhabited. The land was divided into large domains ruled over by lords but occupied chiefly by an illiterate peasantry.

Essentially each community was a self-sufficient unit of settlement. To be sure, the lord of the land and the retainers who lived with him in his castle and the officers of the army who maintained his rule could make use of foods, articles of clothing, and luxuries brought at high cost from distant places. But the great majority of the people lived on what they produced from the immediate locality.

Under the traditional agricultural system the soils of Europe did not give large yields. The brown forest soils soon declined in productivity when used repeatedly for grain crops without the addition of fertilizers. To cope with this fact the "three-field system" of farming was used. Rye or wheat was planted in a field one year; the following year the same field was used for barley or oats; and in the third year the field was permitted to stand idle or in fallow. Animal manures were not used, even where there were cattle. Under this system the yields of wheat were only six to ten bushels to the acre, and few of the communities were safely beyond the danger of famine caused by local crop failure. The density of population was closely related to the quality of the soil for grain-farming.

The Emergence of the Industrial Society.   The emergence of the industrial society and the appearance of modern Europe involved a number of basic changes in the distribution of people and the relation of settlement to the physical earth. The inhabitants of the island of Great Britain played an important role in these changes.

Why should such important cultural developments have appeared first in Britain? There is certainly no simple answer to this question. It is true that Britain enjoys a stimulating climate, with frequent changes of weather and without great extremes of heat or cold, flood or drought. It is true also that the British people were made up of a variety of ethnic strains. The channel which separates the island from the mainland gave just enough protection from repeated invasion and conflict to permit early political unification and more attention to nonmilitary matters than the people of the mainland could afford. The British people turned to the sea, and their ships sought commercial connections in the most distant parts of the world. The homeland was mostly too wet or too steep to make first-class agricultural land, yet the island was not lacking in products for export. Traders came early to exploit the tin ores of the Scilly Islands off the tip of southwestern Great Britain. After the forests had been cleared from the Pennine Hills in central England, the abundant moisture throughout the year supported a rich growth of grass, and on the grass sheep were pastured. This practice did not cause land destruction, as in the Group IV regions of the Mediterranean, because of the difference in climate. The sheep provided Britain with one of its earliest export products—wool. The market was across the Channel in the clothing manufacturing towns of Flanders. The British traders, moreover, had sailed to much more distant places, and had come back laden with the exotic products of many lands; and with the experience of travel and trade came new ideas to challenge the traditional ways of doing things.

The fact is that the first attack on the traditional way of living of the Occidental world was delivered in Great Britain. The first people to challenge the political and economic power of the landlords over an illiterate peasantry were the British. The first country to become dependent on distant sources of food for the support of all the people was England, which has been dependent on imports of wheat since 1750. The first change in the traditional three-field system of farming was made in England. During the second quarter of the eighteenth century the British farmers adopted a system of crop rotation. A field was used one year for wheat, another year for a cultivated forage crop, and a third year for hay. With the use of more fields for feed crops rather than for human food directly, the acreage in wheat dropped; but the yield rose to between ten and twenty bushels to the acre. This was accomplished through the use of animal manures. The animals greatly enriched the diet of the British, and at a cost low enough so that meat was available not only for the very wealthy but also for a large part of the population. More recently the use of chemical fertilizers has raised the wheat yields of Europe to thirty or forty bushels to the acre.

Inanimate power was first placed under effective human control when James Watt perfected his steam engine in 1769. The technical skill was now at hand greatly to increase the use of power in production and transportation. The age of more and more complex machinery brought about an unprecedented increase in the need for fuels and metals, and it was in Great Britain that the first steps in this direction were taken. The first iron bridge was built in 1779 over the Severn near Coalbrookdale in England not far from the border of Wales. In Coalbrookdale, also, anthracite coal was first used experimentally in the smelting of iron. The traditional fuel for making iron had been charcoal, but the forests of Great Britain were already so seriously depleted that a new kind of fuel was urgently needed. The steam engine itself was tried out as a replacement for direct water power, and steam was first used to turn the wheels of a textile factory in 1785. A number of railroads run by animal power or by gravity were in use in England during the eighteenth century for carrying coal from inland mines to the seacoast. Early in the nineteenth century, steam engines on wheels replaced animal power on several of these railroads. The first experiment in moving a boat with steam power was made on Dalswinton Loch in Scotland in 1788. These are the important first steps that marked the beginning of the Industrial Revolution.

Changing Patterns of Occupance. Within a relatively few years the significance of the physical features of the earth with respect to the distribution of population in the Occidental world began to require fundamental reinterpretation. Among the many changes in the relation of man to the land which have appeared and are still in process of appearing, we shall discuss four: (1) changes in the pattern of circulation; (2) changes in the significance of barriers to circulation; (3) changes in the location, complexity, and size of cities; and (4) changes in the use of raw materials.

The Patterns of Circulation. One of the distinguishing features of Occidental culture—a feature which has been given new emphasis by the Industrial Revolution—is the movement of people and goods from place to place. This is described by the general term *circulation*. We have already shown that the movement of people and goods is by no means limited to areas of Occidental culture. The caravans crossing the Sahara were de-

The Industrial landscape of Halifax, in Yorkshire, England (British Information Services).

A river steamer in the Rhine gorge above Koblenz. In the background are terraced hillsides with vineyards (photo by the author).

scribed in connection with the Muslim occupance; the connections of ancient China both by sea with India and by land with the markets of Turkestan and Persia, as well as the internal movements within China proper, have been discussed. But in comparison with the volume of movement within the Occidental world these other patterns of circulation are insignificant.

The kinds of routes selected in Occidental culture areas have changed with changes in the technology of transportation. In the pre-industrial era of horse-drawn vehicles, canal boats, and small sailing vessels, certain kinds of surface and coastal features were important in the selection of routes. But the same features are not so important in the era of railroads, motor trucks, and large ocean ships, and they are quite irrelevant to the patterns of air travel. In many instances the pre-existing patterns have survived the changes in technology because, once established, they could not easily be shifted. However, there are numerous examples throughout Europe of old market towns or ports that have declined because they have been by-passed by the modern routes.

In general, men seek the shortest route from starting point to destination, but they swerve from the straight course to avoid obstacles. Some people, like the Romans, are accustomed to building very straight roads, and are deflected from the shortest lines only by the most serious obstacles; while other people's roads wind this way and that in obedience to the slightest local advantages of travel. Roads are fixed at either end on the surface of the earth, and, to a greater or lesser degree, at other critical points along the way—for example, at passes or low points in hilly country, or at river crossings. In crossing an upland the route which requires the least ascent and descent is usually chosen, but not uncommonly this is modified by the selection of the easiest approaches. To people crossing a river, firm landing places on either bank are fully as important as shallow water. At such points the roads are fixed in position; but in between they conform to slight local advantages of grade or to stretches of dry soil. In most parts of Europe the natural lines of travel for people on foot or with horses were discovered and utilized by the earliest inhabitants.*

Surface features, however, are not the only controls of the road pattern. In many regions the road patterns conform to an arrangement prescribed by the survey of land properties. Whether the property lines conform to the pattern of roads, or the roads assume a pattern determined by the survey of properties, depends on which of these two things came first. The main highways in Europe usually antedate the property lines, and, in fact, form the skeleton to which the latter are articulated. The secondary roads, however, are in many instances fixed in position by the land divisions.

Quite different is the pattern of settlement based on railroads. The route selected for a railroad may or may not follow a route previously selected for a road. By making use of cuts, fills, bridges, and tunnels, a railroad can follow a less devious course through hilly country than can a road, and it is deflected less by swamps and rivers. But because railroad grades cannot be so steep as road grades, rail routes are tied more closely to the major advantages of terrain than are highways.

World Distribution of Railroads. The present world pattern of railroads is the product of only about a century, yet it reveals strikingly the present-day distribution of what we call Western civilization. Since 1825 when the first passenger railroad was put into operation between Stockton and Darlington in northern England, the strands of the railwebs and railnets have been woven into a closely knit fabric near the great Occidental cities. Away from these cities the fabric has a looser weave, until outside the chief areas of Euro-American settlement only long, isolated tentacles have been extended, forming the present-day pattern (Map 48).† Western Europe

---

* Gordon East, *An Historical Geography of Europe* (London, 1935).

† Mark Jefferson, "The Civilizing Rails," *Economic Geography*, Vol. 4 (1928), pp. 217–231. Professor Jefferson suggests the terms adopted here: *railweb* indicates that no part of an area is more than ten miles from a railroad; *interrupted railweb* indicates that a few patches more than ten miles from a railroad exist; *railnet* describes a wider spacing of the railroads in which each twenty-mile zone appears as a distinct band; *rail tentacles* are the isolated lines extending into territory otherwise lacking rail facilities; and *river-links* are those detached bits of railroad connecting two sections of a navigable stream.

and eastern North America stand out conspicuously with their closely woven railwebs; other centers of Occidental occupance, chiefly in the different parts of Groups IV and V, are distinguished by interrupted railwebs or railnets; but beyond the parts of the world dominated by the machine culture the rail lines are few and far between. China possesses a net of the loosest weave, and even that is the result of European activities. The railroad is a distinguishing trait of Occidental culture, and its distribution is an excellent measure of the spread of that culture. The importance of the European regions of Group V in terms of rail transportation is obvious.

Highway Transportation. Motor vehicles appeared before World War I, but it was not until after that war that they became common. The increase in the number of trucks and passenger cars accompanied an increase in the mileage of all-weather paved roads. At first motor trucks were used chiefly to bring goods to the railroads; but little by little, as the network of paved highways was developed, trucks began to compete with railroads for many classes of goods.

The pattern of highways now closely resembles the pattern of railroads in the Occidental parts of the world. The island of Great Britain leads the world in the ratio of road mileage to total area. The high-speed, divided highways with limited access have greatly facilitated the movement of people and goods by motor vehicle for long distances. In addition, the fact that even the secondary roads are often paved gives motor-truck transportation a much greater degree of flexibility than transport by rail.

Ships and Ports. Railroads and highways come to a focus on a relatively few large ports, and between these ports ocean ships provide the necessary connections. However, the size of modern ocean ships is so much greater than that of sailing ships that only a few of the older ports are deep enough to receive them. Most of the older ports were established as far inland as navigation on the rivers permitted. Places like London, Paris, Bremen, and Hamburg are now beyond the reach of large ocean ships; so they make use of new outports such as Southampton, Le Havre or Cherbourg, Bremerhaven, and Cuxhaven. Smaller ships can still reach these great cities, but the river ports are too crowded to accommodate more than a small fraction of the huge volume of shipping required by the modern industrial society.

If a world map could be made to show the position of every ship on a certain day, it would reveal clearly the pattern of circulation of the Occidental world. Most of the ships would be clustered along the same coasts that show railwebs on the railroad map. There would be a great number of ships in the North Sea. Similarly, many ships would be clustered along

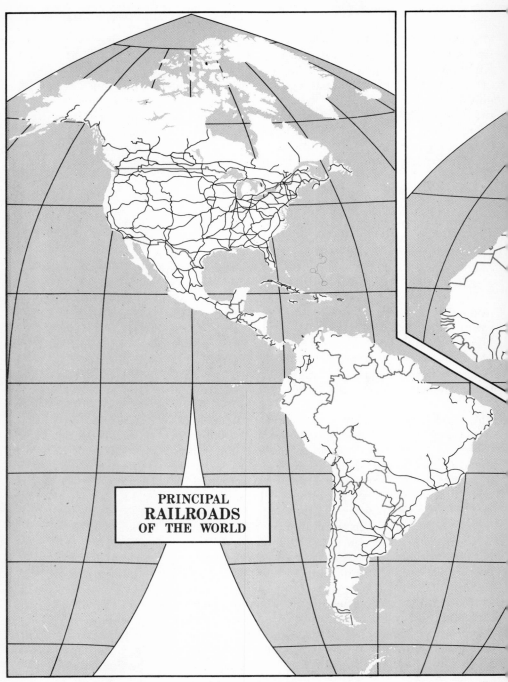

PRINCIPAL
RAILROADS
OF THE WORLD

Map 48

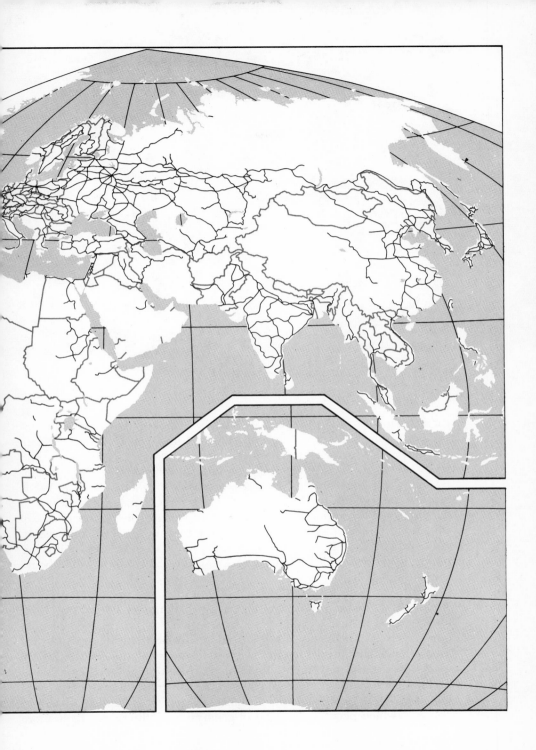

Atlanta Expressway Connector opened in 1964 (Wide World Photos).

the eastern coast of North America. In the open ocean the greatest number of ships would be following the North Atlantic route between North America and Western Europe, for the most active movement of people and goods is between the countries of the industrial society. The chief concentration of ships outside the North Atlantic route would extend from Western Europe through the Mediterranean, the Suez Canal, the Red Sea, to the Persian Gulf and the oil fields of that region. Smaller numbers of ships would be seen following routes to the ports of southern and eastern Asia and of Australia and New Zealand. Ships would also be following routes to Latin America. On vast areas of the oceans there would be no ships at all.

Air Lines. The development of air transportation since World War I has forced people to look at world geography with a new perspective. The old familiar maps of middle and low latitudes, with north at the top and with most of the high latitudes left out, were good enough for people whose only means of overseas movement was by ship. As a result of looking at these maps, however, many geographical errors have crept into popular thinking. One is the peculiar habit of thinking of north as "up" and south as "down," which persists as a kind of geographical illiteracy. Even more

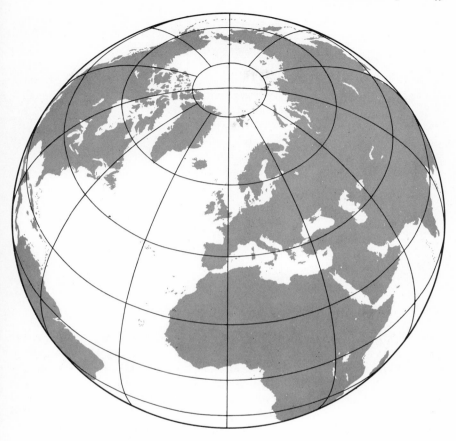

Map. 49. The principal hemisphere.

serious is the idea that the Atlantic and Pacific oceans separate the continents, as well as the failure to see Europe in its new global relationships.

As you look at the world as a whole (which can best be done on a globe),
the position of Western Europe takes on a new significance.   It is a good
exercise in modern geography to pick up a globe and turn it until you find
the position which permits you to see the largest proportion of the world's
inhabited lands. From such a viewpoint it will be seen that the hemisphere, or half of the earth, that centers on Nantes in France contains almost 90 per cent of the land outside of Antarctica. Only some 10 per cent
of the world's lands are on the opposite side of the earth. In the *land hemisphere* (Map 49) are to be found 94 per cent of all the people in the world,
and 98 per cent of all the world's industries. Western Europe occupies a

central position in relation to the global arrangement of lands and peoples, and other parts of the world must be measured in terms of remoteness from Europe. No other great trading area occupies such a strategic position: 94 per cent of the great commercial cities of the world are closer to Europe, on the average, than to any other region of the world. Most of those cities are within twenty-four hours' flying time of Europe.

The world's air routes are much freer to follow great circles than are water routes. Air lines connect the chief centers of population and production, just as railroads concentrate in these areas; and from these centers long tentacles are extended to remote places. The high latitudes, long avoided by the world's chief routes of circulation, are now no barrier to high-flying planes. From the chief centers of Europe air routes extend to other parts of the world, departing only slightly from great circles. The air lines to North America pass over the North Atlantic, over or close to southern Greenland, and over Labrador or Newfoundland. From the Scandinavian countries an air route passes over northern Greenland and Canada to the western United States. Air lines from Europe pass over Southwest Asia on the way to southern and eastern Asia, and to Australia and New Zealand. On the way to Latin America the air lines pass over the Sahara, crossing to Brazil between Dakar and Natal.

The Significance of Barriers.   What constitutes a barrier to transportation? What features of the terrain are important because they impede or prohibit the circulation of people and goods, or because they offer advantages of military defense? The answer cannot be given without reference to the kind of human society which is present. The search for terrain features which would be advantageous as political boundaries is something which has been of concern in Europe during all the centuries since political boundaries were first drawn.

France, for example, was able to achieve national unity behind the protection of a series of physical barriers. The eastern boundary of France took advantage of the Alps, the Jura, the Vosges, and the Ardennes, along which lines of defense could be maintained against the east (Map 46). The fact that there were gaps between each of the hilly or mountainous areas, and that the plains offered easy access around the western end of the Ardennes, has long been of importance to France. In war after war, important and critical battles have been fought in that strategic area between the Ardennes and the sea.

The nature of modern warfare, like the nature of peaceful economic pursuits, has so changed in this period of changing technology that the significance of the terrain is now very different from what it was even during World War I. No longer are ridges and hills of such importance as strong points in defense as they were in that war and earlier wars. With mechanized armies moving rapidly in motor vehicles, the existence of paved roads is more important than the existence of commanding heights. Actually a larger force may be needed to guard the movement of an enemy along paved highways in hills than in level plains because of the many hidden places along the winding roads of the uplands. World War II demonstrated the ease of military movements in the Ardennes, a region long considered as a major strategic barrier. Strong points of defense in that war were offered by the stone houses and narrow streets of the small towns where roads came together and around which it was not possible to pass without leaving the roads. Now, with the use of air-borne armies and rocket projectiles, the significance of terrain must be interpreted anew.

The Location, Complexity, and Size of Cities. There is an intimate relationship between the pattern of circulation and the pattern of cities. Every urban development of whatever size is the center of converging routes of travel. The area within which the routes converge on a central point is approximately the area that the city serves—the *service area*. But

The town of Vianden in Luxembourg, in the heart of the Ardennes (Ewing Galloway).

Marksburg on the Rhine (F. Henle).

cities, like the means of circulation, have developed in a period of changing technology. Very few indeed are model cities, laid out on previously unoccupied land in accordance with an overall plan. Most cities have grown without plan or vision, and are handicapped by the forms and features inherited from previous periods of sequent occupance which cannot easily be wiped out for a new start. Most cities are so ill-adapted to modern life that they are frustrating, irritating, and costly for the people who live in them. Most cities are not at all like the dream cities that modern technology and social understanding would make possible.

In medieval Europe there were three kinds of functions for which cities came into being: commercial, religious, and administrative. Most towns started with one of these functions and quickly added one or both of the others. In cathedral towns the church was the commanding structure, visible from afar over the low buildings around it (for example, Köln, in Germany). People came to worship but stayed to trade. In other cases the commanding structure was the castle of the lord of the land, built on a hilltop if one were available, with the town nestled at its base. From the castle the king or duke carried on the administration of the political area that he controlled. In market towns, the public square in the town center was usually the focus of life. In any case the medieval towns were compact within their walls, and there was little to distinguish one part of the town from another. Workshops, salesrooms, and living quarters were all combined in one structure; and the buildings lined narrow, winding streets which were chiefly for the use of pedestrians.

The new technology, which greatly increased the mobility of people and the capacity to transport goods, enlarged and diversified the functions of the urban centers. The volume of commerce grew enormously. Financial and banking services began to concentrate in certain key cities. As the administrative function was extended, government activities were housed in new, imposing buildings, and the castles became museums. A great variety of social functions developed: religious shrines continued to serve people from outside the cities, but there were also university centers for education, centers of art and music, and medical or health centers. In modern life more people seek recreation in cities than in remote rural areas. All these various functions are services performed in central cities for the people of the service areas.

When steam power, and later electric power, was used in factories, large specialized industrial structures made their appearance. The kind of location sought by an industry depends on such factors as accessibility of raw materials and power, supply of labor, and proximity to markets. Industries such as paper manufacture, in which the manufactured product has much less bulk than the raw material, tend to be located close to the supplies of the raw material, often in places where no towns existed before. Industries that are dependent on especially skilled workers tend to be located in previously established cities where workers are available. Industries that turn out products of high value per unit of weight, or products that are perishable, tend to locate close to markets. Since the largest cities are themselves the largest markets and have the largest pools of trained workers, there is a tendency for such cities to grow larger and larger. More and more industries of all kinds are attracted because of all the other services available. Even the basic steel industry, once closely tied to coal supplies, now tends to select locations as close as possible to the largest industrial centers, where steel is used in the greatest quantities.

All these various functions—commercial, administrative, industrial, and social—are often performed in the same city. But now, unlike the undifferentiated medieval city, the new cities are sharply marked off into distinctly different districts. The center is usually a place where the commercial function is focused. This is the *central business district*. Similarly, the other functions are concentrated in distinct *functional areas*. Filling in the spaces around the functional areas, the land in between is occupied by residences which are often built without any overall plan to guide the development of the urban pattern.

The changes in the technology of transportation made all this development of cities possible. Before the railroad era food could not be brought to any one place in sufficient quantities to support so many non-food-producing urban people. Furthermore, when people had to move about by foot or by horse, they had to live as close as possible to the buildings in which they worked. It was the coming of the electric street-car lines that first made it possible for people to live at some distance from their places of work. For the first time the "journey to work"—a distinctive feature of modern Occidental life—became a problem. Along the street-car lines, or around the stations reached by steam commuter trains, those who could afford to do so left the center of the city and settled in the suburbs. Cities expanded along radiating lines. Later, when the automobile and motor bus permitted commuters to break away from the rail lines, expansion went even farther.

Since the number of new kinds of employment increased to a much greater extent in the cities than in the rural areas, more and more people came to live in cities. Whereas in a country like China less than 10 per cent of the population lived in large cities before World War II, in countries of the industrial society it is not uncommon today to find that 70 to 80 per cent of the total population are city people. The proportion of people employed in agriculture has declined because many people who formerly lived in rural areas now make their living in cities. A large increase in the number of "rural, non-farm" homes has been made possible by the automobile.

The result of these changes has been a rapid increase in the number of great cities in the world. There probably had never been a city with a million inhabitants before London reached that size in 1802. Since then city after city has grown so fast that the present census figures for city populations enumerated within the old political city limits have little real meaning. Geographers define *metropolitan areas,* or *conurbations,* as areas which include the connected, continuously built-up suburbs and outlying industrial districts as well as the central city. According to this definition, there were about 20 cities of one million or more in 1920. By 1935 the number had increased to 51, and by 1955 to 71. In 1965, there were well over 100 such cities. Table I of Appendix F (pp. 533–536) lists the world's great cities by culture areas.

As cities throughout the Occidental world grew in size and importance, there was a tendency for one city in each country to become pre-eminent. In this one center people could find the greatest variety of goods and services, the rarest articles, the best professional and artistic skills, the greatest development of the business institutions that facilitate trade. To this one center came the most able people because here was the place with the greatest economic opportunity. As the supremacy of one city became more and more apparent, not only traders and business people were attracted to it but also artists, musicians, and people of wealth who wished only to enjoy city life. The result was that one city in each country grew out of all proportion to the other cities. This is what Mark Jefferson calls the "law of the primate city."* Among the larger countries of the Occidental world there are eighteen in which the chief city is more than three times the size of the second city; there are twenty-eight in which the chief city is more than twice the size of the second city; and there are very few where two cities of nearly equal size are competing for primacy (as in Canada, Australia, and Brazil).

The Use of Raw Materials.   People who live in cities are sometimes seriously ignorant of the relationship between their economy and the resources of the land. Before the Industrial Revolution, however, few indeed were the people, literate or illiterate, who did not appreciate the basic need for forming a workable connection with the land, for in those times economies were closely related to the resources of the immediate locality. The Industrial Revolution has brought a greater and greater capacity to produce goods, and this, in turn, has led to an enormous increase in the volume and variety of the basic raw materials. Water is the raw material consumed in the greatest quantities. For industrial purposes it is now used on such a scale that even in rainy parts of the earth many cities suffer from water shortage. More than 250 tons of water are required to make a ton of steel, and the water demands of some other industries are even greater. The world rainfall map (Plate 12, p. 568) was never more significant than it is today as an aid in understanding the arrangement of people on the earth. But water is only one raw material. In addition to the old, familiar substances, such as coal, oil, copper, tin, iron, lead, and zinc, there are now many newer items such as the hardeners of steel—manganese, tungsten, nickel, chromium, vanadium, molybdenum. Among the other newer natural resources are bauxite, the ore of aluminum, and uranium, used as the basis for nuclear power.

None of these resources is evenly distributed over the earth. Even water, though abundant in some places, is lacking in others. Iron minerals are widespread among the rocks of the earth's crust, and iron ore has been mined in many parts of the world. But the demands of modern industry are so great that no longer is it possible to rely on many small-scale min-

* Mark Jefferson, "The Law of the Primate City," *Geographical Review,* Vol. 29 (1939), pp. 226–232.

ing operations, which are excessively costly per unit of product. Only by means of large-scale mining operations can the raw materials be produced at low enough cost per unit and in large enough quantities to supply the industrial needs of modern society. One of the basic principles of twentieth-century economic geography is that production of all sorts tends to localize in a few specialized areas. Meanwhile the industrial society has been using up the richer ore bodies at rates even more rapid than the rate of population growth. As lower-grade ores are developed, the cost of production increases—not suddenly, but by small steps. There are some economists who point to the possibility that gradually increasing costs could wipe out the advantages of large-scale production and could bring the industrial society itself face to face with disaster. It seems that the Occidental world is engaged in a race between continued technological progress and resource exhaustion.

Coal is the basic raw material of the industrial society because it is used not only as a source of power but also in the metallurgy of iron and steel, and as a raw material from which many by-products, ranging from aspirin to nylon, are made. Yet awareness of coal as a basic natural resource is relatively recent. In the thirteenth century, when the forests of the more accessible part of Britain had already been largely cut off, King Henry III gave his consent to the mining of coal at Newcastle. The people of London protested against this new fuel on the grounds that it fouled the air and endangered health. By 1650, however, two sailing vessels were regularly employed in carrying coal from Newcastle to London, and English coal was also being used in Belgium and France. By 1700 there were six hundred sailing vessels carrying coal to London. Coal mining began in France in 1715, and at about this same time coal was used in a small way in England to smelt iron at Coalbrookdale. After 1769 the demand for fuel increased very rapidly. But it was not until after 1856 that the method of using coke made from bituminous coal in steel manufacture led to an unprecedented expansion of coal mining. And it was only then that large numbers of people concentrated in industrial cities were located where coal was near at hand.

As a result of these developments, the geography of the world's coal took on a new significance. There proved to be large supplies of high-grade coal in Great Britain and in parts of Europe, especially in the valley of the Ruhr in Germany (Map 50). Later discoveries indicate that something like 90 per cent of the world's coal reserves are in the United States and Canada, China, and the Soviet Union.

After the development of the technology of using bituminous coal in making coke and, in turn, using coke in the manufacture of steel, deposits of bituminous coal for the first time attracted large-scale industrial development. The Ruhr before 1856 was a poor, farming area, its sandy soils

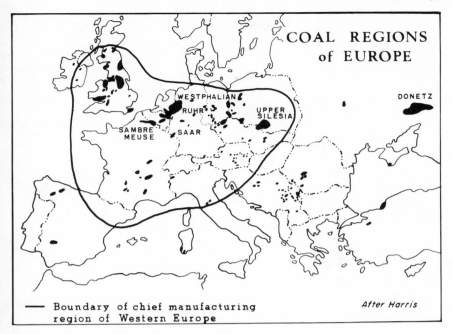

Map 50. Coal regions of Europe.

useful only for pasture. After 1860 it became the industrial heart of Europe and one of the world's major areas of productive capacity. The present urban development of the Ruhr and neighboring areas is shown on the map (Map 51). The black areas are solidly built up with factories, warehouses, railroads, and residences.

The Ruhr became the productive heart not only of Germany but also of Europe. In a world of divided sovereign states, Germany had the coal and France had the iron. From the Ruhr came 90 per cent of the bituminous coal of prewar Germany, and about half of all the coal in Europe outside the Soviet Union. Of the coal mined in the Ruhr before World War II, some 48.5 million tons a year were used in the manufacturing industries of the Ruhr itself; 39.6 million tons were sent to other parts of Germany; and 39.6 million tons were exported to the Netherlands, Belgium, France, Luxembourg, Italy, Switzerland, the Scandinavian countries, the Balkans, Spain, and other places. Thus a very considerable part of the productive capacity of Europe was based on Ruhr coal.

A great variety of manufacturing industries were established in the Ruhr. Close to the coal mines and the huge coke ovens, blast furnaces and rolling mills turned out great quantities of steel of different kinds. All

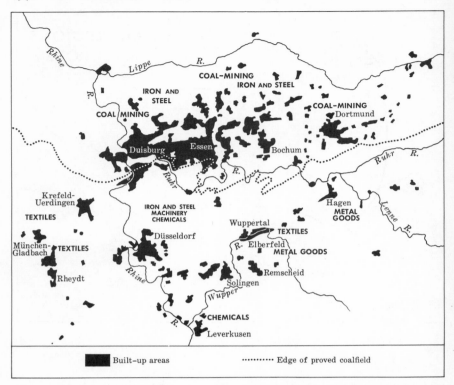

Map 51. Urban development in the Ruhr district (after Chauncy D. Harris).

kinds of plants for making things out of steel were located close to the steel mills. Close by, also, were chemical and dye industries, which used by-products such as coal tar and its numerous components. There were synthetic fiber plants and pharmaceutical industries, all based on the same materials. The present great concentration of people in this area (Plate 7) includes only a small proportion of the total number of people both inside and outside Europe whose economic life is directly or indirectly tied to the productivity of this one place.

The European Economic Community. The people and the resources of Europe are divided among twenty-eight sovereign states, and the boundaries between these states are matters of the greatest significance. The rise of the spirit of nationalism accompanied the rise of the industrial society, and, in fact, was largely produced by it. Yet one of the basic contradictions of Occidental thought at the present time is the existence of ideas of

Heavy industry in the German Ruhr (Koenig, from Black Star).

international economic interdependence along with ideas of national economic self-sufficiency and international political irresponsibility. The continent of Europe has the physical resources, the technological skills, and the manpower to form one of the major aggregates of economic power on the earth, comparable to that of the United States or the Soviet Union. But Europe, split into sovereign states, plagued by the fear of aggression from neighboring states, hampered by the pre-industrial concept of economic self-sufficiency, and dominated by the hatreds engendered by two great wars, was unable to achieve the economic strength that the new technology made possible.

In the 1950's, however, the people of Europe achieved a major change in attitudes and objectives. They took the first hesitant steps toward accepting the principle of international interdependence in 1952, when six European countries—the Netherlands, Belgium, Luxembourg, the German Federal Republic, France, and Italy—agreed to pool their coal, iron ore, and scrap metal and to send these commodities freely, without tariff restriction, into any of the participating countries. In 1954 refined steel was added. This is known as the European Coal and Steel Community, developed by what has been called the Schuman Plan. The result was an increased production in all these items.

In 1957 two revolutionary new international agreements were ratified by this same group of countries. These agreements established Euratom and the European Economic Community (the Common Market). Like the Coal and Steel Community, each of these undertakings is guided by an executive commission responsible to an Assembly of 142 members: 36 each from France, West Germany, and Italy; 14 each from Belgium and the Netherlands; and 6 from Luxembourg. The members of the first assemblies were selected by the parliaments, but in the future members will be elected by the citizens of these countries. There is also a Court of Justice to decide on cases of disagreement. The basic purposes of the two organizations are to pool atomic knowledge and resources, to eliminate tariff barriers and other trade restrictions, and to permit the free movement of capital and workers from one country to another.

The results have been spectacular. The value of all goods and services produced in these countries took a sudden upward spurt. The market for all kinds of consumer goods expanded beyond all precedent. Large numbers of families could afford to buy automobiles, and for the first time could experience the new kind of mobility. Automobiles opened the markets for a long list of new products that came suddenly into demand. Some people outside of the Economic Community were fearful that trade with other parts of the world would be reduced. But it is one of the basic principles of economic geography that the greatest volume of trade flows between two industrialized countries. In anticipation of an increased flow of exports and imports, a wholly new port—Europoort—is being built at the mouth of the Rhine, near Rotterdam. The development of a third great center of economic and military power in the world is a major step in the maintenance of world peace.

Hay cut and drying in southern Germany. In the background is a field of wheat (photo by the author).

EASTERN NORTH AMERICA

The second of the two major areas of Occidental occupance in the regions of Group V is in eastern North America (Map 52). The area of the mid-latitude mixed forest lands of North America is only a little less than that of the similar regions of Europe, but it is occupied by a much smaller population. Within these regions in Europe there are twenty-one cities with more than a million inhabitants; in Anglo-America there are fourteen such cities. In Europe the density of rural population is generally more than 100 people per square mile; in eastern North America the density is mostly between 25 and 50 (Plate 6). But the North American area stands foremost in the whole world in terms of productive capacity, and so in the living standard of its people.

In some ways the eastern part of North America is remarkably similar to Western Europe. As Carl Sauer points out, "it would be impossible to cross an ocean anywhere else and find as little that is unfamiliar on the opposite side."* The mid-latitude mixed forests of both areas contain many of the same kinds of trees. The climate of both areas is characterized by variable and stimulating weather, and by an abundant, but not excessive, supply of moisture. To be sure, the winters of eastern North America are colder than those of Western Europe, and the summers are hotter; but the difference is not so great that important changes in clothing or housing are necessary. The surface of the land, too, was familiar to the Europeans—there are similar landforms resulting from geological processes already observed in Europe. And there is the further element of similarity, which became important after the emergence of the industrial society, in that both parts of the world are abundantly supplied with coal.

The Early Periods of European Settlement. The native Indians had been living in the forests of eastern North America for a long time before the arrival of the Europeans. They depended for their food supply on hunting and fishing, supplemented by a shifting cultivation of maize, squash, and beans. In many places the Europeans found openings in the forest where the Indians had made clearings and planted crops. The settlers called these openings "Indian oldfields." Through the forest the Indian trails marked the easiest routes over the hilly terrain for men on foot.

To this thinly occupied land came the English, French, and Dutch settlers during the first few decades of the seventeenth century. The English settled near Chesapeake Bay in Virginia in 1607, and in New England in 1620. The French established Quebec on the St. Lawrence River in

*Carl Sauer, "The Settlement of the Humid East," in *Climate and Man*, 1941 Yearbook of the U. S. Department of Agriculture, pp. 157–166.

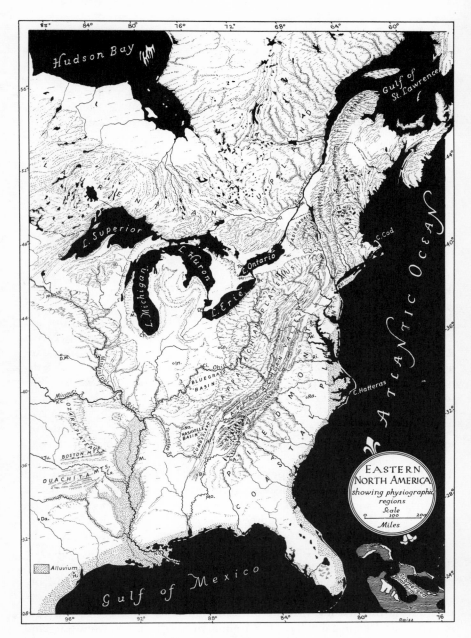

Map 52. Eastern North America.

1608. The Dutch settled along the Hudson Valley in 1614; but in 1667 the Netherlands ceded this colony to the British in exchange for the sugar-producing colony of Surinam in the Guianas. In the century that followed these first settlements, four different culture areas developed, in each of which a new and distinctive way of living was forged in an American habitat. Such areas in which cultures have their origin can be called *culture hearths*. The traditions of modern United States and Canada were derived from the mixture of ideas and skills from these different sources and from the original culture hearth in Great Britain. The four culture hearths were: (1) French Canada; (2) New England; (3) the Southern Colonies; and (4) the Middle Colonies.

The French colonies were the only ones situated where there was an open water route to the interior. French missionaries and fur traders went up the St. Lawrence River to the Great Lakes, and on to the great rivers of the backlands—the Mississippi, the rivers leading to Hudson Bay, and the Mackenzie that led to the Arctic Ocean. Some of the French spread thinly over this vast area, while others remained as a closely-knit French-speaking group of farm settlers along the lower St. Lawrence River. These people today form the core of French Canada.

The New England colonies were established in a habitat characterized by severe winters and cool summers, and by thin sandy soils interrupted in many places by outcrops of bare rock. With incredible labor, the farm settlers cleared the land of trees and rocks, gathering and piling the latter in their famous "stone walls." They learned from the Indians how to grow maize, squash, and beans, and they also tried the more familiar European grains—wheat, barley, rye, and oats. They found their chief source of income from the sea. Not only did the forests provide good timber for building ships, but the sea off New England provided one of the world's finest fishing grounds. New England merchants sent their ships out over the world's oceans on risky trading ventures. Those who stayed at home were devoted to building the institutions of democracy, including the "town meeting" with its emphasis on the use of persuasion rather than force in the settlement of public issues. The New Englanders built schools and colleges to provide their children with free public education.

The Southern Colonies, on the other hand, were established in a climate of mild winters and hot, rainy summers—a climate remarkably similar to that of East Asia. The southerners found that agriculture could be made to pay handsome profits to the landowners. At first they tried tobacco, for which a new expanding market was found in Great Britain. Then they turned to cotton planting. To do the work they imported Negro slaves. The southerners, too, were devoted to democracy—but the democracy did not apply to the slaves. They too insisted on education, but education for the children of the landowners taught by tutors in their homes.

A settlement in the hilly upland of New England (Philip Gendreau).

The Middle Colonies were not like any of the other culture hearths of eastern North America. These were located in eastern Pennsylvania and nearby Maryland and New Jersey. To this area came people of many origins—Dutch, Swedes, and Germans, as well as English, Scots, and Irish. Many different religious denominations were represented. The colonists established themselves on their own small farms, where each family formed a largely self-sufficient unit. The parents taught children to read the Bible, to write, and to do simple arithmetic. Here, too, a frontier kind of democracy flourished. And from this area came an amazing series of inventions. These farmers were the first to use the Indian grain, maize, to fatten the European animal, the hog. They built log cabins, and four-wheeled wagons later known as "prairie schooners." They invented the long rifle and the potbellied stove. From the Middle Colonies came a stream of pioneers, moving restlessly westward.

The Pioneer Movement. From the three culture hearths of English-speaking America settlers spread and mingled. As late as 1700 the areas of settlement along the east coast were still separated by unoccupied country. But by 1790 the colonies had spread along the country east of the Appalachians, forming a continuous belt of settlement all the way from what is now Maine to the border of Georgia. The New Englanders had moved northward into northern New England and westward into New York. But the chief currents of movement had come from the Middle Colonies and the Southern Colonies.

The greatest tendency to advance the frontier settlement appeared in the Middle Colonies. Pioneers spread first southwestward along the valleys between parallel ridges that mark the eastern side of the Appalachians. Some of them went up the Susquehanna River and its tributary the Juniata to the east-facing front of the Allegheny Plateau. This was the most serious barrier, which was nevertheless crossed in central Pennsylvania. Beyond, the winding headwaters of the Ohio River brought the pioneers to Pittsburgh. Daniel Boone was the famous person who led settlers southwestward through the Appalachian Valley all the way to Cumberland Gap—an opening in the long escarpment that extends southwestward from the western side of the Hudson Valley all the way to Alabama (Map 52). Through Cumberland Gap the way was open to the Blue Grass Basin in Kentucky, and the Nashville Basin in Tennessee.

Meanwhile a very different kind of pioneer movement had developed in the Southern Colonies. The success of cotton-planting as the basis for a prosperous economy was secured by two technological developments. By 1785 in England, steam had been applied to the textile factories, and the demand for a greatly enlarged import of raw cotton made the British look all over the world for low-cost sources of this fiber. And Eli Whitney's invention of the cotton gin in 1793 (patented 1794) made it possible for one worker to do what had formerly required 200 in removing the seeds from the fiber. The Southern Colonies became the world's lowest-cost source of cotton.

Cotton planting in the United States began to spread rapidly from the original area on the piedmont of the Carolinas and Georgia. New plantations were carved out of the forest to the west. Cotton planting swept round the southern end of the Appalachians in Alabama and on to the Mississippi, then across the river onto the black prairie soils of Texas as far as climatic conditions permitted. Cotton planting was tried as far north as Rhode Island. But it was found that where the growing season, or the period between the last killing frost of spring and the first killing frost of fall, was less than 200 days, the yield per acre of cotton was not enough to make it profitable. As a result of the balance of costs and prices, the line marking the northern boundary of the 200-day growing season became a critical climatic limit to the northward expansion of the cotton belt.

It is only since World War II that cotton-planting in the south has entered the latest phase of sequent occupance. Traditionally, since the Civil War, the crop has been planted by a tenant or share-cropper, cultivating a small hillside farm with a mule and plow. This kind of farming in a region with torrential summer rains resulted in widespread soil erosion, and so in increasing poverty for the rural people. But with the invention and use of the cotton picker and other cotton-farming machinery, the whole relation of people to the land has been changed. Cotton has largely disappeared from the hilly lands, where the cotton picker cannot be operated. Now it is concentrated on flat land—along the coastal plain of the Carolinas instead of the piedmont; on the floodplain of the Mississippi instead of the area back from the valley bluffs; and on the black prairies of Texas, or the irrigated lands farther west. On much smaller areas, and with many fewer workers, cotton is now produced more abundantly than ever before.

Settlement Patterns. Settlement in eastern North America, as in most Occidental regions, was first established along the main pre-existing lines of travel. The Indian trails and the rivers which were navigable for canoes were the first routes along which settlement advanced. The map of Michigan shows the relation of the Indian trails to the terrain, and suggests the extent to which the aboriginal pattern of settlement focused on the same points which later emerged as great cities (Map 53). Detroit owes its location to the existence of firm gravelly banks which permitted easy landings on both sides of the Detroit River. The Indians used it so frequently that the French placed their trading post there. Many of the main automobile highways of the present day follow very closely the routes first laid down by Indians on foot.

In 1785 the Federal government of the United States adopted a uniform pattern of land survey—a rectangular pattern based on square mile sections (see Figure 4, p. 298). In most parts of the country settled before 1785 there are irregular field boundaries and winding roads. The parts of the country settled after 1785 are dominated by the right-angle pattern, oriented to the cardinal points of the compass. However, in many parts of the forested regions, the first routes of penetration were still the Indian trails, which conformed to no systematic pattern. Main roads, therefore, in many cases cut at an angle across the north-south or east-west roads. The basic pattern, too, is interrupted in places by such natural obstacles as lakes, swamps, rivers, or steep slopes. These features are illustrated in topographic detail on the map (Map 54).

In North America, as in Europe, the first settlements were made in the era of horses, and roads were fixed in accordance with the factors previously discussed. Later, when railroads were built, some notable readjustments were made. The best farm lands in the hilly interior of New Eng-

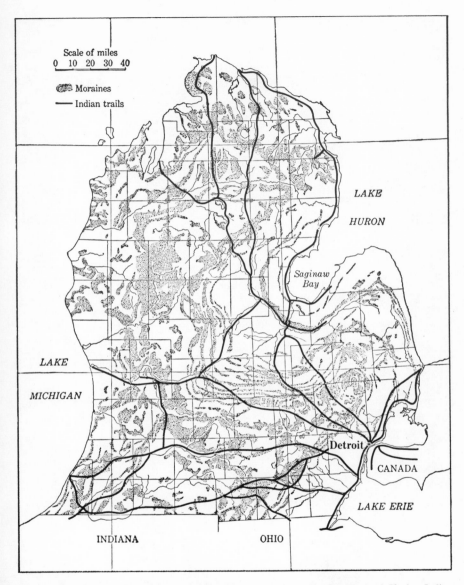

Map. 53. Moraines and Indian trails of Michigan (moraines after Leverett and Taylor; Indian trails after Hinsdale).

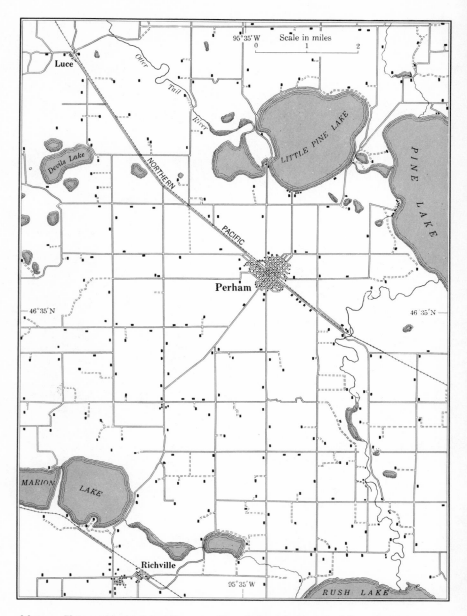

Map 54. Topographic detail in Minnesota (from Perham Quadrangle, Minnesota, United States Geological Survey).

land are generally, but not in every case, on the uplands. The valleys, filled with sandy and gravelly glacial deposits, are generally poor for agriculture. So the earliest towns were on the uplands—for example, Grafton and Sutton (Map 55), on either side of the Blackstone Valley in Massachusetts. When textile industries first appeared in New England they were placed at small water-power sites, such as Millbury. And later the railroads ran through the valleys to avoid the steep grades by which the uplands were reached. Millbury grew; but Sutton and Grafton became sleepy little villages until summer visitors from the large cities not far away came to them for summer homes. In many instances hill towns have declined or

Map 55. Sequence of settlement patterns in Massachusetts (a portion of the Blackstone Valley).

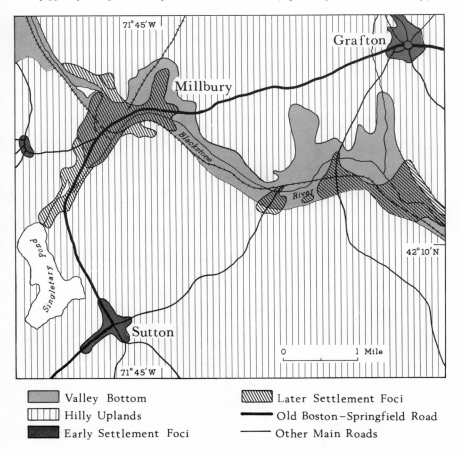

Valley Bottom	Later Settlement Foci
Hilly Uplands	Old Boston–Springfield Road
Early Settlement Foci	Other Main Roads

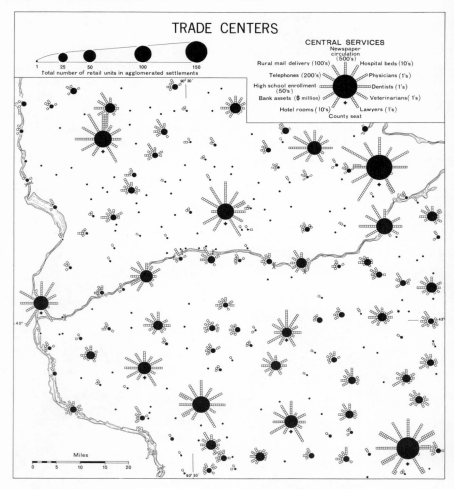

Map 56. Trade centers, showing central services (courtesy of the Geographical Review).

disappeared.   But the new towns along the railroads have prospered. There are examples of whole communities which have been moved down-hill into the valleys.   There are other examples of towns which have been extended to nearby railroads, such as Princeton, Illinois, where the result has been the development of two trading centers.

An essential part of the pattern of settlement as it has developed in eastern North America is the arrangement of trade centers.   Within the service areas of towns and cities there are many scattered smaller places—hamlets, villages, small towns—in which the rural people find a variety of urban services. The map of central services performed in the small trade centers of a part of southwestern Wisconsin (Map 56) illustrates a characteristic feature of the American Mid-West.* Twelve different kinds of central services are mapped. The smaller trade centers developed in the period before 1880 when transportation was by horse and wagon. When railroads were built, the trade centers on the rail lines grew larger and added more services, while the centers that were not on the rail lines declined. In some cases the latter have lost all their previous service functions and are now nothing more than clusters of residences. The automobile has led to the continued concentration of central services in the larger centers; yet at the same time it has brought about a scattering of single-service centers, such as gasoline and service stations, which did not exist before.

Cities and Industries in the Eastern United States. Manufacturing industries appeared in the United States shortly after the Revolutionary War. To be sure, there had been small-scale iron smelters and other manufacturing of local significance long before; but New England was the first part of the United States to become predominantly industrial. Now the largest concentrations of industry are outside New England. In the late eighteenth century or early nineteenth century it would have been very difficult to predict what kinds of industry would localize in different places. One could scarcely have failed to predict the pre-eminence of Pittsburgh and Chicago, but none of the other great industrial areas were so obvious.

The way in which the human factor operates in establishing the original patterns of industry can be illustrated by the story of the first cotton mills. Many Americans, after the Revolution, wanted to build machines such as they had seen or heard of in England, but no one had been able to build such machines, and the English would not permit their export. In response to a prize offered in Philadelphia for information about textile machines, a young man named Samuel Slater came to America with enough information in his head to reconstruct a workable machine from memory. However, the Philadelphians, with characteristic caution, refused to risk their money on Slater's machine. New Englanders, on the other hand, were ready to back him; and in 1790 he built a cotton mill on the Blackstone River in Pawtucket, Rhode Island, near Providence. Thus New England rather than Pennsylvania became the leading cotton textile region of the United States because of the attitudes and temperament of the people, not because of any advantages of location.

Furthermore, the distribution of the textile industry within Massachusetts and Rhode Island can only be explained in terms of sequent occu-

*John E. Brush, "The Hierarchy of Central Places in Southwestern Wisconsin," *Geographical Review*, Vol. 43 (1953), pp. 380–402.

pance.   When Slater showed that machines could be built to produce cotton thread, knowledge of steam engines to furnish the power had not reached America.   The only source of power was falling water, used directly through a mill wheel to turn the machinery.   Since each factory had to be within a hundred feet or so of the mill wheel, there was room for only one factory at each power site, or at the most two, if both sides of a stream could be used.   Small water-power sites were therefore just as valuable as large power sites.   Along all the New England streams there are numerous falls and rapids, and at each place where a small dam could be inexpensively built, small industrial towns were established around a mill.   Industries were scattered all through the valleys of interior New England.

Scarcely thirty years later the significance of these resources was wholly changed.   The application of steam power gave an advantage to mills located at tidewater, for the coal had to be imported by barge along the coast.   Within a short time, however, railroads, which were built rapidly after 1830, provided adequate connections for all the scattered little industrial towns.   Where canals had been started (as in the Blackstone Valley above Providence), they were promptly abandoned in favor of the cheaper railroads.   The many small manufacturing towns were therefore able to survive and to this day can be found in the hilly New England interior.

The study of each industrial concentration brings to light a story similar to that of the early New England textile mills.   Once a district becomes known for a specialty and skilled workers become available, there is a definite economic advantage for other similar or closely related industries to select the same locations.   So it is that the Providence–Fall River area became the chief center of high-grade cotton textiles in New England, and has survived even the removal to the South of most of the cotton textile industries which require less skill.   Woolen textiles were concentrated north of Boston, and Boston itself became one of the largest of wool depots.   Shoe manufacture was localized in eastern Massachusetts.   The lower Connecticut Valley was noted for its metal industries and its manufacture of complicated machinery.   Holyoke, in Massachusetts, was a center of paper production.   In recent years the electronics industry has had a large and rapid growth in various parts of New England.   In all these industrial districts of New England, which cover less than 1 per cent of the area of the United States, there are about 5 per cent of the people of the United States, and 10 per cent of the manufacturing in terms of value.   More than 75 per cent of the people of New England live in towns and cities, leaving large areas of surrounding countryside almost empty of human inhabitants.

Changes in the pattern of industry are constantly taking place.   Consider, for example, the story of steel manufacture.   It was only during the second half of the nineteenth century that steel began to replace iron,

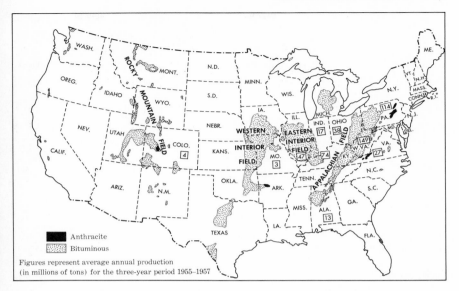

Map 57. Coal fields and coal production in the United States.

which was proving inadequate to meet the requirements of the new machines and of the railroads. In 1867, a few years before steel began to be produced regularly in open hearth furnaces, the United States manufactured only about 22,000 tons of steel. In 1900 it manufactured 10,000,-000 tons; and since World War II its steel-producing capacity has passed 100,000,000 tons in some years. Steel has become the most widely used of all manufactured substances.

To produce so much steel requires an enormous volume of raw materials. A century ago coal was the raw material needed in largest amounts, and as a result most of the first steel centers were located where coal was abundant, as in the Ruhr district of Germany. In the United States the Pittsburgh-Cleveland district became the major center of steel manufacture. Coal suitable for making coke was at hand (Map 57). At Pittsburgh there was also iron ore, and sources of limestone were close by. As the volume of production increased, iron ore was brought by lake boat from the great Mesabi Range in Minnesota, west of Lake Superior. The large steel center which was built round the southern end of Lake Michigan used coal from the Illinois fields not far away.

In the modern period, since World War II, the continued improvement of the technology of making steel requires a continued reappraisal of the relationships of industrial development to resources. Steel manufacture today requires many raw materials that were unknown during the early years of the industry: to supply these new materials the United States must reach out to ore bodies in fifty-seven different countries. During World War II the reserves of high-grade ore in the Mesabi Range were severely depleted. Ore containing a lower percentage of iron is crushed and made into pellets near the mines. Increased costs of mining, however, are offset by lower costs of transportation, and by large savings in the operation of the blast furnaces where the pellets are a more efficient source of iron than the unprocessed high-grade ore. Meanwhile new sources of iron ore have been developed. A body of high grade ore has been found in Canada north of Lake Superior. A major mining development has taken place at Schefferville on the border between Quebec and Labrador in eastern Canada. A new major source of iron ore has also been opened up in Venezuela. The construction of the St. Lawrence Seaway and the deepening of the Welland Canal (between Lake Ontario and Lake Erie) facilitate the movement of ores from these new sources to the Great Lakes industrial districts. New centers of steel manufacture have been built on the Delaware River and at Sparrows Point in Maryland. In 1963 plans were announced for the construction of a vast new steel-making complex at the southern end of Lake Michigan where the new oxygen process would further reduce the costs of manufacture. As a result of these changes, bituminous coal is no longer a major factor in the localization of the steel industry.

Blast furnaces of a huge steel plant about twenty miles northwest of Pittsburgh on the Ohio River (Jones & Laughlin Steel Corporation).

The skyline of the automobile city of Detroit. The lake boat in the foreground is probably carrying iron ore (National Film Board of Canada).

Since the beginning of the twentieth century there has been an enormous increase in the production of many different kinds of manufactured goods in the United States; and during this time the per capita production of each worker has been increased. New centers of manufacturing have developed in parts of the country other than the east coast—notably in the Tennessee Valley, where electric power is abundant, and on the Gulf coast of Texas, where new chemical industries are making use of the abundant resources of oil, gas, and sulfur. The greatest concentration of industries, however, still remains in the manufacturing belt of the northeast. The map (Plate 14, p. 572) shows this area extending from New England to Baltimore, and running westward through New York State and along the southern margin of the Great Lakes. It includes western Pennsylvania, Ohio, Michigan, Indiana, and Illinois to the western side of Lake Michigan. At least the eastern part of the Corn Belt can now be better characterized as a manufacturing region than as an agricultural region. About 76 per cent of all the factory workers in the United States are employed in this manufacturing belt of the northeast. In terms of value added by manufacture this belt accounts for 77 per cent of the United States total.

New York. The primate city of the United States is New York. This is the one urban center which stands out above all others, and in it are concentrated many millions of people, many of the most important skills in the United States, and huge aggregates of financial power. The city performs all the urban functions: it is a commercial and financial center of world-wide significance; it has an enormous concentration of manufacturing industry, chiefly of consumer goods; it is a city which provides recreation for many millions of people from distant places; it is a major center of art, music, and literature; and in recent years it has become the seat of the United Nations organization. On it are focused the interests and hopes of the entire world.

The geographical city of New York extends far beyond the political city. In the east it includes politically independent cities at least as far as the border of Connecticut. It includes Brooklyn, Manhattan, and the Bronx east of the Hudson River. West of the river in New Jersey the metropolitan area of New York takes in Jersey City and Bayonne along the Hudson, and, west of a belt of marshes, Elizabeth, Newark, Passaic, and Paterson. The heart of all this enormous metropolis is Manhattan (Map 58).

New York City owes its location to a variety of factors. The Dutch at

Lower Manhattan, the Upper Bay, and the Narrows (Fairchild Aerial Surveys).

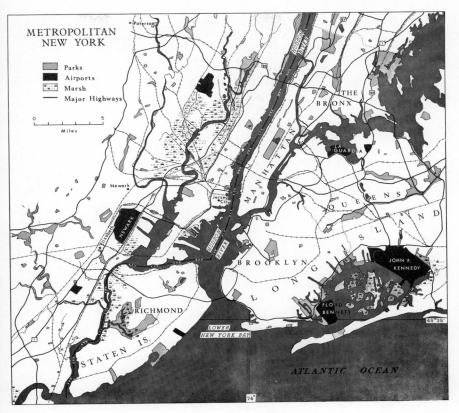

Map 58. New York.

an early date recognized the strategic value of Manhattan Island, commanding the outlet of the easiest route of travel across the Appalachians. Warfare restricted the value of this route until after 1812, and its full value was not realized until after 1825, when the Erie Canal provided low-cost transportation throughout the Great Lakes. The development of New York's connections to the Middle West took place just at the beginning of the period of great expansion westward. Then, also, few great cities are built on sites which possess such natural advantages. The Hudson River is wide and deep; Manhattan Island and the nearby shores of Long Island and New Jersey are firm and rocky. The East River and the Hudson meet in the Upper Bay, which is large enough to accommodate a vast amount of shipping. The Port of New York has a water frontage of some 770 miles, not all of which is yet developed. But all these advantages could scarcely have resulted in the growth of so large a metropolis were it not for the location of New York with reference to Europe. The exchange of people, goods, and ideas with Europe is a fundamental fact of American life, and New York is as much a reflection of these currents of exchange as it is of local advantages. Nor could New York have appeared at all except for the rise of the industrial society, with all the attitudes, objectives, and technical skills implied by that term.

Summary

We return, then, to the questions raised at the beginning of this chapter, regarding the concentration of so large a proportion of mankind in the regions of Group V. It is clear that the conditions of the habitat that attracted settlers in any one place and at any one time have differed from those that were significant in other places and times. The causes of the concentration of people are too complex to permit any single, or simple, explanation. Whereas the rice farmers of China concentrated with greater and greater densities on the river floodplains where rice would grow abundantly, farmers in a similar habitat in southeastern United States avoided the floodplains until recently. Furthermore, the features of the habitats that were significant in the past are in many cases no longer significant in attracting concentrations of people. Review, for example, the changing significance of bituminous coal as a factor in the location of population. In the Ruhr, although coal was mined it was not sold more than twenty miles from the pits until modern transportation made low-cost bulk shipment possible. Not until after the invention of the Bessemer process in 1855 and of the open hearth process in 1856 were large quantities of bituminous coal essential for the manufacture of iron and steel. The large concentrations of people and industry on or near the coalfields began in the 1860's. At that time it took twice as much coal as iron to produce a given quantity of steel: therefore the steel industry tended to locate at the coal rather than at the iron. But even before World War II these relationships of coal to iron had been altered, making it possible to locate the steel industry close to markets rather than close to raw materials. The industrial concentrations already established were not abandoned, but new industrial developments appeared near the markets. Clearly bituminous coal is no longer a major factor in the development of dense concentrations of people.

We have illustrated this principle again and again: that the significance to man of the physical and biotic features of the habitat is a function of the attitudes, objectives, and technical skills of man himself. This does not mean that man is emancipated from dependence on earth resources; but rather that with each change in the elements of the culture the significance of the resource base must be reinterpreted.

UNIVERSITY
BOOK STORES
— 49 —

1 3 OCT 71

$011.95 — 2
$008.25 — 3
$000.75 — 1
$020.95 SUB TOTL
$000.63 — TAX

$021.58 TOTL

The Mid-Latitude Grasslands

THE MID-LATITUDE GRASSLANDS cover about 9 per cent of the earth's land surface, and are occupied by 7 per cent of the earth's population. On the generalized global pattern of habitats (Figure 12, p. 424) these grasslands occupy an intermediate position between the dry lands and lands once covered with forests. As in the case of the tropical woodlands and savannas of Group III, it is now believed that forest or woodland at one time extended to the margins of the arid lands, but that repeated burning by people who were seeking game has had the effects of pushing back and sharpening the forest boundary and of creating pure grasslands. Nevertheless, these mid-latitude grasslands have appeared in a particular part of the global pattern of habitats, and they have existed long enough to form a distinctive type of soil which is unlike the soils developed under forests (Map 59).

If the grasslands occupy an intermediate position among the major regional divisions of the earth, they are nevertheless distinctly marginal with reference to the centers of population. As we have already seen, a large proportion of the earth's human inhabitants occupy the mixed forests of middle latitudes and the semideciduous forests of the Asian low latitudes. Recently, settlement has pushed out from these forests onto the contiguous grasslands, so that now parts of Group VI share with the mixed forest lands those spectacular developments of the machine culture which we have just described. In fact, it is from the more accessible grasslands that the major portion of the grain and meat supply for the support of the great urban populations is now derived. Where the grasslands have been subject to agricultural settlement, a transformation of the primitive landscape no less remarkable than that of the forest clearings has taken place. The present distribution of such settlements illustrates once again the vital role played by culture in the establishment of geographic limits.

The Habitat

VEGETATION AND CLIMATE

In the transition zone of the middle latitudes between the deserts and the forests there are two chief kinds of grasslands. On the dry margins are the short-grass *steppes;* and on the wet margins are the tall-grass *prairies.*

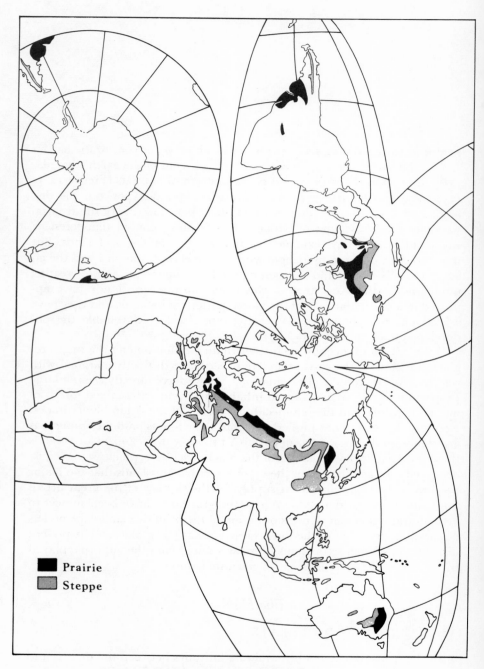

Map 59. Mid-Latitude Grasslands.

■ Prairie
▨ Steppe

An encampment on the Kirghiz Steppe.

The Steppes. The change from scattered xerophytic shrub vegetation of the regions of Group I to the steppes of the semiarid portions of Group VI brings a notable difference in the landscape. The actual boundary between the two is not everywhere easy to identify when it is sought in topographic detail, although in some parts of the world the limits are sharp enough for this. Generally speaking, the vegetation of the dry lands fails to form a complete cover over the surface of the land; if grass is present, as in the "desert shrub–desert grass" formation, it grows in bunches with bare ground between the plants. The steppes, on the contrary, are covered with a continuous mat. At maturity the steppe grasses are only a few inches in height, although in unusually wet years taller grasses give the vegetation cover an uneven appearance. Normally the steppes resemble a closely pastured meadow—a landscape of striking monotony which extends unbroken to the horizon.

The short grasses of these regions are developed in areas deficient in moisture. Like the xerophytic shrubs of the deserts, these plants are adapted to long periods of drought. After a rain they spring quickly into activity, completing the life cycle within a short time and then remaining parched and brownish until the next shower brings renewed life. The water is absorbed by the surface layers of the soil, but very rarely is enough received to penetrate to the water table. Soil moisture is available to the grass roots near the surface for a period after a rain, but underneath this surface layer there is a zone of permanently dry soil. Deep underground, as in the deserts, lies the zone of saturation, replenished at rare intervals by unusual rains. It is the presence of soil moisture near the surface that makes possible the growth of the shallow-rooted short grasses.

In general, the steppes appear in the semiarid climates bordering the deserts (Plates 6 and 7, pp. 559–561). However, in many places the deserts are interrupted by high mountains. As a result the actual distribution of steppes in the world is scattered (Map 59). A large, elongated area of steppe crosses Eurasia, north of the deserts, all the way from Manchuria in the east to the northern side of the Black Sea in the west. There is only a narrow belt of steppe in North Africa.

In the other parts of the world similar irregularities may be observed. In North America the steppes are developed only on the east and north of the dry lands. The Great Plains extend from Texas into southern Canada, and a small steppe area in Washington and Oregon borders the northern limits of the dry lands of the intermontane plateaus and basins. In South America the steppes, like the deserts themselves, are much distorted by the Andes. Along the eastern piedmont of the mountains in Patagonia there is a narrow zone of steppe which widens southward toward the Strait of Magellan. The tall bunch grasses of the Argentine Humid Pampa, which lies east of the desert, are mixed with a dwarf scrub woodland known as *monte* along the dry margin, and there is no zone of short-grass steppe between the prairies and the dry lands. Nor is there a steppe bordering the dry-land region of South Africa. In Australia the steppe is limited to the eastern desert border in the basins of the Murray River and the Darling River.

Even in regions where the steppe does form a zone of transition between the arid climates of the desert and the subhumid climates of the wetter lands, the relations to the climatic lines are not always simple. In the classification of climates developed by Wladimir Köppen, a formula was devised by which arid, semiarid, and humid climates might be distinguished on the basis of average monthly and annual figures for temperature and rainfall. This formula is presented in Appendix B, pp. 479–485. The climates are described by letter: an arid climate is represented by the letters *BW*; a semiarid climate by the letters *BS*. The distribution of climates according to the Köppen system is shown on Plate 11 (p. 566).

A comparison of the outlines of the *BS* and *BW* climates with the observed distribution of vegetation shows a number of important differences of pattern. In many places xerophytic shrub vegetation is found well beyond the area of *BW* climate—as in western China or the western interior of the United States. As a matter of fact, in nearly all the vegetation distributions thus far described, forest as well as desert, numerous departures from the generally related climatic patterns can be observed. In part these can be explained by reference to the edaphic conditions, especially the presence or absence of water. But future field studies may also seek explanations for these irregularities in the distribution and activities of prehistoric man.

The activities of prehistoric man, especially his use of fire, had differing results under different climatic conditions. In arid lands there could not be a sufficiently large accumulation of inflammable material to feed a fire; in wet forested areas fires could not easily spread out of control. But in places where there was enough rainfall to support the growth of an abundant vegetation, yet where there were periods of dry weather long enough to dry out the surface of the ground and the accumulation of organic matter lying on it, fires could get a start and spread widely. The question is, where do extended periods of dry weather occur? The average position of the boundary between humid and semiarid climates may be less important than lines that would indicate the frequency of dry years. The *B* boundary, that is the boundary determined by Köppen's formula between the semiarid *BS* climates and the bordering humid climates, has an average position which is shown on Plate 11 (p. 566); but it shifts widely from this average position when it is plotted for individual years. In fact, rarely does the actual border between sufficient moisture and deficient moisture in any one year lie close to, or even correspond in trend with, the average *B* boundary. This condition is illustrated by a map of this critical boundary in the United States in a succession of years. During the period from 1915 to 1924, humid years were experienced as far west as the front of the Rocky Mountains, and dry years were experienced as far east as Minnesota (Map 60).* Russell suggests the possibility that the recurrence of a very dry year (a *BW* year) at not infrequent intervals may serve more effectively to limit the spread of grasslands toward the deserts than does the average condition (Map 61).†

The Prairies. The prairies are quite distinct from the vegetation types which border them. Unlike the grasses of the steppes, the prairie grasses are tall and deep-rooted. At maturity they reach heights of from three to more than ten feet. The grasses of the Argentine Pampa are said to have risen above the head of a man on horseback. Few scenes in the New World so impressed the early travelers from Europe as did the sight of the great expanses of grass billowing in the wind. Around most of these prairies the edge of the forest is sharply defined. Except for the galeria forests along the streams, the prairies, when the Europeans first saw them, were entirely treeless.

Toward the steppes the prairies are limited by a fairly definite moisture supply. Where the zone of moist soil extends for as much as two feet below the surface, the tall grasses are able to gain a foothold at the expense

* H. M. Kendall, "Notes on Climatic Boundaries in the Eastern United States," *Geographical Review*, Vol. 25 (1935), pp. 117–124.

† R. J. Russell, "Dry Climates of the United States, II, Frequency of Dry and Desert Years, 1901–1920," *University of California Publications in Geography*, Vol. 5, No. 5 (1932), pp. 245–274.

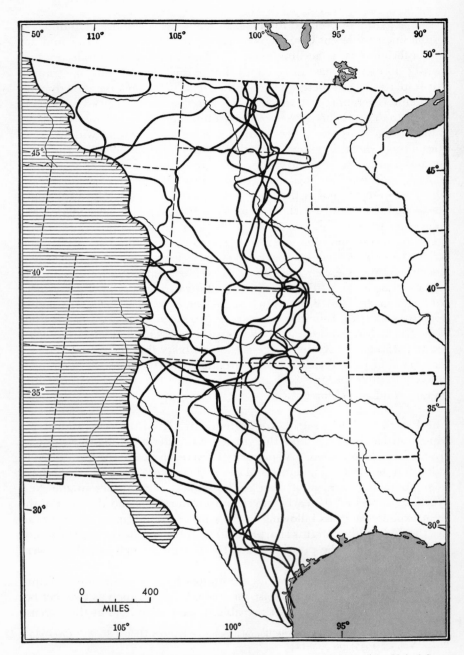

Map 60. Fluctuations of the semiarid/humid boundary in the central part of the United States, 1915–1924 (after Henry M. Kendall).

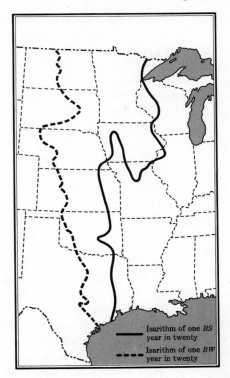

Map 61. Frequency of semiarid (BS) and arid (BW) years in central United States (after Richard J. Russell).

of the short grasses.   Russell finds that in the United States this condition, and with it the prairie-steppe boundary, corresponds closely to the eastern limit of the area which receives at least one very dry (*BW*) year in twenty (Map 61).   In topographic detail this prairie-steppe boundary is much influenced by edaphic conditions.   On sandy soil the depth of the moist surface layer is greater, climatic conditions being equal, than on clay soil. Therefore the tall grasses penetrate well within the areas generally deficient in moisture on sandy soils, but short steppe grasses are found on clay soils well within the humid lands.

The boundary between the prairie and the forest is not so clearly related to climatic or edaphic conditions.   In the United States the prairie-forest border bears only a very general relationship to the eastern limit of climates with one dry year (*BS*) in twenty.   The eastward extension of the prairie south of Chicago is well within a climate humid enough for tree growth, and where trees are planted they grow without difficulty.   Similar wet prairies occur along the Gulf coast of Texas and Louisiana, in the Humid Pampa of Argentina, in Uruguay and southern Brazil, in Hungary and on the northern side of the Russian steppes, in South Africa, in Manchuria, and in Australia.   In all these places the prairies are treeless, except for galerias, and the prairie-forest border is sharp.

That the treeless wet prairies owe their origin to fires set by prehistoric man seems well established.   Such fires, started perhaps to aid in the hunting of game or to improve the feed for game animals, spread out of control.   The intense heat killed the young trees that might otherwise have regained a foothold on the prairies, and in the course of time pushed back and sharpened the forest edge.   Nevertheless, when Europeans first came upon these prairies, they had been in existence long enough to have developed as a distinctive natural habitat, with their own peculiar soils, and their own peculiar animal population adjusted to life in a treeless environment.

SURFACE FEATURES

Most of the regions of Group VI are either plains or plateaus.   Although in some cases the surfaces are broken by sharply defined ravines and even so-called "bad lands," and in some cases are surmounted by hills, only rarely can the surfaces be classified as hilly.   Where there are hills or low mountains there is likely to be a more abundant rainfall; these features also impede the spread of fire.   Where mountains interrupt the plains— such as the Black Hills in South Dakota—they are forest-covered.

As in the case of the drainage features of Group III, the streams in the semiarid parts of Group VI flow in braided channels during the dry periods, and spread out in sheet floods during heavy rains.   On the other hand the rainfall in the prairies is usually sufficient to support permanent streams.

SOILS

Some of the world's most productive soils for grain farming are under the mid-latitude grasslands, especially the prairies.   The contrast between the dark-colored prairie soils and the lighter-colored soils of neighboring forests of Group V is very great.   In order to understand the pre-eminence of the grassland soils we must review briefly the soil-making processes.

A Review of the Soil Processes.   The development of a regolith is the first step in the construction of a soil.   Under the influence of the atmosphere, the process of weathering results in the disintegration and decomposition of the exposed rock material at the earth's surface.   To be sure, the character of the climate affects the nature of this weathering process; for chemical decomposition, producing a fine-textured regolith, is emphasized in hot and moist climates, while physical disintegration, producing a relatively coarse regolith, is emphasized in dry climates, especially those with a temperature range that crosses the freezing point. But the differences of texture and composition of a regolith in any climate are closely related to the nature of the parent material. The geologic map furnishes the pattern for the map of regolith.

The production of a soil on the surface of the regolith is the result of three processes. The percolation of water through the surface layers on its way down to the water table is responsible for the first two of these: leaching and eluviation (pp. 106–107). Leaching, like all other chemical processes, is at a maximum in hot and rainy climates; eluviation also goes on most rapidly where an abundance of water is moving down through the regolith. Both leaching and eluviation cease where there is no percolation of water, whether this is due to a desert condition, to a permanently waterlogged condition as in a swamp, or to a permanently frozen condition as in the polar regions. These processes are only retarded, of course, in places where droughts, floods, or frosts recur seasonally. Under any given type of climate, however, both leaching and eluviation proceed much more rapidly where the regolith is coarse in texture than where it is fine and compact.

The third soil-making process is the accumulation of humus. This goes on most rapidly not only where the largest amount of organic litter is provided by the vegetation but also where the destruction of this litter by bacteria is not too rapid. Bacterial action is at a maximum in hot, moist climates, and declines with lower temperatures or decreased moisture. Although the tropical forests supply a considerable amount of litter in the form of dead leaves and twigs, the bacteria, together with the destructive activity of ants and other small animals, quickly destroy this material. The rate of humus accumulation in the forest lands increases as one proceeds toward cooler climates. Whereas the tropical forest soils as well as those of the lower middle latitudes are characteristically light-colored, those of the higher middle latitudes (north of Chesapeake Bay in eastern North America) are somewhat darker in color. No forest vegetation, however, can supply such an abundance of organic material as can a grass cover, with its yearly increment of dead stems and its mat of fine roots. The grassland soils are black or dark brown in color.

As these soil-making processes continue they produce a gradual change on the surface layers of the regolith. In the course of time three horizons become more and more clearly distinguished. The surface, or *A horizon,* is one which has felt the maximum of leaching, has been rendered somewhat coarser in texture than the original regolith by the process of eluviation, and has been mixed with whatever amounts of humus are available. The

B horizon is a zone of accumulation, rendered finer in texture than the original material by the addition of the fine particles brought down from above. Underneath is the *C horizon,* the unleached and uneluviated parent material.   The depth and character of these horizons reflect the balance of the soil-making processes as controlled by the climate and the cover of vegetation. Not until the first signs of these horizons appear, however, is the regolith said to have a cover of soil.   As the horizons become more and more clearly defined the soil is said to become mature.   Theoretically, given a long enough time, the soils lose the characteristics imparted to them by the underlying parent material, and throughout the broad regions of similar climate and vegetation cover the mature soils all take on the same kind of profile.   The patterns of soil distribution which are related to the underlying geology are gradually obscured by the broader patterns related to the climate.

Mature soils, however, can only develop where the regolith is undisturbed.   On steep slopes where creep or flow is active, the *A* and *B* horizons are stripped off as fast as they are formed, and fresh regolith is brought to the surface.   On river floodplains fresh alluvium is laid down before any soil horizons can be formed in the older deposits.   Similarly, in areas of active loess accumulation mature soil profiles should not be expected. Mature soils can develop only on level or gently rolling surfaces free from active deposition and exposed to the soil-forming processes for a sufficiently long period of time.   In hilly lands only minor portions of an area can have mature soils; nowhere but on the more level plains are any extensive areas of such soils to be found.

Grassland Soils.*   Over the wide expanses of rolling to level plains in Group VI, however, the soils are able to reach maturity and to reflect closely the transitional features of the climate.   A succession of soil types, from the humid forest margins across the prairies and the steppes to the dry lands, conforms to the changes in moisture and vegetation cover.   On the rainy margins of the prairie a deep soil is formed which is so abundantly supplied with organic material that it is dark-colored even in the *B* horizon (Figure 3, C).   This is the *black prairie soil.*   But near the dry margin of the tall-grass prairies a very important change in the moisture

---

* See the classic treatment of the Great Plains of the United States: C. F. Marbut, "Soils of the Great Plains," *Annals of the Association of American Geographers,* Vol. 13 (1923), pp. 41–66; J. B. Kincer, "The Climate of the Great Plains as a Factor in Their Utilization," *Annals of the Association of American Geographers,* Vol. 13 (1923), pp. 67–80; H. L. Shantz, "The Natural Vegetation of the Great Plains Region," *Annals of the Association of American Geographers,* Vol. 13 (1923), pp. 81–107; O. E. Baker, "The Agriculture of the Great Plains Region," *Annals of the Association of American Geographers,* Vol. 13 (1923), pp. 109–167; see also F. Shreve, "Rainfall, Runoff and Soil Moisture under Desert Conditions," *Annals of the Association of American Geographers,* Vol. 24 (1934), pp. 131–156.

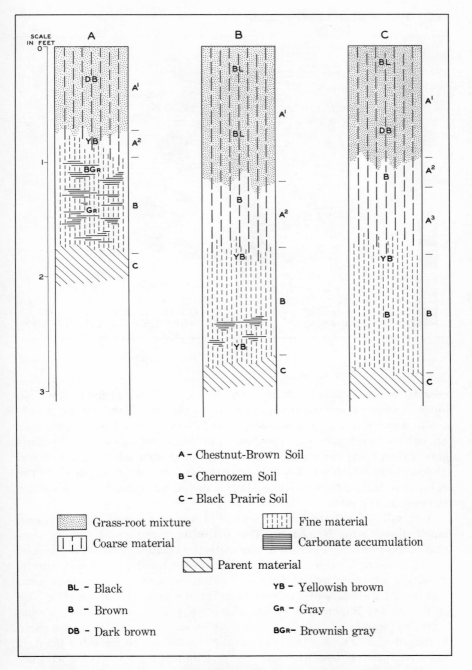

Figure 3. *Generalized mature soil profiles developed under grasslands (after Jenny).*

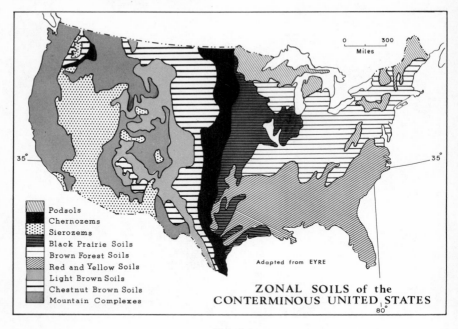

Podsols
Chernozems
Sierozems
Black Prairie Soils
Brown Forest Soils
Red and Yellow Soils
Light Brown Soils
Chestnut Brown Soils
Mountain Complexes

Adapted from EYRE

**ZONAL SOILS of the
CONTERMINOUS UNITED STATES**

Map 62.

conditions takes place, a change which is critical in soil formation. No longer, except at rare intervals, does enough rain fall on the ground to percolate through to the ground-water table. Whereas the black prairie soils are subject to leaching like all other humid soils, the soils on the dry margins of the prairie cannot be similarly robbed of their soluble constituents. The minerals which are dissolved near the surface are carried down to the *B* horizon, but no farther. The result is the accumulation of these soluble minerals in the subsoil.

Two soil types share this peculiarity of having mineral accumulations, chiefly lime, in the *B* horizon. The first of these, occupying the dry margins of the prairies, is known as the *chernozem* (Figure 3, B). The color of the chernozem is even darker than that of the black prairie soil, and its fertility is increased by the decreased effectiveness of the leaching process. The humid boundary of the chernozem is not easy to identify, for this type grades almost imperceptibly into the black prairie soil through a zone where the small and scattered lime concretions occur only here and there in the subsoil. The dry boundary of the chernozem, on the other hand, is quite distinct. It coincides with the prairie-steppe boundary, where, because the depth of the moist surface soil becomes less than approximately two feet, the tall grasses give way to the short grasses. The smaller supply of humus from the short grasses is reflected in a change from the black color of the chernozem to a chestnut-brown color; and the more active evaporation and shallower penetration of the rain water result in the formation of a continuous layer of lime salts much close to the surface than in the case of the chernozem (Figure 3, A). This is the *chestnut-brown soil*.

The distribution of these soil types, where they have been adequately studied, conforms closely with the vegetation and climatic patterns. The black prairie soils are apparently rather unusual; the largest area of these, probably, is in the United States. The chernozems and chestnut-brown soils in both North America and Eurasia, where they have been carefully mapped, straddle the boundary between humid and semiarid climates.

The Occupance

Studies of sequent occupance in the mid-latitude grasslands offer still another illustration of how people with different cultural traditions react differently to very similar habitats. There are parts of the world where the occupance of the steppes by pastoral nomads is very ancient, and where even today this form of occupance persists. But in most regions the grasslands were thinly occupied by hunters until Europeans with domestic animals pushed out the earlier inhabitants. The use of the grasslands for agriculture began, with very few exceptions, during the second half of the nineteenth century, after a series of technological developments had radically changed the significance of these habitats.

PASTORAL NOMADISM

Pastoral nomadism as a distinct way of life appeared first and persisted longest on the steppes of Eurasia. In popular writing, the nomad is usually associated with the desert; and as we have seen in the chapter on Group I, the nomadic life has been important during certain periods of sequent occupance in the Sahara and Arabian Desert, and in the deserts of central Asia. But even here the nomadic peoples made their homes on the steppe margins of the deserts and only traveled to the desert oases when it was harvest time, or when there were goods to be carried by caravan. Pastoral nomadism is more properly associated with the mid-latitude grasslands around the deserts than with the deserts themselves.

Furthermore, pastoral nomadism could develop only on those grasslands where there were people with grazing animals. Of the thirty species of animals that are useful to man, all but four were first domesticated in southwestern, southern, southeastern, or central Asia. In none of the other great grassland regions of the middle latitudes were there people with domestic animals to practice nomadism.

The word "nomad" implies the absence of a fixed location. Nomadic peoples are free from the close attachment to the earth which of necessity characterizes the agriculturists. To be sure, certain of the forest dwellers, carrying on migratory agriculture, establish only temporary attachments to the land which are periodically broken; and other peoples, making use of the resources of contiguous regions, may make more or less regular seasonal migrations from one locality to another. Such peoples may be termed *seminomadic*. But the true nomad at no time thinks of his encampment as in any sense fixed; and even if the passage of the seasons finds a nomadic tribe moving regularly back and forth between neighboring areas, as between a mountainous region and the plains close by, the routes of travel are seldom the same, except, perhaps, where a mountain range enforces the use of a certain pass, or where the crossing of a large stream is possible at only one point. A map of the distribution of nomadic peoples would show always the same pattern of scattered groups, but the position of the groups would be ever-shifting.

The nature of the nomadic occupance enforces this freedom. The wealth of the nomad is represented solely by the number and condition of

A shepherd with sheep on the steppe in Iraq (courtesy of G. B. Cressey).

his animals. He has no other possessions that he cannot quickly pack and move on the backs of his horses or camels. From his flocks and herds he gets the material for his clothing, his house, his rugs, and his implements; from them he gets his meat and milk; from them he derives a surplus to exchange with the sedentary agriculturists for grain, dates, tea, or other agricultural products; and it is on his animals that he relies for the mobility which is an essential part of his life. In these lands of uncertain rains the pasturage is dependent on the scattered showers. When the nomad hears of a rain, he must be ready quickly to move his animals into the section which has been moistened, in order to take advantage of the brief period of rich growth that will follow. Rainy years to these people mean years of plenty, even of luxury.

Not uncommonly, nomadic peoples take advantage of complementary regions. The people of the Kirghiz Steppe, for instance, used to move their flocks into the high plateaus of the Altai Mountains during the summer, returning to the grasslands for the winter. Many of the nomadic peoples of the Sahara, who claim ownership of the various oases, enter the deserts only during the winter, leaving them either for the high pastures of the Atlas Mountains or for the savannas south of the desert during the summer months.

In comparison with their numbers, the steppe nomads have wielded a very great political power. For various reasons they have since time immemorial established their control over the neighboring sedentary agriculturists. These two contrasted groups of people, so necessary to each other, are traditional enemies. The nomad, because of his military organization and his mobility, is usually the conqueror; but the agriculturist, because of his permanence and the strength of his attachment to the land, has always survived and at last absorbed his conquerors.

The steppes that formed the ancestral home of the Mongolian nomads extend in a belt along the northern side of the deserts all the way from Manchuria into Europe north of the Black Sea—reaching even as far as the Plain of Hungary south of the Carpathians (Map 59). The Mongols who lived in central Asia in what is now western China pastured their sheep, goats, horses, and camels on these grasslands. But repeatedly throughout history they have erupted from central Asia in waves of conquest. Invasions of horsemen from the steppes started the forest peoples of Western Europe on the move, leading all the way to the Iberian Peninsula and through Italy to Sicily. In the thirteenth century A.D., Mongolian conquests again swept westward into Europe, southward into Mesopotamia and India, and eastward into China. It is thought that such periodic waves of migration and conquest may have been set off by long-continued droughts that dried up the pastures and forced the nomads to flee from the steppes.

OCCIDENTAL OCCUPANCE

Before the middle of the nineteenth century the world's mid-latitude grasslands held little attraction for people of European origin.   Only in Russia north of the Black Sea was agricultural settlement attempted in wide areas.   Everywhere else agriculture was marginal, and the open grasslands were largely left for the cattlemen.   Around the margins of the grasslands there were endless conflicts between the ranchers and the farmers.

In Latin America during the colonial period there was a great demand for mules to do the heavy work of carrying gold and silver from the mining centers to the ports.   The mule is the sterile offspring of the mating of asses and mares; and although the mule is hardy enough to survive high altitudes and poor pastures, asses and horses require good pastures. The most accessible parts of the grasslands were used to breed mules. There were three major breeding areas: 1. along the southern side of the Paraná River in Argentina, where mules were raised to be used in the Andes of Peru and Bolivia; 2. in Uruguay, where mules were raised for use in Brazil north of Rio de Janeiro; and 3. along the Gulf Coast of Texas, where mules were raised for use in Mexico.

After the middle of the nineteenth century, however, there was a movement of farm settlers onto the mid-latitude grasslands of the world. In the United States this movement began after the Civil War, and was especially strong between 1870 and 1900.   In Argentina the settlement of the Humid Pampa in back of Buenos Aires took place chiefly between 1880 and 1910.   In Australia the conflict between the "squatter" cattlemen and the farmers began about 1860, and by 1884 the farmers were victorious.   In Russia a great eastward stream of pioneer settlement followed the construction of the Trans-Siberian Railroad which was started in 1891.   The eastward migration along the belt of grasslands was especially strong between 1907 and 1912.   Still more recent is the farm settlement in the Canadian prairies.

What events took place during the second half of the nineteenth century that suddenly made the prairies and steppes habitable for farmers?   We shall look at the record of sequent occupance in four parts of the world: 1. in the prairies and steppes of the United States; 2. in the Humid Pampa of Argentina; 3. in the steppes of Russia; and 4. in the grasslands of Manchuria.

THE UNITED STATES

The prairies in the United States occupy the western part of the Central Plains (Plates 1 and 10, pp. 553 and 564).   Before 1860 farm settlement had reached the western edge of the forest and had moved out along the valleys farther west.   But on the open prairie the land was left to the cattlemen.   There was no way to build fences that would keep the cattle out of the grain fields in places where there was no timber.   As railroads were extended westward the railheads became places to which the cattle were driven for shipment to the eastern markets.   And all around the margin between grassland and forest, cities were established to provide facilities where the exchange of goods between contrasted regions could be carried out.   These towns are now great cities: Minneapolis–St. Paul, Chicago, Indianapolis, St. Louis, Kansas City, Dallas–Fort Worth.   In Canada, Edmonton and Winnipeg were located along the same regional border.

The Settlement of the Grasslands.   The spread of farm settlement onto the grasslands was made possible by a series of inventions.   As a result of this spread of new settlement the grasslands were transformed from low-value range land to high-value farm land excellently suited for the low-cost production of grain and meat.   The first invention that made all this possible was the railroad itself, for without the capacity to ship bulky products at low cost per unit, the products of the prairie farms could never have been moved to the markets in the eastern cities.   Another important early invention was the steel plow, first manufactured in 1837.   The earlier iron-shod plow could not turn the heavy prairie sod.

A major problem for the farmers, however, was how to keep animals from the fields of grain.   The system of agriculture practiced in the forests of Ohio and Indiana was inherited from the Middle Colonies—it consisted of raising maize and feeding it to hogs and cattle.   This combination of grains and livestock on the same farm had been found remarkably profitable, in part because the animal manure could be used to maintain the productivity of the Brown Forest Soil.   On the open range the manure was lost.   And on the grasslands where timber was scarce, it was not possible to build effective fences.

The problem was solved in 1873, when a farmer named James Glidden in DeKalb, Illinois, invented barbed wire.   This simple device made it possible to keep cattle out of the fields of growing crops with three strands of wire and fence posts at some distance apart.   But along with the invention there was another element to complete the picture.   In nearby Chicago there were large steel industries, ready to invest capital in machinery for the manufacture of barbed wire.   Within a decade after 1873, barbed wire was being supplied in large quantities to the grassland farmers, and arrangements had been made with firms in Great Britain and Belgium to manufacture the new product for sale elsewhere in the world.   Barbed wire at last made low-cost fencing possible, and for the first time in history

Cow punchers rounding up their cattle on the ranges of the Great Plains in Texas.

cattle and grain could be raised on the same grassland farm. For the first time the rich black soil under the prairie sod could be used for grain farming without excluding cattle from the region.

The fences, however, created a whole series of new problems, which also had to be solved. On the open range cattle could easily walk to nearby streams to get water; but when the pastures were fenced, water had to be provided. Digging a well was possible, but not easy, until the invention of well-drilling rigs. Then came the problem of how to bring the water to the surface. Windmills had been known in Europe for many centuries, but the European mills were cumbersome affairs, requiring stone or a good supply of lumber for their construction. On the treeless prairies the materials for making windmills were lacking. In 1854 Daniel Hallady of Connecticut designed a new kind of windmill that could be manufactured in quantity from wood, and could be assembled on the prairie farms at relatively low cost. Along with the windmills and the drilling machines came other inventions: large harvesting machinery made it possible for one farmer to harvest a large enough acreage to support himself and his family where yields per acre are low; new and more efficient plows and harrows raised productivity per farmer; silos made possible the storage of fodder for the winter feeding of animals in the severe-winter climate; and new varieties of wheat and maize raised the yield per acre where the rainfall was not abundant.

The Transformation of the Habitat. As a result of the settlement of farmers on the grasslands, the landscapes of these regions have been profoundly modified.   Before the arrival of settlers in any important numbers, the "balance of nature" remained virtually undisturbed.   There was an equilibrium between the various forms of plant and animal life living together in the same area.   The native grasses were those which had developed a resistance to the hazards of the environment; the native animals had established a balance between their natural rate of increase, the food supply, and the depredations of their enemies.

Into this organized community came man.   First he killed off, either for sport or for food, many of the larger native animals.   Then he plowed up large areas of the native grasses and replaced them by cultivated grasses. But the effects of these simple acts went much farther than could have been predicted.   Certain of the native animals of the region enjoyed either an elimination of their natural enemies or an increase in the supply of food, or both, which made possible a sudden and large increase in their numbers.   The killing off of certain birds, for instance, was followed by a rapid increase in the gopher population.   Some of the insects which had previously maintained a bare existence on the native grasses now found the nonresistant wheat or maize much more to their liking.   The chinch bug, for example, probably fed on the native bunch grasses, where it returned to pass the winters; but during the summer season this little native of the North American plains played havoc with the maize, wheat, and oats. Among the native plants, the sunflower, which now rapidly covers an idle field, once maintained itself precariously in competition with the prairie grasses.   Thus many of the insect pests and weeds which, as a part of the natural grassland region, were effectively held in check by the competition of their enemies, were suddenly freed from this competition, so that their numbers increased enormously and they came to form hazards against which man's agriculture had to contend.

There are spectacular stories of the introduction of new species into these regions.   The Hessian fly, for instance, is a grass-feeding insect introduced accidentally into the United States from Europe.   The great wheat fields of the North American prairies provided an ideal environment for this insect, and it multiplied at a rapid rate.   Lacking any natural enemies in these new surroundings, it encountered little to check its ravages until special resistant varieties of wheat were developed.

The introduction of trees was the cause of a change of another kind in the grasslands.   Around the farmsteads and villages forests were planted, so that today the buildings are all but hidden in the foliage during the summer months.   On the prairies, where settlement is close, trees have been added to the landscape in such numbers that no longer is the horizon visible.   At first glance these modified grasslands seem closely to resemble the cleared forest lands.   The landscapes of the Corn Belt of the United States, whether in the eastern previously forested part, or in the western

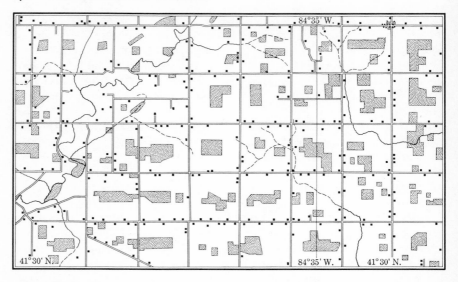

Map 63. North American Corn Belt landscape in a previously forested region. The wood lots are relict patches of the native oak-hickory forest (from the Pioneer Quadrangle, Ohio-Michigan, United States Geological Survey).

prairies, are strikingly similar. Yet there is a difference. The relict wood-land patches in the eastern part are not uncommonly left in the centers of the sections, away from the roads (Map 63); but in the prairies the planted wood lots are mostly located around the farmsteads, close to the roads (Map 64).

The patterns of settlement developed in this period are remarkably uniform over large areas. This is owing in part to the absence of strongly marked relief features, but also in part to the ease with which roads in a grassland can be shifted to conform to a general settlement plan. On forested plains the first lines of travel away from the rivers, which developed even before the stage of pioneer settlement, are more or less fixed as the framework to which later settlement is joined. Even where the standard survey of properties was later applied, the persistence of the first roads along the Indian trails is notable, as is illustrated by the map of Perham (Map 54). But in the grasslands the roads are not so rigidly fixed because they are not hemmed in by trees. Even where a regular line of travel exists across a prairie, a well-defined road is not necessarily impressed upon the landscape. As the ruts of the wagon wheels score the prairie sod too deeply, a new way is picked to one side. The result was that when the uniform pattern of properties was established the shift of the roads to conform to the right-angle lines was easy. Because the tradition of the dispersed settle-

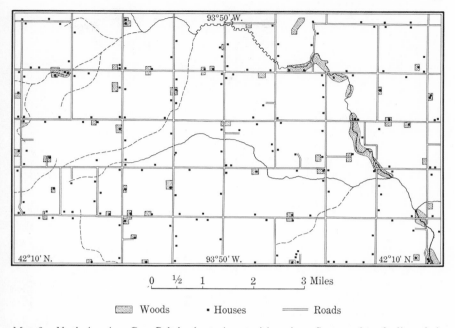

Map 64. *North American Corn Belt landscape in a prairie region. Some patches of relict galeria forest follow the streams, but most of the wood lots have been planted around the farmsteads (from the Boone Quadrangle, Iowa, United States Geological Survey).*

ment had become established west of the Appalachians, for reasons previously described, this same pattern was carried on westward into the grasslands (Figure 4).

The Corn Belt. The agricultural region that developed on the Central Plains of the United States as a result of the spread of farm settlement onto the prairies is known as the Corn Belt. The practice of feeding maize to hogs and cattle, and marketing the fattened animals, which came originally from the Middle Colonies culture hearth, was first developed as an agricultural system in Ohio and Indiana, in the forested regions of Group V. But in the 1870's the movement onto the prairies carried this same agricultural system westward across Illinois, Iowa, and northern Missouri to the eastern part of Nebraska. When the Corn Belt filled out its present outline in the 1880's it reached 800 miles east and west, from central Ohio to eastern Nebraska. In the east it was about 150 miles wide, but in the west it was as much as 500 miles north and south. As a result of the application of the new technology, and as a result of the existence of a growing market for food products, in which meat was preferred to corn bread, this region became the world's most prosperous farming area. Here the combination of

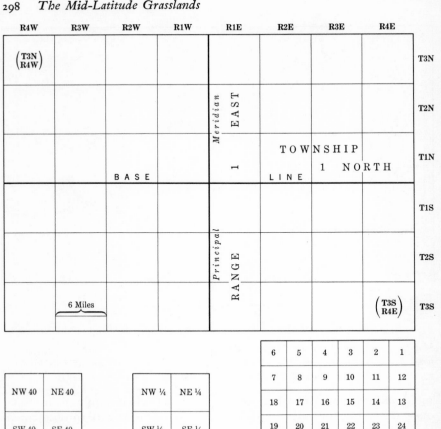

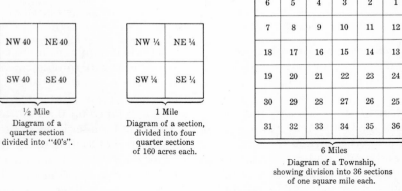

Figure 4. Diagrammatic layout of the General Land Office survey of the United States. (The survey is governed in various parts of the country by a number of different principal meridians and base lines. Sample description of a forty-acre property: The NE forty of the NW quarter of section 17, township 2 N, range 4 E of the fifth principal meridian.)

A Corn Belt farm in Iowa (J. C. Allen, from Ewing Galloway).

climate, level surface, productive soil, skilled farmers, economic institutions, and freedom from tariff barriers offered an unequalled opportunity for a farm system that could yield a profit to the farmers. No small part of the explanation of the development of the Corn Belt was the geographic position of this region in the center of the expanding nation, closely accessible to the great urban markets.

In 1862 the United States Congress passed the Homestead Act. This opened the public lands of the nation to settlement by individuals at no cost except registry fees. But the individuals had to undertake to farm the land assigned to them. Each individual farm family could lay claim to 160 acres, or a quarter section, as surveyed by the General Land Office (Figure 4). As settlers made good their claims by plowing the land and raising crops, and by building farm homes and barns on their properties, these properties increased in value. Many thousands of small farmers who had come into possession of the land almost free of charge found themselves the owners of valuable property. Such an increase of land value resulting from the process of settlement is what the economists describe as "unearned increment." There are parts of the Corn Belt today where land is valued at well over $500 per acre. In the small towns of the Corn Belt there are retired farmers, living on the income from mortgages; and the more prosperous of the farmers have been able to retire to California or Florida. Never before in the history of mankind have individual small farmers been able to profit in such large numbers from the economic system of which they were a part.

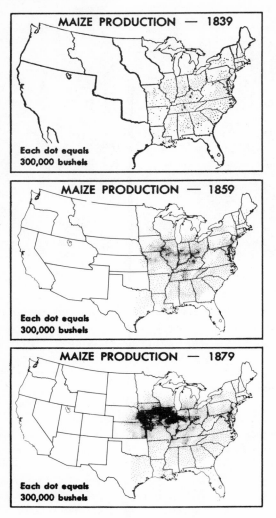

Map 65.

The concentration of maize production in the Corn Belt took place step by step (Map 65). Before the Civil War there was scarcely any sign of the developments to come. But by 1879 the enormous productivity of the prairie farms in Illinois and Iowa had already become apparent. The maps of hogs and cattle show a corresponding development (Maps 66 and 67).

In many ways the Corn Belt is almost ideal for the kind of farming that developed there. Maize is a tropical plant that requires much heat and humidity for its best growth. Furthermore, it needs something like 150

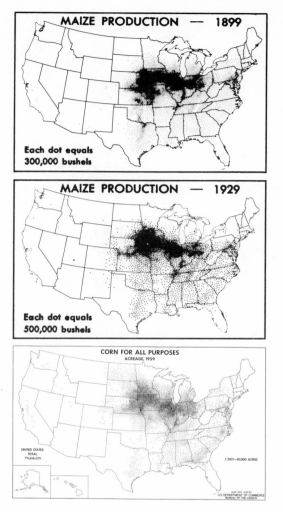

days of growing season to ripen the grain. Because of the continental climate, although the winters are severe, the summers are very hot. And although much of the Corn Belt is only moderately rainy, the greater part of the rainfall comes during the summer months. Toward the north the Corn Belt type of farming gives way to hay and dairy where the growing season is too short and the summers too cool for maize to ripen. In this region maize is cut green for silage. The Corn Belt is limited toward the south by hilly terrain. It extends westward as far as the isohyet* of eight inches of rainfall in the summer months. In addition to the favorable cli-

*An isohyet is a line connecting points of equal rainfall. (See Appendix A, p. 459.)

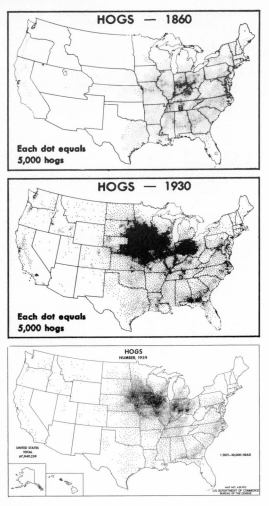

Map 66.

mate, however, are the vast areas of level land, and the remarkably sustained fertility of the Black Prairie Soil and the Chernozem.

Crop Combinations in the Corn Belt.   In previous chapters the effect of transportation development in supporting crop specialization in certain favored localities has been described.   We have seen how certain vegetables and fruits are intensively cultivated in those small areas where a combination of climate, soil, surface, and drainage is peculiarly favorable.   We must now amplify this principle; for although maize exhibits a notable localization in the Corn Belt, this region is also ideally suited to other crops

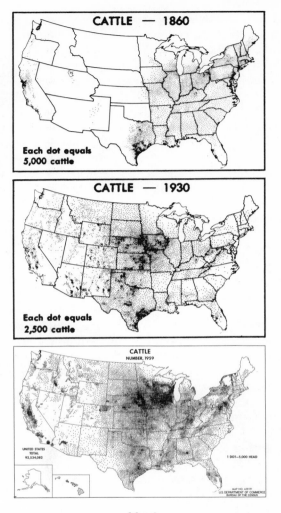

Map 67.

that are not similarly concentrated there, and although this is the leading maize-producing region of the world, less than half of the acreage of crop-land is planted with maize.

There are certain tendencies in agricultural land use leading toward a specialization of crops, and there are other tendencies leading toward crop diversification. We have seen that, with nothing more adequate than horse-drawn vehicles, each community is forced to depend on nearby sources of food, and under these circumstances there is little chance of crop specialization. Only very valuable products, for which the cost of shipment represents but a small part of the total cost, can be cultivated to the exclusion of other crops—and then only in places where the factors of land, labor, and capital can be favorably combined. The development of railroads and steamships results only in a relative change in the operation of this economic principle. Still it is the crops having the larger value per unit of weight which respond most clearly to the forces leading to specialization. Such are most of the crops produced by Occidental plantations in the tropical forest regions: sugar, cacao, coconuts, coffee, bananas, and others. Such, also, are the fruit and vegetable crops previously described as examples of localization. The sugar beets and potatoes which in certain parts of the Corn Belt interrupt the prevailing crop combinations have become localized in those places in response to this principle. These very valuable products take precedence over maize, and where they are grown there is little diversification.

Specialization of crops is also apparent in the zones around the large cities. In these places, however, localization is brought about by accessibility to market rather than by any special quality inherent in the soil. Where land is expensive, only those crops can be grown which bring large returns in money income. Truck-garden zones are established on the periphery of most cities of the world, in many cases despite adverse conditions of climate, soil, or slope.

Among the more bulky products, such as the grains, it not uncommonly happens that two or more crops are in competition for the same territory, all of them finding especially favorable physical conditions. This is the situation in the prairies of the Corn Belt, where both maize and wheat find excellent conditions of growth. In these circumstances, provided there is a market for all the competing crops, those which are otherwise most narrowly limited by physical requirements generally get the first choice of the land.

The diversification of crops arises chiefly from two causes. In the first place, experience has shown that the productivity of the soil, which is quickly exhausted by such crops as maize or wheat, can be maintained by a rotation of crops and by the application of animal manures. During the past century, as we have seen, crop rotation and domestic animals have become important features of Occidental grain-farming. Then, too, the most efficient use of labor throughout the year is gained by crop diversification. In a one-crop system the work of planting, cultivating, and harvesting is concentrated at certain times of the year, and periods of relative idleness intervene. But the labor demands of different crops are spread differently over the seasons, so that a more uniform distribution of work is possible in regions of diversified agriculture. For these reasons other crops are associated with the dominant crop in the Corn Belt.

The operation of these various principles leads to the appearance of such specialized agricultural regions as the Corn Belt. The outlines of the re-

A cotton picker on the Mississippi flood-plain in Mississippi. This machine does not work on hilly land.

gion represent an adjustment between these economic principles and the physical qualities of the land. The land, however, remains as a relatively permanent basic factor; it does not become a positive force in the man–land equation unless it is significantly changed during the course of settlement —unless it is destroyed, perhaps, by wasteful farming methods. Otherwise, the positive element in the equation is the balance of costs and prices determined by the economic conditions, for it is these factors that determine the significance of the features of the habitat.

The Agricultural Revolution. In an industrial society, continued attention to research and development produces a continuous stream of new technical devices and new methods of producing things. Change has become a way of life, for better or for worse. Just since World War II a second agricultural revolution has taken place in the United States.

A large number of new and improved agricultural machines have been developed. Even before 1940 the replacement of horses by tractors resulted in a decrease in the acreage needed to provide feed for work animals. During the 1930's the development of "hybrid corn" more than doubled the yield of maize per acre. But since 1950 this process of technical improvement has gone on at a spectacular rate. New breeds of beef cattle and hogs can be fattened on less feed than before; improved breeds of dairy cattle produce more milk per cow with less feed. New kinds of

The corn harvester removes the ears from the stalks, husks them, and chops the leaves and stalks—all in one operation (J. I. Case Company).

insecticide have brought many insect pests under control for the first time in history—although the widespread use of these chemicals has produced other unexpected results, such as the killing of fish downstream. New chemical fertilizers and soil conditioners have converted poor, sandy soils into high-yielding soils, so much so that the natural fertility of a soil is no longer as critical a matter as it once was. Soil conservation practices have returned worn-out lands to production, and are reducing the rate of new destruction.

Farming today requires a large capital outlay. A tractor may cost $32,000, and a modern plow about $7000. Yet only these modern devices can do the work fast enough and with sufficient efficiency to make the use of high-value land profitable. The modern hay-baler is an example: before 1940 two men with pitchforks would take a whole afternoon to load ten tons of hay; the modern baler makes it possible for one man to bale ten tons of hay in an hour. In 1910 it took 147 man-hours to produce one hundred bushels of corn; in 1964 it took four man-hours to produce the same amount. Between 1935 and 1940 a farmer could raise enough food to feed himself and about ten other people: in 1963 one farmer could raise enough food to feed himself and more than thirty other people. This enormous increase of productivity per farmer results from large capital investment applied to first-class land. The small 160-acre farm, operated by a farmer using his muscles and the muscles of his animals, is a high-cost producer of food—whether or not it is considered to be socially desirable. Today nearly a quarter of all the farms in the country are large ones, covering at least 640 acres, and marketing between $10,000 and $50,000 of farm products each year. These large-scale operations produce 72 per cent of the crops and livestock of the United States. The Corn Belt is being rapidly transformed as a result of the consolidation of former small farms into larger units, and as a result of the necessary large capital investment in farming.

Another result of these changes is the reduction of the number of people employed in farming. In 1940 about 20 per cent of the working force of the United States was employed in agriculture; in 1962 only 7.5 per cent of the working force was in agriculture. Yet food production increased. The people no longer employed in agriculture were being absorbed in manufacturing industries and in service occupations in the cities. By 1960 the Corn Belt was more of a manufacturing region than an agricultural one.

The Wheat Regions. Wheat, unlike maize, is mostly used directly as a human food. It must therefore be shipped in the form of grain, not in the form of fattened animals. Wheat is well adapted to this method of marketing, for the hard, dry kernels can stand rough handling, and can be shipped even through the rainy tropics without deteriorating.

Wheat was carried onto the grasslands of North America along with maize, but before 1870 it showed little tendency to concentrate (Map 68). In the decade between 1870 and 1880, however, the binders and large power-driven threshing machines were invented, making possible large-scale farming. The settlers advanced westward onto the drier grasslands in three

Grain elevators along a railroad in Oklahoma (Philip Gendreau).

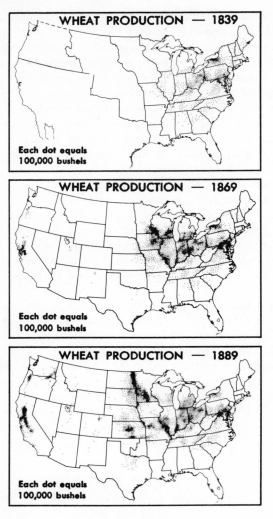

Map 68.

places: in the Red River plains of Minnesota and North Dakota, in southern Nebraska and Kansas, and in the Columbia Plateau portion of Washington and Oregon. The next decade witnessed an enormous increase of production in these areas, especially on the Red River plains. The pattern of distribution as outlined by 1899 has remained essentially the same except for amplification of its details.

Advantages of the Grasslands for Wheat.   To interpret wheat distribution it is necessary to consider briefly the advantages of parts of these

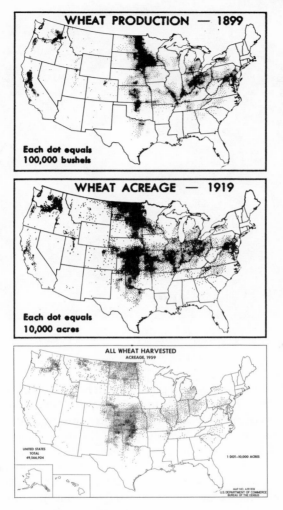

WHEAT PRODUCTION — 1899

Each dot equals 100,000 bushels

WHEAT ACREAGE — 1919

Each dot equals 10,000 acres

ALL WHEAT HARVESTED
ACREAGE, 1959

UNITED STATES TOTAL 49,566,924

1 DOT—10,000 ACRES

grasslands for wheat production, advantages which have led to the establishment of wheat as a chief crop. We are not concerned here with those areas where wheat is a minor crop, as in the Corn Belt, although these regions account for an important part of the world production. On the dry margins of the prairies and on the steppes, wheat is not only dominant but, in places, occupies nearly all the cropland.

Wheat will grow under many different climatic conditions. By a process of seed selection, numerous varieties have been developed which are adapted to conditions altogether different from those of the Mediterranean region. Quick-maturing varieties, for instance, have pushed the cold limits

Harvesting wheat (Wide World Photos).

far poleward. Only barley and potatoes can be pushed farther north. Up to the present time, however, no kind of wheat has been developed that can mature in less than ninety frost-free days. Nor can the seed be ripened with certainty unless the average temperature of the three summer months is at least 57°. Most of the world's wheat is planted in the fall, starts its growth before winter sets in, and is ready for the harvest early in the following summer. This is known as *winter wheat*. Where the winters are very cold (averaging below 20° in the coldest month), winter wheat is unable to survive unless the ground is regularly protected by a deep covering of snow which is not blown into drifts. In the northern wheat areas—the Dakotas and part of the Washington–Oregon area—wheat is planted in the spring after the frost is out of the ground and is harvested in the late summer. This is called *spring wheat*.

In its native habitat wheat is adapted to cool, moist winters and hot, dry summers. The largest yields of wheat are associated with a cool, moist period in the early stages of growth; but a hot, dry harvest season is required for the best quality of grain. Although very large yields are produced in western Europe, the resulting wheat is soft and starchy and is considered to be poorer in quality than the hard, protein-rich varieties, which require hot, dry summers.*   In regions of heavy rainfall, too, wheat is subject to numerous diseases.   The rainfall limits within which the crop is grown vary with the temperature.   On the poleward side the wheat concentrations lie between the 10-inch and 40-inch rainfall lines, but in the warmer wheat-producing regions the rainfall limits become 20 inches and 70 inches. Wheat is grown both above and below these amounts, however.

The grasslands, then, especially those with severe winters, do not possess the best of wheat climates.   They do possess one feature in common, how-ever, which makes wheat-growing possible on a large scale: the great ex-panses of level land permit the use of machinery, and wheat is now essentially a machine-cultivated crop.   As the decreasing rainfall or the increasingly unfavorable winters result in diminished yields per acre, machinery makes possible the cultivation of more acres per farm.   Thus, wheat has become established on the chernozem belts of the world, where the climatic conditions have made it possible to compete on more even terms with maize, and where the deep, rich soils have maintained their pro-ductivity in spite of continued use.

The Dry Margins.   The settlers who pushed the agricultural frontier westward across the grasslands of the United States usually raised wheat at first, and only changed to maize later.   But as the wheat farmers moved westward they did not stop at the western margin of the chernozem belt. The chestnut-brown soils beyond lured the pioneers on with promises of quick wealth, especially after a series of wet years.   In the northern Great Plains three years of more than normal rainfall from 1914 to 1916, and es-pecially in 1915, started a wave of settlement.   Far out on the steppes the pioneers plowed up the short-grass sod and planted wheat.   From the vir-gin soils large yields were gained, and, aided by wartime prices, the set-tlers found themselves prosperous beyond their hopes.   But then came the inevitable cycle of dry years, from 1917 to 1919—all years of crop failure. Many of the farmers who managed to survive the drought, with their farms heavily mortgaged, were ruined by the drop of land values which followed the conclusion of World War I.   The fields were left to grow up in weeds; the tide of abandonment was almost as strong as the tide of settlement.

A similar story can be told for western Kansas.   In one county the total income from wheat farming for a 640-acre farm for the whole period from

---

*Early in its growth the wheat plant sends up additional stalks from buds near its roots.   Only as many heads are developed as there are stalks.   Branching is promoted by cool, moist wea-ther during the early period of growth, a condition which is best provided by the cool marine climates of the continental west coasts.   The largest yields of wheat occur in these regions, but the much-desired hard wheats, with their high protein content, do not thrive in these wetter cli-mates.

1912 to 1934 was $21,167.   This means an average income of about $1000 per year for a farm of this size.   But such a statistical average is far from the actual income per year.   The fact is that of the total income quoted above, $20,472 was received in one year, 1920, when the farmers in that county enjoyed a rare combination of favorable rainfall and high prices. Obviously this is a system of farming which is entirely speculative, and one which requires a considerable outlay in the form of relief funds from the government.

The farmers on the dry margin who have managed to survive have learned a number of important lessons.   A different agricultural technique was necessary on these dry margins in order to make permanent settlement possible.   It was found that by allowing the land to lie fallow for a year, enough moisture might be stored up to permit the production of a crop the following year.   Thus a part of the cropland is left bare each year— carefully plowed and harrowed to reduce the evaporation.   Wheat grown with such *dry-farming* methods may yield only from six to ten bushels to the acre, although in wet years the yield may be much more than this.   But, aided by machinery, the farmers ceased to care about the yield per acre, provided they could cultivate a sufficient numbers of acres.   The Homestead Act had been changed in 1909 to permit settlers to occupy a maximum of 320 acres, and in 1916 the limit was further raised to 640 acres. Field studies in Montana led to the conclusion that 1280 acres, or even

Eroded land in the spring wheat area of South Dakota—on the dry margin
(Soil Conservation Service).

Cattle grazing on the steppes of eastern Montana (United States Forest Service).

twice this number, were needed to provide security.* Furthermore, it has been found that on the steppes farming and cattle-ranching ought to be combined, so that in the dry years range cattle can provide some income to compensate, at least in part, for the crop failure.

Even with the best techniques, however, the settlement of the dry margin of the Great Plains remains precarious. No part of the region is free from the threat of drought, and no one has yet found a way to predict with accuracy when a drought will begin or end. Sometimes droughts last for only a few months; sometimes a number of years pass without a single shower. Sometimes the farmers of one county watch in despair as a heavy shower drenches a neighboring county. Sometimes, when the air is very dry, a shower forms, but the rain evaporates before it reaches the ground. From 1950 to 1956 there were large parts of the southern Great Plains which had no rain at all. The drought was so prolonged that even the cattle had to be moved away. With the droughts come the dust storms that

* See the studies of pioneer settlement in I. Bowman, *The Pioneer Fringe,* American Geographical Society, Special Publication No. 13 (New York, 1931); and *Pioneer Settlement* (by twenty-six authors), American Geographical Society, Special Publication No. 14 (New York, 1932).

blow the fertile topsoil from vast areas of plowed land being used for dry farming.   As a result, only ruined land and abandoned buildings remain.

THE ARGENTINE HUMID PAMPA

Another of the world's mid-latitude grasslands is the Argentine Humid Pampa (Map 69).   When the Spanish settlers came upon this region in 1536 they established a base at Buenos Aires.   The land along the southern side of the Paraná and Plata rivers was covered by tall, waving grass without a sign of a tree.   It was inhabited by hunting Indians who made a poor living from two native animals, the rhea (a kind of ostrich), and the guanaco (a small relative of the llama).   The Spaniards brought horses and cattle ashore at Buenos Aires and some of them escaped.   Within a few years, herds of wild cattle and horses were roaming the Pampa, and the Indians, having learned to ride horses, soon killed so many game animals that the resource base of their existence was destroyed.   The Spaniards tried to use the land for agriculture, but found that to clear the tall grass was almost impossible with the tools at their disposal.   They abandoned Buenos Aires and moved up-stream to Asunción in Paraguay.   Buenos Aires was occupied again in 1580 as a naval base.

Studies of this region conclude that before the coming of the Indians the xerophytic brush, characteristic of the Dry Pampa to the west, grew lux-

A dust storm approaching in the western Great Plains (Soil Conservation Service).

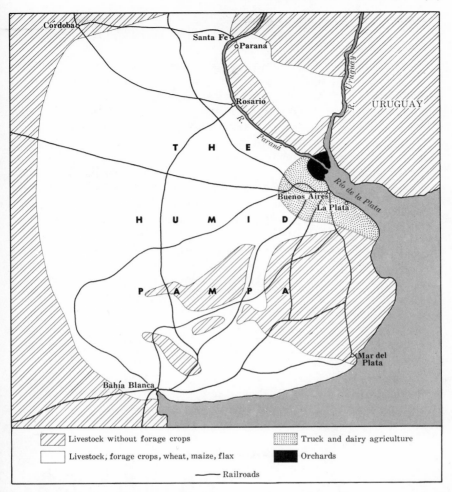

Map 69. Agricultural divisions of the Argentine Humid Pampa (adapted from Preston E. James, Latin America 3rd Edition, New York, 1959).

uriantly on the Humid Pampa. The brush may have been thick enough to be described as a woodland. Buenos Aires, with an average of 36 inches of rain per year, has a climate in which trees could grow. The absence of trees is interpreted as the result of fires set by the Indians to help in the hunt.

The only use that the Spaniards could find for the region was to raise mules and cattle. Along the Paraná shore, the animals were left on unfenced pastures and only rounded up by the seminomadic *gauchos* when it was time to drive the animals to a market. The rest of the area today included in the Humid Pampa remained empty except for roving bands of marauding Indians.

The settlement of the Humid Pampa, except for the northern rim, did not begin until the second half of the nineteenth century, three hundred years after the first settlement. The first railroad was built with British capital in 1857, and the British offered the Argentines a market for cattle, after the first refrigerator ship in 1877 made it possible to ship meat across the equator. By that time barbed wire from Great Britain made fencing possible so that the breeding of the animals could be controlled. The British were not interested in the lean animals that fed on the Pampa grasses: they wanted fat beef, and they were willing to send breeding stock to help the Argentines raise the kind of beef that the British market demanded.

The settlement of the Pampa went along quite different lines from those described for the North American prairies. In Argentina the tradition of the large private estates remained unchallenged. The Humid Pampa was cleared of Indians by 1881, and was quickly divided among some 300 families, each with an estate of more than 100,000 acres. Furthermore, the owners of the estates were interested only in raising high-grade animals, not at

Crowded conditions at the old docks at Buenos Aires. A large new port has been built north of this area (Sawders, from Cushing).

all in farming. But it was soon found that the new British beef cattle could not thrive on the Pampa grasses, and that some kind of a feed crop would have to be provided for them. It turned out that this region was ideally suited for the production of alfalfa. The soil is mostly a deep accumulation of wind-blown dust, or loess, and the water table is close enough to the surface to be reached by the roots of the alfalfa plant.

The problem was to clear the Pampa grass. This was still difficult, as it had been in 1536. But it was found that if wheat could be planted, the wheat would keep the grass from coming back, and thus, after a few years, prepare the land for the planting of alfalfa. To do this work, the land-owners hired immigrant tenants, mostly from Italy and Spain, who moved temporarily onto parts of the estates, plowed the land and planted wheat for three or four years. Then, by contract, the tenants would plant alfalfa and move to another piece of land. The alfalfa remained productive for four or five years, after which the process might be repeated. In the decade between 1880 and 1890 the present outline of the Humid Pampa had been developed, filled in mostly with fields of wheat and alfalfa—except for an area of maize production around Rosario, and a dairy and truck-farming district close to the big city of Buenos Aires.

This kind of farm settlement moved westward toward drier country. In the north, where temperatures are higher, the farm settlement went about to the 23-inch rainfall line; and in the south, about as far as the 16-inch rainfall line. These average amounts of rainfall—about 20 inches—became known as humid; but places where rainfall was less than these amounts were called semiarid or arid. The dry country was left for open range, with agricultural settlement only where the land could be irrigated. What determined that approximately 20 inches should form the boundary between humid and semiarid? It was not the natural vegetation. The monte brush was at one time widely spread over what is today the Humid Pampa, and in spite of the Indian burnings, it is not probable that a geographer in the sixteenth century could have identified the present border of this region. The sharp difference between the Humid Pampa and the Dry Pampa was produced by the process of settlement: and settlement went westward as far as this type of farming was profitable. If the price of meat had been higher in the 1880's and 1890's, or if the price of wheat had been double what it was in those decades, it would then have been profitable to carry this type of farming farther westward. Perhaps even the concept of what is "humid" might have been extended to somewhat drier country.

During World War II, when all available ships had to be used to move the armies across the seas and to supply them, the British decided to cut down on imports of wheat in favor of meat. In Argentina, the large land-owners dismissed their tenants, and turned the wheat acreages into alfalfa pastures. Wheat acreages were reduced to less than a third of the pre-war figure. The tenants were quickly absorbed in manufacturing employment, and in various public works in the cities. Since the war the supply of tenants has not been built up again by new immigrants, and even today the acreage of wheat and maize is not nearly so great as it was before 1940. Argentina, struggling with problems of industrial development, and with the solution of political problems, has yet to bring the Humid Pampa back to its potential productivity.

THE GRASSLANDS OF RUSSIA

The third of the regions we shall look at in this survey of the mid-latitude grasslands includes the prairies and steppes of Russia, now the Soviet Union. The chernozem soil that lies under the prairie is the famous "black-earth belt" of Russia, extending from the northern side of the Black Sea northwest of Odessa eastward to the edge of the mountains near Barnaul, and in scattered patches even as far as Irkutsk near Lake Baikal (Plate 10, pp. 564–565, and Map 70). The black-earth belt forms a narrow band between the forests farther north and the steppes and deserts to the south. This is the chief agricultural area of the Soviet Union, and also the part with the greatest density of population (Plate 7, pp. 560–561). The Russian grasslands, unlike those of the United States, occupy that part of the world pattern that borders the dry lands in the north (Figure 12, p. 424). In this position they are comparable to the prairies and steppes of Canada.

The climatic hazards that farmers must face in this region are serious. Agriculture is limited to the north by cold and by the shortness of the growing season, and to the south by lack of rainfall. Within the black-earth belt, and the forest margin to the north of it, both cold and drought are frequently experienced. During the winter, cold air masses from the northern interior of Siberia and from the Arctic pour unimpeded across the open plains, bringing very low temperatures. Because cold air masses are very dry and the winds are strong, the little snow that may have fallen on the black-earth belt is blown away or evaporated, thus depriving the soil of much-needed moisture for the spring planting. During the growing season the whole area is frequently visited by droughts. Records indicate that serious droughts occur, on the average, once every two or three years. Only in the westernmost part of the black-earth belt does the rainfall average more than 20 inches a year. These climatic hazards are only partially compensated by the excellence of the soil.

The grasslands of European Russia were the first such regions in the world to be successfully occupied for grain farming. In accordance with the pre-industrial tradition the land was divided into large private estates, and the work was done by the labor of serfs. Armed only with the most primitive agricultural implements, the prairie sod was broken largely by

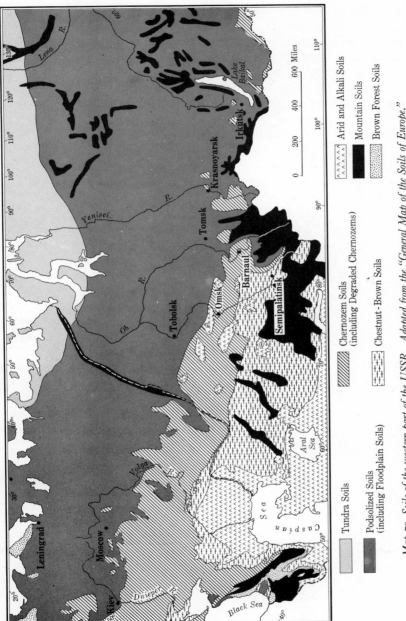

Map 70. Soils of the western part of the USSR. Adapted from the "General Map of the Soils of Europe," Warsaw, 1928; and "Soils of the U.S.S.R." in Pioneer Settlement (New York, 1932), p. 248.

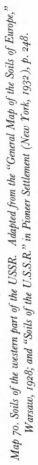

	Tundra Soils		Chernozem Soils (including Degraded Chernozems)		Arid and Alkali Soils
	Podsolized Soils (including Floodplain Soils)		Chestnut-Brown Soils		Mountain Soils
					Brown Forest Soils

0   200   400   600 Miles

the power of human muscles supplemented by domestic animals. Under a system of virtual slavery, work was accomplished which elsewhere proved impossible until the age of machinery. After the freeing of the serfs, a small proportion of the peasants were able to acquire farms of their own, but most of the agricultural workers were employed on the lands of the large owners. The average size of the peasant farms was between seven and ten acres, which is too small for the support of a family in the grasslands.

Wheat was raised on the black-earth belt, not as a food for the peasants, for they generally ate rye bread, but for export. The grain was carried by

Map 71. Topographic detail from a portion of the Starya Ushitsa sheet. Prepared by Army Map Service, Corps of Engineers, U.S. Army Washington, D.C., July 1962 printing.

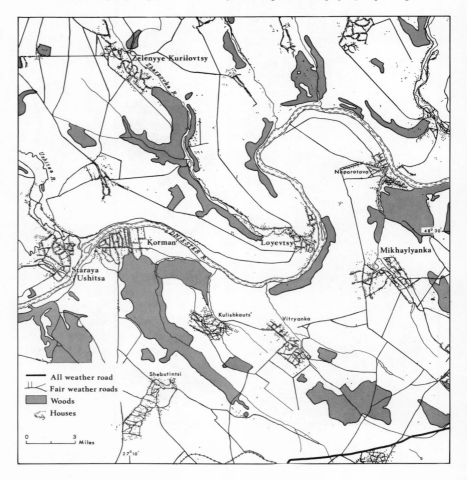

Fertilizing sugar beets on a state farm in the U.S.S.R. (Sovfoto).

wagon to the Volga River, and thence by river and canal to St. Petersburg (now Leningrad), where it was loaded on foreign ships for export to other European countries. In 1891 the Trans-Siberian Railroad was started, and a stream of pioneer settlers spread eastward into western Siberia, following the advance of the rails. Between 1897 and 1917 the population of Siberia doubled, and most of the new settlement was in the black-earth belt.

The Soviet government has reorganized the agricultural system. The first step was the elimination of the small private farm, and the combination of farm properties in large collective or state farms. This change involved no rearrangement of the people, for the rural population has traditionally been grouped in compact rural villages (Map 71). In 1958 there were some 78,000 collectives, averaging more than 3000 acres in size. They were operated by work brigades, using new machinery supplied from the factories. There were also 5000 state farms, run by the government, having an average size of 6000 acres.

The agricultural system in the Soviet Union is quite different from that of the United States, or of the Humid Pampa. In the grasslands of European Russia the crops include winter wheat, maize, sunflowers (for oil), hemp, sugar beets, and tobacco. The pastures for beef cattle and dairy cattle are separate from the crop lands, and animals must be watched by herders because very little of the land is fenced. Farther to the north, on the border between the grasslands and the forests of Group V, spring wheat replaces winter wheat, and there are also winter rye, maize, barley, and oats. Around the outskirts of the cities there are zones where cabbages and potatoes are raised, and dairy cattle are pastured. Toward the east, along the line of the Trans-Siberian Railroad, the farms grow spring wheat, rye, barley, oats, and flax.

Soviet agriculture is not highly productive. In part this is due to the recurring natural hazards of cold and drought which affect even the better farm lands of the Ukraine near the Black Sea. Toward the north and east the climatic hazards increase. Yet the Soviet planners have pushed grain farming farther and farther into areas of low rainfall. In 1954 the "Virgin Lands" program was started: spring wheat was planted on 100 million acres of steppe land in Western Siberia where the average annual rainfall was between 8 and 16 inches. The planners knew that this was a gamble on a huge scale, but there was pressing need for more wheat. The idea was to compensate for low yields by planting a vast acreage, and to expect frequent years of crop failure. Continued crop failure, together with serious wind erosion from the plowed fields, demonstrates that climate still remains largely beyond human control. The Soviet government in 1964 was forced to abandon the Virgin Land program and to purchase large amounts of grain from the other grasslands of the world—chiefly from Canada and the United States.

The lack of adequate farm production in the Soviet system seems also to be due in part to the system itself. It is an interesting fact that all over the world people who devote their lives to farming have a deep desire to work on their own land. The individual farmer learns how best to manage his own land, and resents the arrival of the "expert." In the Soviet Union it would seem that too much emphasis has been placed on maize, especially in areas where soil, water, or climate is not suited to maize. In some places maize is best planted in rows, in other places it does better when planted in squares. But the Soviet planners paid scant attention to the need for adjusting farm practices to local variations of land quality. The Soviet government has also yielded to the farmers' demands by permitting the use of small plots of land by individual farm families for private production. Although these private holdings amounted in 1962 to only 1.4 per cent of the Soviet agricultural area, and only 3.3 per cent of the area of planted crops, from them came 33 per cent of the harvested crops and 50 per cent of the livestock. The communists have not been able to change the basic attitudes of the farmers toward the land.

MANCHURIA

In all the great grassland regions of the world the experience of man in his attempt to form permanent fixed settlements has been similar. In a general way there are the same problems of securing water, of clearing the

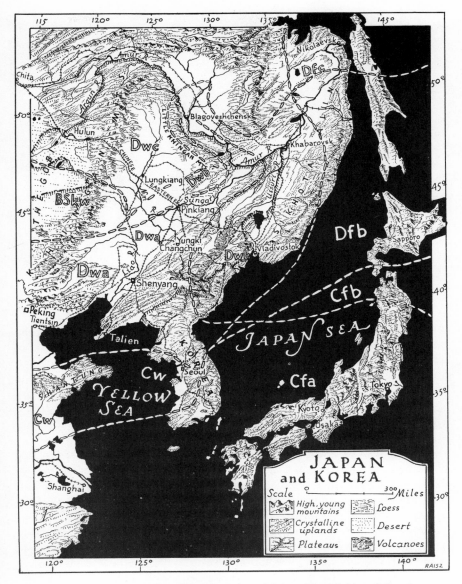

Map 72. Japan and the neighboring portions of Asia. (For definition of climatic symbols, see Appendix B, pp. 480–487.)

Manchurian roads become all but impassable in the summer rainy season (Triangle Photo Service).

grass sod, of combating insect pests, of building houses to withstand the extremes of weather in a land without the shelter of trees or hills, and of finding a suitable form of economy to make the settlement workable. But in each region we have described, differences in human culture—in the attitudes, objectives, and technical abilities of the settlers—have produced different relationships between people and land. Underlying the broad similarity of all the regions of Group VI are the detailed differences that make each area and its problems unique.

This is illustrated with special force in the story of the Chinese occupance of Manchuria, another of the great mid-latitude grasslands of the world. Manchuria (Map 72), is a region of long and very cold, dry winters and short, hot, rainy summers. At Harbin, now called Haerhpin, the average temperature of January is $-1.7°$. From October to April the ground is frozen and generally bare. The roads at this time of the year are easily passable. When the short summer comes (from May to September) the weather is hot and rainy, vegetation springs to life, the landscape changes from brown to green, and the roads are deep with mud and all but impassable. Into this region, once occupied only by pastoral nomads, came the agricultural Chinese.

The Chinese settlement of Manchuria began over a century ago; for between 1821 and 1851, colonies were established as far north as the Sungari River. Not until 1878, however, was colonization given official sanction.

During the last two decades of the nineteenth century, a slow but steady movement of Chinese was filling the southernmost parts of Manchuria. When the railroads were built, after 1900, the stream of settlement, as in the Occidental grasslands, was rapidly augmented. It was not until 1926, however, that the numbers of immigrants into Manchuria became spectacular. From 1926 to 1928 over a million people a year moved northward, probably the greatest migration in human history. Most of these colonists came from the famine zones of North China, chiefly from Shantung. After their arrival in Manchuria a few took advantage of the railroads, but the greater number struggled northward on foot to find room for settlement.

The Chinese mode of expansion on this frontier is quite different from the expansion on Occidental frontiers. The North American pioneers, for instance, traveled far beyond the margins of established settlement and located their homesteads in a zone of very thin and scattered population. Similarly, the older Russian expansion eastward along the black-earth belt sent colonies far out in advance. Not so the Chinese. This frontier spread northward "like a drop of oil," presenting a solid front of dense settlement against the unsettled grasslands beyond the frontier, still occupied by pastoral nomads.

The story of settlement in Manchuria is greatly complicated by the fact that this region is of interest not only to the Chinese but also to the Soviet Union and to Japan. For some 2000 years, up to the end of the nineteenth century, Manchuria was important chiefly as a marginal part of China. To the Chinese it is known as the "three eastern provinces," and only the foreigner uses the name Manchuria. In 1896, however, the Chinese government permitted Russia to build the Chinese Eastern Railway to serve as a shortcut on the Trans-Siberian line to Vladivostok. The Russians, seeking an ice-free port, built a branch southward from Harbin (Haerhpin) to Port Arthur (now Lüshun), near Dairen (now Talien). The activities of the Russians brought them into conflict with the Japanese, who desired both protection from the advance of the Russians into eastern Asia and also the right to exploit the mineral resources of Manchuria, which include both coal and iron ore. As a result of the Russo-Japanese War of 1904–1905, Japan took over the southern branch of the railroad and renamed it the South Manchuria Railway.

These railroad lines were administered by essentially independent corporations, which therefore made them lines of Russian and Japanese penetration into Chinese Manchuria. The corporations were responsible for the policing of zones on either side of the rails, and they built mines and factories and developed cities. When the Japanese seized Mukden (now Shenyang) in 1931 and set up a puppet government for "Manchukuo," the chief purpose was not to find new lands to colonize, but rather to have a free hand to develop and utilize the commercial resources of the country. In comparison to the millions of Chinese, few Japanese ever came to Manchuria. But the Japanese developed the coal mines, especially the mines at Fushun near Mukden, where the thickest coal seam in the world (417 feet) is located. At Anshan, south of Mukden, large iron and steel works were built. For Japan, poor in coal, the control of Manchuria seemed essential. As a result of World War II many of these industrial establishments were destroyed or removed.

Since the rise to power of the communist government in China, the situation in Manchuria has changed again. No longer can Japan exert influence in this area. With the help of the Soviet Union, the Chinese have rebuilt the big steel plant at Anshan and have reopened many of the mines that were destroyed during the war. From the Manchurian base the communists gave support to North Korea in its war against the forces of the United Nations. The communist line was pushed almost as far south as Seoul (Map 72). Manchuria is still a focus of conflicting interests. As one or another of the interested countries becomes relatively stronger or weaker, the balance of influence in the region is shifted.

The Agriculture. Settlement in Manchuria was formerly based on subsistence grain-farming. Even today the most important subsistence crops are a giant sorghum known as kaoliang, millet, and wheat. Before World War II, however, the soybean had become more and more of a commercial crop, after the mode of the Occident. This remarkable plant is a native of eastern Asia and has been cultivated in China for many centuries. Its introduction into Manchuria was very successful. In 1908 a shipment to England found an overseas market, and until World War II exports of soybeans, bean cake, and bean oil brought a steady cash income. The soybean had become particularly important to the Japanese as a fertilizer for their heavily overworked agricultural lands. Since the war Japan has lost this valuable import.

Summary

The mid-latitude grasslands of the world form a distinctive kind of habitat, occupying a specific part of the generalized global pattern of habitats. It is a well-established fact that where grasses alone cover the land this is the result of widespread burning, for under natural conditions grass and brush or scrubby trees are intermingled. The over-grazing of the short-grass steppe, on the other hand, may result in an extension of the dry lands. There are numerous places on the desert margins where xerophytic shrub vegetation has moved onto land which within historic time has been covered with grass sod.   These habitats, wherever they occur, pose certain similar problems for people who would put them to effective use.

The solution of these problems differs according to the ways of living of the people involved.   We have noted the considerable contrasts in the sequent occupance of the North American grasslands, the Argentine Humid Pampa, the steppes of Russia, and the grassy plains of Manchuria.   Similar contrasts would have been brought to light by the study of such other grassland regions as those of Australia and Canada.   In North America the revolution in agricultural technology which has come about since World War II has enormously increased the productivity of these regions. The technical skills and knowledge exist greatly to reduce the world's hunger, and the obstacles to the spread of this knowledge are largely man-made.

The Boreal Forest and Woodlands

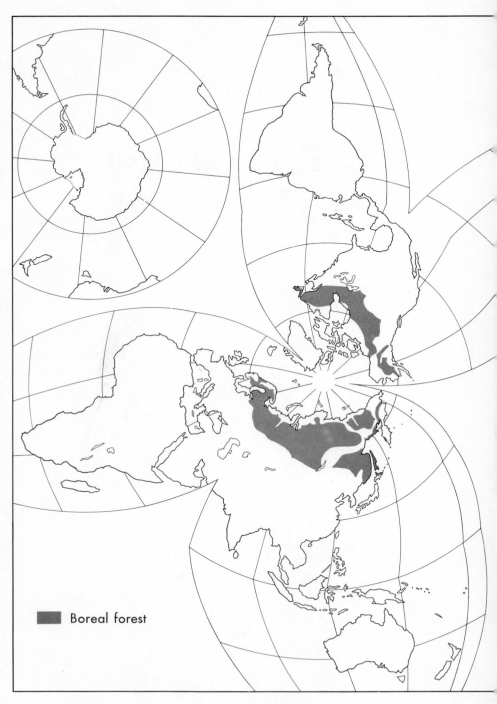

Boreal forest

Map 73.

S EASONAL CHANGE reaches a maximum in the boreal forest and woodlands. In no other part of the world does the aspect of the face of the
earth undergo such a radical transformation rhythmically, in the
course of the year, as in these forest lands of the higher middle latitudes of
the Northern Hemisphere (Map 73). The intense cold and long hours of
darkness during the winter enforce on the vegetation a long period of rest.
During this time the contour of the land is smoothed by a blanket of snow,
and the rivers and lakes are locked in a casing of ice. At first the longer
hours of sunlight in the spring seem to make little impression on the frozen
land; but suddenly, in May or June, the bare ground is revealed, the ice
breaks up and is carried downstream in great thundering, chaotic masses,
and the long-slumbering vegetation almost bursts into vigorous life. A car-
pet of flowers quickly covers the ground left bare by the melting snow, and
the air is filled with myriads of insects. This is the brief period of breath-
less activity for all the inhabitants of the forest—all except man, the intruder, who finds travel difficult when he tries to penetrate the thick forests and bogs away from the navigable rivers. Only where agriculture is
attempted is this a busy period for the human inhabitants. With the first
touch of fall the broadleaf trees turn yellow or red, the insects disappear,
and the land animals seek a shelter for the long winter hibernation. Great
numbers of migrating animals, especially birds, start southward. First with
a touch of frost, then more firmly with a grip of ice and snow, winter fas-
tens its fingers on the land. The long, dark night sets in. Then, from their
summer refuge near the rivers, men move out into the forest, traveling easily on skis or snowshoes or sledges over the snow-covered surface or along
the smooth ice-covered rivers. These are the hunters, trappers, and lum-
bermen who extract from the forest at this time its toll of timber and furs.
No landscapes, not even those of the tropical savannas, could change more
than this in the course of a year.

The climatic background of this seasonal change is related to an extreme
continental position. Great temperature ranges are associated with wide
land expanses, for only at a distance from the oceans can great contrasts
between warm summers and cold winters be developed. Range of temperature, we have said previously, increases with increasing latitude and
distance from the sea. Since all the continents taper to the south, no large
expanses of land occur in the middle latitudes of the Southern Hemisphere;

Trappers making camp in northern Quebec (Canadian National).

only north of the equator is land and water distribution effective in producing extreme continental climates. The northern lands where these extreme climates prevail are the regions of Group VII.

The Habitat

VEGETATION AND CLIMATE

The boreal forest and woodlands which extend from west to east across the continents of the Northern Hemisphere, poleward of the deserts and grasslands, are dominantly coniferous. Farther equatorward on both the eastern and the western sides, as we have seen, lie the mixed forests of Group V. The predominance of conifers north of the mixed forests does not mean that the rigorous climatic conditions of the higher middle latitudes are more suitable to these trees, for actually conifers grow much better in regions of milder climate. But in the north they can compete on more or less even terms with the broadleaf species.

The Taiga.* The northern coniferous forest, or *taiga,* can be contrasted

* "Taiga" is a Russian word referring to the northern virgin forests.

in almost every respect with the tropical selva. To be sure, both are ever-green; but this resemblance is only superficial, for the evergreen conifers of the taiga do not enjoy the year-round growing season of the evergreen broadleaf species of the tropics. Then, the taiga is composed of a few sim-ple associations instead of a great variety of kinds of trees. Spruce, fir, larch, and pine are the chief conifers, and these are combined with such broad-leaf species as aspen, birch, beech, maple, and willow. These forest re-gions, except in northern Manchuria, lie north of the range of the oaks. Among the most common associations are the spruce-fir forests of North America, with larch (tamarack), cedar, and maple occurring along with spruce and fir in the swamps; or the fir, birch, and aspen forests of western Siberia; or the larch and fir forests of eastern Siberia. Pure stands of pine are found on some of the sandy soils, much as on the similar lands farther south in Group V. The conifer forests are interrupted by broadleaf en-claves along the river banks or in some of the swampy areas, or where these species have sprung up as second-growth forest after the conifers have in one way or another been removed.

The density of the stand of trees in the taiga varies greatly from place to place, but even in the most favored spots these forests do not form such a thick cover as the selva. Although many valuable stands of timber are found, probably the greater part of the land is covered by poor, stunted, and knotted trees having little value as timber. At the northern limits of

Near the northern limit of the taiga in Alaska (Three Lions).

this group of regions the forest gives way to a woodland in which single mature trees, centuries old, have reached only the stature of small bushes. In marked contrast to the selva, the forest floor in many areas is littered with fallen trunks and branches or with bundles of up-turned roots, which, because of the high pitch content of the wood and because of the cool climate, decay very slowly. Especially in the swampy places the underbrush is so thick that passage through the forest may be extremely difficult.

The pitch content of the conifer renders it peculiarly liable to destruction by fire. Where lumbering operations are being carried on, sparks from the mills or camps frequently catch in the piles of slashings. In dry weather fires start very quickly, and once well under way are almost impossible to check. Few, indeed, are the northern forests in which charred trunks do not give evidence of at least one destructive fire.

The clearing of the taiga, whether by extensive lumbering or by fire, is not followed by a rapid return of the original species. At first only a low growth of bushes appears among the stumps. Then, instead of conifers, the first trees to gain a precarious foothold on the land are the broadleaf

Floating logs down a Siberian river (Sovfoto).

Lake and boreal forest in Norway, fifty miles north of Oslo (J. Allan Cash, from Rapho-Guillumette).

A coniferous forest in Western Canada (WIB Photo).

types, chiefly birch and aspen.   In Siberia this second-growth enclave of broadleaf types is called "white taiga," as opposed to the dark-green fir forests, which are called "black taiga."   Only after a long period of time does the slow growth of conifers reproduce the climax forest.

The Native Animals of the Taiga.   In another respect the taiga differs from the selva.   Instead of lacking large ground animals, it is the habitat of an animal population of extraordinary variety and number—an animal population which derives most of its food supply from the aquatic life in the numerous rivers, lakes, and swamps.   In fact, in the more northerly sections the forest animals are of much greater value as a resource than the timber that shelters them.   In these forests roam the world's chief fur-bearing animals: minks, martens, muskrats, foxes, wolves, badgers, bears, beavers, squirrels, sables, and ermines are included in the long list.   There are also several large ungulata, chief of which are the deer, the moose, the caribou, and the close relative of the caribou—the reindeer.

The Climate.   Temperature is the most significant climatic element in these regions.   Fundamental in the production of the boreal forest landscapes, with their marked seasonal contrast, is the alternation of long, severe winters and short, cool summers.   Especially in the continental interiors very large ranges of temperature between the average of the coldest and warmest months are experienced.   For example, Winnipeg, in Manitoba, has a range of 70.3°, between an average of − 3.9° in January and 66.4° in July; and Dawson, in the Yukon, has a range of 82.4°, from − 23.1° in January to 59.3° in July.   As might be expected, the most extreme ranges of all are found in the interior of the largest land mass, Eurasia.   The little town of Verkhoyansk, in northeastern Siberia, holds the world's record for the range between the average temperature of its coldest and its warmest months.   January averages − 58.2°, and July averages 59.9°—a range of 118.1°.   The lowest temperature ever recorded at Verkhoyansk is − 90°; but at this same place a July temperature of 93.5° has also been recorded.   Even lower winter temperatures have been reported from a place called Oymyakon.   Both these places are located in valleys among the low mountains of northeast Siberia where air drainage during calm, clear nights produces exceptionally low temperatures.   Generally the winter temperatures in the northern parts of Group VII are not quite so low as these extremes: − 78° at Fort Yukon in Alaska, − 81° on the lower Mackenzie River in Canada, − 88° on the lower Lena River in Siberia. At all these places summer temperatures in the 90's are normal.

The winter temperatures are by no means so critical as the summer temperatures and the length of the growing season.   Even though the summers are short, this is more than compensated by the long hours of sunshine.   Poleward of latitude 55° or 60° N., the number of hours of possible sunlight per day during June increases rapidly to a maximum of twenty-four hours near the Arctic Circle (Map 74).   At these latitudes it is not sufficient to measure the growing season in terms of frost-free days.   Instead, it must be measured by the total number of hours of sunlight which come while the air temperature is over 42.6° (below which the vegetation growth ceases).   Because of the very rapid rate of growth resulting from the long hours of sunshine, wild plants and crops extend considerably farther toward the north than might be expected.

The forests of Group VII, like those of Group V, run diagonally across the continents (Plate 10, pp. 564–565; Map 73; Fig. 12, p. 424).   On the west coasts the boreal forest is more than 10° farther north than on the east coasts.   The southern limit of the forest in Alaska is about 55° N., and in Scandinavia about 60° N.; in northern Maine and in eastern Siberia the southern limit is south of 45° N.   The diagonal arrangement is owing, as we have seen, to the contrast of warm and cold ocean water on the two sides of the continents in higher middle latitudes.   There is an important difference to be observed, however, between the northern limit of the boreal forest in Europe and North America.   In Europe the warm North Atlantic Drift

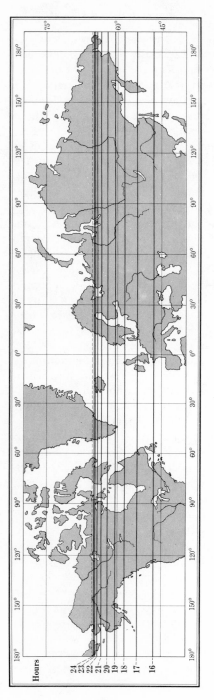

Map 74. Hours of sunshine north of 45° on June 21. Based on sun's center and corrected for refraction (computed by A. D. Maxwell).

runs northward along the coast of Norway into the Arctic Ocean, bringing ice-free conditions around northern Norway and even some distance beyond (Map 83, p. 363). But the barely submerged range of mountains that forms the Aleutian Islands shuts out the warm Kuro Siwo from the Bering Sea. As a result the boreal forest does not reach the coast of Alaska, which is tundra-covered even in the Aleutian Islands well south of 60° N.

The boreal forest and woodlands are not broken by the dry lands in the continental interiors, as are the forests of Group V. They extend all the way across the Northern Hemisphere continents north of the grasslands. Their limits are closely related to the temperatures of the summer months. The northern limit, where the boreal woodland borders the arctic tundra, corresponds closely to the isotherm of 50° average temperature for the warmest months. The southern limit, where the boreal forest borders the mixed forests of Group V, is very close to a line drawn though places which have three months averaging over 50° and a fourth month which averages just under 50°. Where four months average over 50° the summers are long enough so that the oaks and other trees characteristic of the forests of Group V can compete successfully with the conifers except on areas of porous soil or where man has intervened.

The rainfall over most of the boreal forest and woodlands is low. Only on the continental margins is the total annual precipitation greater than 10 inches. Furthermore, most of the rain comes in summer, and the winters are characteristically dry and clear. This is owing to the position of these regions in the world pattern of climates. We may recall that the cold air masses that move southward over the middle latitudes of the Northern Hemisphere originate over the Arctic Ocean, Greenland, and the higher middle latitudes of North America and Eurasia in winter. Although there may be heavy frosts where cold air is accumulating, there can be no precipitation because air is settling rather than rising. The skies are cloudless, which promotes the radiation of heat from the ground and the further chilling of the air in contact with the ground. During the winters the area of cold air accumulation is so large that no warm air masses can bring moisture to it. Only on the continental margins is there much snowfall (Map 75). Contrary to popular belief, supported generally by the "movies," Siberia in winter is a land of little snowfall; the ground is mostly bare or covered with accumulations of frost. Because of the intense cold and the lack of a protecting blanket of snow, the small rivers and marshes freeze solid, and the ice on lakes and larger rivers is so thick that it can support the heaviest trucks and machines, even locomotives pulling loaded trains.

The average annual rainfall of the regions of Group VII is much less critical than the temperature, however. Because even in summer the

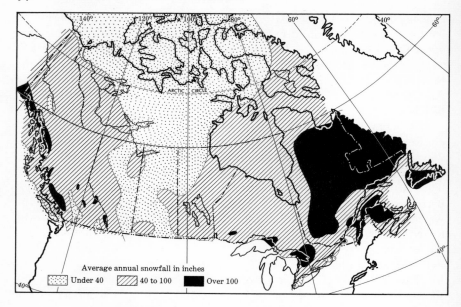

Map 75. Mean annual snowfall of Canada (after Koeppe).

temperatures do not average very high, the evaporation is never very great.   At Verkhoyansk, for example, where the average annual rainfall is only 5.2 inches, the evaporation is so low that crops can be raised with no thought of irrigation.   Actually a large part of the area of Group VII is covered by swamps and bogs, some of them permanently frozen underneath.   In summer, when the ice melts and the surface of the ground thaws out, large areas become all but inaccessible for people who must travel on the land.

SURFACE FEATURES AND DRAINAGE

The prevalence of lakes and swamps in Group VII, however, is not solely the result of low evaporation.   The surface features and drainage also contribute to this condition.   Two chief processes have been at work in sculpturing the landforms of these regions: glaciation and running water.   In both cases, for reasons we shall see, lakes and swamps are commonly produced.

The Surface Configuration of Group VII.   On both sides of the North Atlantic Ocean, in northeastern North America and northwestern Europe, there is a remarkably similar development of the surface features (Plates 1 and 13, pp. 553 and 570–571). This part of North America is occupied by the Laurentian Upland, in the midst of which is found the great indentation of Hudson Bay. The southern end of this hilly region in southern Canada and in parts of the United States is within the borders of Group V. In Europe the Scandinavian Upland occupies part of Finland and most of Sweden and Norway. In the midst of this upland is the Gulf of Bothnia. Both uplands are made up of knobby hills rising above extensive swampy or lake-filled valleys. Within the uplands major terrain features are formed by long and sharply-marked escarpments following old fault lines through the ancient geologic formations here exposed at the surface. Both uplands rise gradually from the continental interiors toward rims that face the Atlantic. The sea face of this escarpment in Labrador and in Norway is steep and rugged, forming what looks from the sea like a range of high mountains; yet only in southern Norway and in northern Labrador can it be classified as mountainous, for elsewhere, on climbing to the top, one finds a rolling hilly surface sloping gradually inland. Both uplands are bordered around their margins by cuestas that mark the up-turned edges of the resistant sedimentary formations.

Bordering these hilly uplands and their marginal cuestas are vast plains extending from the lower middle latitudes of both North America and Eurasia northward to the Arctic Ocean. These lowlands in the north are drained by three great north-flowing rivers: the Mackenzie, the Ob, and the Yenisei.

Immediately east of the Yenisei in Siberia, the moderately-dissected plateau of eastern Siberia rises abruptly from the lowlands of the west. This vast level-topped upland fills most of the area between the Yenisei and the Lena, reaching from the mountains of central Asia to the shore of the Arctic Ocean. A similar kind of terrain is found in the Yukon Valley of Alaska between the Alaska Range and the Brooks Range. The Yukon and its tributaries pass through this plateau in steep-sided valleys.

Northeast Siberia, east of the Lena Valley, is composed of ranges of high mountains, rising distinctly above a low mountain country. Along the arctic coast there is a wide coastal plain, and another narrowly confined lowland connects the Bering Sea with the Sea of Okhotsk north of Kamchatka.

The Extent of Glaciation. These various natural divisions of Group VII have been sculptured in detail by two quite different processes. A considerable area was never covered by the ice of the continental glaciers, and here the landforms have been produced chiefly by the work of running water. Glacial landforms, however, have been only very slightly modified by post-glacial erosion in the other parts of the group.

Since glaciers can be formed only where so much snow falls during the

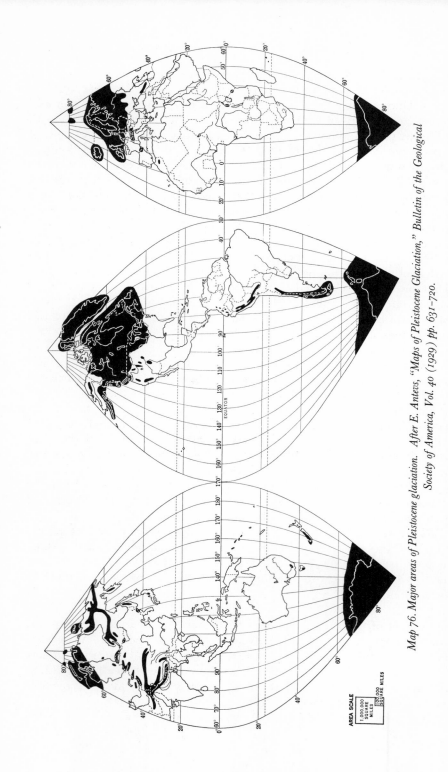

Map 76. *Major areas of Pleistocene glaciation. After E. Antevs, "Maps of Pleistocene Glaciation," Bulletin of the Geological Society of America, Vol. 40 (1929) pp. 631–720.*

AREA SCALE

1,000,000 SQUARE MILES

100,000 SQUARE MILES

winter that it does not all melt away during the summer, the places most favorable for ice accumulation are in the regions either of heavy snowfall or of cool summers, or of both. Such places are found in the high latitudes or on the snowy continental margins of higher middle latitudes. It is believed that a climate not radically different from that of today was needed to produce the continental ice sheets of the Pleistocene.

The areas of the world covered by Pleistocene ice are shown on the map (Map 76). In North America the chief centers of accumulation were in the far west on the snowy mountains of the west coast, and on the Plateau of Labrador, east and south of Hudson Bay. From these centers the ice spread chiefly south, east, and west. The Labrador ice sheet extended as far south as Long Island. Its southern boundary crossed the Appalachians north of Pittsburgh, and thence followed roughly the line of the Ohio and Missouri rivers into the central part of the continent. A small area in Wisconsin was never covered by the ice, although it was at one time entirely surrounded. The ice crossed Hudson Bay and covered the plains of central Canada as far north as the Arctic Ocean, but the Yukon Plateau was never glaciated. Ice still covers Greenland and parts of Ellesmere Island. In Europe the chief center of ice accumulation was the northern part of the Scandinavian Peninsula and Finland, from which the ice spread southward over most of the British Isles and, on the Continent, as far as the mouth of the Rhine and the highlands of central Europe. Eastward, however, glaciation probably extended only a short distance beyond the Urals. Most of the great interior of Siberia, with its light snowfall, was never glaciated. In the Southern Hemisphere glaciation was extensive in the southern Andes and the New Zealand Alps. The largest area of accumulation was the Antarctic Continent, which is still ice-covered.

Lakes and Swamps. In glaciated territory, whether the landforms are dominated by the processes of erosion or of deposition, innumerable depressions, large and small, are formed. If these are deep enough, they hold lakes. On the crystalline rocks of the hilly uplands the ice carved a surface of alternating low rocky ridges, smoothed and bare of soil on top, and bog-filled or lake-filled hollows. The similarity of the landscapes developed chiefly by glacial erosion on the crystalline rocks of the Laurentian and Scandinavian uplands is striking. In Finland alone, for example, there are some thirty-five thousand lakes, covering nearly a tenth of the total area of the country (see Map 101, p. 506). In North America a series of large lakes have been formed along the margin between the crystalline rocks and the sedimentaries. In the south are the Great Lakes. Northward, arranged along this geologic boundary, are Winnipeg, Athabaska, Great Slave, and Great Bear lakes. In addition to these larger water bodies, smaller lakes or swamps nestle in almost every depression.

Travel by airplanes, equipped in summer with pontoons and in winter with skis, is an easy matter in these regions, where landing places can be found every few miles.

On the lowlands the glacial landforms are chiefly those of deposition. Here the greatest variety and confusion of surface topographic features appear, marked by only a vague festooning of the moraines. Some of these areas contain even more lakes and swamps than the hilly uplands.

In whatever manner lakes may be formed, they are only temporary features of the land in point of view of geologic time. Not only are their outlets being cut down, thus lowering the level of their waters, but also their basins are being filled with material washed into them. Throughout these glaciated regions all stages in the extinction of lakes can be found, from open water bodies to marshy flats from which all signs of open water have disappeared. Along with the gradual filling of such depressions, there is

Figure 5. Diagram to illustrate the filling of a pit lake by vegetation (after C. A. Davis).

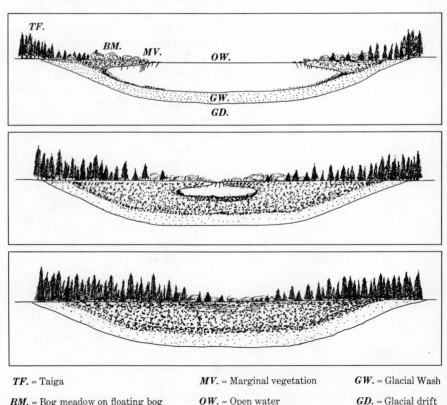

| **TF.** = Taiga | **MV.** = Marginal vegetation | **GW.** = Glacial Wash |
| **BM.** = Bog meadow on floating bog | **OW.** = Open water | **GD.** = Glacial drift |

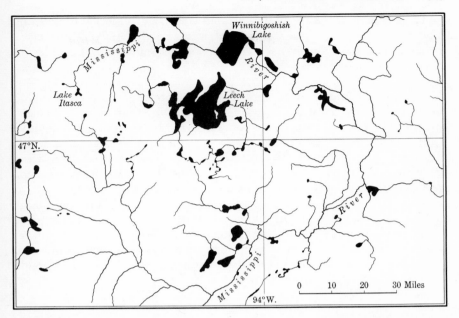

Map 77. Irregular drainage of a glaciated area: the headwaters of the Mississippi River in Minnesota (United States Geological Survey).

a fairly definite succession of vegetation (Figure 5). First, water lilies and sedges grow on the margins of the open water. These gradually form a floating bog that extends out from the solid shore. The floating bog becomes thicker until it fills in sufficiently to form a swamp, and various shrubs and bushes soon crowd out the sedges. The first trees to appear are usually larch (tamarack) in pure stands; later, as the marsh becomes more solid, in the regions of Group VII spruce follows and crowds out the larch. These various elements in the succession can all be identified in more or less concentric arrangement around lakes in process of extinction.

Rivers in Glaciated Territory. The drainage patterns in glaciated country are very different from those developed by more normal processes. Because of the blocking of preglacial valleys and the character of the surface left after the retreat of the ice, the rivers in such country are extremely irregular and winding in their courses. In many cases they wander aimlessly from lake to lake, completely changing their direction of flow as they proceed downsteam (Map 77). In unglaciated territory, on the other hand, the stream patterns are the usual dendritic or trellis types.

The regimen of the rivers in glaciated country is remarkably uniform. The many lakes regulate the flow of water so that·only a protracted drought can have much effect, while sudden rains must be excessive to produce much of a rise.

Floodplain Swamps. An exception to this statement, however, is found in the cases of the great north-flowing rivers of this group—the Mackenzie, the Ob, the Yenisei, and the Lena. These rivers are subject to extensive spring floods, and the lowlands, even where they are not glaciated, do not dry out rapidly after the water recedes. This irregular regimen arises from the conditions of the spring thaw. Since the headwaters are freed earliest, while the lower portions of the rivers are still incased in ice, great jams are the result, and behind these jams the water backs up over a large territory. The floods of the Ob are as much as thirty-five miles wide in some sections. Permanently water-logged surfaces, in many places underlain by peat, are common in all these regions, covering as much as 75 per cent of the total area in the lowlands north of Tobolsk. In Canada the name "muskeg" is applied to such surfaces.

THE SOILS

The mature soils of Group VII are well developed only in the unglaciated areas. In the regions covered by glacial deposits, the time that has elapsed since the retreat of the ice has permitted only the beginnings of soil development. In both glaciated and unglaciated territory, moreover, no mature soils can develop in swampy places.

The soil type toward which the immature regoliths are developing, and which is represented in mature form over much of Siberia, is the *podsol*.* The podsol profile is distinctly shallower than any of the other mature profiles (Figure 2, A, p. 219), in few places reaching depths greater than from eighteen inches to two feet. Soil development is slow because of the long period each year when the land is frozen. For various reasons, notably the absence of earthworms, the humus layer on the surface is not mixed with the soil, but remains as a very black, highly acid accumulation. The lower part of the A horizon in mature podsols is leached to a gray or even white color. The B horizon is reddish from the accumulation of part of the leached material, and is very compact. These soils quickly lose their fertility under cultivation.

In parts of Group VII there is a permanently frozen subsoil. This is the case in the far northern part of European Russia, in Siberia east of the Yenisei, and in parts of Canada and Alaska—all regions of light snow

---

*A Russian word meaning "ash-colored underneath."

cover and intense winter cold.   This frozen subsoil, by prohibiting the percolation of water, is a further reason for the extensive development of
swamps.   Because the removal of the vegetation cover has in some places
resulted in the thawing out of this ice, it is thought that perhaps this phenomenon has been inherited from the intense cold of the glacial epoch.   It is
known as *permafrost.*

The Occupance

The boreal forest and woodlands rival the deserts in scantiness of
human inhabitants.   Although these regions constitute 10 per cent of the
world's land area, they are occupied by only about 1 per cent of the
world's population.   Furthermore, most of the inhabitants are recent
comers who have, for one reason or another, migrated to these more remote regions.   The Asian steppe nomads, fleeing from the periodic droughts
of the grassland regions, not only pushed westward into the forests of
Europe and eastward into China but also northward into the taiga, where
certain of the steppe tribes sought refuge from their warlike neighbors.
More recently the Occidentals have extended their frontiers of settlement
into these regions, and scattered outposts of settlement are found in
the most isolated places, supported by such extractive industries as mining,
lumbering, fishing, and trapping.

A Seaplane at Uranium City, Saskatchewan (National Film Board of Canada).

OCCUPANCE BY NONOCCIDENTAL CULTURES

The several different tribes that were pushed northward into the Siberian taiga from the steppes of central Asia have readjusted their modes of life to this new environment in various ways. Some have given up their horses in favor of cattle; others, such as the Samoyeds of northwestern Siberia, adopted the reindeer and remained pastoral nomads. Perhaps the most adaptable of all these "native" peoples were the Yakuts, who occupied the basin of the Lena River in the heart of the world's "cold pole." They learned to supplement their cattle with fish and game, to raise agricultural products and sell them to the Russian settlements, and even to act as traders between the Russians and the more remote forest tribes along the Lena and its tributaries. They have even been able to adjust to the communist system introduced by the Soviet Government. The still more primitive peoples of the Canadian forests, who live by hunting and fishing only, are believed to have migrated from Asia through Siberia and Alaska into the New World before mankind had advanced to the domestication of other animals than the dog.

Contacts with the European and American settlements or trading posts have seriously disorganized the native ways of living. In Siberia only the Yakuts are still increasing in numbers. In both Siberia and Canada the Occidental demand for furs led to an increase of winter trapping. Men with their families start out into the wilderness in the fall and establish themselves in remote and isolated places, where they spend the winter gathering a supply of pelts. With the melting of the snow in spring, when travel is limited to the rivers, they return to the trading posts and there exchange their skins for articles manufactured in the Occident, such as foods, rifles and ammunition, clothing, and strong drink.

OCCIDENTAL OCCUPANCE

This fur trade of the Europeans with the inhabitants of the taiga, both in Siberia and Canada, is now many centuries old. As early as the eleventh century the merchants of Russia were carrying on trade with the inhabitants of the Ob Valley. Trading posts were established during the sixteenth and seventeenth centuries, mostly at the mouths of the rivers down which the "natives" brought their loads of skins in the spring. The famous Hudson's Bay Company received its charter from King Charles II in 1670, and proceeded to locate posts first around the shores of James Bay and later along the western shore of Hudson Bay (Map 78). For some time the Company did not find it necessary to penetrate inland, as the Indians brought their furs over great distances in order to purchase the white

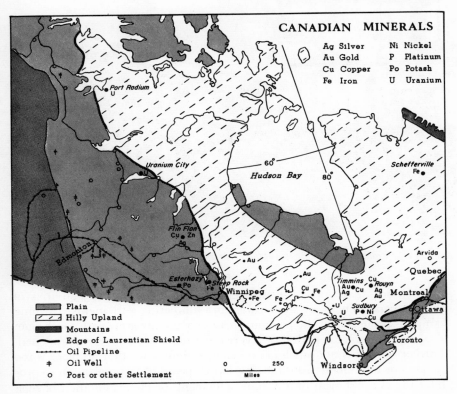

Map 78. Trading posts, mining centers of Canada.

man's products. Competition with other fur-trading companies. however, forced the establishment of posts in the interior, mostly at important river junctions or at portages between river systems. Meanwhile the Russians had pushed their trading activities across Asia and into Alaska, and even southward along the Pacific coast to the Spanish settlements in California. Only the mountains separated them from the domains of the Hudson's Bay Company. Through the activities of these big trading companies vast areas of the boreal forest and woodlands came under the control of two nations: Great Britain and Russia. In 1867 the United States purchased Alaska from Russia. Today railroad tentacles have been extended into these regions, and the posts at the railheads are the chief points of concentration of the fur traders.

Mining and Lumbering. Meanwhile other types of Occidental occupance have appeared which have done more to transform the landscapes of the

A gold dredge at work in a stream of the Yukon Plateau (Machetanz, from Three Lions).

forest lands than have the isolated trading posts or the activities of the trappers. These are the mining and lumbering settlements. Mining camps associated with the precious metals commonly grow with mushroom rapidity, and after a period of feverish existence are entirely abandoned. Furthermore, it is not much of an exaggeration to say that no place is too isolated or too remote from the developed means of transportation to prohibit the establishment of a mining settlement for the exploitation of such minerals as gold, platinum, and uranium, provided the ore bodies are sufficiently rich. Placer gold was exploited as early as 1830 in the territory just west of the mountains of central Asia between the headwaters of the Ob and the Yenisei. Other gold camps sprang into being, flourished, and declined. Today the chief centers of placer gold-mining in Siberia are located along the valley of the upper Lena and its tributary, the Vitim, northeast of Lake Baikal (Map 79). Placer gold, too, was the cause of the great gold rush of 1898 into Alaska. Auriferous gravels are widely distributed throughout the Yukon Valley and its tributaries (Map 80).

Somewhat more permanent are the mining communities based on ores of minerals used in modern manufacturing industry. The ancient crystalline rocks contain such ores as iron, nickel, platinum, copper, lead, zinc, cobalt, and uranium. Prospecting for these vein minerals, however, is difficult since it must be done in summer when travel away from the rivers is all but impossible. The great ore body of Sudbury, north of Lake Huron, was discovered in 1883 when the Canadian Pacific Railroad was being built. In the process of digging a cut through a range of rocky hills, the presence of rich ores was made known. Today Sudbury is one of the

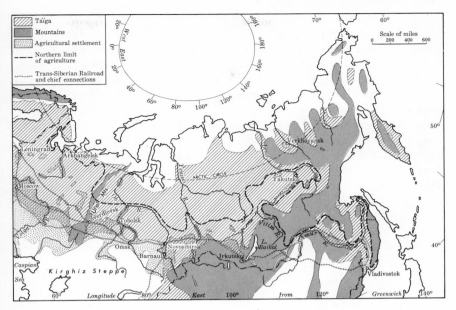

Map 79. Occidental settlement in the northern U.S.S.R. (after P. Camena d'Almeida).

world's leading sources of nickel, but in addition the Sudbury mines produce silver, lead, zinc, copper, gold, and platinum. Large smelters refine
the ores before they are shipped to the industrial centers.

A major source of high grade iron ore was discovered in 1887 in the hilly
country northwest of Duluth in the state of Minnesota. This is the famous

Map 80. Cropland, mining centers of Canada.

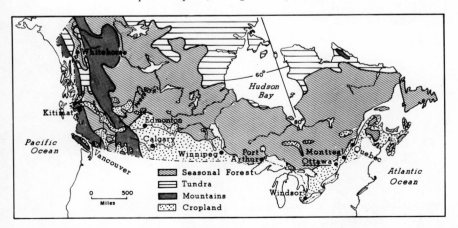

Mesabi Range that provides a major part of the ore for steel plants located along the southern shores of the Great Lakes.   The location of the Mesabi Range permits a short rail haul to the big ore docks on Lake Superior, and then low-cost bulk shipment in ore carriers to the ports around Chicago, Detroit, Cleveland, and Buffalo.   The ore body is near the surface and can be excavated with mechanical shovels without expensive tunneling.   An enormous volume of ore (65 per cent iron, and with a low percentage of impurities) was dug out of the ground to support the expanding steel industry of the United States.   But as World War II drew to a close it was clear that additional sources of iron ore would have to be found, since by that time only relatively low-grade ore remained at Mesabi.   New technology in the handling of low-grade ore, however, insures the continued importance of this mining area.

Meanwhile, many new ore bodies have been discovered in Canada, located in the mineral-rich crystalline rocks of the Laurentian Uplands. These new discoveries are not the result of exploration by individual pros-

An open pit mine in the Mesabi Range, from which high-grade ores have now been completely removed (Ewing Galloway).

pectors, or the chance strike resulting from railroad or road construction. Large mining companies now invest millions of dollars in surveys carried out with the aid of the newest technical devices. A major source of high-grade iron ore has been found in a belt running through northern Quebec and Labrador. Schefferville, in Quebec Province, is now reached from the St. Lawrence River by a rail line 375 miles long. In 1964 a huge ore body containing copper, zinc, and silver was found near Timmins 130 miles northwest of Sudbury. This place was at one time a major producer of gold, but the ore bodies had been exhausted when this new strike was made. The company, owned in the United States, that discovered the Timmins ore body had spent an average of $400,000 a year for six years, drilling more than 80 test borings in the search for ores. To uncover the ore will require the investment of another $20,000,000. A huge open-pit mine will be excavated, mining machinery installed, and the area will be connected by rail with the industrial centers to the south. These and other mining communities in the Boreal Forests and Woodlands of Canada are shown on the map (Map 79).

There are similar mining communities in the crystalline rock areas of northern Europe. The Bergslagen ores of Sweden, located about 120 miles northwest of Stockholm, were mined as early as the thirteenth century. Swedish wrought iron was recognized as superior in quality, and the demand for Swedish iron ore in the iron-poor Ruhr was greatly increased after 1860. About 1900 another large body of iron ore was dis-covered at Kiruna, 165 miles from the head of the Gulf of Bothnia. A railroad was built through the highlands 80 miles to the ice-free port of Narvik in Norway, thus permitting the year-round shipment of ore from this far-northern mining community.

Lumbering operations are another source of wealth and another basis of settlement in the regions of Group VII. And lumbering camps are no more permanent than settlements around the mines. Many are the towns on the northern shores of the Great Lakes that flourished at one time as the timber was being cut in back of them, and many of these places are now ghost towns. Some of them, and new towns along the northern shore of the St. Lawrence, are now flourishing again as centers of paper manufacture. The use of the forest to provide pulp-wood goes on faster than the annual rate of growth. The logs are made into paper as close to the forests as possible because paper is less bulky to ship than the logs. Canada in 1960 supplied about half of all the paper for newspapers used through-out the whole world. Lumbering operations are prosperous, also, in Sweden, along the western shore of the Gulf of Bothnia. Sweden at one time had a virtual monopoly on the manufacture of wooden matches. But all these wood-using industries must eventually face the problem of slow forest growth in these regions of short, cool summers.

Agricultural Settlement.   Agricultural settlement in the boreal forest and woodlands has been pushed far to the north, even beyond the Arctic Circle, yet the areas of such settlement are small and isolated.   They represent inhabited islands in the midst of the thinly peopled forests.   Like all Occidental pioneer settlements, they are located along the chief lines of travel—the navigable rivers or the rail tentacles.

The chief axis of settlement in Siberia is the Trans-Siberian Railroad (Map 79).   This follows the black-earth belt of the grasslands until it enters the forest in the neighborhood of Tomsk.   Clearings along this line in Group VII are scattered from Tomsk to Irkutsk, and beyond Lake Baikal in the valley of the Amur and its tributaries as far as Vladivostok. Penetration into the taiga to the north follows the valleys: along the Dvina nearly to Arkhangelsk, along the Ob to Tobolsk and beyond, and along the middle portion of the Lena to Yakutsk.   Isolated spots of settlement are found in the valleys even within the Arctic Circle, the most northerly of these being Verkhoyansk.

In Canada the chief axes of settlement have been the St. Lawrence River in the east and the railroad lines across the grasslands beyond Winnipeg in the west (Map 80).   Penetration of the forests to the north by agriculturists has been successful only in isolated localities.   The occupance of the Laurentian Upland has been especially difficult, in spite of the proximity to the large cities along the St. Lawrence.   Only in the Lake St. John lowland, and in the clay belts south of James Bay which have been opened up by the railroads, as around Cochrane, have agricultural settlements persisted.   As in Finland and northern Sweden, this region seems little suited to agricultural occupance.   The clearings north of Edmonton along the Peace River, however, are analogous to those of the Siberian taiga.

Agricultural settlement in Alaska has also been slow in developing.   Although agricultural products of good quality have been raised at Fairbanks on the Tanana River (Map 81), the difficulty of reaching a market has proved very great.   During the decade before World War II, a new pioneer colony was established in the Matanuska Valley around Palmer, along the railroad north of Seward and Anchorage.

Though the patterns of occupance on this northern pioneer fringe resemble those of the early stages of Occidental settlement in the other forest lands of the world, it is not at all certain that they can be elaborated as the others have been.   Agriculture is handicapped in the boreal forest and woodlands in numerous ways.   The severity of the winters, the shortness of the growing season, the isolated and spotty distribution of the areas of favorable soil, and the difficulty of reaching a market are all major obstacles to this form of occupance.   As the climate becomes more rigorous toward the north the importance of the edaphic elements in limiting the areas

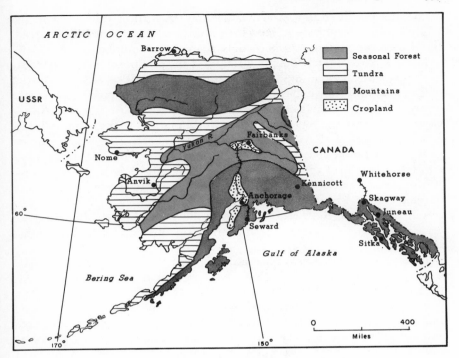

Map 81. Cropland of Alaska.

of potential settlement becomes greater. In spite of the optimism expressed in some of the propaganda, there is considerable doubt as to whether these isolated forest clearings can ever be incorporated in the main area of Occidental settlement by the conquest of the surrounding territory. This may be possible in certain areas along the southernmost margin of the taiga, but in most of the lands of Group VII widespread agricultural settlement under present conditions will probably not be feasible.

Animals and Crops. The pastoral and agricultural products that might support pioneer settlement in the boreal forests and woodlands are numerous. Most important at present are the animals raised for meat or dairy. In terms of acreage, the feed crops are more important than the food crops, and many of the grains are cut for hay and stored for winter feeding. Although cattle can scarcely compete for the large city markets in the regions of Group V, they can be marketed in nearby lumbering or mining communities. Reindeer, however, might well compete with cattle raised in places closer to the markets. Reindeer do not need to be sheltered or fed on stored hay during the winters, for they can take care of themselves.   Reindeer meat has actually been successfully sold in the United States, as it has been for a long time in the Scandinavian countries. But a pastoral economy supports only a small total number of people.

In a few parts of the regions of Group VII the production of spring wheat has provided economic support for settlement.   The Peace River District of Canada, for instance, has been organized around the production of this grain, as have also the similar clearings in southwestern Siberia.   An increase in the demand for wheat in the world markets would perhaps result in an extension of these wheat-growing communities; for wheat can be raised on favorable soils as far as the limit of ninety frost-free days and as far as the isotherm of 57° average temperature for the three summer months. If suitable soils can be found, the temperature conditions would permit the development of wheatlands even north of the Peace River District and in certain small areas in Alaska.   However, the production of wheat in these areas must remain marginal both in the economic and in the geographic sense.

Beyond wheat other crops reach the farthest limits of agriculture.   The hardiest of all the grains is barley; in the most northerly agricultural settlements of Siberia, Canada, and Alaska the usual crop combination is composed of barley, hay, and potatoes.   Vegetables and berries of rich flavor find suitable conditions of growth at these high latitudes and, with the establishment of canneries, might conceivably provide a commercial basis of settlement.   Vegetable gardens are planted even in the delta of the Mackenzie River not far from the margins of the Arctic Ocean.

Summary

Man is still the intruder in these regions.   Various cultures, driven by necessity to seek a refuge in the forests, have been able to maintain themselves, even if they have succeeded in doing little more than this.   The Occidentals, in their search for the primary materials with which to fashion the structures and implements of their civilization, have established mining and lumbering centers even where all the necessary foodstuffs have had to be brought in from other regions.   They have done the same in other parts of the world.   These regions have now also been penetrated by the fringes of Occidental settlement.   In especially favored places the isolated communities of pioneer farmers may prove permanent, but they are not likely to lose the flavor of the frontier for a long time.

The Polar Lands

COLD WEATHER, even in summer; sparse vegetation or no vegetation at all; snow and ice visible in the landscape, at least in patches, throughout most of the year—these are the outstanding characteristics of the polar lands. All these things can be experienced at one or another place and time in various parts of the world; but nowhere else, save on the poleward margins of the neighboring groups, can one find the long winter nights when the sun never comes above the horizon, or the long summer days when there is no darkness.

The polar night of the lower arctic latitudes, with its strange beauty, has been vividly described by the explorer Nansen:

The sky is like an enormous cupola, blue at the zenith, shading down into green, and then into lilac and violet at the edges. Over the ice fields there are cold violet-blue shadows, with lighter pink tints where a ridge here and there catches the last reflection of the vanished day. Up in the blue of the cupola shine the stars, speaking peace, as they always do, those unchanging friends. In the south stands a large red-yellow moon, encircled by a yellow ring and light golden clouds floating on the blue background. Presently the aurora borealis shakes over the vault of heaven its veil of glittering silver—changing now to yellow, now to green, now to red. It spreads, it contracts again, in restless change; next it breaks into waving, many-folded bands of shining silver, over which shoot billows of glittering rays, and then the glory vanishes. Presently it shimmers in tongues of flame over the very zenith, and then again it shoots a bright ray up from the horizon, until the whole melts away in the moonlight, and it is as though one heard the sigh of a departing spirit. Here and there are left a few waving streamers of light, vague as a foreboding—they are dust from the aurora's glittering cloak. But now it is growing again; new lightnings shoot up, and the endless game begins afresh. And all the time this utter stillness, impressive as the symphony of infinitude.*

How very different are these same scenes during the polar day! The colorful beauty of the night is lost in the white glare of the brilliant yet heatless sunshine. Instead of the awe-inspiring displays of light and shadow on white snow surfaces, the day brings pale skies, a horizon veiled in fogs, and a foreground of barren rocks and patches of ice or snow now pitilessly revealed in the daylight.

For the whole twenty-four hours of the earth's revolution the sun circles the horizon, bringing real warmth only to the slopes which are steep

*F. Nansen, *Farthest North* (New York, 1898), pp. 252–253.

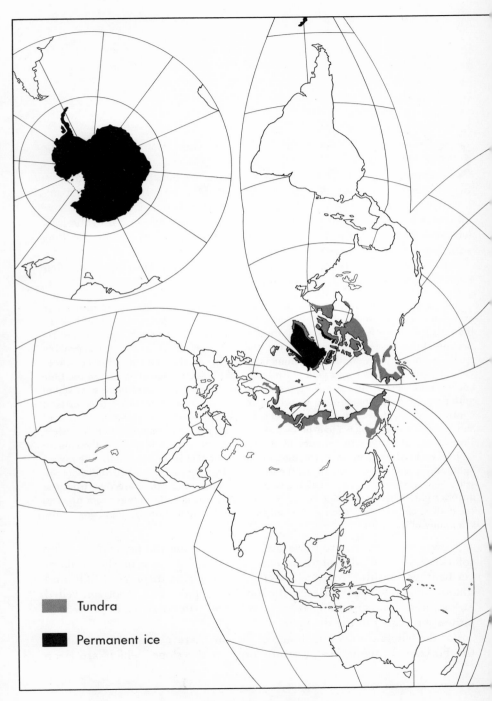

Map 82. The Polar Lands.

Tundra

Permanent ice

enough to receive its rays nearly perpendicularly. In the shade, on the north-facing slopes at noon, or on the south-facing slopes at midnight, the air is cold. Bare ground appears from beneath the melting snow, and the ice on the polar seas breaks up in jumbled masses. In the far north, sheltered places, warmed by the reflection from neighboring cliffs, are filled with a luxuriant cover of quick-flowering plants. Near the southern margins of the arctic regions, where the summer temperatures climb well above freezing, the land is covered with a mat of mosses, lichens, grasses, and flowering plants. Here only the surface thaws out, soaking this mat of vegetation like a sponge and providing breeding places for swarms of mosquitoes.

Except for the cool summers and cold, dark winters, the two polar regions of the earth are very different in character. The arctic is composed of a deep ocean basin, bounded by the northern coastal plains of North America and Eurasia, with their fringes of island clusters. Just the opposite condition is found in the antarctic; for here there is a continent five million or so square miles in area, larger than Europe, and bordered by the stormy southern oceans (Map 82). Whereas the arctic shores are sparsely inhabited by men, the Antarctic Continent is totally uninhabited.

The Habitat

VEGETATION AND CLIMATE

In many respects the polar lands resemble the dry lands. Both are deserts in the sense of being largely uninhabited and also in the sense of possessing a meager cover of vegetation. The one is a desert of drought; the other, a desert of cold. Both of them, moreover, are bordered by a margin of semi-desert, a transition zone that separates them from the world's forest lands. Around the dry deserts are the grasslands of Group VI; around the cold deserts are the tundras.

As in the dry lands, there are few places in the polar lands entirely without vegetation. Glaciers present to the eye a glittering white surface without vegetation cover; and there are many areas of bare rock. But even the bare rock, on closer examination, usually proves to support mosses and lichens and scattered plants.

Every Arctic traveller remembers his surprise and delight when for the first time in high latitudes he came on meadows of rich grasses, bright with tall, yellow buttercups, luxuriant saxifrages, violet cuckoo flowers, blue polemoniums, or many other flowers; moorlands purple with saxifrage as a Scottish hillside is with heather; peat bogs white with myriad tufts of waving cotton grass; dry banks with their hundreds of sturdy white and yellow poppies, clumps of red and yellow saxifrage, dryas, campions, an other blooms; or some wind-swept summit on which the Arctic poppy triumphantly flowered.*

The Tundra. The characteristic vegetation of the polar regions is the tundra; but the tundra itself, like the grasslands, is composed of transitional types. From the margins of the taiga, northward to the absolutely barren polar desert, three chief kinds of tundra are recognized: these are the *bush tundra,* the *grass tundra,* and the *desert tundra.*

The first of these is found on the edge of the taiga and in a few especially well-sheltered spots farther to the north. Here the flora is composed of dwarf trees, chiefly willow, birch, alder, and mountain ash. Where conditions are particularly favorable a scrub woodland of birch is found, as in southernmost Greenland; but mostly the tallest individuals rise no more than three feet above the ground. The bush tundra grades off rapidly into the broader zone of the grass tundra, which is composed of a nearly continuous mat of sedges, mosses, and lichens, mixed with bushes that lie prone on the ground. This grass tundra, like the other polar types, rests on a permanently frozen regolith; and when the surface thaws out during the summer the water does not drain away, but is soaked up by the spongy vegetation. Summer travel over these tundras is described by the expressive term *mushing.* Still farther poleward the grass tundra breaks up into detached "oases" in the sheltered hollows, separated by expanses of bare rock or regolith. This is the desert tundra.

The Animals of the Polar Lands.   In view of the severity of the polar winter, the richness and variety of the fauna of the arctic regions are remarkable. Many of the land animals of the taiga migrate northward onto the tundra during the summer months. The reindeer of Eurasia and the similar, but smaller, caribou of North America are the most important of these. Another large herbivore found far within the arctic is the musk ox, or ovibos, generally now surviving only in isolated herds which graze on the more luxuriant patches of desert tundra. Two small herbivora—the arctic hare and the lemming—are also widespread in the arctic.

Following the herds of reindeer, caribou, or musk ox are a number of predatory animals, such as the wolf and fox. Most of these carnivora, however, belong typically to the taiga fauna and are intruders in the polar lands. The drift ice of the polar sea or the immediate coastal margin is the habitat of the polar bear, preying chiefly on marine life; the seal; and the walrus.

Birds and insects are particularly numerous. Mosquitoes are probably present in greater numbers in summer over the tundra than anywhere else on earth and are a terrible plague to the human and animal inhabitants,

*R. N. Rudmose-Brown, *The Polar Regions* (New York, 1927), p. 112.

Tree line gives way to shrubs and then pure tundra plants (Mac's Foto Service).

although not as carriers of disease. Bees and butterflies perform their usual function of the fertilization of flowers. Flies are abundant, especially near human habitations. Attracted in part by this abundance of insect life, many a migrating bird in summer makes the tundra his goal. The rocky shores of the arctic seas provide breeding places for a great number of the birds well known in middle and even low latitudes. The land birds which remain in the regions during the winter include the ptarmigan, the snowy owl, the gerfalcon, the raven, and the snow bunting.

Sea life is rich. Although reptiles, amphibians, and fresh-water fish are either entirely absent or very rare, the inhabitants of the polar oceans are varied and numerous. The seal, the walrus, the whale, the narwhal, and the sea elephant are among the most typical forms of sea life.

In the antarctic regions a land fauna is practically nonexistent, although the sea life is abundant. The largest known land animal on the Antarctic Continent is a wingless mosquito, found in only one single protected locality. There are no land mammals; no land birds. Because of the absence of predatory animals, the penguins find conditions on the coasts and on the isolated islands of the southern oceans ideal as breeding places. These birds, unable to fly and awkward on the land, could scarcely exist in the presence of a land enemy.

The Polar Climates. These various zones of vegetation with their associated fauna correspond closely to the summer temperatures. All the polar climates average less than 50° in the warmest month. In the Northern

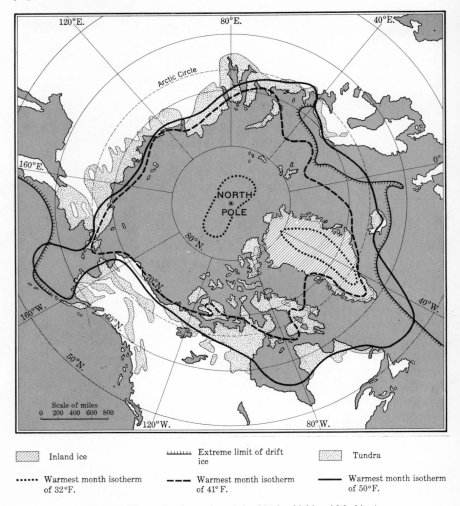

Map 83. The north polar regions (after Nordenskjold and Mecking).

Hemisphere this isotherm corresponds to the boundary between the taiga and the tundra. The continuous vegetation cover of the bush and grass tundras is found mostly within the regions that have warmest-month temperatures between 50° and 41° (Map 83). Where the temperatures drop below 41° in the warmest month, only the desert tundra can exist. The polar desert, including the areas covered by ice, corresponds with the places where the warmest month averages below 32° (in the Northern Hemisphere only Greenland and possibly a portion of Ellesmere Island).

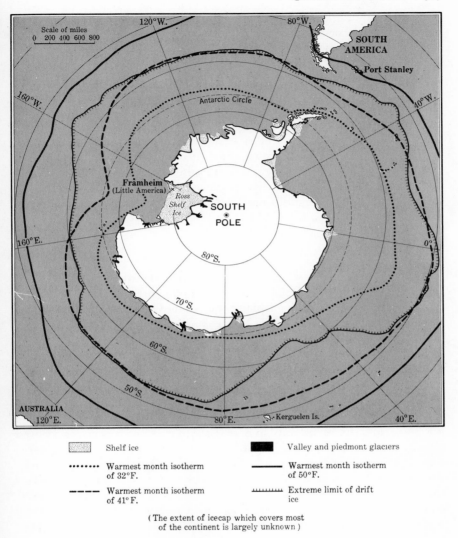

░░ Shelf ice	■ Valley and piedmont glaciers
•••••••• Warmest month isotherm of 32°F.	——— Warmest month isotherm of 50°F.
----- Warmest month isotherm of 41°F.	⊥⊥⊥⊥⊥ Extreme limit of drift ice

(The extent of icecap which covers most
of the continent is largely unknown)

Map 84. The south polar regions (after Nordenskjold and Mecking).

In the Southern Hemisphere very little of the Antarctic Continent extends far enough northward to reach the isotherm of 32°. Only in these
few places is any vegetation found (Map 84). A very peculiar type of
polar climate exists in southernmost South America and some of the
islands of the South Atlantic and South Pacific Oceans. Here, although
the warmest month averages under 50°, the coldest month is over 32°. This

is an extreme of marine conditions—the result of great expanses of open sea. Tierra del Fuego, in spite of its position with reference to the isotherm of 50° for the warmest month, is covered by a broadleaf forest, mostly of antarctic beech.

The polar climates are not necessarily colder in winter than are the climates of higher middle latitudes. The lowest air temperature ever recorded at the surface of the earth was observed at an altitude of 11,220 feet, near the South Pole (−126.9°). But close to sea level the temperatures are not so low as those of Siberia. From both Greenland and Antarctica, especially the latter, come great outblasts of cold air that move at high velocities and blow along great quantities of snow. Mawson names the Antarctic Continent "the home of the blizzard." The neighboring oceans in the higher middle latitudes of the Southern Hemisphere are among the stormiest in the world.

SURFACE FEATURES

The surface features of the polar lands include all varieties of relief, from low, marshy coastal plains to high ice plateaus and glaciated mountains. In the Northern Hemisphere the Arctic Ocean is bordered for the most part by the Eurasian and North American coastal plains (Plates 1 and 13, pp. 553 and 570–571). These lowlands are interrupted by the Urals, a chain of low mountains extending into the polar ocean through Novaya Zemlya, and by the highlands of Greenland and the neighboring islands. Part of the Canadian arctic archipelago is composed of low-lying detached pieces of the North American coastal plain, underlain by horizontal stratified rocks; but the easternmost coasts which face Greenland, notably of Ellesmere and Baffin islands and of Labrador, stand up as ice-scoured hills and low mountains still partly covered by glaciers. The ice-free coasts of Greenland are similarly composed of heavily glaciated uplands. Iceland and Svalbard are also mountainous and harbor small accumulations of ice. But none of these existing glaciers is so extensive as the inland ice which masks the greater part of Greenland (Map 85). In the Southern Hemisphere the continent of Antarctica is covered by the world's largest existing icecap.

Landforms. In contrast to surfaces exposed to a tropical rainy climate, which are attacked dominantly by chemical decomposition and are speedily covered by a thick mantle of fine-textured regolith, the surfaces in the polar regions are attacked dominantly by physical disintegration, the exposed rock being shattered and broken into angular fragments by frost action. Nowhere else, except on the summits of high mountains above the timber lines, is frost action so potent a force in fracturing the rock surfaces.

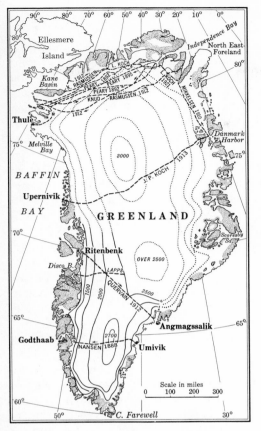

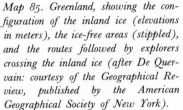

Map 85. Greenland, showing the configuration of the inland ice (elevations in meters), the ice-free areas (stippled), and the routes followed by explorers crossing the inland ice (after De Quervain: courtesy of the Geographical Review, published by the American Geographical Society of New York).

The lower slopes of cliffs broken up in this way are covered with accumulations of rock fragments, much as in the deserts. Plateau surfaces not covered with ice are mantled with angular blocks of rock loosened by frost action, forming a very rough surface known as a *rock field*. In the course of time such rock fields may be modified by continued frost action until a coarse, gravelly regolith is produced.

Erosion is carried on by processes very different from those of the rainy lands. Even more than in the case of the dry lands, running water is limited to the exotic rivers. River valleys exist, to be sure, along the courses of the north-flowing rivers of Canada and Siberia. Except for summer streams pouring from the front of melting glaciers, however, other streams in the polar regions are poorly developed. As a result the water from the melting snow and ice during the arctic summer forms extensive ponds and marshes on the surface.

Glacial erosion is at a maximum.   Where the formerly more extensive glaciers of the ice age passed through mountain valleys they produced typical glacial troughs.   Near the coast, where the valleys were deepened below sea level by ice scour, the drowned glacial troughs are known as *fiords*. However, while the ice had the effect of smoothing the hills and deepening the valleys, it seems to have had little effect on high-level plateaus; in fact, it seems to have preserved them from weathering.   The high-level surfaces of Labrador and Norway are little touched by erosion; instead, they are mantled with rock fields apparently of postglacial origin.

Along the coasts a feature common in the polar regions is the *strand flat*. This is a marine terrace bordered on the landward side by an abrupt sea cliff and extending seaward in a fringe of rounded, polished islets known as *skerries*.   In some places the strand flat broadens out to ten or twelve miles in width; in other places it may be very narrow or entirely lacking. The flat-topped rock ledges and the partially submerged skerries are persistent elements of the arctic coastal landscapes of the hilly or mountainous sections.

In addition to the landforms produced by glacial action, there are also vast lowlands which were never ice-covered (Map 76).   These are monotonously flat and poorly drained.

The Occupance

Man in the polar regions maintains his existence only by continuous effort.   Along with the driest deserts, these regions are among the world's least favorable habitats; and along with the deserts, the polar lands have been the least penetrated by Occidental settlement.   When Occidentals did enter these regions they found two chief native cultures, and the patterns of population distribution developed by these contrasted modes of occupance were quite distinct.   The Eskimos, chiefly of North America, were the only people who established themselves permanently in the arctic lands.   Since their occupance was based on the hunting of the seal they were nomadic or seminomadic, and they never placed their villages far from the seacoast.   On the other hand, the Eurasian tribes, whose occupance was based on the domesticated reindeer, were pastoral nomads, living on the tundras only during the summers and seeking refuge in the forests during the winter months.   Their summer villages were placed back from the coast.   Occidental contacts with these peoples at first were largely through the activities of traders, explorers, miners, and missionaries, and more recently have come from the establishment of air bases and from other military activities.   The result has been the virtual annihilation of these native cultures.

The population of the polar regions is entirely limited to the Northern

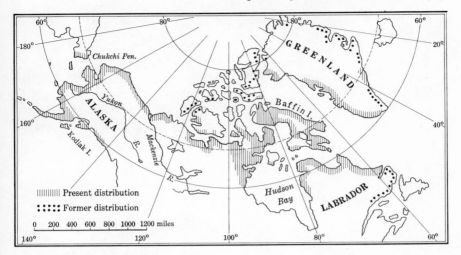

Map 86. The maximum distribution of the Eskimo culture, with an indication of the lands from which the Eskimos have withdrawn (from Ludwig Mecking, Die Polander, *Leipzig, 1925).*

Hemisphere. The great Antarctic Continent is surrounded by a stormy, ice-filled ocean which has so effectively barred the access of man that until the airplane could be used for exploration large parts of its coast were unknown.

OCCUPANCE BY THE ESKIMO CULTURE

The Eskimos occupied the margins of the polar seas from the extreme northeast of Siberia across northern North America to eastern Greenland and Labrador. Their present distribution, and the whole territory over which the signs of Eskimo occupance have been found, are shown on the map (Map 86). Over these many miles of arctic coast there are scattered some 50,000 Eskimos; of these nearly 23,000 are in Greenland and nearly 16,000 are in Alaska.*

The Eskimo culture represented an amazing adaptation to the harsh conditions of arctic living. Agriculture was entirely lacking, and very few of the products of the plant world were utilized in any way. The seal provided the basic support; from this animal came clothing, food, implements, and even fuel. Only a very few small tribes of Eskimos lived inland and depended on the migrations of the caribou. Hunting was a serious business, for, in spite of a high degree of skill and almost continuous effort, game was

* G. H. T. Kimble and D. Good (editors), *Geography of the Northlands,* (New York, 1955).

Eskimos in their kayaks along the coast of Labrador (Philip Gendreau).

not always plentiful and starvation was the consequence of failure. The best season of the year for seal-hunting was the winter, except for the darkest period in December. The surface of the polar sea is frozen, and travel long distances by dog sled was relatively easy. The Eskimos learned that if the nearer hunting grounds were visited too frequently the game would be driven away; during the winter, therefore, they frequently traveled for weeks at a time to distant places where seals were reported to be plentiful.

The seal, however, had to be supplemented with other game. Numberous sea animals were hunted during the summer with the aid of the kayak, or skin boat. At this season also the large land animals, especially the caribou and the musk ox, were sought; although their meat was less satisfactory than that of the seal or the walrus, owing to the small amount of fat it contains, nevertheless it provided a pleasant variety and a much needed supplementary supply to be "cached" as a provision against later want. Birds and birds' eggs were also much prized as offering a change in the steady diet of seal meat. Yet throughout the year the Eskimos ate little else but meat: meat eaten cooked but more often eaten raw, or frozen, or rotten; meat served without salt.

Eskimo Settlements. The nomadic or seminomadic type of life was essential in such a culture. Migrations of the game were closely followed by migrations of people. Only in the places where water and ice conditions were especially favorable for the seal—so favorable that a dependable supply of that animal was certain year after year—could the Eskimos become in any way sedentary. Even the land animals in the territory of Eskimo occupance have been the cause of migrations. The absence of both sea game and land game from the outermost islands of the Canadian arctic archipelago was reflected in the absence of Eskimos from this region.

Yet the Eskimos were not without attachment to certain sites. During the winter they gathered together in villages near the water known to be frequented by seals.* The immediate locations of these villages depended on such features as ease of approach over the sea ice, protection from high winds, supplies of drinking water (usually from stranded icebergs), and other local factors. In all the centuries during which the Eskimos occupied the shores of the polar seas, they returned to these same places again and again. The stone houses used during the winter were first built before the memory of the oldest inhabitants; they had been repeatedly abandoned and reoccupied. The movements of these people, therefore, were between points more or less definitely fixed.

During the summer the Eskimo became more completely nomadic. With his skin tent he traveled along the coast to visit the summer sealing grounds or the cliffs on which great numbers of birds breed. Small groups, too, traveled inland to hunt the caribou and the musk ox, so that at this season the distribution of people was less rigidly attached to the coast or to any particular sites.

Contacts with Occidentals. Contacts with Europeans and Americans have completely transformed the traditional Eskimo culture in all but the most remote places. The Eskimos have been described for years in elementary geography texts as an example of the close adjustment of a way of living to the meager resources of the polar lands. The Eskimo culture belonged to the Stone Age, but it was one in which a certain few skills were developed to perfection. When contacts with European traders and mis-

---

* See the description of the life of the "Polar Eskimo," the northernmost of the world's human inhabitants, who occupied the peninsula of Thule in western Greenland north of latitude 76° N., in W. Elmer Ekblaw, "The Material Response of the Polar Eskimo to Their Far Arctic Environment," *Annals of the Association of American Geographers*, Vol. 17 (1927), pp. 147–198, and Vol. 18 (1928), pp. 1–24.

Native dwelling north of the Arctic Circle in Alaska (Sawders, from Cushing).

sionaries brought the rifle to the Eskimos so that they could hunt the seal much more effectively than with a spear or harpoon, the first result was an unprecedented abundance of food. Hunting the land animals in summer was also made easier. The Eskimos seemed to be well off indeed. After a time, however, the seals began to leave their accustomed waters. The Eskimos had no product of great value that they could sell to the traders. The seal on which the Eskimos depended for food, clothing, and heat is the hair seal. (The furs used for making sealskin coats come entirely from the large herd of pelagic "fur seals"—*Callorhinus alascanus*—which returns every year to breed on the Pribilof Islands, off Alaska.) When the hair seals were killed off too rapidly by hunters with rifles, the Eskimos could no longer occupy their arctic homes. Here is a case where a technical change resulted in a decrease in the habitability of an area. The Eskimos began to decline rapidly in number so that by 1920 there were probably not more than 33,000 of these people left.

Now the process of cultural change has gone a step further. Some individuals among the Eskimos have had a capacity for making a fundamental change in their way of living. Not every person can give up traditional ways and learn entirely new ways; but among every people, even the most primitive, there are some who can do this. In Greenland the Eskimos have moved into the settlements of the ancient Norse and the Danes, in many cases have intermarried, and are today scarcely to be distinguished from other Greenlanders. Likewise, many native Indians in the United States are no longer distinguishable from other Americans.

OCCUPANCE BY THE EURASIAN CULTURES

Probably the whole Eurasian tundra does not support more than thirty thousand people, and during the winter the population is much less than this. The various peoples of the taiga, chiefly the Samoyeds and the Chukchi, who have domesticated the reindeer, migrate northward with these animals during the summer, much as the wild herds of reindeer used to migrate and as the caribou of North America still migrate. These nomadic peoples have no permanent villages, either in summer or in winter, but move their herds from place to place to take advantage of the slow-growing pasturage. When the snow begins to fly, they move into the taiga and abandon their skin tents in favor of pits dug in the ground. These Siberian tribes are therefore only partly dependent on the polar habitat. Their diet of meat is supplemented by fish from the rivers and by berries, roots, and nuts from the forest. Furthermore, the possession of do-

Winter travel by dog sled in the Siberian tundra (Sovfoto).

mestic animals frees them from the fortunes of the chase. They are not so close to the margin of existence as the Eskimos used to be, nor are they so harmoniously adjusted to the conditions of arctic living.

Contacts with the European traders have been as detrimental to most of these people as in the case of the Eskimos. Among all the Siberian forest and tundra tribes, only the Yakuts are increasing in number. Apparently none of these cultures can survive except in greatly modified form— perhaps organized for the production of a meat surplus from the reindeer herds in exchange for which the white man's industrial and agricultural products can be purchased.

OCCIDENTAL OCCUPANCE

There is little to record concerning the occupance of the polar regions by Europeans and Americans. While these regions have attracted parties of explorers since classical antiquity, little permanent settlement by white men has ever taken place. The trading posts, which are the only permanently inhabited spots along the Eurasian arctic littoral, are engaged in the handling of the products of the taiga (chiefly furs) and are located at the mouths of the north-flowing rivers. Igarka and Noril'sk on the lower Yenisei River are lumber exporting ports. A number of similar posts in North America have been established within the polar lands, but they are not supported by polar products.

Whaling and mining have also attracted Occidentals to these regions and have led to the establishment of settlements. The whaling industry, so important before the days of mineral oil, shifted from the vicinity of Svalbard to the more remote parts of the world as the whales were killed in increasing numbers. Modern mechanical equipment threatens the final exhaustion of this resource. Until recently the whaling industry required land bases for the extraction of the oil, and such bases were established where protected harbors provided shelter for the whaling fleet. A number of these stations were located in the arctic, as at Herschel Island off the mouth of the Mackenzie River, and in the antarctic, as at Stanley, on the Falkland Islands. With the invention of the modern whaling ships, which are, in reality, floating packing plants where the carcasses are turned into a variety of products, the land stations have declined in importance.

Mining too has supported more or less permanent settlement in a few localities in the north. The coal mines of Svalbard are perhaps the most important, although gold in Alaska continues to provide a somewhat unsteady basis for such communities as Nome.

A major problem of Occidental occupance is the maintenance of lines of transportation. This is a matter of great concern to the Soviet Union. Only the westernmost part of the Soviet Arctic coast remains ice-free

A landing strip on the Mackenzie River near Aklavik, Northwest Territories (National Film Board of Canada).

throughout the year.   Ships can sail around the northern tip of Norway to the port of Murmansk even in winter; and with the aid of ice-breakers a channel can be kept open all winter to Arkhangelsk.   The part of the Arctic Ocean into which the Ob and Yenisei rivers empty has an open season from July to October because it is protected from the Arctic ice pack by islands.   But east of the Taymyr Peninsula (about longitude 100° E.) all the way to Bering Strait the ice pack is driven against the shore by north winds, and prevents all navigation except during a two- or three-month period between July and September.   Soviet ships make this trip regularly each summer, providing connection with the ports along the lower courses of the Siberian rivers.   But even in summer the ships must go in a convoy following the new nuclear-powered ice breaker and accompanied by airplanes and helicopters to spot the openings in the ice.

The airplane now makes any part of the arctic or antarctic regions more easily accessible than it ever could be by land travel.   Regular commercial air routes cross the polar regions, but an examination of the arctic regions on a globe shows that the actual air routes connecting major concentrations of people cross only the margins of the polar lands.   The air routes from the United States to eastern Asia pass over southern Alaska; those from eastern United States and Canada to western Europe may pass over the southernmost tip of Greenland.   However, two vital needs—the need of defense in the arctic regions, and the need of scientific observation in both the arctic and antarctic—have resulted in the establishment of permanent or semipermanent settlements in the polar regions. A system of military air bases and radar warning nets stretches for 3000 miles across the arctic regions of North America, and it may be assumed that similar systems have been built in Northern Siberia. A large number of bases have been set up in the polar regions for the observation of meteorological phenomena and other matters of interest to students of the physics of the earth.

Summary

The Occidental peoples have not yet found a resource by which permanent polar settlement can "pay its way." Hitherto, occupance has been based on resources of other regions seeking an outlet through the arctic, or on temporary extractive industries, such as whaling and mining. Agriculture being physically impossible, permanent settlement would have to rest on pastoral activities, probably those associated with the reindeer. But the permanence of the arctic pastures under heavy grazing has yet to be demonstrated. The native cultures, so intimately adapted to the region, have been disorganized by the introduction of Occidental tools and foods, and are threatened with annihilation. On the whole the landscapes of the polar lands have been modified by human occupance to a lesser degree than those of any other group.

The Mountain Lands

MOST PEOPLE THINK they know what a mountain is. Yet when we compare such relatively small and inconspicuous features as the Turtle Mountains of North Dakota with such imposing heights as the Berkshire Hills of Massachusetts, we find that we cannot depend on popular impression and terminology for our definition of mountains. The dictionary says that a mountain must rise to sufficient elevation and with sufficient abruptness to stand out conspicuously from its surroundings; also that it must have a relatively small summit area, as opposed to a plateau, which has a large summit area. This definition admits of considerable range of interpretation, for the feature which would stand out conspicuously on the plains of North Dakota would remain quite incidental in a hilly land such as New England. Nor is elevation above sea level a safe guide to the definition; for there are many examples of mountainous surfaces at low elevations, and many plains which rise gradually to high elevations. As a matter of fact, any definition must be arbitrary because no sharp distinction exists in nature between high hills and low mountains. There is a complete series of steps from almost featureless plains to plains with many steep slopes but of slight relief, to low hills, to high hills, to low mountains, and finally to the highest mountains. Only in certain places do mountain fronts stand imposingly above extensive plains. For the purposes of classification in this book we have adopted as a working definition of "conspicuous" the concept that the elevation must be sufficient to bring about a vertical differentiation of the vegetation cover. We shall explain this definition and its limitations more fully as we proceed.

The mountain lands differ from the other eight groups of habitats in several important ways. In the first place, the chief criterion for the recognition of mountain areas is the surface configuration, whereas the other groups are recognized primarily by the various kinds of vegetation and climate. The characteristic features of mountain landscapes are associated with ruggedness of terrain. According to the definition we have adopted for mountains, vertical differentiation of vegetation types is an essential characteristic. The occupance also is commonly arranged in layers. In other words, the major landscape differences are found in Group IX by ascending or descending the slopes; not, as in the other groups, by traveling horizontally north, south, east, or west. Another characteristic of mountain geography is the intricacy of the patterns of distribution as com-

Map 87. *The Mountain Lands.*

pared with the relative simplicity of the patterns developed on more level lands. To follow the winding course of an isotherm, for example, through the valleys and around the ridges of a mountain region requires a much larger-scale map than is necessary in order to observe the same degree of accuracy in plotting the relatively simple course of the isotherm on a level surface. Unlike the monotonously similar landscapes over large areas on the plains, the mountain landscapes are spotty; they are arranged in a mosaic of small units, each contrasted sharply with the surroundings, resembling the patterns on a crazy quilt. Still another characteristic of mountain lands is the difficulty of moving over their rugged surfaces or steep slopes. As a result these regions are isolated and offer places of refuge for the survival of relict flora or fauna or even cultures; they are areas of survival of ancient ideas and modes of life, not areas where new ideas originate. As a further result of the difficulty of movement over them, mountains play the role of barriers to the spread over the earth of plants, animals, and man. Mountains cover 12 per cent of the earth's land area, and of the world's population about 12 per cent occupies the regions of this group (Map 86).

Distribution of Mountains. The arrangement of high mountains on the surface of the earth was described in the introduction to this book (Map 2, and pp. 6–10). The chains of mountains tie the continents together and differentiate the ocean floors into submarine regions. Like all surface features, however—and unlike the climatic features—mountains are irregularly placed. The regions of Group IX do not appear on the diagram showing the generalized global pattern of habitats (Figure 12, p 424) because these features, along with the outlines of the continent, are unique for each land mass. They constitute interruptions of the generalized global pattern of climatic features. The student who would develop a clear concept regarding the global arrangement of habitats will memorize the unique surface patterns of each continent, as he would memorize the distinguishing features of his friends' faces. The actual distribution of the regions of Group IX is shown on Plates 1–5 and 13, pp. 553–558, and 570–571.

The Habitat

SURFACE FEATURES

Of fundamental importance in producing the intricacy of the distribution patterns in mountain regions are the surface features. Mountain surfaces are of the greatest variety not only in their topographic details but also in their broader aspects. Nevertheless, in spite of this variety, certain characteristic designs are repeated in almost all the world's high-mountain

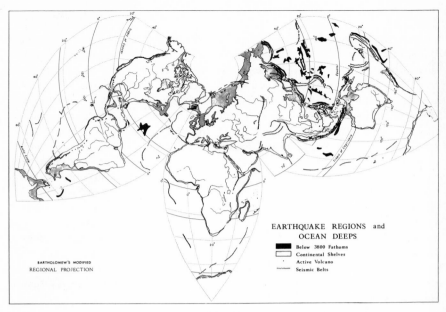

EARTHQUAKE REGIONS and
OCEAN DEEPS

■ Below 3800 Fathoms
□ Continental Shelves
· Active Volcano
~~~ Seismic Belts

BARTHOLOMEW'S MODIFIED
REGIONAL PROJECTION

Map 88.

regions. For example, there is a tendency for the ranges to take on an arcuate, or festoon, arrangement. Commonly, also, the mountain arcs are backed on their concave sides by more or less extensive tectonic basins; and off the middle of the convex sides there are usually rift depressions, in many cases ocean "deeps."

These general patterns, characteristic of all mountain regions, are the result of the common geologic processes that produce mountains. Over long periods of geologic time the breaking apart and drifting of the continental masses have produced pressures and strains in the rocks of the earth's crust (Map 1). The rock layers are crushed, folded, wrinkled, broken, and pushed up or dropped down along certain zones of crustal weakness. These are the zones where the chains of mountains appear, where volcanic activity is common, and where earthquakes may be expected (Map 88). The various kinds of rock structure, or tectonic forms, are discussed in Appendix C (pp. 489–515).

As soon as rock structures are lifted above sea level they are exposed to the various processes of destruction or denudation which, if continued,

long enough, could wear the uplifted surfaces down again to plains (pene-
plains or pediplanes) close to sea level. These processes are also discussed
in outline in Appendix C, and are made the subject of more intensive
study in courses on geology and geomorphology. Exposure to the weather
results in the breaking of the surface of the rock into fragments, so
that eventually a mantle of loose rock debris is formed, which we have previously described as regolith. Rain falling on the upraised surface runs off
or sinks into the regolith depending on the porosity of the regolith, the rate
of the rainfall, and the protecting cover of vegetation. The landforms that
are produced by running water, solution, gravity, freezing and thawing, and
other agents of denudation are the ones that characterize the surfaces of
mountain regions today. Of greatest importance is the action of running
water in cutting valleys on these upraised portions of the earth's crust.

There are many other processes, however, that produce strongly marked
surface features in places where they have been in operation. Glaciers
form on high mountains wherever the snowfall of winter is so deep that it
does not all melt off during the summer. They are therefore most common in climates with heavy precipitation and cool summers. The climates
of higher middle latitudes on the continental west coasts fill this description most fully, and in these regions glacial landforms are most conspicuous;
but even on the equator, if one climbs high enough, one finds the mountain-
tops permanently covered with snow. The various landforms produced in
mountain areas as a result of glaciation are shown in a series of block
diagrams in Appendix C (p. 509). Since the ice was everywhere more extensive in the Ice Age, these various forms are to be observed where
glaciers no longer exist. The places where mountains or mountainous
escarpments border the sea, and where the ice-deepened valleys are
drowned, are today clearly visible, even on small-scale maps, as fiorded
coasts. The map of a part of the coast of South Chile (Map 89) illustrates
this feature. Similar coasts are to be observed in British Columbia and
South Alaska, in Norway, in Labrador, and in New Zealand. Glacial
landforms in the interior are similar to those near the coast except that
more of the valley bottoms and sides are visible. Long, narrow marginal
lakes, however, are commonly found along the edges of glaciated mountains, such as those of the Italian piedmont, or the eastern front of
the Rocky Mountains in Montana (Glacier National Park). Some of the
world's most spectacular mountain scenery is to be found where glaciers
have had a chance to sculpture the surface.

Of the other processes of denudation that work on the sloping land of
mountainous areas we need only mention the work of gravity which produces rock slides and avalanches. In mountain regions where steep valley
slopes are subjected to soaking and drying with the passing seasons, avalanches are common, and the scars of ancient slides are to be observed in

A glacier on Susten Pass, in the Swiss Alps.

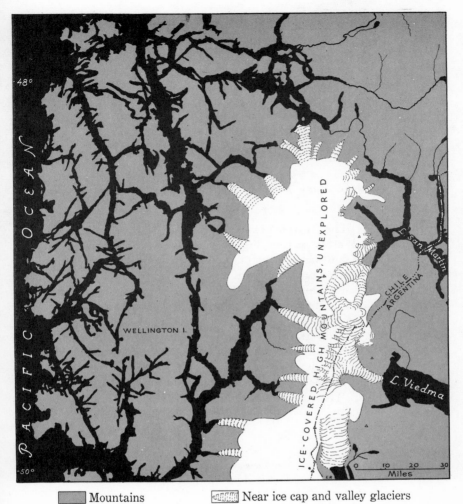

| | Mountains | | Near ice cap and valley glaciers |

Map 89. A near icecap in the southern Andes, with detail of the fiorded coast of South Chile (from the Map of Hispanic America, published by the American Geographical Society of New York).

many places. The characteristic landforms produced by avalanches are suggested by the drawing (Figure 6).

All these many kinds of landforms are infinitely varied by the underlying rock structures. In some mountain areas the structures are produced by simple folding (as in the case of the Jura Mountains, shown in the *a* cross section Figure 7). Most high mountain regions, however, are more com-

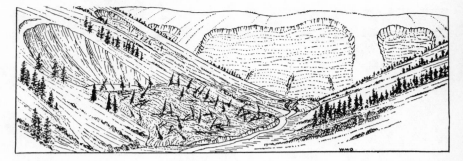

Figure 6. Landforms produced by landslides (reproduced from a drawing in W. M. Davis, "The Lakes of California," California Journal of Mines and Geology, Vol. 29 (1933), pp. 175–236.

plex than this. The Alps, for example, are tightly folded and faulted (as shown in the *b* cross section Figure 7). Other mountain regions are formed by block faulting, in which large masses or blocks of the earth's crust are broken and lifted or dropped in relation to bordering blocks. Rocks, therefore, are broken and contorted into very complex structures, and in many places these structures are masked by a covering of volcanic material—old lava flows or deep accumulations of ash. Each kind of rock formation differs in its resistance to the forces of denudation. Some rocks are weak and easily eroded; others are resistant. As the processes of denudation work on the underlying structures the work goes forward rapidly on weak rocks, whereas resistant rocks stand out boldly as cliffs or still uneroded heights. The result is the extraordinary complexity of mountain terrain.

Figure 7. (a) Cross section of the Jura Mountains; (b) cross section of the Alps (generalized from A. Heim, Geologie der Schweiz, Leipzig, 1919–1921, Vol. I, Table 23; Vol. II, Table 18.

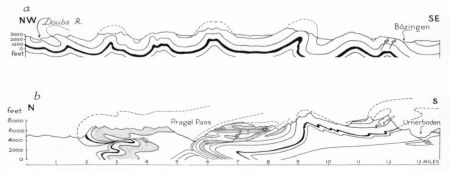

Figure 8. Block diagram illustrating characteristic intermont basins.

In many of the mountain regions of the world, areas which are nearly flat or gently sloping occur in the midst of steeper and higher surfaces. These are intermont basins, which are distinguished on the plates (Plates 1–5, 13, pp. 553–558, and 570–571) by solid black. The block diagram (Figure 8) suggests two ways in which intermont basins can form: on the left where a downfold of the rock structures forms a basin; on the right where a depression between two mountain blocks is partly filled with alluvial material washed down from the higher slopes. Intermont basins are formed upstream from places where the rivers pass through resistant rock formations and where, as a consequence, the downward cutting of the valley is retarded. They are formed where volcanoes block earlier river-cut valleys with flows of lava or falls of ash. In these and many other ways intermont basins are formed, some of large extent, others too small to show on the maps.

It is important to notice that the major ranges of mountains in the world in most places do not form the divides between river basins. A close examination of the maps will reveal example after example of rivers that rise outside of mountain areas and pass through the mountains in gorges. An outstanding example is the Danube, where it passes through the Iron Gate on the border of Romania and Yugoslavia. The Yangtze and the Columbia are two other examples among many. Such rivers are said to be *antecedent* because they were established in their courses before the mountains rose across them, and as the mountains were slowly lifted up they were able to continue their downward cutting. Th Amazon is an example of a river which was unable to maintain its course because the Andes rose so fast; as a result it turned and found a way out to the Atlantic, but its valley is still widest along the eastern front of the Andes and gets narrower downstream. At Obidos the floodplain is only twenty miles wide, below which place it becomes wider again (Map 16).

CLIMATE AND VEGETATION

Climatic distribution in mountain areas is also extremely complicated. Although most of the major types of climate found in other parts of the world occur in mountain regions, the significance of these types in Group IX is largely obscured by the many important local variations. Nowhere else are "local climates" developed in such large numbers, and nowhere else do they exert such a critical effect on the character of the landscape. Yet this seeming confusion of climatic distribution can be understood through the interplay of two of the principles of mountain geography: the principle of vertical differentiation, based on the effects of change in altitude; and the principle of spotty distribution, based on the effects of different exposures to sunlight and of differences in rainfall.

Vertical Differentiation.   The most important climatic element leading to the vertical differentiation of landscapes in mountain areas is temperature.   Generally speaking, lower temperatures may be found either by traveling along the surface of the earth toward the poles or by ascending vertically above the earth.   However, one would have to travel many miles along the surface to find as great a contrast of temperature as is concentrated in only a few miles of vertical distance (Figure 9).   The isotherms that reach sea level in high or middle latitudes rise steeply toward the margins of the low latitudes, gaining their greatest altitude between 20° and 30°, especially over the hot deserts.   Although sagging somewhat over the equator, they remain high between the tropics.   So it is that mountains on the equator rising to fifteen thousand feet can reach all the average temperatures that are spread over the thousands of miles of horizontal distance between the equatorial and polar regions.

We must not suppose, however, that because a place at a considerable

Figure 9. Vertical arrangement of the average annual isotherms (after Clayton and Ramanathan).

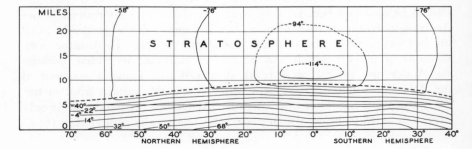

elevation in the low latitudes has the same average temperature as a place at sea level in middle or high latitudes, it also has the same climate. At high altitudes on tropical mountains none of the climates of middle and high latitudes are found. There are none of the cyclonic storms or associated weather changes which are essential characteristics of the middle latitudes. Furthermore, with increase of altitude, there is a decrease of the range of temperature between summer and winter. This effect is most noticeable in the low latitudes, where temperature ranges are small even at sea level. The average monthly temperatures at Quito illustrate this condition (Appendix F). Quito is located nearly on the equator in the Andes of Ecuador at an elevation of 9350 feet. Its average annual temperature is 54.60, but its range between the average of the coldest and warmest months is no more than 0.3°. In middle-latitude and high-latitude mountains, on the other hand, the ranges of temperature are not so low as in the tropics, and seasonal change is an important feature.

Snow Lines and Tree Lines. As a result of these vertical distributions of temperature, almost all the landscape features which are affected by temperature not only have horizontal limits bounding their areas of distribution but also vertical limits. One very important altitude limit is the snow line, the boundary of the area covered by permanent snow or ice. Horizontally, the areas of permanent snow and ice are restricted to the polar regions; but the vertical limits are reached by the higher mountain summits even on the equator. As in the case of all altitude limits that are governed in whole or in part by temperature, the snow line corresponds in pattern to the vertical arrangement of the isotherms (Figure 9). It rises to its greatest elevation near the margins of the low latitudes and declines to its lowest elevation in the high latitudes. Near the equator it is necessary to climb about 15,000 feet to reach the snow line—a little higher than this on Mount Chimborazo near Quito, and a little lower on Mount Ruwenzori in Uganda. Southward along the Andes the snow line rises to about 16,000 feet near Lima and to more than 20,000 feet at the Tropic of Capicorn in Northern Chile. South of this, however, it drops rapidly. In Middle Chile it is between 11,000 and 14,000 feet. In Tierra del Fuego it lies a little below 2500 feet. The snow line, however, is obedient not only to temperature but also to snowfall and other things. At any given latitude it lies somewhat lower on the wetter sides of the mountains and somewhat higher on the drier sides, and it descends farther on shady slopes and remains higher up on sunny slopes.

The altitude limits of the various types of vegetation also correspond to the pattern of vertical temperature distribution. Roughly, the same succession of types is found in ascending mountains near the equator as is found on proceeding poleward along the continental east coasts. The tropical forests occupy the lower slopes; higher up are the mixed forests of broadleaf types; and beyond the upper limit of trees but below the snow line is a zone of alpine meadows not unlike the tundra of the polar margins. Conifers do not appear at higher altitudes south of Nicaragua. Since tree lines are generally higher in rainy mountains and lower in dry mountains, whereas snow lines vary in just the opposite way, it follows that the zone of alpine meadows is widest in dry regions and narrowest where the rainfall is heavy.

As far as vegetation and other forms of life are concerned, the vertical differentiation reaches a maximum in the low latitudes. Here we find the greatest variety of zones. Vertical differentiation remains a conspicuous feature of mountains in the middle latitudes, but it disappears altogether in the high latitudes. The criteria suggested in the introduction to this chapter for the recognition of "conspicuousness" in mountains can be used, therefore, only in the middle and low latitudes, not in the polar zone (Figure 10).

Other Climatic Elements. Certain of the other elements of climate act to reinforce the effects of temperature in producing a vertical differentiation. Rainfall, for instance, develops something of a vertical zoning. Up to six thousand or seven thousand feet in the middle latitudes, and somewhat higher in the low latitudes, the rainfall on mountain slopes increases; but above this zone of maximum fall the amounts diminish. At higher altitudes the specific humidity of the air becomes very low. Unbroken ranges of high mountains are very effective barriers to the passage of moisture.

Pressure is another climatic element which decreases with increasing altitude. Its results, however, are of less significance than those of temperature and rainfall. At elevations above twelve thousand or fifteen thousand feet many human beings are affected by altitude sickness, and at very high altitudes the difficulty of breathing forms a distinct limit to occupance. Decreased pressure also lowers the boiling point of water so that the cooking of foods by boiling takes much longer, or may become altogether impossible without pressure cookers. When Marco Polo observed this phenomenon in his journey across high Tibet, he explained it as the result of the low temperatures. "Even the fire," he wrote, "is not hot enough to cook foods."

Spotty Distribution Patterns. The vertical differentiation of mountain landscapes, resulting from the variation of these several factors with altitude, is greatly modified by the irregularity of the terrain. Steep slopes oriented at various angles to the sun's rays; narrow valleys with winding courses; mountain-rimmed bits of flattish valley floor or delta plain: all these features combine to add complexity to the otherwise simple arrangement of things in vertical zones.

Figure 10. Diagrammatic cross section through the mountains of North and South America, showing vertical zones of vegetation (modified from J. Paul Goode).

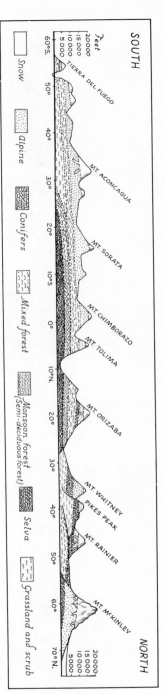

Looking up the Vorder-Rhine Valley in Switzerland. Note the contrast between the ubac and the adret (Swiss National Tourist Office).

Local contrast in exposure to sunlight is one of the important causes of spotty landscape patterns. Slopes which face toward the sun not only absorb much more heat than those which receive the sun's rays more obliquely, but they also enjoy many more hours of sunshine. In the Northern Hemisphere the north sides of east and west valleys, such as the upper Rhône Valley in Switzerland, are much warmer than the south sides at the same altitude, and these temperature differences are reflected in striking landscape contrasts—contrasts in natural vegetation, in occupance, and even in landforms. So great are these differences that the two sides have been distinguished by the names *adret*, meaning "sunny side" and *ubac*, meaning "shady side."*

*"The matter of sunlight is so dominant that each dialect of European mountain peoples has a set of terms for sunny side and shady side. Thus the German, *Sonnenseite, Schattenseite; Sonnenberg, Schattenberg;* French, *adret* (Latin, *ad directum*), *ubac* (Latin, *ad opacum*); *endroit, envers;* Italian, *indritto, inverso; adritto, opaco;* Catalan, *sola, baga; solana, ubach; soula umbaga.* One may so name a village or a shady portion of a village, as Envers de Fontenille or Inverso Pinusca." From R. Peattie, "Height Limits of Mountain Economies," *Geographical Review,* Vol. 21 (1931), pp. 415–428.

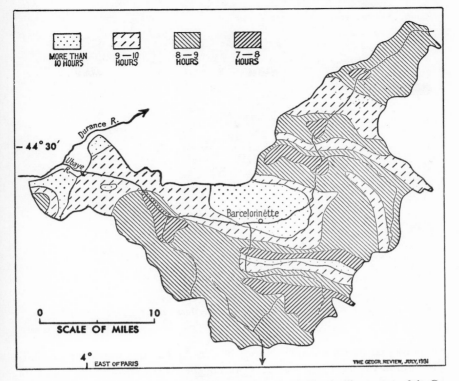

Map 90. Hours of sunlight in the valley of Barcelonnette (by A. Levainville; courtesy of the Geographical Review, published by the American Geographical Society of New York).

The adret and the ubac are generally not arranged symmetrically on the two sides of the valley, however; for where towering peaks cast shadows over the neighboring terrain, the patterns of light and shade are amazingly intricate. A map of the average daily hours of sunlight in the valley of Barcelonnette, in the French Alps, suggests at least one reason for the characteristic spottiness of mountain landscapes (Map 90). The resulting temperature contrasts from place to place may be sufficient in any locality to wipe out quite completely the general decrease of temperature with increase of altitude, and so to obscure the vertical zoning.

Another climatic element which contributes to the intricacy of mountain patterns is rainfall. While it is true that rainfall exhibits a certain vertical arrangement—increasing, as we have pointed out, up to a zone of maximum, and decreasing beyond that—still in most mountain areas this feature is only vaguely developed. Vertical zoning of rainfall is most apparent on mountain sides which present a relatively unbroken wall to the

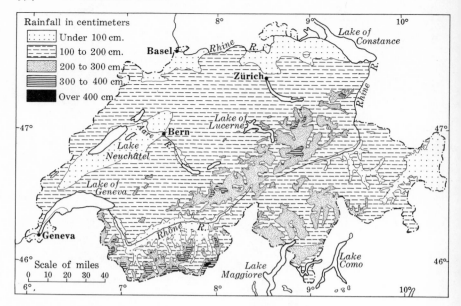

Map 91. Rainfall of Switzerland (after J. Maurer and J. Lugeon, 1928).

air currents, as the eastern slopes of the Andes, the southern slopes of the Himalayas, and the western slopes of the Sierra Nevada of California. In most mountain areas the great contrasts in the amount of rain received, even on neighboring slopes which are oriented somewhat differently to the rain-bearing winds, make it difficult or impossible to observe any general increase or decrease with altitude (Map 91). As we have seen, the world's heaviest rainfalls occur on the windward slopes of mountains up which warm, moist air is rising buoyantly (Kauai and Cherrapunji). Where the mountains are high, the windward slopes are generally much wetter than the lee slopes, which lie in a *rain shadow;* but where the mountains are lower, the clouds that form over them may drift to leeward and bring more rain to that side. Basins and deep valleys into which the wind must descend are usually dry; but, on the other hand, where the wind blows up through a valley, it may bring copious rainfall. The actual rainfall distribution in a rugged mountain region composed of slopes standing at various angles to the winds forms a pattern even more intricate than that of the hours of sunlight. Furthermore, these two patterns in no way correspond; so that the landscape features, which are in part conditioned by sunlight and in part by rainfall, find in mountain regions the most extraordinary number and diversity of combinations of these elements. If to these things

A basin on the high altiplano of Bolivia, near La Paz—elevation over 12,000 feet (Three Lions).

is added the variety of edaphic conditions, we can appreciate the basic reasons for the spottiness of mountain landscapes.

The Occupance

Mountains resemble the deserts in the persistent effect they exert on the distribution of the human occupance. In most parts of the world the character of the occupance patterns is largely determined by the culture which produces them, and a succession of cultures in any one area may result in a series of occupance patterns which are radically different one from another. In the mountain lands, on the contrary, the location of settlements and the routes of travel established by different cultures are as closely fixed by the rugged terrain as they are in the dry lands by water. Only in topographic detail can they vary. The general characteristics of mountain distribution patterns may be illustrated not only from the physical elements but also from elements of the occupance. Vertical differentiation appears in many forms; spotty arrangement reflects the

A branch of the Sogne Fiord, Norway, latitude 61° N., in summer (Carl Tietz).

diversity of habitat background; and the barrier nature of mountains leads to the convergence of routes on the passes and to the historical persistence of these routes.

VERTICAL DIFFERENTIATION

The vertical differentiation of occupance is developed in almost all the mountain regions which have gone beyond the pioneer stage. Even early in the progress of settlement, when the main routes of travel are of chief importance in guiding the arrangement of population, a vague altitude zoning is usually apparent; but as settlement is elaborated, vertical zones, differing from one another in the modes and forms of occupance, become more and more sharply differentiated. While this stratification is an almost universal feature of mountain regions, the actual modes of occupance at the various levels differ from place to place. In the low latitudes, for instance, the occupance has a tendency to become static, with little movement from one altitude to another; but in the middle latitudes in most mountain regions a regular seasonal migration up and down the slopes is

The same scene as that on the opposite page in winter. Note that the fiord is not frozen over (Carl Tietz).

developed. Throughout the world the differing cultures of the mountain dwellers find expression in the many and various methods in which the resources of the several altitude zones are utilized. In other words, while some form of vertical arrangement appears in the occupance of almost every mountain region, the ways in which this arrangement is worked out are in large measure unique for each group of people.

Altitude Limits. The altitude limits of the various forms of human settlement are in many respects similar to the horizontal limits of these same forms in the other groups of habitat regions. In most cases such limits are a reflection more of the culture of the people than of rigidly imposed natural barriers. However, in general, the same crops reach the upper limits of agriculture as reach its poleward limits, and there is a similar sequence of crops down the slopes or equatorward.

The extreme upper limits of settlement differ in the various mountain regions not only with such natural features as the snow line and tree line but also with the historical and cultural background of the inhabitants. The highest human habitation is reported by Bowman in the Andes of

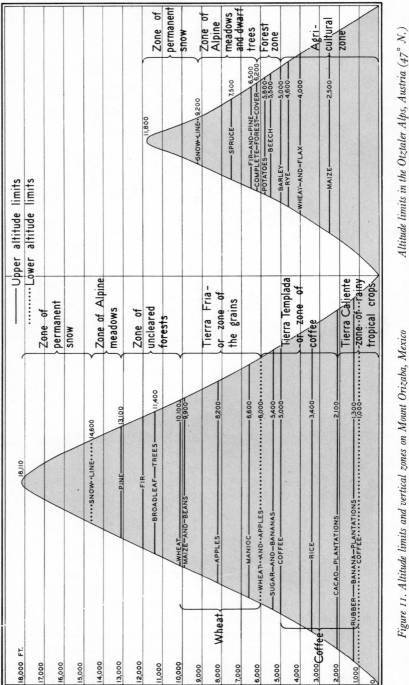

Figure 11. Altitude limits and vertical zones on Mount Orizaba, Mexico (19° N.) (after Sapper).

Altitude limits in the Ötztaler Alps, Austria (47° N.) (after Sapper).

southern Peru, at an elevation of 17,100 feet, only a little below the snow line.* Settlement at this great elevation, however, is the result of certain peculiarities of the occupance in this region. Neither of the major culture groups in the Peruvian Andes, namely, the Indians and the Europeans, would, if left to itself, have established a permanent settlement at such an altitude. But the European has appropriated the better lands at altitudes suitable for his commercial crops, and the poor Indian has been forced to seek refuge at still higher altitudes where a scanty pasturage for his sheep and llamas may be had. In each mountain region the upper limits of settlement represent a compromise between the traditional mode of occupance, the historical background of the people, and the peculiarities of the local terrain. We may say in general, however, that the highest settlements are usually associated with mining; in fact, some mining communities have been established above the snow line. The next highest settlements are commonly supported by the pasturage of domestic animals. Lower down, the various types of agricultural settlement appear.

Both the animals and the crops supporting these settlements show fairly distinct upper limits in any one region. Because sheep can exist on much scantier pasturage than cattle, they are the domestic animals which are driven highest in the mountains. Cattle and horses usually occupy the richer pastures lower down. Of the crops, the potato reaches the highest altitudes, just as it reaches the highest latitudes. Lower down, the various grains arrange themselves in the expectable sequence: barley, rye, wheat, maize, and rice in descending order. The tropical crops occupy the lower slopes of low-latitude mountains.

Vertical Zones. Most mountain people recognize in the region they inhabit fairly definite zones of altitude, to which they give distinguishing names. For the reasons previously suggested, the number of these zones is greatest in the low latitudes. In any region, however, these popularly recognized zones, when analyzed, prove to represent a generalization of a considerable number of altitude limits: crop limits, limits of various types of settlement, even limits of racial groups. A few specific examples will illustrate this more clearly.

On the slopes of Mount Orizaba in Mexico, at about latitude 19° N., six vertical zones are given popular recognition (Figure 11).† The two upper zones are simple concepts, each based on one dominant feature. At the top is the zone of permanent snow, lying above 14,600 feet (to the peak at 18,110). The zone of alpine meadow lies between 13,100 feet and

---

*See the chapter on the Andes by I. Bowman, in J. Brunhes, *Human Geography* (Chicago, 1920), pp. 453–498; reference on page 468.

†Karl Sapper, *Allgemeine Wirtschafts- und Verkehrsgeographie* (Berlin, 1930), pp. 66–67. The altitudes on the diagram on p. 398 and in the corresponding parts of the text are translated from the metric system to the nearest round numbers of feet.

the snow line.   The forest zone is not so simple as the upper two, for it is differentiated by the altitude limits of the various trees into three parts: a lower part of mixed broadleaf trees and conifers, a middle part of pine and fir, and an upper part where pine alone can exist.   The upper limit of agriculture as practiced on Orizaba lies about 10,100 feet above sea level. This corresponds to the upper limit of wheat.   At various altitudes below 10,100 feet are found in succession the upper limits (in some cases the lower limits) of the various crops.   As a result of certain typical combinations of crops, however, the agricultural occupance is divided into three zones.   The *tierra fria* (roughly from 6000 to 10,100 feet) is essentially the zone of wheat cultivation.   Manioc, apples, maize, and beans are associated with wheat at the bottom of this zone, but all these other crops disappear, one after another, as one ascends.   Below the *tierra fria* is the *tierra templada* (from 2100 to 6000 feet).   This is primarily the zone of coffee culture, although coffee does not quite reach the top, nor does its cultivation stop at the bottom.   Associated with coffee up to their respective altitude limits are sugar cane, bananas, and rice, as well as maize, manioc, and beans. The lowest zone is the *tierra caliente*.   This is the zone of rainy tropical crops: cacao, bananas, rubber, sugar cane, rice, maize, manioc, and beans.

The vertical zones recognized in the Otztaler Alps in Austria, at the head of the Adige Valley, are similarly composed of various individual limits (Figure 11).   The zone of permanent snow is above 9200 feet.   Below this lies the zone of alpine meadow and dwarf trees, within which, however, pine, fir, and spruce have their successive upper limits.   The zone of continuous forest cover begins at about 6200 feet, while the upper limit of the agricultural zone is about 5000 feet.   Within the forest zone are found the upper limit of broadleaf trees (beech) and the upper limit of crops (potatoes).   Only one agricultural zone is recognized, although it is diversified by the limits of barley, rye, flax, wheat, and maize.   There is no *tierra templada* or *tierra caliente*.

Contrasts between the Low and Middle Latitudes.   In the low-latitude regions regular seasonal movements up and down the mountain slopes are of relatively minor significance.   Not that such movements never occur. There are places where people move uphill to escape summer heat (Rio de Janeiro to Petropolis, Manila to Baguio), or downhill to get warm (Mexico City to Cuernavaca); but one may suspect that the social life is as much a factor as temperature.   In other places there is a shift of the agricultural occupance up and down the slopes in harmony with the rains (as on the eastern slopes of the Andes).   Such movements, however, are of small importance.   On the whole, the stratification of people and crops in the low-latitude mountains is static.   In fact, the vertical contrasts in occupance become well enough established so that locally important currents of trade are developed between the lowland dwellers and the highland dwellers, based on the vertical differentiation of products.

There are two reasons why the occupance in most middle-latitude mountains does not achieve this permanence of stratification. In the first place, there are fewer vertical zones and so less opportunity for the development of different layers of contrasted types of occupance. There are no zones of tropical products or of coffee below the zone of grain-farming; and as one proceeds poleward, even the zone of grain-farming is forced to lower and lower altitudes until it disappears altogether, and the forest zone descends to sea level. In the second place, the marked seasonal change, which is lacking in the low latitudes, renders the higher mountain slopes productive only at certain seasons. There is a tendency, therefore, for the mountain peoples to establish their homes at the lower altitudes and to ascend each summer with their domestic animals to take advantage of the excellent pasture lands of the alpine meadows.

Transhumance and Seasonal Seminomadism. The movements up and down the slopes of middle-latitude mountain ranges in response to the rhythm of the seasons are of two chief kinds. There are movements involving only the herds or flocks of domestic animals accompanied by a small number of attendants, and there are movements involving not only the animals but also the whole human group. These kinds of movement are called, respectively, *transhumance** and *seasonal seminomadism.* Transhumance is a widespread phenomenon. It is reported from nearly all the lower middle-latitude mountain regions of the world, with one striking exception to be described later. The flocks of sheep of the pastoral nomads who used to occupy the steppes of Central Asia were driven into the bordering high mountains during the summer. The Soviet government has now ended nomadism by settling these people on irrigated areas, but the practice of transhumance still continues. Hay crops are raised on the irrigated areas in summer to feed the animals during the winter. A similar form of transhumance is to be found in southern Argentina and Chile. In the mountain regions of western North America transhumance without any form of nomadism is the rule: sheep are driven to the higher pastures

---

* "Transhumance" is a word borrowed from the French. It is derived from a combination of *trans,* meaning "across" or "over," and *humus,* meaning "the ground." As a term, "transhumance" denotes the periodic, or seasonal, movement of flocks or herds of domestic animals between two areas of different climatic conditions. Such climatic differences within relatively short distances are found in mountains, and the term "transhumance" is therefore associated with the seasonal movements of domestic animals in mountain areas. A distinction is made between the Greater Transhumance, involving movements between a mountain region and its surrounding lowlands or plateaus, and the Lesser Transhumance, which includes movements within the mountain region from lower to higher slopes. E. H. Carrier, *Water and Grass, a Study in the Pastoral Economy of Southern Europe* (London, 1932).

Terrace farming near Cuzco, Peru (Three Lions).

above the timber line, and cattle and horses to pastures at lower elevations, many of them in the open forests of these regions. Similar movements of animals take place in Australia and New Zealand.

Transhumance combined with seasonal seminomadism was formerly an outstanding feature of the mountain occupance of Europe, especially southern Europe, where the nomadic tradition was a culture trait of the mountain peoples. These movements of the people as well as of the animals continue even today, but in a form much modified by modern transportation. In some of the mountain valleys of the Alps an exceedingly complex series of migrations up and down the slopes takes place. After passing the winter in stables in the valleys, the animals are started up the mountains early in the spring. They are driven first to the lower pastures (known as the *voralps*), and then, as the snow melts, they proceed by stages to the pastures above the tree line (known as the *alps*). Meanwhile the human group carries on various activities at different levels—now climbing to harvest a crop of hay from the alpine meadows, now descending to care for grains or vegetables planted in the valleys, now ascending again to make cheese at the settlements on the alps.

The most complex of such movements, in the Val d'Anniviers in Switzerland, was described by Jean Brunhes.* In this valley, the inhabitants used to have several permanent villages at different altitudes, each family owning homes in each of the villages. At almost all times of the year people could be found ascending or descending the mountain trails between the different habitations. Their activities extended from vineyard cultivation in the Rhône Valley to cheese-making in the alpine meadows near the snow line. This self-contained community that once made such effective use of the different parts of the habitat has now been radically changed. To be sure, animals are still driven up to the high pastures during the summer and down again to the valleys in winter. But now the whole area has been discovered by tourists: in summer, hotels and lodges offer accommodation for hikers and mountain climbers; and in winter this has become one of the more popular ski resorts. The people are now mostly engaged in serving the needs of the visitors.

The Lack of Transhumance in Japan. Japan is a notable exception to this general rule of mid-latitude mountain occupance. Until recently there was little or no pastoral utilization of the mountain slopes to supplement the intensive agricultural use of the valleys and coastal lowlands. The Japanese culture contains no traditional familiarity with domestic animals, for other than draft purposes, to suggest the use of the mountain pastures; nor are the pastures of much value in the high mountain area of Japan, owing to the growth of nonedible bamboo grass and sedge. A distinct vertical zoning is developed which remains undisturbed by important vertical movements, in spite of the rhythm of the seasons. Agriculture, based primarily on rice, is concentrated in the valleys, the intermont basins, and the coastal lowlands (Maps 92 and 93). Certain dry-land crops, such as tea or mulberry, are planted on the lower slopes. Above this zone of cultivation the Japanese mountains are forest-clad, and into this zone come a few charcoal-makers during the summer months. Still higher are the unoccupied alpine meadows, just below the snow line.

SPOTTY DISTRIBUTION

The mountain lands resemble the dry lands in the prevailing scantiness of population. Yet, as in the dry lands, there are in these regions numerous small areas of very dense population—some of the densest in the world. The concentration of the occupance in the valleys, basins, delta plains, or other bits of flattish land at appropriate altitudes is an outstand-

---

* See Chapter VIII in J. Brunhes, *La Géographie humaine* (Paris, 1925); and also P. Arbos, "The Geography of Pastoral Life," *Geographical Review,* Vol. 13 (1923), pp. 559–575.

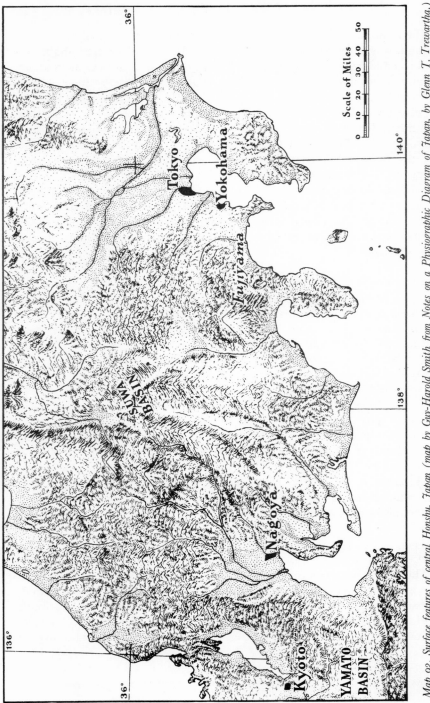

Map 92. Surface features of central Honshu, Japan (map by Guy-Harold Smith from Notes on a Physiographic Diagram of Japan, by Glenn T. Trewartha.) Courtesy of the Geographical Review, published by the American Geographical Society of New York.

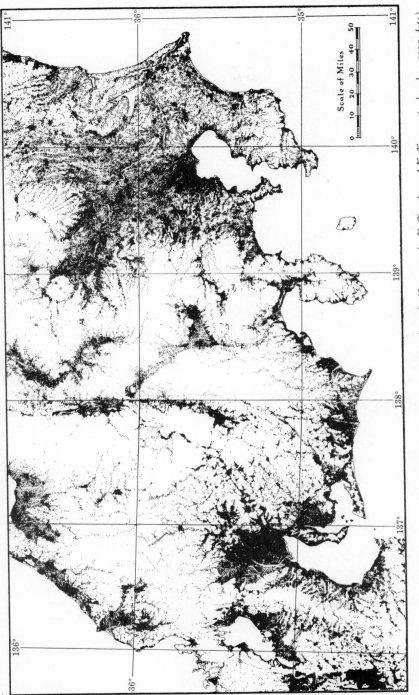

Map 93. Population of central Honshu, Japan. Each dot represents two hundred people (from map by K. Tanaka and K. Yamamoto, based on 1925 data).

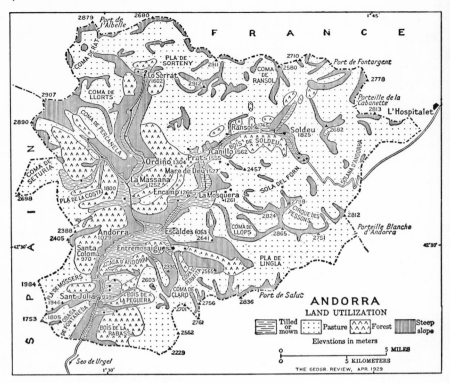

Map 94. Land and settlement in Andorra (by R. Peattie; courtesy of the Geographical Review, published by the American Geographical Society of New York).

ing feature.   The resulting patterns of occupance are no less spotty than the background of the physical setting.   The areas of concentrated settlement are of various sizes and shapes, but each community is more or less isolated from other communities by uninhabited slopes over which communications is very difficult.

Relation of Settlements to Landforms.   Among the mid-latitude mountain regions there are many illustrations of the concentration of people and their settlements in the small areas of favorable land.   The densely populated lowlands, with their big cities, form a striking contrast to the scantily populated highlands in such small countries as Switzerland and Austria.   The canton of Zürich in Switzerland, a lowland canton, has more than seven hundred people per square mile, whereas the canton of Valais, in the highlands, has only about sixty per square mile, and these are mostly in the valley of the upper Rhône.

A map of the land utilization in Andorra brings out these relationships quite clearly (Map 94). Agriculture in this mountain state in the Pyrenees is limited to a few cultivated crops and to hay cut from untilled meadows. The agricultural lands follow the valley of the Río Balira and its tributaries. The sequence of widened intermont basin and narrow, steep-walled gorge, which is characteristic of mountain streams descending over rocks of varying degrees of resistance, is revealed in the pattern of the agricultural land. The concentration of the small villages in these basins can be seen, and also the location of the chief town, Andorra, in the midst of the largest basin. Only a small proportion of this little country is devoted to agriculture; much more of the area is alpine pasture with a few patches of forests. But the various parts of the territory are divided into small units by slopes too steep for any kind of use—slopes which follow either the sides of the main valleys or the mountain crests.

The relation of population distribution to areas of relatively level land is also illustrated by two maps of the central mountainous part of the Japanese island of Honshu (Maps 92 and 93). The number of people in any given territory is in rather strict proportion to the size of the plains and basins, much as in the dry lands, where the population of an oasis is strictly proportional to the available supply of water. Tokyo and Yokohama occupy the Kanto Plain, the largest in Japan. Other large cities, such as Nagoya and Osaka, occupy other plains of considerable extent. Many small villages and towns are strung along the coast on the smaller delta plains and coastal terraces, while back in the mountains each intermont basin and narrow valley bottom stands out clearly on the population map. Yet the greater part of the territory is only scantily inhabited, so rugged are the slopes.

Although this tendency to concentrate on the lowlands is repeated by various cultures in the mountain lands, there are a few regions where the lowlands have been avoided in favor of the higher intermont basins. This is notably the case in most parts of Spanish America. So common is the concentration of settlement in the highlands, leaving the low coastal regions almost uninhabited, that many writers have insisted that this was a result of the avoidance of the hot lowland climates. The historical fact is that the Spaniards came to the New World seeking gold or other sources of quick wealth, and also large numbers of sedentary Indians who could be converted to Christianity and set to work in the mines or fields. Such groups of Indians at the time of the Spanish conquest were to be found in the intermont basins of Mexico, Guatemala, Colombia, Ecuador, Peru, and Bolivia. To these places the Spaniards directed the main streams of settlement. But where the largest number of Indians were found in the lowlands, the Spanish settlements were also established in the lowlands, as in the Dominican Republic and in Nicaragua. The Mexicans in the high

The Cochabamba Basin, Bolivia, is about 15 miles long by six wide, at an elevation of about 8500 feet. It is occupied by more than 300 people per square mile (Three Lions).

Basin of Mexico found the continuously cold climate so tiresome that they established a resort city, Cuernavaca, in the *tierra templada* close by. In other words, the kinds of places sought for the establishment of settlements in mountain regions depends on the cultural traditions of the people; but in any case, the chief areas of concentrated settlement are to be found on the relatively gentle slopes. Settlements on very steep slopes are usually associated with mining, or are found to be places of refuge, such as Machu Picchu in Peru.

Relation of the Settlements to Local Climates. Few generalizations can be made concerning the relation of settlements to the various local climates of these mountain lands. In dry mountains, for instance, the rainy places are preferred; but in rainy mountains the inhabitants commonly seek the sunny, dry, lee sides, as in the Hawaiian Islands. In the mid-latitude regions the sunny slopes are usually so much more desirable than the shady slopes that a definite separation of the wealthier people from the poorer people takes place, the former occupying the adret, the latter the ubac.

In the low latitudes, on the other hand, the shady side is chosen first, and the poorer settlements occupy the sunny slopes. The greatest variety of local adjustments is possible. Thus there may arise not only a vertical stratification of people, as in the Andes, but also a complex rearrangement within the same vertical zone to conform to the different details of slope and local climate.

MOUNTAINS AS BARRIERS

Because of the steep slopes, the narrow valleys, and the rigorous climates of high altitudes, especially in the middle latitudes, mountains have played the role of barriers to the movement of people on the earth. The mountains tend to isolate and separate the communities within the mountain regions, and also the peoples on either side.

The Isolation of Mountain Communities. The isolation of mountain communities is difficult to overcome. Steep slopes require the construction of zigzag trails which cling precariously to the ledges of the valley side. Avalanches, especially on the rain-soaked valley sides of tropical mountains, frequently obliterate parts of the trails and render communication uncertain. If the trails reach considerable altitude, the obstacles of snow, high winds, and low temperatures are added to the difficulties of rugged surface. Yet, in spite of these difficulties, it is quite commonly easier to gain access to an intermont basin by climbing over its mountain rim than by attempting to follow the narrow, steep-walled gorges along the river. It is in such places that anthropologists look for survivals of older races and cultures, which, without the protection afforded by the isolation, would have been submerged.

The resources of mountain lands, moreover, are in many regions insufficient to pay the huge cost of railroad and highway construction. Those mountain basins which happen to lie close to a pass route may find the problem solved with relative ease, but the more remote Occidental communities must pay their own way if they are to be connected with the urban centers. Probably the chief support for railroad development away from the pass routes has come from mining and lumbering. Industrial development—especially of such industries as the manufacture of paper or matches, which can make use of both timber supplies and water power—has resulted in railroad construction. More recently tourist establishments have supported the building of railroads and highways.

Pass Routes. Mountain ranges, also, play the role of barriers between the territories on either side. In this capacity mountains have shaped the course of history at many critical times. The importance of the Alps and

The Uspallata Pass between Chile and Argentina (Lanks, from Caterpillar Tractor Company).

Carpathians in shielding the growing cultures of the Mediterranean lands, or of the Himalayas in shielding India, can scarcely be overemphasized, although both these barriers were crossed at one time or another by conquering peoples. Because mountains are barriers, the interests of the inhabitants of a wide extent of territory are focused on the pass routes. These become nodal points of great strategic importance, not only from the military point of view but also from the commercial and political points of view.

Pass routes across mountain ranges are developed not only as a result of the existence of an easy natural line of travel, but also in response to a demand for communications. Many easy natural passes are followed by little-used trails, as in the southern Andes, because the arrangement and needs of the people on either side bring about no insistent demand for a line of travel. On the other hand, many of the actual roads or railroads which cross mountain barriers in places where the demand for communications from a large territory is concentrated follow very difficult routes. Fortunate, indeed, are those few places where world routes of travel come to a focus on a relatively easy pass, such as the Isthmus of Panama. In any case, few pass routes bear any relation whatsoever to the local resources of the mountain area; they are developed in response to conditions elsewhere in the world. The greatest contrasts may therefore be found between the settlements along the routes themselves and the settlements of the mountain dwellers only a short distance away.

Considering the arrangement of the mountains in the world as a whole, we can place pass routes in two categories. There are the passes which cross the mountainous rim of the Pacific Ocean, and there are the passes which cross the great east-west mountain barrier of southern Asia and Europe. But the rim of mountains around the Pacific is broken in the north and south and especially in the southwest. There is no barrier problem involved in sailing from the Indian Ocean into the Pacific. In Asia also the chief difficulties standing in the way of overland communication between China and the Western world are not those of mountains but, rather, those of aridity combined with low winter temperatures. The mountain rim of the Pacific is most effective as a barrier in the great north-south extent of the American ranges. To illustrate the development and historical importance of pass routes over these great barriers, let us consider a few examples.

The Panama Route. The importance of the Panama route is especially great because, at least up to the present, this route has no competitors close by. Not only the great width of a large part of the continents of North and South America, but also the height of the passes over the western mountains, has helped to emphasize the focus of lines of travel on this point

An air view of the Miraflores Locks in the Panama Canal (Jim Mitchell, from Black Star).

in the barrier. In the country of Panama the mountain backbone of Middle America drops to such a low elevation, while still retaining the characteristics of steep slopes and narrow valleys, that a passage from one side to the other may be had by a climb of only two hundred and eighty-five feet through the Culebra Pass. The surface here has been deeply eroded under rainy tropical conditions, resulting in steep slopes, deep clay soils, and the danger of frequent landslides. The whole region was originally covered with a selva.

The Isthmus became the focus of transportation routes as soon as the commercial-minded Europeans had explored and colonized the world's continents. A road from Portobelo, on the Caribbean (northwestern) side, crossed the mountains by the Culebra Pass and descended to the Spanish colonial town of Panama, on the Pacific (southeastern) side. Panama was the base from which proceeded the conquest of western South America; and later the entire trade between Spain and its South American colonies was limited by law to the route by way of Panama. Ships from

Spain brought goods to Portobelo; thence the goods were carried by mules over the Isthmus to Panama and there were reshipped south. The road across the pass, used chiefly by mules, served until about 1850, at which time the stream of American gold-seekers, on their way from the eastern part of the United States to California, stimulated the construction of a railroad.

In 1876 the French, encouraged by their success in Suez, sent a mission to Panama to survey a route for a canal. In 1881 a French company started work near Colon, attempting to dig a waterway like the Suez, without locks. Two things blocked success. The construction of a canal at sea level was much more difficult in Panama than at Suez, for in the latter case there was no mountain range to cross, but only a low ridge; and the rainy tropical climate of Panama, with its disease-carrying mosquitoes, was very different from the desert climate of Suez, where there is little penalty for poor sanitation. But the canal project was too important, considering the geographical position of the Isthmus, to permit its abandonment. In 1904 a project under the control of the United States was undertaken, beginning with an expensive and widespread program of sanitation. The draining of swamps and the clearing of luxuriant vegetation cost too much for the average tropical community; but if yellow fever, malaria, and other diseases common only in the tropics were to be eliminated, it had to be done by the elimination of breeding places for the mosquito. The new canal project included the construction of a huge dam at Gatun and the flooding of the valley of the Río Chagres (Map 95). Access to the lake, which is 85 feet above sea level, is gained through locks. The Gaillard Cut carries the canal across the divide to the Pacific side, and here two sets of locks are used to permit descent to sea level. The work was completed in 1914, the first ship passing through the Canal on August 3 of that year.

In return for its independence and the defense of its territory, Panama, formerly a part of Colombia, has leased to the United States a strip of land ten miles wide known as the Canal Zone. Within this zone the usual tropical landscapes, many of them still primitive, have been transformed by the magic touch of money and commercial interest. Instead of being left in the wild confusion of a tropical forest or being closely packed with the squalid wooden houses of an isolated tropical city, the country has been cultivated like a park, and the cities of Cristobal (on the Atlantic side) and Balboa (on the Pacific side) are built with wide, paved streets, shaded by trees and bordered by widely spaced white bungalows, and are kept scrupulously clean. The contrasts are extraordinary between the landscapes, both rural and urban, which result from centuries of occupance in Panama, and the landscapes in the Canal Zone, which reflect unlimited

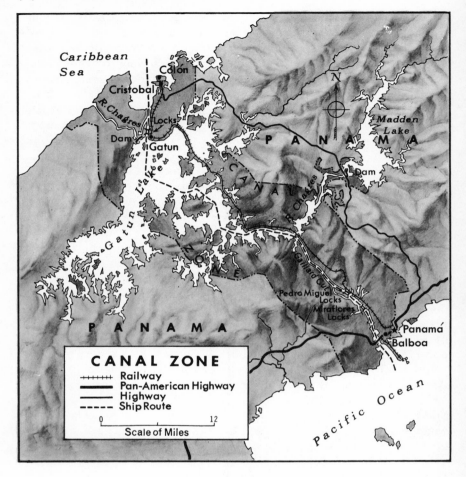

Map 95. The Canal Zone.

financial backing at a focal point in world trade.   From the results
attained in the Canal Zone, however, it is not possible to conclude that all
tropical lands can be similarly developed.

The Brenner Pass.   The Brenner Pass, across the Alps, is not so significant to the world as a whole as the Panama route; nor is it so important
a crossing of the European mountains as either the Bosporus and Darda-
nelles straits in the east or the Rhône-Saône Valley in the west.   The
Brenner Pass, however, has played a very important historical role.   From
Verona in Italy to Munich in Germany the crossing of the Alps by this route

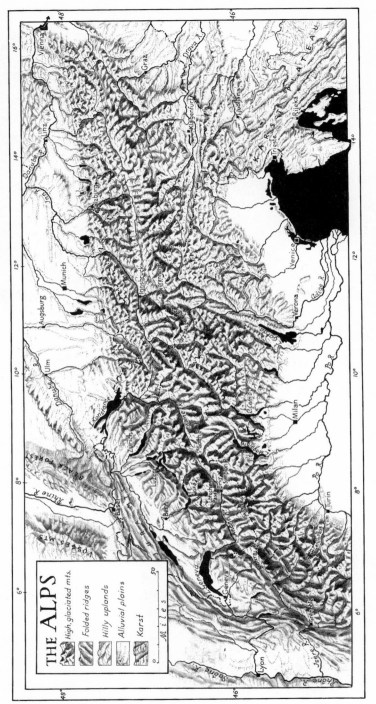

Map 96. The surface configuration of the Alps and neighboring territory.

Western approach to Susten Pass, Switzerland, near upper limit of pasture (photo by the author).

requires an ascent of 4470 feet (Map 96). From the Plain of the Po the Adige Valley, a broad glacial trough, provides an easy route of approach to the divide. From the crest the descent by way of the Inn Valley is only 2767 feet. In this way the Alps may be crossed by a single climb, although elsewhere more than one range must be crossed through higher passes with steeper approaches. As a result the Brenner Pass has been of importance from an early period in history. By this route the Cimbri invaded the Po Valley; and later the Roman forces, marching out to the frontier posts on the Danube, followed it, building a road so that supplies could be sent out to them. Over this pass came the amber from Germany on its way to Rome in exchange for fabrics and wines. The German emperors of the Middle Ages invaded Italy over the Brenner Pass, and later the road through the pass was traveled by people from the north attracted by the culture of Venice. The trade which was carried on over this pass from Venice resulted in the early flourishing of such cities to the north as Augsburg, Regensburg, Nürnberg and Leipzig. The first carriage road over the Alps, and later the first railroad, followed the Brenner route. To this day the Brenner is one of the chief lines of travel between central Europe and Italy. Within the mountain area there are only glistening steel rails traveled by heavily loaded trains, and highways over which motor cars or trucks pass back and forth; yet the effect of the pass is felt in the lowlands on either side through the growth of the pass cities—Verona to the south and Munich to the north.

The Khyber Pass.   Many mountain ranges cannot be crossed by a single pass like the Brenner.   Instead, several ranges must be crossed by means of long, tedious ascents and equally difficult descents.   Thus the caravans from the oases of Tashkent and Bukhara seek the markets of India over the ranges of the Hindu Kush by a series of difficult passes (Map 97). From the Amu Darya and the piedmont oasis of Mazar-i-Sharif, they cross several lesser divides, finally surmounting the main range of the Hindu Kush Mountains over the Hajikhak Pass at 12,188 feet.   Thence they cross the Paghman Mountains by the Unai Pass to Kabul at 5740 feet, and finally, after passing through the narrow gorges of the Kabul River and the Khyber Pass at 6825 feet, they descend to the town of Peshawar and the Indus Valley.   Over this and neighboring routes have come the repeated invasions of India which, in the course of history, have peopled that land with such a variety of races.   Until recently, in addition to the dangers and difficulties of the road, the pass was dominated by Afghan tribesmen,

A zigzag route through the Hindu Kush Mountains (Philip Gendreau).

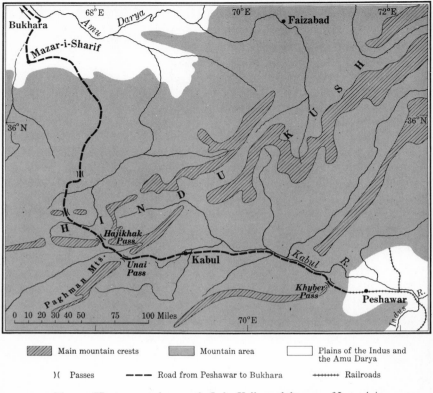

Map 97. The pass route between the Indus Valley and the oases of Inner Asia on the margins of the Turkestan.

who for centuries collected toll from the passing caravans and not infrequently resorted to pillage. Across this series of passes there is no railroad —only a road with steep grades and sharp turns, traveled in large part by loaded bullocks. However, at either end of the pass cities have grown up; Peshawar and Kabul are the two places that are most directly dependent on the Khyber Pass. Farther on, Bukhara is the focus of pass routes, not only from the south but also from the high basins of inner Asia to the east.

Summary

In more than a surficial sense mountains are major features of the earth's face. Not only do they stand out conspicuously from their surroundings, but their influence is felt far beyond the limits of this group in the conti-

This village in Khyber Pass is a stopping place for passing caravans
(Deane Dickason, from Ewing Galloway).

nental patterns of climate and vegetation and in the general arrangement
of the occupance. On a continent without mountains the major patterns
of the landscapes would be simple; the areal scene could be painted, as it
were, with broad sweeps of the brush. But mountains complicate the picture. The differences between the simple patterns shown on the generalized continent and the actual patterns on the face of the earth are to some
extent the result of irregularities of coast line; but in large part they are
the result of the distortion of climatic lines by mountain barriers. These
effects are felt beyond the mountain borders: within the mountain regions
there is an intricacy of design not equaled in any other parts of the earth.

The landscapes are composed of such a complexity of detail that only large-scale topographic studies can reveal their essential qualities. A general vertical differentiation of the landscapes can be discerned, but this fact is obscured in detail by the spotty design of all the landscape elements. It is this remarkable variety of scenery as well as the imposing grandeur of snow-capped peaks against the sky that gives to the mountain lands their fascination.

Principles and Problems of Man–Land Relations

IN THIS STUDY of the changing significance to man of the physical and biotic features of his habitats we are concerned with the areal associations and causal interconnections among things of unlike origin. This is the nature of geographic study: to examine the complex interactions of physical and biotic processes in the development of habitat regions; and to identify the changes in the significance of the habitats to man that result from economic, social, and political processes. An important part of such study is taxonomic, in that it deals with the grouping of things in categories, making up systems of classification. The purpose of such study has been achieved if the student gains a mental image of the major regional differences on the face of the earth, and of the processes that have formed them. No part of the earth's surface, land or water, should remain so blank in the student's mind that it would be impossible to reconstruct, on the basis of the principles presented in this book, its probable physical, biotic, and cultural characteristics, and the probable interconnections among these features.

The regional concept is central to the structure of geography. The region is defined in terms of areal associations and interconnections among diverse features: as when certain kinds of vegetation and soil occur together with certain types of climate; or when, at certain periods of Occidental culture, steel industries are located near supplies of bituminous coal. The region is a segment of the surface of the earth within which there is a distinctive association of causally interconnected features. The region is homogenous in terms of the criteria by which it is defined, and differs from neighboring areas. The distinctive characteristics of the region are best discerned in the regional core, and toward its borders the characteristics of neighboring regions are intermingled. Cores, therefore, are more important than boundaries.

THE GLOBAL PATTERN OF HABITATS

In this book we have defined nine major categories of habitat regions. We have recognized groups of regions, because each category of region occurs in separate parts of the earth. But this recurrence of analogous regions accords with a predictable pattern, resulting from the interacting processes that produce the regional characteristics. We have identified

two principles in the global pattern of habitat regions: One is the principle of regularity which relates to all those features of the face of the earth
that are associated with climate; the other is the principle of irregularity
which relates to all those features associated with surface form.   As a result of the principle of regularity, it is possible to forecast the kinds of associated features that can be expected at any given latitude and at five
longitudinal positions: west side of an ocean basin; east side of an ocean
basin; west side of a continent; interior of a continent; or east side of
a continent.   But as a result of the principle of irregularity these regular
patterns are somewhat distorted in each specific continent and ocean basin.

We have already introduced the idea of the generalized continent

Figure 12. Generalized global pattern of habitats.

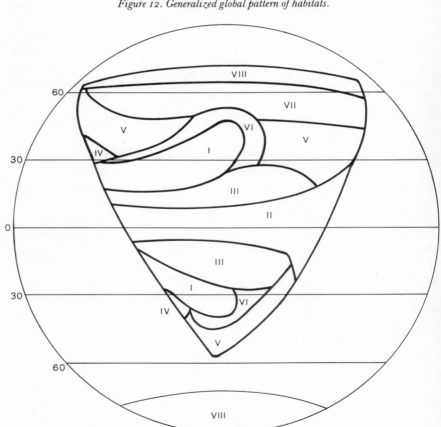

(Figure 1, and discussion on pp. 206–209). It is now possible to plot the generalized global pattern of habitats, by showing the position or positions of each group of regions in relation to this continent (Figure 12). Since the generalized continent is drawn with smoothed coastlines, and without mountains, it can show only those regions which accord with the principle of regularity—namely, Groups I to VIII. Group IX, together with the irregularities of each specific continent, provides the distortions observed on the actual maps of the habitat regions (maps at beginning of text on each group). The position of each of the first eight groups is described in Table 4, and the proportion of the land area of the earth included in each group is shown in the table on p. 23.

TABLE 4. The Position of Groups I to VIII in the Global Pattern

GROUP	NORTHERN HEMISPHERE	SOUTHERN HEMISPHERE
I. The Dry Lands	Western side between 20° and 30° bending inland and poleward to 45°	Western side between 20° and 30° bending inland and poleward to 40°
II. The Tropical Forest Lands	Zone about 10° on both sides of the equator, broadening on the eastern side to about latitude 25° in both hemispheres	
III. The Tropical Woodlands and Savannas	On western side and interior forms transition zone between I and II	On western side and interior forms transition zone between I and II
IV. The Mediterranean Lands	Western side between 30° and 40°	Western side between 30° and 40°
V. The Mid-Latitude Mixed Forests	Western side between 40° and 60°, extending inland between VI and VII: Eastern side between 25° and 45°, extending inland as far as VI	Rim around southern end of continent, extending to 25° on eastern side, and to 40° on western side
VI. The Mid-Latitude Grasslands	Border zone around I	Border zone around I
VII. The Boreal Forests and Woodlands	Crosses northern continent from west to east: from 60° on western side to 45° on eastern side	none
VIII. The Polar Lands	Northern fringe of continents	Antarctica

POPULATION

During the nearly two million years since the genus *homo* appeared on the earth, probably in East Africa, man has spread from his original tropical habitat into all the various groups of regions in the world. In so doing he has learned more and more about the nature of his habitat, and he has developed new skills for creating useful things out of earth materials. Only yesterday, in the human time scale, he learned how to use inanimate power and machinery to do the work he had long done himself or with the aid of his animals. And only yesterday he began to learn how to organize a society in which every last individual might be treated with dignity and in accordance with law.

How is it, then, that the contemporary world is filled with fear and insecurity? How is it, in spite of the newly acquired ability to produce the necessities of life in abundance and to move vast volumes of things rapidly from place to place, that the great majority of the world's peoples are still hungry and getting hungrier?

The Industrial Revolution and the Democratic Revolution have brought fundamental changes to those areas they have reached. Both started around the North Sea in Europe, and both have been in process of spreading. In the freedom of North America, Australia, and New Zealand— and also of Scandinavia and certain other parts of Western Europe beyond the rim of the North Sea—both revolutions have advanced rapidly. Elsewhere, however, the spread has been retarded. As the new technologies and the new concepts regarding the status of the individual were brought into new areas, they encountered new sets of conditions. They entered regions with different resource endowments; they came into contact with people of different cultural traditions. Few parts of the earth, however remote, remain truly untouched by these changes; but the ways in which the changes have affected life in different parts of the world are by no means uniform. It is possible to identify some eleven culture regions in the world, in each of which the problems and conditions arising from the impact of the two revolutions on pre-existing cultures are more or less homogeneous. The origin and development of these culture regions are examined in another book.*

As a result of these complex processes the world has become very unevenly populated. The maps (Plates 6 to 9, pp. 559–563) show the pattern of population density in each of the continents, and the percentage of the world's population in each of the groups of habitat regions is shown in Table 5.

*Preston E. James, *One World Divided* (New York, 1964).

TABLE 5. Estimates of World Population by Regions, 1650–1961

POPULATION IN MILLIONS

DATE	WORLD	ANGLO-AMERICA	LATIN AMERICA	AFRICA	EUROPE[a]	ASIA[b]	OCEANIA	OCCI-DENTAL COUN-TRIES[c]
1650	545	1	12	100	103	327	2	118
1750	728	1	11	95	144	475	2	158
1800	906	6	19	90	192	597	2	219
1850	1171	26	33	95	274	741	2	335
1900	1608	81	63	120	423	915	6	573
1920	1834	115	92	136	485	997	9	701
1930	2008	134	110	155	530	1069	10	784
1940	2216	144	132	177	579	1173	11	866
1950	2406	166	162	199	594	1272	13	935
1961	3490.8	204	218	261	648	1721	16.8	1086.8

From Carr-Saunders and United Nations

[a] Including U.S.S.R.
[b] Excluding U.S.S.R.
[c] Including Anglo-America, Latin America, Europe including U.S.S.R. and Oceania.

Population Growth. The population map is a picture of the distribution of man at a particular moment of time. In order to understand the significance of the map it is necessary to examine the process of population change, and to look at the population historically as well as geographically.

We find that changes in population density are closely related to changes in culture, especially in the technology of production and in the organization of society. When prehistoric man found out how to cultivate plants and to domesticate animals, a large population increase became possible in those habitats that were suitable for crops and animals. In other words, the population could increase because more people could be fed. When, at the dawn of written history, man found out how to organize society under codes of law, an increase in the production of food was made possible and, again, population could increase.

Changes in technology do not always mean that population can increase in any one area. We have seen what the importation of the rifle did to the food supply of the Eskimos. When the plow replaced the hoe in certain agricultural societies, it was found that hilly lands could support fewer people than before. The meaning of the features of the physical earth changes, especially when they are examined in topographic detail. Although population as a whole is permitted to increase as a result of technological change, such change may also lead to a rearrangement of people in relation to the land.

Even when technological changes and changes in social organization permit population increase, however, growth does not always follow. During the long history of man on the earth, the death rates have risen and fallen suddenly and unpredictably. Famines, due perhaps to fluctuations of climate, are not predictable, nor are epidemics. Population increases when the death rate is lowered; it decreases when there is a rise in the death rate. Throughout long periods of time the ratio between the death rate and the birth rate has been so closely balanced that the net population growth has been very slow. The three chief factors that affect the death rate are hunger, disease, and war. These are what Malthus called the positive checks to population growth, that operate to keep the population in balance with the food supply. Of these, hunger (including famine and malnutrition) and disease are the most important. War causes a rise of the death rate because of the decrease of the food supply or the spread of disease rather than because of the actual slaughter of people in battle.

The changes in technology during the past two centuries include advances in the knowledge of medicine. At first medical knowledge increased less rapidly than did the methods of controlling the earth's physical resources. In the first half of the nineteenth century the control of disease and even the understanding of the causes of disease were beyond man's science. Little by little, scientists such as Louis Pasteur uncovered the causes of disease. Since 1900 both understanding and skill have increased enormously. In 1900 the chief causes of death were tuberculosis, pneumonia, infant diarrheas, typhoid fever, scarlet fever, diphtheria, yellow fever, and malaria. By 1950 these diseases were largely under control wherever modern medicine was applied. The chief causes of death in the United States were cancer, heart disease, and hypertension. All of this meant that more people survived to old age. In England and Wales, for example, a man born in 1880 might expect to reach the age of 44; a man born in 1945 might expect to live beyond the age of 65.

Population Growth since 1650.   Very little exact information exists regarding the world's population. As late as 1800 most population data were based on estimates. The census taken every ten years since 1790 in the United States is almost unique in the world. Even today the methods of gathering data in different countries vary so greatly that the census of one country is seldom comparable with that of another. Figures for birth rate and death rate based on actual count are available for only 30 per cent of the world's population. Nevertheless, more or less reliable esti-

mates of the world's population have been made for the period since 1650.*
These estimates are presented in Table 5.

According to the table, the population of the areas of Occidental settlement began to increase rapidly after 1800 and continued to increase during the nineteenth century. Although the concentration of people in the
European regions of Group V began to appear only after 1800, the population of Europe as a whole increased 119 per cent during that century.
In the same period the population in all the parts of the world occupied
by people of Occidental culture increased at least three times as fast as in
those parts occupied by other cultures.

The most rapid growth of population ever achieved by any large area
of the world was recorded in the United States in the nineteenth and early
twentieth centuries. In 1775 there were only 2,500,000 people in the colonies; and to the west the whole expanse of the continent as far as the Pacific Ocean was only thinly occupied by Indians, fur trappers, and Spanish cattle ranchers. The westward movement of the frontier, including
the occupance of the grasslands, was accompanied by the rapid growth of
large cities and urban industries. This era of rapidly-expanding economy
resulted in the creation of a vast amount of widely-distributed wealth, and
left an attitude of optimism clearly stamped on the American character.
The westward movement was supported by the arrival of millions of immigrants, some of whom came freely from Europe and other continents,
and some of whom came from Africa as slaves. Most of the immigrants
came to America because they had heard that it was a land of opportunity; and because they came it *was* a land of opportunity.

In the late nineteenth and early twentieth centuries great changes began to appear in the death rates of the Occidental world. It was at about
this time that medical science began to gain control over the ravages of
childhood diseases. More recently the discovery of sulfa drugs and antibiotics, and the use of DDT in the control of disease-carrying insects, have
resulted in a still greater drop in the death rates in those parts of the world
where modern health measures have been put into operation. Death rates
as low as 10 or 12 per thousand can now be achieved.

There has also been a drop in the birth rate in the areas of the industrial society. This decline has been especially noticeable among those who
live in cities. In the United States the birth rate, which had dropped below 20 per thousand in the 1930's, rose again to nearly 25; and the death
rate was brought to 9. In the pre-industrial society birth rates remained
generally above 40, and death rates were only a little lower. In the indus-

* A. M. Carr-Saunders, *World Population: Past Growth and Present Trends* (Oxford, 1935); W. F.
Willcox, *Studies in American Demography* (Ithaca, New York, 1940); *The Determinants and Conse-
quences of Population Trends*, Population Studies No. 17, United Nations (New York, 1953).

trial society the present trend is toward a situation characterized by low birth rates and low death rates, which is in striking contrast to the high birth rates and high death rates of other parts of the world.

The Population Prospect.   The question is what will happen to the populations of countries not now included in the industrial society when the new technology of the Industrial Revolution is adopted and when the methods of modern medical science are applied to the improvement of public health.   Demographers, who are students of population processes, warn against the idea that the cycle of events that took place in the industrial society will necessarily be repeated elsewhere.   It is clear that in countries like China a decrease in the death rate must be followed by a "population explosion."   How long might it take such a country to achieve a low birth rate–low death rate situation?   Sociologists believe that declining birth rates are associated with a relatively high level of economic well-being.   This was brought about in the industrial society by increasing the production of goods and services at a faster rate than the increase of population.   But in the industrial society the Industrial Revolution came just at the time when settlers were entering new and previously almost unoccupied lands which had been rendered highly productive by new inventions.   The advance of the frontier onto these new lands accompanied the rise of the cities and the development of manufacturing industries.   Markets expanded as production increased.   Can a similar situation be created again through a series of new inventions that will change the potential utility of the present thinly-peopled or empty areas of the world?   No certain answer to this question can be given; yet on it hinges the population prospect of the decades ahead.

As a result of the revolutionary changes brought about by the new technology and by the new concept of the status of the individual, all the world's cultures are going through various processes of rapid readjustment. This is a time of conflicting values; but it is also a time of opportunity for anyone with the courage to face such changes and to seek solutions for the inevitable conflicts.   All kinds of economic, social, political, and military problems have arisen which demand the closest attention of the world's wisest people.   These problems need to be approached from as many different points of view as possible.

To make application of the geographic point of view to an understanding of these problems of our time, four fundamental facts are required. First is the population pattern—where people are located on the earth and in what density.   The second is the arrangement of the significant features of the habitat, the resource base.   The third is the pattern of contrasted cultures, or ways of living. And the fourth is the division into political areas. It is from an understanding of the complex areal relationships of population, habitat, culture, and political area that all kinds of modern problems of readjustment can be approached geographically. The geographic analysis of the meaning of the observed areal relationships must proceed from a knowledge of the processes of change that are going on. Such analysis can throw new light on the causes of poverty, hunger, insecurity, and conflict, and on the methods of combating them.

Maps

By Hibberd V. B. Kline, Jr.

Cartography. The word "cartography" by its derivation means the making or drawing of maps or charts. To the geographer it is the content of maps that is significant. The full and accurate understanding of content must, however, be based on sound knowledge of the advantages and limitations inherent in cartography. These are related to the basic considerations of space and distance, to map "projections" that present the spherical form of the earth on a two-dimensional surface, and to symbols which stand for facts and ideas.

The Map as a Tool for Analysis and for Synthesis. The cartographical method serves the geographer as a tool or instrument for analysis. On the map he can record any phenomena, physical or cultural, which are observed on the face of the earth. It must be remembered that the framework upon which these facts and inferences are plotted is that of the earth, or a part of the earth, itself. The geographer may derive his data from original observation in the "field," which in a sense is his laboratory, or from secondary sources. No matter what the derivation, he plots his information on the map. It is thus reduced to comprehensible size and concreteness. The cartographical method also serves the geographer as a means of synthesis and generalization. By use of the map he may combine two or more phenomena for study, or present their relationships to each other. The map is a method of summing up spatial phenomena that have two or three dimensions. The geographer, whose interests are in the significance of differences from place to place, therefore finds the map to be both a means and an end in his field of study.

I. Basic Requirements of a Map

Direction.   We may consider the map to be a representation of the earth itself or of selected items that have areal distribution over the earth.   To be more than a diagram or picture, a map must show measurement of distances, and position or direction with reference to the points of the compass.   Direction may be represented in several ways, all of which are based upon a convention commonly accepted by all the nations of the world today.   That is, direction is given with reference to an imaginary grid related to the axis of rotation of the earth.   This grid of latitude and longitude gives the four cardinal directions of N., E., S., and W. and permits direction from any given place to be considered in terms of arcs of a circle, according to any of the systems for dividing a circle.   Direction, then, becomes a matter of stating how a line drawn on the face of the earth trends with relation to the grid of the earth or to a circle drawn around some point on that line.   Direction in a circle is measured in terms of an arc, or azimuth.*

The instrument most commonly used to determine direction is the compass.   Since the magnetic compass conforms to the magnetic lines of force of the earth's field, which is not in perfect correspondence with the axis of rotation of the earth, a correction must be applied in most places to convert magnetic readings to azimuths, or to bearings.

Scale.   Distance is based more simply on a direct comparison between linear measurements on the earth and on the map.   A map that is the same size as the portion of the earth it represents would be similar to a pattern used by a dressmaker or toolmaker.   Maps are not patterns and are therefore, without exception, smaller in size than the size of the corresponding segment of the earth.   It is obvious that a ratio must exist between a linear measurement on the earth and its facsimile on the map.   This ratio is *scale.*   Any distance on the map is taken as unity, or 1.   The corresponding number of units which this same distance has on the earth provides the remainder of the ratio (or the denominator to the numerator of 1).   Thus a scale of 1:10,000 is a ratio in which one unit on the map (in inches, centimeters, spans, pipestems, or any other measurements) equals 10,000 of the same units on the earth.   A scale of 1:1 would be "pattern-size."   A scale of 1:100,000 is ten times *smaller* than 1:10,000 be-

---

* Azimuth is stated in degrees from 0° to 360°. Two systems are in common use, reading clockwise from either the north or the south point. Bearings are stated in quadrants (quarter circles), using the nearest meridianal point and the direction from it. For example, S. 75° is the bearing of azimuth 105° (from north point) or azimuth 285° (from south point).

cause the unit on the map stands for 10 times as many units on the ground. Scale may be written as a fraction (1/10,000), sometimes designated as R.F. or representative fraction. Scale also may be expressed in words that translate the ratio of like units into other equivalents. For example, a scale of one inch to one mile has a ratio of 1:63,360 (viz. 5280 feet in one mile × 12 inches in one foot = 63,360 inches in one mile). Therefore, if one unit is one inch in the numerator, the 63,360 units in the denominator equal one mile. Scale may be expressed also as a line drawn on the map and divided into distances representing the distances on the earth. This is an appropriate convention because it makes measurement possible by direct comparison with the subdivided line.

It must be emphasized that scale is a linear comparison between map and earth. The greater the disparity between these two measurements the smaller is the scale. This may be readily appreciated and remembered by recalling that ½ is larger than ¼, and thus 1:10,000 is larger than 1:100,-000. Areal comparisons between scales, in accordance with the principles of geometry, are in terms of the squares of their linear measurements. Thus, in the last example above, the linear difference is 10 times but the areal difference is 100 times, since area implies the measurement of two directions at right angles to each other.

Position.   The third attribute that makes a map, that of position, is a consequence of distance and direction, and it is often expressed in terms of the other two (so far in such a direction from a known point). Absolute position may be stated as an intersection of the geographical grid lines in terms of latitude and longitude;* for example, Washington National Observatory, 38°55′ N., 77°04′ W. Other systems of coordinates may be used, such as the town and range systems of the U. S. Land Survey (Figure 4, p. 298); the arbitrary coordinates of a military grid; and the network lines on an atlas page.

A map, then, is a representation of the surface of the earth, or some portion of it, in which directions, distance, and position are shown as truly as possible, or with sufficient accuracy for the purposes of the representation. That perfect representation from a mathematical point of view is impossible will be demonstrated subsequently.

* Latitude is the distance north or south of the equator expressed in degrees from 0° at the equator to 90° at each pole. Lines measuring latitude extend east and west around the earth parallel to and including the equator. These lines, therefore, are "parallels of latitude." Longitude is the measurement of distance east and west on the earth. Since no obvious starting point for such measurement exists, an arbitrary line must be selected. Many such "prime meridians" have existed, but today the meridian of Greenwich, England, is commonly accepted as zero. The north and south "meridians" marking the intervals of longitude are numbered from the prime meridian westward to 180° and eastward to 180° to complete the circumference of the earth.

II. Measurements for Mapping

Base-Line and Triangulation.   Maps have their origin in the measurement of the earth.   Since most maps either are concerned with the land and water bodies of the earth, or relate their subject matter to this distribution, it is apparent that this primary distribution must be determined. The precise determination is known as surveying.   The basic concepts of surveying are simple, although the exact methods and applications may be exceedingly complex.   Surveying is based on straight lines.   A straight line is most easy to sight along, to measure, and to draw.   Therefore, direction (line-of-sight) and distance (along the line) may be simulated by a proportionately smaller straight line drawn upon a piece of paper or map. The place where two or more straight lines intersect is a fixed position, which also may be plotted upon the map.

Surveying, or sighting along straight lines, takes two fundamental forms. The first is the *traverse,* in which, starting from a known position, the direction and the distance is measured along each of a succession of straight lines.   Points of positions not on these lines may then be related to this framework by additional straight lines drawn and measured to them.   The second method is *triangulation.*   In this method the measurement of angles takes the place of the measurement of lines, except that at the beginning a *base-line* must be measured carefully.   Triangulation makes use of the triangle, or three-sided geometrical figure.   Given the measurements of the angles of a triangle and the length of one side, the lengths of other sides can be determined by the simple trigonometry to which virtually every school child in the Occidental culture is exposed.   Thus triangulation is the building of triangles in which the directions of the sides are known and the distances are computed after measuring the angles between sides.   It has an advantage over the traverse in that many observations can be made from one point and in that the tedious and exacting measurement of lines is avoided, save for the necessary base-line.   This method, like the traverse, supplies a framework of known lines and positions to which other detail can be added by further sighting and measurement.

Complexities are added to these simple methods by the fact that instruments are not perfect and man is not infallible; by the irregularly oblate spheroidal shape of the earth, which introduces problems of spherical trigonometry; by the influences of gravity and magnetism, which differ from place to place; by the presence of vegetation, atmospheric refraction, and other handicaps to observation; and by the irregularities in altitude and slope that occur on the surface of the earth.

Elevation.　The measurement and mapping of the surface irregularities of the earth require that some point be chosen to which to relate places of higher, lower, or equal elevation.　This point is most often the ocean at some aspect of its level (as "mean sea level" or "lower low water"), and the point is transformed into a geometrical figure of area to become the "datum plane."　Since the distance from the center of the earth to the surface of any ocean is affected by gravitational differences from place to place, and since all the oceans have differing "levels," the altitudes obtained from different datum planes are not directly comparable.

Elevation with reference to the datum plane is measured by a procedure called "leveling."　Leveling consists of determining the altitude of points the horizontal position of which is known by surveying.　The method is to measure the distance between points and their differences in vertical angle from each other.　This may be done with a number of different instruments for measuring these two elements.　In the United States the telescopic alidade and the leveling rod are commonly employed.　The former is focused on the latter.　The number of marked intervals on the rod intersected by the cross hairs in the lens of the telescope gives the distance.　The angle of the instrument focused on the rod is given by a measuring arc in terms of degrees of elevation or depression from the horizontal.　The two figures entered into a table give the difference in elevation between the known position and the new position.　The map representation of differences in elevation and the form of the surface require the use of symbols.

The impact of earth-orbiting observatories upon the measurement of the earth for mapping, and upon the gathering of many kinds of geographic data, is a subject of much interest to geographers and to other scientists concerned with the surface of the earth and with the atmosphere.　A variety of *remote sensors,* such as infrared radiometers, high resolution radars, and multiband cameras, can be placed in space and used for "looking at" and recording observations about the earth.　These tools promise great speed, precision over broad areas, and efficiency as compared to traditional earth —or atmosphere—bound instruments, through whose use the earth's surface is still poorly known in many of its dimensions and aspects.　Contemporaneous world-wide mapping will become possible; seasonal changes in cloud, snow, and vegetation cover, in surface waters and sea ice, and in other cyclic phenomena will be recorded through time-lapse series; transportation flows will be measured at a given moment of time; urban and rural land settlement and use data will be available in a variety of detail never before possible.　The very richness and volume of information that will be amassed through the new techniques using remote sensors will require a parallel development of techniques that will permit the effective

The first unmanned Mercury Spacecraft to orbit the earth photographs the West African Coast. From the Strait of Gibraltar to Cabo Yubi, Morocco. Cloud cover hangs close to the coastal area and the Atlantic Ocean appears in the top left of the picture. (NASA).

and flexible handling of the data. The information acquired must be processed, organized, stored, retrieved from storage, compared and recombined, and referenced to place and to time. Much of the new knowledge gained in this new age of exploration which is upon us will be recorded and used in the traditional form of the map.

III. Map Projections

The Properties of Map Projections.   Reduction of measurements made on the face of the earth to scale representations on the map is a simple procedure provided that only a few square miles of the land surface are involved. Areas of greater extent are more complex because the curvature of the earth's surface and the flat plane of the surface of the map are different geometric forms. The whole earth, or any major segment of it, cannot be simulated to scale except by a globe or a part of a globe, any more than a ball or other round object can be flattened without distortion. By acknowledging and understanding this distortion, the earth spheroid can be represented on a plane surface. This is the *map projection** in which the geographical grid (latitude and longitude lines) of the earth is systematically arranged on a plane surface in order to achieve some desired qualities or properties. The properties that may be obtained are:

a. Conformality (orthomorphism), in which angles formed by intersecting lines are the same on the map as on the globe. This quality results from right-angle intersection of meridians and parallels on the map (as they are on the earth) and the same scale along these lines (not necessarily the true scale) at the intersection.

b. Equivalence (equal area), in which the ratio between any area on the earth and the corresponding area on the map is constant. This quality is obtained by adjusting the spacing of parallels and meridians so that the area enclosed by any quadrilateral composed of these lines is of the same size proportionally to the similar area on the earth, as is any other quadrilateral. Equivalence applies to the whole map, although shapes must be distorted on any equal-area map in order to keep areas in the same proportion to the earth everywhere.

c. In conjunction with either of the above properties, another quality known as *azimuthal* (or zenithal) may be obtained. Azimuthal projections are those in which direction is truly represented from the center of the projection.

d. Some projections fail to possess any of the above properties, but are *compromises* which sacrifice exactness in order to attain the approximate appearance of the earth, or part of it.

e. The property of showing curved lines on the globe as straight lines on the map.

The variety of map projections that it is possible to construct is almost infinite. However, a limited number of projections are commonly used. The following pages are devoted to those which are commonly encountered, although two pure, but extreme, perspective forms of little actual significance are used to introduce some of the principles involved.

Cylindrical Perspective Projections. The basic concept of the "perspective" projection is that the geometrical figure upon which the geographical grid is "projected" must be developable. That is, the figure must be one

---

*The term "projection" is in good repute even though most projections are mathematically computed and are not true perspective arrangements of the geographical grid "projected" onto a geometrical figure.

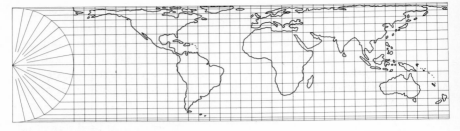

(A)

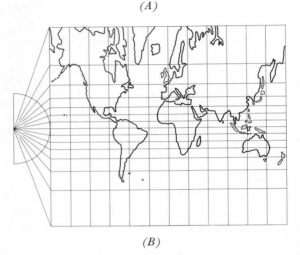

(B)

Figure 13. (a) *Cylindrical equal-area projection;* (b) *central cylindrical perspective projection.*

that can be flattened out into a plane surface without distorion. One such figure is the cylinder which, after cutting, may be unrolled. A paper cylinder may be wrapped around a globe representing the earth, and the geographical grid may be transferred from globe to paper. If a paper cylinder tangent at the equator (the usual case) is of the same height as the diameter of the globe, and if it is intended to represent the whole globe, then a map projection such as Figure 13, A, is obtained. This is the *cylindrical equal-area projection,* in which the lines of perspective are assumed to come from infinity as parallel lines. Clearly the equator is truly represented, since the length of the equator on the globe is the same as on the tangent cylinder. However, the poles, which on the globe are points, are elongated by this perspective projection into lines the same length as the equator. This results in great east-west stretching in high or polar latitudes as well as crowded parallels. Observe that half of the circumference of the globe is compressed into the distance representing the length of the diameter of the globe, and that the spacing between parallels decreases away from the equator.   This projection, then, is so objectionable in high latitudes as to be little used.

The cylinder of paper may once more be wrapped tangent to the equator of the globe, and the origin of the perspective lines transferring the geographical grid to the paper may be placed elsewhere.   If the origin be placed in the center of the globe, *the central cylindrical perspective projection,* shown by Figure 13, B, results.   Once again the equator is truly represented, but obviously the poles can never be shown, since they lie parallel to the tangent cylinder.   High latitudes are so grossly exaggerated in area and shape that this is hardly a satisfactory projection.

Mercator.   Using the ideas contained in the above projections, it is possible to construct other cylindrical projections that do have significance. Gerhardus Mercator in 1569 published one that bears his name.   It had great significance in the age of exploration by sea, and it is the best known projection today.   It is also most commonly misunderstood.   Mercator compromised between the cylindrical equal area and the central cylindrical perspective projections by spacing the parallels not according to any perspective arrangement but mathematically, so that expansion of the area north and south of the equator is at the same scale as expansion east and west in any given latitude.   For example, the parallel of 60° latitude is, on any cylindrical projection, just twice as long as on the earth, and 80° latitude is six times as great.   Mercator made his distortion in the N.–S. direction in these same proportions.   The projection is, therefore, conformal, but of increasing scale and decreasing fidelity of larger shapes away from the equator; and the poles cannot be shown.

The Mercator projection owes its fame to the fact that a *straight line* upon it cuts all meridians at the same angle and is a *rhumb line,* or line of true compass direction.*   It is not necessarily the shortest line between two points on the earth (unless they are on the same meridian or both are on the equator), but it is one the direction of which is easily ascertained, and also it can be steered by compass in a ship or airplane.   Therefore, navigators generally use the Mercator map or chart to determine their direction of movement.   *Great circles,* or shortest routes between widely spaced points, are often approximated by traveling along a series of rhumb lines obtained from the Mercator projection, rather than trying to steer a constantly changing compass course.   The Mercator projection has obtained

---

*A line of true or constant direction on the globe that trends in one of the cardinal directions (E., W., N., or S.) is a straight line since it is a parallel or meridian of the geographical grid. Any line trending in any other direction must cut across the geographical grid and, on the globe, follows a spiral path, or *loxodrome,* which curves toward the nearest pole, but theoretically never reaches it.   The spiral path of the loxodrome may be demonstrated by drawing a line on the globe that everywhere trends northeast, for example.

the sanction of established use to such a degree that it is often mis-used where equal-area projections or other projections of the whole world would be more appropriate. Much confusion over the size and positions of areas on the earth, such as the relative areas of Greenland and South America (compare the projection in Figure 15, B, with Figure 13, B) or the idea that North America is located between Europe and Asia, arises from the inappropriate use of the Mercator projection.

Elliptical Projections. The tangent cylinder lends itself to other perspec-tive and mathematical projections.* A related class consists of those oval or elliptical projections of the whole earth in which the meridians are not parallel to each other, but are less widely separated toward the poles. In these projections the diameter of the globe forms the N.–S. axis, while the E.–W. axis is taken as twice this value. This relationship of distance from pole to pole, being one half the distance along the equator, is the same as on a globe and is the basis for equality of area. Three equivalent projec-tions on this scheme are shown in Figure 14. *Mollweide's homolographic* and the *Sanson-Flamsteed sinusoidal* projections both possess meridians equally spaced on the parallels, and the latter are truly parallel as on the globe. They differ from each other in that the homolographic diminishes the in-terval between parallels toward the poles, thereby expanding E.–W. the shapes of the lands in the high latitudes; the sinusoidal expands the inter-val between parallels toward the poles, thereby contracting the E.–W. extent of lands in high latitudes. The *Hammer-Aitoff* projection (Figure 14) effects a compromise by departing from the parallelism of the parallels of the globe. Despite the curved parallels, equivalence is maintained by decreasing the spacing of the meridians toward the margins of the projec-tion. The result is a pleasing projection in which shapes of land areas are well shown.

A drawback to all the oval projections is that only the areas adjacent to the central meridian have good shapes. One solution is to lengthen the points that represent the poles to lines parallel to, but not as long as, the equator. Such projections are those of *Eckert* and *Denoyer's semi-elliptical*. They may be made equivalent, but they introduce their own errors of shapes, for, obviously, the poles cannot truly be shown as lines.

A second rationalization consists of "interrupting" the world projections so as to create several central meridians around each of which is plotted a segment of the geographical grid. This reduces the errors of shape very materially while retaining equality of area. Carried to its extreme, these

*O. M. Miller, "Notes on Cylindrical World Map Projections," *Geographical Review*, Vol. 32 (1942), pp. 424–430.

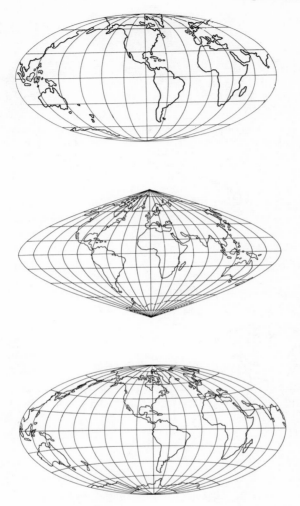

Figure 14. Projections.

interruptions would be the "gores" of paper with which an inexpensive globe is covered (Figure 15, A). One interrupted projection is *J. Paul Goode's homolosine* projection. Close examination of Figure 15, B, will reveal that Goode has used Mollweide's homolographic projection from 40° to the poles, and the sinusoidal between the equator and 40°, in order to get the best shapes for each area, and that he has "interrupted" the

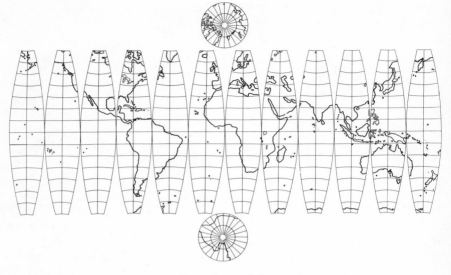

Gores for a globe

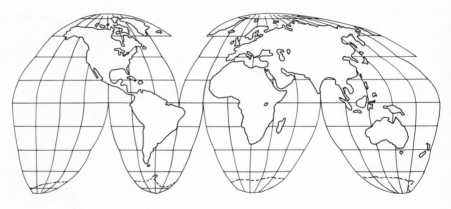

Goode's homolosine projection

Figure 15. (A) Gores for a globe; (B) Goode's Interrupted Homolosine projection.

oceans to maintain the continents as units. Another edition of this projection interrupts the continents to give continuity to the oceans. V. C. Finch has provided a useful interruption of the Hammer-Aitoff projection by eliminating some of the landless areas of the earth and fitting the Australian–New Zealand segment into the position normally occupied by the Indian Ocean (Plate 14). A common reaction to these interrupted projections is objection to the fragmentary appearance of the geographical grid. Once it is appreciated how the various fragments fit, the realistic shapes and equivalent areas must be acknowledged to be an advantage over other world projections.

The sinusoidal projection is used in this book with a three-lobed interruption (see Map 76, p. 342). The lobe containing Europe and Africa uses the central meridian of 20° E., but each of the other two segments has a different central meridian north of the equator from that south of the equator because the land mass of South America is distinctly east of North America and the center of Australia is about 40° east of the approximate center of Asia.

Projections to a Plane. Another group of projections is derived by the perspective extension of the geographical grid from a globe to a plane that is tangent to that globe. Since a plane is used, and not a cylinder, only one half or less of the earth can be depicted. Moreover, these projections are azimuthal, since all great circle lines that pass through the tangent point (center of the projection) are straight lines and therefore directions are truly shown from the center of the projection. Three points are commonly chosen as the origin of the perspective lines: infinity, to produce the *orthographic projection;* the circumference of the globe at the point diametrically opposite the tangent plane, giving the *stereographic projection;* and the center of the globe, called the *gnomonic projection.* These projections may be prepared in three different forms or cases: *equatorial (normal),* with plane perpendicular to the equator; *polar,* with plane perpendicular to the pole; and *oblique,* with the plane in some intermediate position.

The orthographic projection shows considerable compression of the marginal areas of the hemisphere (Figure 16, A), just as perspective lines from infinity compress the high latitudes of the cylindrical equal-area projection. However, this is a useful projection because it has approximately the appearance of a globe, viewed from a distance, or a photograph of a globe. It is not exactly the same because neither the human eye nor the camera is at infinity.

The stereographic projection (Figure 16, B) has a geographical grid which expands away from the tangent point. It is conformal, but exaggerates areas near its margins as do all projections that show angles correctly.

On the gnomonic projection (Figure 17), with perspective lines derived from the center of the globe (similar to the central cylindrical perspective projection), the margins of a hemisphere cannot be shown since they lie in

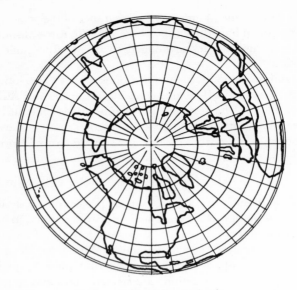

Orthographic polar projection

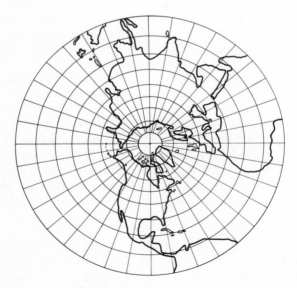

Stereographic polar projection

Figure 16. (A) Orthographic polar projection; (B) Stereographic polar projection.

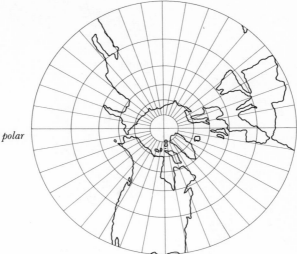

Figure 17. Gnomonic polar projection.

a plane parallel to the tangent surface. Indeed only a small part of a hemisphere can be shown without excessive expansion of shapes and sizes of areas. There is one unique property of the gnomonic projection which makes it useful in spite of its obvious defects. This is the fact that all straight lines drawn on the projection are great circle routes (i.e. great circle or circumference lines on the globe become straight lines on the projection). It is therefore possible for the navigator to determine readily the shortest distance between two points by plotting them on the gnomonic chart and connecting them with a straight line. Points along this line can be transferred to the Mercator chart (where they will form points on an arc unless they lie wholly on the equator or on a meridian) to obtain azimuths or directions (rhumb lines) by which to steer to approximate a great circle course.

The principle of the tangent plane may be used with the perspective lines originating elsewhere than stated above. It also may be followed in mathematically locating the geographical grid without recourse to perspective. There are two well-known projections of the latter type, one of which was constructed by the French cartographer Lambert in the eighteenth century. *Lambert's Azimuthal Equal-Area* projection gives satisfactory shapes to large areas of approximately equal dimensions and is therefore well adapted to use for continents, as in the plates in this book (Plates 3 and 5 are in the equatorial case; Plates 4 and 13, the oblique case). It is sometimes employed for hemispheres, but here the distortion of the peripheral areas becomes noticeable as in Map 49, p. 245.

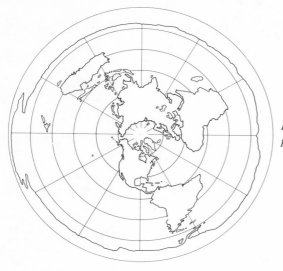

Figure 18. Azimuthal-equidistant polar projection.

The *Azimuthal-Equidistant* projection derives its name from the fact that any line drawn outward from the center of the projection not only has a true azimuth but also is true to scale throughout its length (Maps 83 and 84, pp. 364 and 365).   Since these are the two properties desired, shapes and areas cannot be considered important, and the projection may be extended to contain the whole world within its circumference.   If this projection is plotted around the North Pole (Figure 18), Antarctica occurs everywhere around its periphery, since all directions are south from the North Pole and must inevitably lead to the South Pole; and, on this projection, the South Pole is at its true scale distance—the radius of the projection.   If plotted around a point between pole and equator, both poles will be shown as centers from which the geographical grid curves and loops outward (Figure 19).   This projection has practical value for example, to radio engineers, since radio waves travel along straight lines outward from the center of propagation.

Conic Projections.   When map-makers and map-users are interested in areas of less than hemisphere proportions, they may employ parts of the foregoing projections or they may turn to a series of projections based on the concept of another developable geometric figure placed tangent to the globe.   This new figure is the cone, which is a surface intermediate between a cylinder and a plane and may be "unrolled" to become a plane. Commonly the apex of the cone is considered to lie on the polar axis of the earth extended into space, so that the cone is tangent to a selected *standard parallel*.   Following the analogy of the cylinder, this parallel must be of true

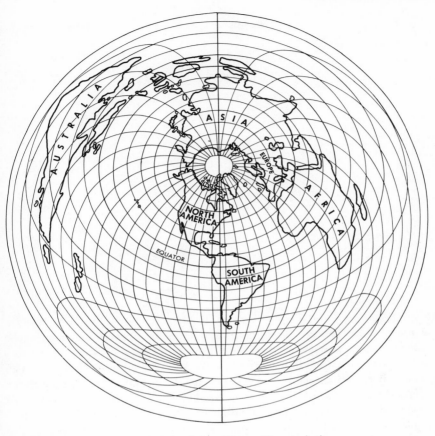

Figure 19. Azimuthal-equidistant oblique projection.

length and scale, since it is a line on the globe and the cone both. When the cone is unrolled and opened out into a plane surface, the standard parallel becomes an arc of a circle. All *other* parallels remain parallel to the standard parallel and are therefore concentric arcs on the map projection. The meridians are straight lines radiating outward from the apex of the cone.

In its simplest form, the conic projection is derived by perspective from the center of the globe so that the parallels are unevenly spaced, becoming farther apart away from the standard parallel. The ordinary *simple conic projection* has the parallels equally spaced at an arbitrarily chosen interval, and is particularly suited to areas of middle latitudes which extend a greater distance from east to west than from north to south. An improvement in scale can be attained by giving the conic projection *two standard*

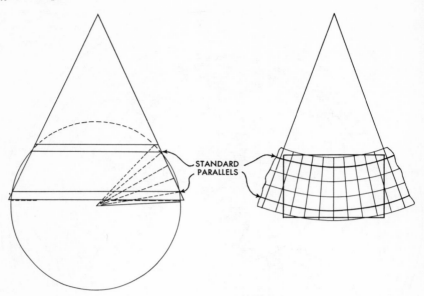

Figure 20. Conic projection with two standard parallels.

parallels. The concept here employed can be likened to passing the cone through a portion of the circumference of the globe, making the surface of the cone coincide with the two parallels (Figure 20).* The overall result is better, since scale errors are reduced, compared to a simple conic.

To add the desirable property of equivalence or of conformity to conic projections with two standard parallels it is necessary to space the parallels to get quadrilaterals proportionately the same as on the globe, or to space the parallels so that scale along parallel and meridian is the same at their intersections. The former spacing is known as *Alber's Equal-Area* projection and may be recognized by the fact that outside of the standard parallels the spacing of other parallels decreases. The latter is *Lambert's Conformal Conic* projection, and its parallels are increasingly wider apart beyond the standard parallels. Once again, these conic projections are best adapted to areas extending primarily east and west. By careful selection of the standard parallels, either projection will give a map of the United States, for example, with very little scale error.†

*Obviously a cylindrical projection also may be constructed secant to the globe rather than tangent. Such a projection, for example, is Gall's Stereographic in which the parallels of 45° N. and 45° S. become standard parallels, true to scale.

†Both of these projections have been calculated for the United States by the United States Coast and Geodetic Survey. Alber's Equal-Area, with standard parallels at 29½° N. and 45½° N., has a maximum scale error at 1¼% in the United States. Lambert's Conformal Conic, with standard parallels at 33° N. and 45° N., is 2½% off at the maximum, within the United States.

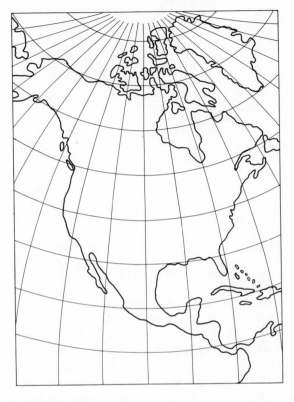

Figure 21. Bonne's projection.

The simple conic projection may be modified in other ways than the above. *Bonne's projection* (Figure 21) is commonly encountered in atlases for continental areas having the north-south axis longer than the east-west (North America or South America for example). The equally-spaced concentric arc parallels are retained, but the meridians are curved so that they meet at the pole, rather than extending as straight lines meeting in space at the apex of the cone. The spacing of meridians on the parallels gives quadrilaterals of true proportion to similar ones on the earth, and thus the projection is equal-area. Shapes are good along the straight central meridian only.

Another modification of the conic is particularly well known to Americans because it is the projection used for the detailed maps of the United States comprising the "Topographic Atlas," issued in the form of the familiar quadrangle sheets. This is the American polyconic projection in which not one cone but a whole series of cones are considered to rest tangent on the globe, each at a different parallel but with their apexes in a

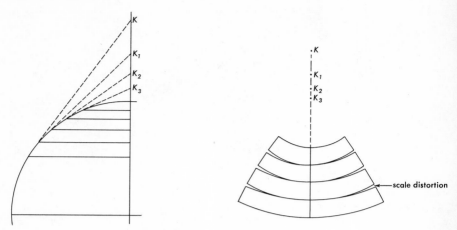

Figure 22. Polyconic projection.

common line.   Each parallel then is an arc of a circle, but the circles have different centers so that the arcs are not concentric to one another. Meridians drawn through the parallels at their true scale positions will yield one straight central meridian, and the remainder curved (Figure 22). Since the principle is one of adjustment northward and southward along many parallels representing many cones, this projection is best suited for areas of great length in those directions and of limited east-west extent.   Although the polyconic projection is neither equal-area nor conformal, its use for quadrangle sheets has been firmly established, probably because of the ease of construction from published figures.*   At the publication size and large scale of the quadrangles, it is not easy to recognize the lack of equivalence or conformality on an individual sheet.   A disadvantage of the American polyconic is that sheets lying along the same parallels will not fit together except by distorting the paper, although any number may be placed in a N.–S. line with perfect coincidence of margins.

The International Map of the World at the scale of 1:1,000,000 is divided into sheets 6° in longitude and 4° in latitude.   It is on the Lallemand Polyconic projection in which the familiar principle of two standard parallels is employed for each sheet and for each of the many cones.   This projection also uses straight-line meridians with two standard meridians on each sheet.   This device permits each sheet to be independently adjusted to one of the secant cones, yet to fit against the margins of the adjacent sheets north, south, east, and west.   Obviously, the Lallemand projection is a compromise and is neither equal-area nor conformal.

*United States Coast and Geodetic Survey, Special Publication No. 5.

The catalogue of map projections is by no means exhausted by the projections named above. Some additional manipulations take the following general forms:

a. Projections onto geometrical figures other than cylinder, plane, and cone. The figure may be a cube or other polyhedron. The geographical grid may be arbitrarily spaced within a conventional surface such as a circle.

b. Turning the cylinder or cone so that the developable geometrical figure is "skewed" with relation to the geographical grid. Examples are the *Transverse Mercator* and the *Transverse Polyconic,* in which the "good parts" along the equator of the Mercator and along the central meridian of the polyconic are given other orientations. Bonne's projection becomes *Werner's* when the tangent cone is fitted across the pole instead of along a parallel. *Werner's projection* becomes *Goode's Polar Equal-Area projection* when interrupted (see Map 7, p. 68).

IV. Map Symbols

It has previously been stated that maps are selective representations of facts of distribution. This is true even of the topographic map, which shows a small area at large scale, because all the manifold aspects of the earth's surface cannot be depicted. The usual combination of selected features on topographic maps falls into five categories:

a. The surface configuration, including form, elevation, and relief.*

b. The drainage pattern, including running water, standing water, and permanent ice.

c. The material works of man, including settlements, structures he erects, transportation ways he builds, and other facts of his land use.

d. Certain invisible aspects of man's use of the land such as political boundaries and air routes.

e. The conventions of the map such as geographical grid, borders, index numbering, and so forth.

Sometimes a sixth category consists of the vegetation cover.

Obviously, the category of invisible facts can be represented on the map only by means of symbols. It is less obvious perhaps, but just as true, that all the other categories also require symbols. How can a railroad track 4' 8½" between rails be drawn to scale, with ties, ballast, and switches? How can a stream be shown that changes its course, its width, and its volume? How would you draw a hill? The use of symbols or conventions that

---

* See the definition of relief given on page 101.

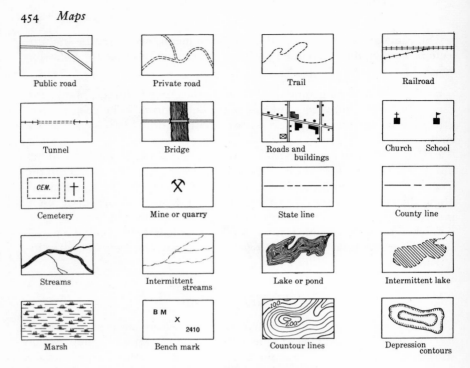

Figure 23. Symbols on U.S. topographic maps.

stand for given facts is imperative. The quality and accuracy of a topographic map depends on the selection of data and their symbolization.

The symbols commonly used on the United States topographic maps are depicted in Figure 23. Those that represent point locations or linear distributions require no explanation, for they are generally a stylized portrayal of a tangible fact as seen from a vertical position,* or an arbitrary representation of an intangible. However, surface configuration has a broad two-dimensional aspect that is difficult to symbolize and a third, or vertical, dimension that must be shown and is even more difficult to present on the two-dimensional surface of a map.

Representing the Vertical Dimension. An oblique (nonvertical) photograph such as that taken out of a window of an airplane shows the vertical dimensions of the land by the principles of perspective, but scale obviously changes away from the camera, and objects are obscured by both distance and intervention of other objects between them and the camera.

---

* This fact will be appreciated by noting that the marsh symbol is viewed from a horizontal position.

The cartographer may render a similar "pictorial" impression of relief. He may adjust distance and scale by changing his position with reference to perspective from place to place on the map. However, he must always displace some portions of the landforms from their true positions and obscure some areas by that displacement, in order to show height and depth. The high volcanic cone of Fujiyama in Map 92 (p. 404), for example, is drawn from an oblique view, whereas the urban areas of Yokohama and Tokyo are seen from a vertical position. The realistic effects of this map by Guy-Harold Smith, or of the "physiographic method" used so effectively by Erwin Raisz (see Maps 10, 11, and 13, pp. 75, 77, and 82, and many others in this book) may compensate for the errors inherent in an oblique view. The physiographic method is, of course, a symbol system because each type of land surface is represented in a particular way, rather than as an individual unique form.* If each mountain were drawn as exactly as possible, which of the numerous oblique views would be representative of it?

The vertical aerial photograph gives some impression of surface forms by the distribution of light and shadow. Unless the contrasts are strong and the relief of the surface is great the nature of the surface may not be readily recognized. This is a common disadvantage of photomaps. Indeed, vertical photographs must be used in stereoscopic pairs† in order to measure slope, height, and relief. The cartographer may employ light and shadow more effectively than most photographs to give the appearance of the vertical dimension on a two-dimensional surface because he can select the amount and the angle of illumination. This method is called plastic shading (as in Figure 24, which should be compared with Map 96, p. 415). It is not susceptible to measurement, unless combined with some other form of relief representation.

A more measurable employment of light and shadow is known as the hachure system. Hachures are short lines drawn vertical to the steepest slope, thin lines representing gentle slopes and thick lines representing steep slopes. In the Lehman system, slopes of 45° or greater employ hachures so close together that they merge into solid black masses. Hachured maps are difficult to draw and difficult to make measurements

---

* Erwin Raisz, "The Physiographic Method of Representing Scenery on Maps," *Geographical Review*, Vol. 21 (1931), 297–304. A considerable degree of realism characterizes the use of these symbols in that the drainage pattern is closely followed, as well as the trends of uplands and changes in slope.

† A pair of photographs which have some part of their area in common but are photographed from different angles so that when placed in a stereoscopic instrument (or properly viewed by the unaided eyes) they produce a three-dimensional image.

Figure 24. Plastic shading with oblique illumination (Switzerland and adjacent areas, from a map of Europe by R. E. Harrison, Ginn and Company, 1958).

from, although the effect of relief is pleasant to the eye, particularly when combined with light and shadow effects (Figure 25). High and flat areas may be difficult to distinguish from low and flat areas, and absolute altitude must be indicated by figures.

While all the above systems have their peculiar merits, cartographers more commonly employ another system, particularly for maps of topographic quality. This is the contour line, which may be defined as an imaginary line on the surface of the ground everywhere at the same elevation above the datum plane for vertical measurements. Successive contour lines above and below each other are separated by an arbitrary contour interval. In reading a map employing contour lines, it is mandatory that we know the contour interval as well as the exact elevation of the lines. Since a contour line is everywhere throughout its length parallel to the datum plane, it neither rises nor falls in elevation, and it must, if traced far enough, come back to close with itself to form an endless line. No two contour lines may touch each other, since they are separated by a contour interval, although a vertical or overhanging cliff, because of the horizontal position of the lines printed on the map, will cause the contours to join or cross each other.

Figure 25. Hachuring with oblique illumination (from the Dufour map of Switzerland).

The way in which certain surface features are represented by contour lines is shown on a relief sketch and map (Figure 26).

Certain basic rules for the interpretation of contour lines are:

a. Contour lines are continuous and do not branch or cross.

b. If a contour line closes upon itself within the area of the map, the land slopes upward from the area outside to the area within the enclosure. Therefore, a group of more or less concentric closed contour lines represents a hill.

c. Contour lines bend when they approach a stream valley so that the bend in the line points in the upstream direction. Relations of valleys to contour lines may be seen in the relief sketch and contour map shown on page 458 (Fig. 26).

d. Contour lines that enclose depressions which have no outlets at the altitude of the contour lines must be specially marked in order to reveal that the enclosed area is lower (see rule *b* above). This marking usually is in the form of hachures pointing downslope drawn along the contour lines, at right angles to the lines.

e. Some map producers emphasize particular lines (for example every fifth line) by greater width of line in order to guide the eye through the complexities of many adjacent lines.

When properly selected as to contour interval and width of line in relation to the scale of the map and the relief of the area, contours may give

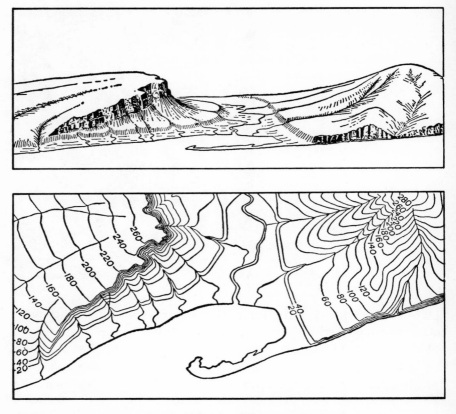

Figure 26. A relief sketch and contour map representation.

a very excellent *visual* impression of the configuration of the surface. Where the contours are bunched together the slopes are great and, if the contour lines are irregular, the surface is rough. Where the contours are closed and concentric the reader sees ridge tops, hilltops, and mountain ranges. Areas of widely spaced contours are low in slope and may represent plains, valleys, or broad upland surfaces according to their relationships to other features. Thus, the qualitative characteristics of the surface may be read almost at a glance and with about as full comprehension as provided by any other symbol system. Quantitatively, it is possible to read altitude within the limits of the contour interval. Spot heights may be used to supplement the value of the lines. It is also possible to determine the vertical relief between two or more points. Horizontal distances being known, the calculation of slope is possible. The contoured topographic map, then, is favored by engineers and others who must have

quantitative data. Some geographers and physiographers have transformed contour maps into relative relief and average slope maps.*

Quantitative and Non-quantitative Data. The principle behind the contour line has been applied to the representation of quantitative data on
maps. These lines are called *isarithms,* or lines of equal value. Examples
of isarithms are furnished in the field of climatology: isotherms (lines of
equal temperature, Map 83); isobars (lines of equal pressure, Map 99);
isohyets (lines of equal precipitation, Plate 12). In these examples the
data are continuous in their distribution and change only in amount or
degree. Some authorities therefore distinguish *isopleths,* or lines of equal
value drawn through data that are discontinuous, such as the distribution
of people on the face of the earth. Very often the interval between isarithms or isopleths is given a color or pattern to focus attention not on the
line of equal value but on the value category comprehended between two
such lines. This principle is used in the snowfall map of Canada (Map
75, p. 340), the average rainfall map of the world (Plate 12), and the population maps of the world (Plates 1 through 6).

Quantitative data may also be represented by dots placed on the map.
These dots may have a uniform value as on the maps of corn production
in the United States (Map 65, pp. 300–301). The visual impression of
distribution may be excellent if the relationships between scale, size, or sizes
of dots and values of dots are carefully considered. However, the difficulty
of counting many dots, and the impossibility of counting merging dots
limits the quantitative use of this symbol system. To obviate this objection,
various schemes have been proposed such as arrangement of dots in count-
able patterns like squares or rectangles; use of open or shaded large circles
through which the individual dots of congested areas may be recognized;
employment of "spherical dots," in which value equals the volume of the
sphere rather than area of the circle or dot; and the erection of square dots
or cubes into piles of blocks. The latter is a step toward a graphical system.
It is possible to place any of the common figures such as pie graphs, bar
graphs, and line graphs on the face of a map.

Non-quantitative distributions are represented by a great diversity of
symbols indicating points, linear patterns, or areal patterns. Sometimes
the symbol selected is purely arbitrary, and sometimes it is a pictorial
effect. Consider as an example the map of the rice-land topography on

* Examples are: C. K. Wentworth, "A Simplified Method of Determining the Average Slope of
Land Surfaces," *American Journal of Science,* Series 5, Vol. 20 (1930), pp. 184–194. E. Raisz and
J. Henry, "An Average Slope Map of Southern New England," *Geographical Review,* Vol. 27
(1937), pp. 467–472. Guy-Harold Smith, "The Relative Relief of Ohio," *Geographical Review,*
Vol. 25 (1935), pp. 272–284.

the delta of the Mahanadi (Map 21, p. 120).   Drainage ditches and un-paved roads use symbols employed on many maps, although the ditch symbol also is used for a wall on some maps.   Coastal bar and waste land is an arbitrary symbol easily drawn and in good contrast to the mangrove and jungle symbol, which attempts to look like the vegetation it presents. One must read more closely and accurately to appreciate that the blank areas are rice land, the avowed subject of the map.   Because symbols are not always self-explanatory, a well-considered map has a legend or key de-fining such symbols.   It is a good map-reading habit to examine the le-gend as well as the scale (and contour interval and projection) before attempting the interpretation of a map.

Greater legibility on maps often is obtained by the use of colors.   Colors may be selected with some relationship to the facts they present, as, for ex-ample, on many atlas maps presenting the world distribution of natural vegetation.   The number of categories being limited, colors may be selected that suggest the vegetative associations portrayed.   The Dry Lands and Grasslands may be assigned grays or yellows whose color density varies in proportion to the floral density.   The forest groups may be designated by greens whose shades and densities may be related to temperature con-cepts.   Tundra and icecaps may then be gray or white.   Colors thus used are easily remembered.   A false impression often is conveyed to the unini-tiated by the hypsometric system used to represent altitude of land sur-faces, particularly on small-scale maps.   Contour lines at large and often irregular intervals separate colors which usually begin with greens at low altitudes and progress through yellows and browns to reds at high alti-tudes.   Because of the infrequency of the contour lines and the wide extent of the color areas, the unfortunate and erroneous impression may be given that elevation changes abruptly at the contact of two colors, and that little change takes place within a given color area.

Legibility of maps is more than a matter of color or of symbol selection. It is related to the function of the map.   Topographic maps portraying many of the tangible features of a landscape and some related intangible data require approximately equal emphasis and clarity among cultural symbols, so that all may be distinguishable, and sufficient emphasis on physical symbols (often obtained through color) so that they form a read-ily intelligible pattern upon which the cultural symbols are distributed. Maps of smaller scale covering larger areas usually place particular em-phasis on a limited number of distributions.   For example, note the em-phasis given to Indian trails in Michigan in Map 53 (p. 263) and to the road from Peshawar to Bukhara in Map 97, (p. 418).   Note the striking symbol used to show the Laurentian hilly upland (Map 78, p. 349).   Note also the distinctive symbol used to show cropland in Alaska (Map 81, p. 355).

V. Map Sources and Collections

Atlases.   Collections of maps brought together in bound or loose-leaf form are known as atlases.   Because of their great utility and handiness compared to individual sheet maps, atlases form a basic reference source comparable to dictionaries and encyclopedias.   The subject area of an atlas may be as general as the world, or as detailed as a county or other minor political division.   Some countries, such as France, Finland, Poland, Czechoslovakia, the U.S.S.R., and Canada, have provided extremely valuable and significant national atlases.   A national atlas for the United States is being prepared.

Sheet Maps.   Unbound sheet maps exist for such a variety of areas and subjects, and in such tremendous quantities, that reference collections are very limited in comparison with the distribution of atlases.   In the United States, local and state government offices and libraries often are well supplied with sheet maps of their particular areas.   For the nation as a whole and for foreign coverage the major sources available to the student or map user are the federal Government and the major geographical societies.   Inquiries concerning domestic mapping may be directed to Map Information Office, U. S. Geological Survey, Washington, D. C.   This office has knowledge not only of the topographic quadrangles and other mapping work of the U.S.G.S. but also of the work of the Coast and Geodetic Survey, the U. S. Department of Agriculture, and all other mapping sections of the Federal Government.   Foreign map collections of real significence exist in Washington at the Library of Congress, Army Map Service (Department of the Army), Hydrographic Office (Department of the Navy), and Department of State.   The most important non-governmental collection is in New York City at the American Geographical Society.

The list of publishers of sheet maps is very extended.   However, a limited number of publishers should be known to every map user.   For the United States, the topographic quadrangles of the U.S.G.S. (supplementary work by Mississippi River Commission; U.S.C.&G.S., Tennessee Valley Authority; and others) are basic.   The largest scale map covering all the United States is supplied by the Geological Survey, at 1:250,000.   In the field of foreign and world mapping, the International Map of the World occupies an important position.   This map is intended to cover the entire world at 1:1,000,000 as a cooperative effort among many nations, following map specifications agreed upon in 1909 and subsequently.   Although far from complete, great progress has been made, particularly during World War II.   The American Geographical Society has completely mapped North America and South America.   European coverage has been completed by various national groups, and reissued by the British government, which also has prepared large parts of Asia and Africa. The British group working on this and many other maps in Europe, Africa, and Asia is the Geographical Section of the General Staff (GS,GS). The American counterpart, which worked cooperatively with GS,GS during World War II to fill in the gaps in world maps at various scales, is the Army Map Service (AMS). Through the latter many universities and public libraries in the United States are participants in a map depository program which features the placement of AMS copies of foreign topographic maps in major population centers throughout the country.

Most topographic maps are of such detail that they must be issued in many individual sheets that form parts of the whole map. These sheets make up a set (or series) of maps. A map set commonly has the same characteristics throughout its sheets, which differ from each other primarily in position. The usual method of keeping records of these sheets is to plot them in miniature on a small-scale index map. All the maps mentioned in the paragraph above are grouped into sets.

Sheet maps that do not constitute sets must be regarded as individual items. Their cataloguing and filing raise problems comparable, but not entirely similar, to problems encountered with books and bound documents. The primary differences between the latter and maps are that area is the map subject of importance, and that a map is physically a thin, and often large, sheet of paper. A number of library systems for maps have been devised, but no general recognition of the merits of a particular one over all others has been forth-coming. However, the most useful systems all depend upon division of the world into arbitrary areas (usually political units). Small-scale maps of large areas are then catalogued with the major divisions of the world, and large-scale maps of small areas with the subdivisions. Maps that present unusual combinations of area are arbitrarily placed in one division and cross-referenced as necessary. In large collections, the designation of area is supplemented with a definition of subject matter of the map. With these principles in mind, it will be found that the library system of any of the major collections may be readily used.

REFERENCES

1. DEETZ, C. H., and ADAMS, O. S. *Elements of Map Projection*. United States Coast and Geodetic Survey, Special Publication 68. Washington, D. C., 1921.

2. DEBENHAM, FRANK. *Map Making*. London, 1936.

3. DEETZ, C. H. *Cartography*. United States Coast and Geodetic Survey, Special Publication 205. Washington, D. C., 1936.

4. HINKS, A. R. *Maps and Survey*. Fourth Edition. Cambridge (England), 1942.

5. FISHER, I. and MILLER, O. M. *World Maps and Globes*. New York, 1944.

6. CHAMBERLIN, WELLMAN. *The Round Earth on Flat Paper*. National Geographic Society. Washington, D. C., 1947.

7. BROWN, L. A. *Story of Maps*. Boston, 1949.

8. MONKHOUSE, F. J., and WILKINSON, H. R. *Maps and Diagrams, Their Compilation and Construction*. New York, 1952.

9. RAISZ, ERWIN. *Principles of Cartography*. New York, 1960.

10. ROBINSON, A. H. *Elements of Cartography*, Second Edition. New York, 1962.

11. GREENHOOD, DAVID. *Mapping*. Chicago, 1964

12. Remote Sensing of Environment, Office of Naval Research, No. 1224 (44) 1963.

13. COLWELL, ROBERT N., et al., "Basic Matter and Energy Relationships Involved in Remote Reconnaissance." *Photogrammetric Engineering*. 29:761–799.

The Atmosphere

I. Some Fundamental Meteorological Principles*

Composition of the Atmosphere. The atmosphere is a mixture of gases. About 78 per cent is nitrogen and about 21 per cent is oxygen; but of the remaining 1 per cent the small proportion of water vapor and carbon dioxide is of the greatest importance in determining the character of the earth's climates. Water vapor is confined almost wholly to the lower layers of the atmosphere, 90 per cent of it lying below twenty-one thousand feet. Its average mass the world over is such that, if it were condensed, it would be the equivalent of a layer of water about one inch deep over the entire surface of the earth.

Insolation. For all practical purposes the sun is the only source of the energy that maintains the temperature of the earth's surface and the atmosphere. The solar energy received at the surface of the earth depends upon four things: (1) the solar output of radiation, which fluctuates slightly in cycles of more or less regular recurrence; (2) the distance of the earth from the sun, which varies seasonally during the passage of the earth around the sun; (3) the inclination of the sun's rays to the plane of the horizon, which varies seasonally owing to the inclination of the earth's axis to the plane of its orbit and which also varies with latitude and local exposure; and (4) the transmission and absorption of the atmosphere. Table I (see reference 6, p. 487) gives the total amounts of solar energy (in

---

*These greatly condensed statements can offer to the student little more than an outline. The demands of time and space in this general survey do not permit a more penetrating treatment of the fundamental elements of geography; the student who plans to go on professionally must go much more deeply into the basic sciences of meteorology, climatology, geology, and geomorphology.

kilogram-calories per square centimeter of level surface) at the top of the atmosphere. From these figures we see that in a year only about 40 per cent as much solar energy is received above the poles as above the equator, and also that the rate of insolation (solar energy received by the earth) falls off most rapidly between latitudes 50° and 60°.

TABLE I.

Latitude	0	10	20	30	40	50	60	70	80	90
Summer half-year	160.5	169	173.5	173	169	160.5	149	139	134	133
Winter half-year	160.5	147	129.5	109	84	58.5	33	13	4	0
Annual	321.0	316	303.0	282	253	219.0	182	152	138	133

Heating of the Earth's Surface. The effect of the distribution of insolation over the earth is to produce, in general, the greatest amount of heating near the equator and the least amount at the poles. This simple latitudinal arrangement, however, is complicated by the *differential heating of land and water*. Water heats more slowly than land and retains its heat longer under similar atmospheric conditions. The relatively slow heating of water is the result chiefly of three facts: (1) the specific heat of land is lower than that of water; (2) water is translucent, so that a given amount of insolation which is concentrated on the surface of the land penetrates through a considerable depth of water; and (3) water is mobile, and so can distribute the heat which it absorbs. Radiation from a water body being less rapid than from the land, the former retains for a longer period the heat which it receives.

Heating the Air. About 37 per cent of the solar energy which reaches the top of the atmosphere is returned again to space by reflection, chiefly from upper cloud surfaces, but in part also from the earth's surface, especially from ice and snow. Of the 63 per cent not immediately returned to space, only about 10 per cent is absorbed by the atmosphere, and the remainder makes its way directly, or as diffuse sky-light, to the earth's surface.

The atmosphere is warmed chiefly by *conduction*, or contact with the earth, and by *radiation* from the earth. Owing primarily to the water vapor and, to a lesser extent, to the ozone and carbon dioxide, the air is able to absorb about 90 per cent of the long-wave terrestrial radiation, whereas it can absorb only about 10 per cent of the solar radiation. Since radiation absorbed in an air stratum is again radiated equally upward and downward, 45 per cent of the outgoing terrestrial radiation is returned again to the earth, and an equal amount finds its way out to space.

Cooling of the Earth.   Eventually as much energy is radiated from the earth as is received from the sun, for if this were not true the earth's average temperature would not remain approximately constant.   The effect of the atmosphere is to let through the incoming solar energy and to intercept the outgoing terrestrial radiation, so that the surface temperature of the earth is somewhat higher than it would be without the protection of its gaseous envelope.   The effect of this absorption of earth radiation is greater as the amount of water vapor increases.   The cooling of the earth's surface by radiation is therefore most rapid at high altitudes and in dry regions where the amount of water vapor is at a minimum.

The Energy Balance in the Atmosphere.   As a result of these processes of energy receipt and energy loss there is a notable contrast in the energy balance of the atmosphere between the part of the earth closer to the equator and the part farther away from the equator.   The dividing line is approximately latitude 38° in both hemispheres.   Within the part of the atmosphere between the equator and 38° there is a net build-up of energy; but within the part of the atmosphere which is more than 38° from the equator there is a net-loss of energy.

Vertical Arrangement of Temperature.   Because the atmosphere is heated chiefly from the surface of the earth, the temperature generally decreases with increasing altitude.   Up to an elevation of from six to nine miles this decrease is about 1° F. for each three hundred and thirty feet of increased altitude.   This is the average *vertical temperature gradient* in the free air. Above six to nine miles (higher over the equator and lower near the poles) the temperature remains fairly constant with increasing elevation.   This upper atmosphere is known as the *stratosphere* (illustrated in Figure 9, p. 388).   The lower zone, in which the temperature decreases with increasing altitude and in which vertical air movements are common, is known as the *troposphere.*

Adiabatic Cooling and Warming of Air.   A mass of rising air is cooled adiabatically; that is, without the removal of any heat from the mass of air involved.   With increase of elevation a rising mass of air expands: it becomes less dense and so its pressure decreases (see section Pressure, p. 468). As air expands it cools.   In a mass of rising dry air this rate of cooling is about 1.6° F. for every three hundred feet.   This is the *dry adiabatic rate.* When an air mass descends, this process is reversed, the air being warmed adiabatically at the same rate.

When the cooling of air results in the condensation of water (section Condensation of Moisture, p. 470), the dry adiabatic rate no longer prevails. Because of the liberation of latent heat in the process of condensation, the rate of temperature decrease becomes less, and the departure of this *retarded adiabatic rate* from the dry rate is greater as the rate of condensation is greater.

Vertical Air Movements.   When the temperature of a mass of air is higher than that of surrounding air, the colder air settles and forces the warmer air to rise. This action is due to the fact that colder air has a greater density than warmer air at the same elevation.   As long as the rising air mass is relatively warmer than the surrounding air at the same level, it will continue to rise.   The relationship between the vertical temperature gradient in the surrounding air and the adiabatic rate in the rising air determines, therefore, whether a vertical movement shall continue or quickly cease.   For if the rising air is cooled so rapidly that it becomes cooler than the surrounding air, it must settle back.   If, on the other hand, the rising air is cooled more slowly, so that the ascending air remains warmer than the surrounding air, the rise is continued.   Anything which increases the vertical temperature gradient or decreases the adiabatic rate tends to increase vertical air movements.   For instance, if moisture is condensing in the rising air mass, the rate of cooling is retarded (section Adiabatic Cooling and Warming of Air); therefore, air in which moisture is condensing tends to be more buoyant than air in which no condensation is taking place.   Buoyancy is also increased if a cold layer of air overriding a warmer surface layer increases the vertical temperature gradient.

In general, then, vertical air movements are common in warm, moist air, and if clouds are present they take the *cumulus* (cauliflower-shaped) form. Cold air, on the other hand, is sluggish and does not rise easily; clouds in such air are commonly *stratus* (sheetlike).

Pressure.   Pressure is the force exerted against a surface by the collision of molecules of gas against that surface.   The greater the density of the atmosphere the greater the force exerted by the bombardment of molecules. Pressure is commonly measured in terms of the height of a column of mercury that will balance this bombardment.   Normal pressure at sea level is about 30 inches of mercury (exactly 29.94 in.).   With increasing altitude the density of the air decreases: at 5000 feet the pressure is about 25 inches; and 10,500 feet, about 20 inches; at 16,000 feet, about 16 inches.

The pressure is not uniform over the earth's surface, however, even at sea level.   Air that is heated expands and has a lower density than cooler air. Air that is chilled contracts and its density becomes greater.

Convection.   The result of the increased density of chilled air or the decreased density of heated air is that gravity pulls the denser air down, replacing the air that is not so dense.   When air in a particular place is heated more than surrounding air, the denser air around the heated air mass is pulled down and over the surface of the earth toward the heated area. The heated air rises, being pushed up by the downward movement of the denser air. In a closed system a complete circulation would become established: denser air descending; air moving over the surface of the earth from cooler to warmer places; air rising over the warmer place; air aloft spilling over from the rising column onto the descending column. Such a circulation is called *convection*. It is important to note that the physical force that produces convection is gravity acting on the denser air.

Deflection Due to the Earth's Rotation. On the surface of our planet, however, all moving bodies are deflected from their courses as a result of the earth's rotation. In this brief summary the causes of this deflection cannot be presented.* The fact is, however, that all moving bodies in the Northern Hemisphere are deflected to the right and that all moving bodies in the Southern Hemisphere are deflected to the left. This deflection is strongest at the poles and reaches zero along the equator.

Winds and Pressures. As a result of this deflection (section Deflection Due to the Earth's Rotation), the winds which otherwise might blow out from a center of high pressure across the isobars (lines of equal pressure) actually move parallel or nearly parallel to the isobars. In the Northern Hemisphere, with deflection to the right, the winds whirl around a high-pressure center in a clockwise direction; and in the Southern Hemisphere, with a deflection to the left, the air movement around a high is counterclockwise. The movement around a low-pressure center is just the reverse: counterclockwise in the Northern Hemisphere and clockwise in the Southern Hemisphere. Over the oceans, where friction with the earth's surface is reduced to a minimum, the whirls are best developed and the winds are most nearly parallel to the isobars; but over the land, where friction retards the effect of the earth's rotation, the winds cross the isobars at larger angles (compare the wind maps on Plate 12).

Humidity. The amount of water vapor which can be mixed with the air depends on the temperature. At higher temperatures more water vapor can be present, but at lower temperatures much less water can exist in the air as a gas. Most of the time the actual amount of water vapor in the air is not so great as the maximum amount possible. The ratio between the water vapor actually present and the total possible amount at a given temperature is called the *relative humidity;* the ratio of the mass of water vapor to the total mass of air is called *specific humidity*. Relative humidity is meas-

*See reference 6 (p. 487).

ured in percentages: saturated air has a relative humidity of 100 per cent; air with half as much water vapor present as might be there has a relative humidity of 50 per cent.

Condensation of Moisture.   In a mass of rising air the temperature is lowered at the adiabatic rate; and as the temperature decreases, the relative humidity, but not the specific humidity, increases.   Eventually a level is reached where the relative humidity is 100 per cent.   As cooling continues, the water vapor is now ready to condense into liquid form.   Condensation must take place around some nucleus.   As a rule there are enough particles of dust carried aloft in the air to provide for condensation; but it has been found that "dusting" certain kinds of clouds with electrically charged particles increases the rate of condensation and may increase the fall of rain. Condensation and the formation of clouds in nature are produced by the rising and cooling of moist air.

Evaporation.   The evaporation of water takes place when the relative humidity of the air into which the water is evaporating is less than 100 per cent.   It increases in rapidity as the relative humidity becomes lower. Water vapor can therefore be picked up rapidly by masses of descending air, since in them the temperature is constantly rising and the relative humidity falling (although, if evaporation is going on, the specific humidity is increasing).   Evaporation is more rapid from warm-water surfaces than from cold-water surfaces; it is more rapid over fresh water than over salt water; and it is more rapid in windy places than in places where the air is still.

Precipitation.   Precipitation includes three forms: rain, snow, and hail. Rain falls when the drops of condensed moisture become large enough to fall through the ascending air currents.   When the drops of water blown upward in the air currents reach temperatures below the freezing point, hail is formed.   When the condensation takes place below the freezing point, snow crystals are formed.

The causes of rain are the same as the causes of condensation (section Condensation of Moisture), although condensation may, of course, proceed only far enough to form clouds from which no precipitation takes place. In nature, rain is caused almost exclusively by the cooling of moist air.   Furthermore, the cooling of air is most effectively, but not exclusively, accomplished by upward movement (section Adiabatic Cooling and Warming of Air).   Air may be caused to rise by the convergence of air masses in motion, especially by the rapid convergence upon a center of low pressure; or it may be forced to rise as it moves onto the shore of a continent or over a range of mountains.   Unless the air is warm and moist, however, rain will not be produced under either of these conditions; for the condition which would produce a rapid rise in buoyant air would cause only a sluggish rise, if any, in cold, dry air (section Vertical Air Movements).

Conversely, the lack of rain in a given area is the result either of the prevalence of descending and warming air masses or of remoteness from the sources of moisture, or both.

II. The Physical Bases of Climatic Differences on the Earth

The Controls of Climate.   The controls of climate may be grouped under seven headings: latitude, land and water, general circulation of air, cyclonic storms, ocean currents, mountain barriers, and a group of other minor controls.

Latitude.   Because of the decrease of insolation with increase of latitude (section Insolation), there is a general decrease of air temperature toward the poles.   However, this arrangement of temperature is much modified by other controls, not only seasonally but also in the average annual conditions.   Even the annual isotherms (lines of equal temperature) do not cross the continents parallel to the lines of latitude (Figure 1, p. 207).

Distribution of Land and Water.   The differential heating of land and water is of chief importance in modifying the effect of latitude as a control of climate (section Heating of the Earth's Surface).   An important distinction is recognized between *marine* and *continental* climates.   Marine climates are characterized by smaller annual ranges of temperature, retarded maximum and minimum of temperature (that is, the maximum occurs in August or later in the Northern Hemisphere instead of in July), greater cloudiness, and a tendency toward fall or winter maximum of rainfall. Continental climates, on the other hand, have relatively large ranges of temperature (in other words, hotter summers and colder winters at the same latitude), the maxima and minima of temperature are not retarded (that is, they come in July and January, respectively, in the Northern Hemisphere), there is less cloudiness (especially in winter), and the rainfall shows a tendency toward a summer or late-spring maximum.

General Circulation of Air.   The general circulation of air in the earth's atmosphere is a part of the mechanism by which the uneven distribution of energy over the earth is equalized.   Warm air must be transferred from lower to higher latitudes and there must be an opposite transferrence of cold air.   But on the rotating surface of the earth, air can move along a straight course only within about $10°$ of the equator.   Elsewhere the deflective effect of the earth's rotation results in the tendency to curve to the right in the Northern Hemisphere and to the left in the Southern Hemisphere. Wherever a persistent flow of air in more or less the same direction is observed, some atmospheric condition must exist to keep the air flow from breaking up into rotating eddies and whirls. The atmospheric condition that permits the development of flows of air in one direction is the uneven distribution of air density.

Fundamental to an understanding of the pattern of surface winds and the regularities of climatic distribution resulting from these winds are the movements in the upper air. Throughout the middle latitudes in both hemispheres there are general flows of air from west to east circulating around the poles; but within this flow there are currents of air moving eastward at much greater velocity than the main body of air. These are the *jet streams*. The jet streams are ribbon-like flows of air, moving up to speeds of 200 to 300 miles per hour, at elevations between 20,000 and 40,000 feet above sea level—near the top of the troposphere (section Vertical Arrangement of Temperature). The jet streams move from west to east in courses that are irregularly shifting—much like a stream of water from a hose nozzle that is being moved from side to side.

In each hemisphere there are three more or less separate jet streams at different latitudes (Map 98). The most persistent of all the streams are the *sub-tropical jet streams,* which circulate in both hemispheres just poleward of 30°. They shift with the seasons, running close to 30° in winter and close to 40° in summer. Poleward of 40° in both hemispheres are the *polar-front jet streams*. And around the Arctic and Antarctic Circles during winter there are the *polar-night jet streams*.

It is believed that these jet streams are major factors in producing the differences of air pressure at sea level. In any stream of air, such as the sub-tropical jet streams, there is a tendency to throw out air to the right in the Northern Hemisphere and to the left in the Southern Hemisphere. Air piles up on the southern side of the jet stream in the Northern Hemisphere, and on the northern side of the jet stream in the Southern Hemisphere. Ridges of high pressure, therefore, are developed at about latitude 30° in both hemispheres. But these ridges are continuous only over uninterrupted expanses of ocean; over the continents they are broken up, leaving cells of high pressure over the eastern sides of the ocean basins at about latitude 30° (Ref. 24, p. 488).

Surface winds tend to circulate around the high pressure cells. Since outward-moving air curves to the right in the Northern Hemisphere and to the left in the Southern Hemisphere, the resulting whirls move clockwise in the Northern Hemisphere and counterclockwise in the Southern Hemisphere. Five such whirls of air can be identified on the wind maps (Plate 12, p. 568): in the North Atlantic, in the South Atlantic, in the North Pacific, in the South Pacific, and in the South Indian. These are the *oceanic*

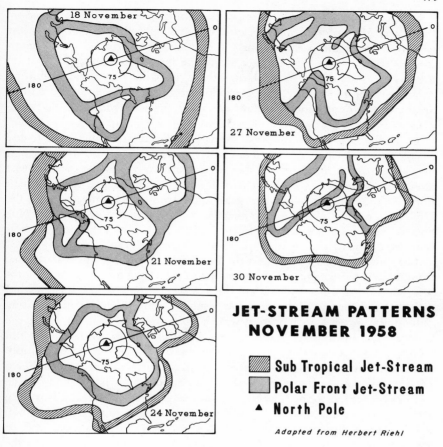

JET-STREAM PATTERNS
NOVEMBER 1958

Sub Tropical Jet-Stream
Polar Front Jet-Stream
▲ North Pole

Adapted from Herbert Riehl

Map 98.

whirls. The North Atlantic oceanic whirl, for example, includes winds over the low latitudes from the northeast. But as one approaches the western side of the Atlantic the winds come from the east, then the southeast. They move onto the continent of North America from the southeast and south. But they continue to curve to the right, changing to southwest winds, then west winds. They cross the North Atlantic in the middle latitudes from the west and northwest, and form the prevailing westerlies of Europe. But they continue to curve to the right, forming north winds over the eastern Mediterranean. Over the Sahara they become northeast winds again to complete the circulation. Since the air circulating around the oceanic whirls cannot move in straight lines they cannot penetrate far into the interior of the continents, excepting within the zone along the equator.

Where the oceanic whirls in opposite hemispheres converge in the equatorial zone they produce much cloudiness and rainfall (Plate 12). On the western sides of the ocean basins the oceanic whirls from opposite hemispheres come closely into contact along the inter-tropical fronts. But on the eastern sides of the ocean basins there are triangular areas of shifting winds between the whirls. These are known as the *doldrums*. Out of these areas currents of air emerge to flow eastward, producing the so-called *equatorial westerlies*. These winds are best seen on the wind map for August (Plate 12). In the eastern Pacific west winds bring heavy summer rains to the Pacific coast of Central America. But the equatorial westerlies are best developed over Africa. In July the warm moist air moves from west to east along the Guinea Coast of West Africa, and continues across the continent north of the equator. The rising air along the west-facing slopes of the Highlands of Ethiopia bring the heavy summer rains that produce the Nile floods. The westerlies descend to the Indian Ocean, and then continue as southwest winds all the way to the southern coast of Asia.

The North Indian Ocean and the borders of Asia have winds that come from opposite directions with the seasons: northeast winds in winter, southwest winds in summer. These are the *monsoons*. The seasonal shift of wind direction was formerly interpreted as resulting from the differential heating of land and water. Air moved, it was thought, from the cooler water to the warmer land in summer, and from the cooler land to the warmer water in winter. The explanation currently advanced is somewhat more complicated. In winter the sub-tropical jet stream moves south of the Himalaya Mountains. The air it piles up on the right produces a surface wind from the northeast—similar to the surface wind on the southern sides of the Northern Hemisphere oceanic whirls. This northeast wind crosses the North Indian Ocean and even reaches eastern Africa and northern Madagascar. In summer, on the other hand, the jet stream breaks up and reforms to the north of the Highlands of Tibet. The equatorial westerlies can move without opposition across the North Indian Ocean and onto the southern part of Asia.

Another pattern of convergence is developed on the poleward sides of the oceanic whirls in the middle latitudes. Cold air accumulates over snow- or ice-covered surfaces. Places of cold air accumulation are Antarctica, Greenland, the Arctic Ocean, and the snow-covered northern parts of North America and Eurasia in winter. Air over these cold surfaces is chilled and becomes dense and heavy. Cold air accumulates to greater and greater depths until it starts sliding out over the surface of the earth toward the nearest area of lower pressure. It is now believed that the outward movement of these cold air masses is related to the position of the polar-front jet streams. When cold air moves away from the area of accumulation it exhausts the pile of cold air. The cold air moves out, therefore, in puffs.

These are the *polar outbursts*. The cold air masses burrow into the poleward sides of the oceanic whirls, producing much storminess. Certain zones of convergence, where the cold air masses come with special force and frequency, are among the stormiest parts of the world. These very stormy areas are around the margins of the Antarctic Continent, in the North Atlantic where cold air from Greenland is felt even in summer, and in the North Pacific where cold air from eastern Siberia is frequently experienced in winter. Cold air masses from Antarctica occasionally penetrate even into the Amazon and perhaps across the equator into the Northern Hemisphere. Frequently cold air is thus transported over the surface to reinforce the high pressure cells over the oceans at latitude 30°.

Cyclonic Storms. In the zones of convergence between different systems of air, whirling storms, known as *cyclones,* originate. The very violent tropical cyclones (known as *hurricanes* in the North Atlantic, and as *typhoons* in the North Pacific) are generated along the zone of contact between the oceanic whirls, especially off the western coast of Africa, 10° or more north of the equator. They move with the pattern of the oceanic whirl, toward the west and then northward along the eastern coast of North America. They follow a similar pattern along the eastern side of Asia. These, however, are especially violent storms: the term cyclone is also applied to those general storms that make up the daily weather maps throughout the middle latitudes. These general storms result from the convergence of the oceanic whirls and the polar outbursts.

As the cold air masses originating as polar outbursts are projected into the stream of relatively warm light air of the oceanic whirls, they become separated from the source region and proceed as homogeneous bodies of air shaped much like drops of water running on an inclined surface; they are steep in front, rounded on top, and trail out behind. The lighter winds of the westerlies ride up over the backs of these cold air masses, the rising air forming clouds and perhaps bringing rain in the process. But the warm light air forms eddies around the front of the cold air mass, eddies which circulate counterclockwise in the Northern Hemisphere and clockwise in the Southern Hemisphere. As the eddies form on the cold front, the cold air mass moves forward, pushing the eddy itself aloft. The result is strong, shifting winds, much cloudiness, and heavy rains. Along the immediate cold front thunderstorms develop in summer when the air of the oceanic whirl has a high temperature and carries much water vapor. In winter the advance of the cold air mass is marked by the familiar signs of an approaching storm—cirrus clouds, then stratus clouds forming a gray pall over the sky, then dark nimbus rain or snow clouds. The blizzards of the plains of North America are carried along by the front of the cold air through which snow is falling from aloft. Then the clouds are swept away and the weather

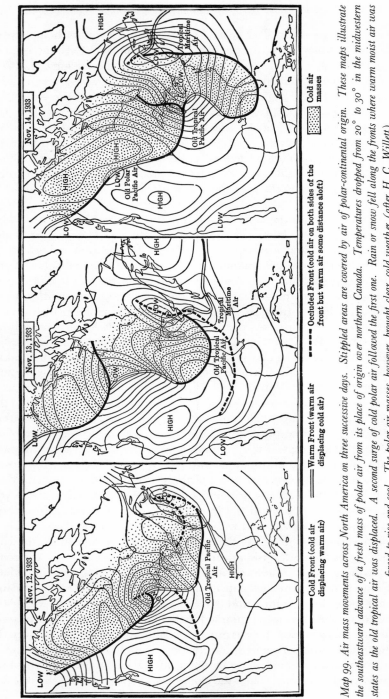

Map 99. *Air mass movements across North America on three successive days. Stippled areas are covered by air of polar-continental origin. These maps illustrate the southeastward advance of a fresh mass of polar air from its place of origin over northern Canada. Temperatures dropped from 20° to 30° in the midwestern states as the old tropical air was displaced. A second surge of cold polar air followed the first one. Rain or snow fell along the fronts where warm moist air was forced to rise and cool. The polar air masses, however, brought clear, cold weather (after H. C. Willett).*

becomes clear and cold.   The alternation of warm, humid air of equatorial origin and clear, cold air of polar origin provides the rapid and extreme weather contrasts which are so characteristic of the middle-lattitude climates.   The accompanying illustrations (Map 99) show the sequence of conditions during the advance of a cold air mass across North America. Since these cyclonic storms produce large-scale updrafts of air, they are major causes of heavy rainfall, especially where the lighter air which they meet is already carrying large quantities of moisture.

Ocean Currents.   Ocean currents are also among the factors that control the world's climates.   The circulation of water in the oceans (Appendix D, section Movements of Ocean Water, p. 518, and Plate 10) brings warm water into high latitudes and cold water into the equatorial regions, and is, therefore, a part of the mechanism that balances the uneven distribution of energy in the world (section The Energy Balance in the Atmosphere).   The arrangement of warm and cold water in the oceans is an element of regularity in the global patterns, and is an important factor in determining the supply of moisture to be carried onto the continents.

Where warm water closely approaches very cold lands there is a frequent and often violent movement of cyclonic storms.   The world's stormiest ocean is in the higher middle latitudes of the Southern Hemisphere surrounding the ice-covered Antarctic Continent.   Very stormy, also, are the warm waters south and southeast of Greenland, and those which approach the coldest part of Siberia in the North Pacific.   These are all regions of maximum cyclonic activity and so of frequent and violent weather changes.

Since cold water yields little moisture to the air (section Evaporation) and since the cooled air is sluggish and heavy, the coasts which have cold water to windward of them are commonly dry.   Since cold water occurs on the west coasts of the continents from about $15°$ to $35°$, this is also a region of low rainfall—especially the center of the belt between $20°$ and $30°$, where the land is arid.   Warm ocean water, on the other hand, is the one major source of moisture in the air, and lands which have warm water to windward are usually wet.

These relationships can be seen clearly by comparing the maps of rainfall, winds, and ocean currents (Plates 10 and 12).

Mountains.   Mountains produce important local differences of climate. Updrafts of air through mountain valleys result in bringing more rain to mountainous areas than to neighboring lowlands.   However, the effect of mountains in producing rain depends to a large degree on the character of the air which blows against them.   Cold air can rise only sluggishly, if at all, and may produce only a low stratus cloud, as along the Peruvian coast. The heaviest rains in the world, however, are received on mountain slopes which lie in the path of warm, buoyant, moisture-laden air (section Vertical Air Movements).

East-west mountain ranges act as temperature divides as well as rain-producers. If the movement of north or south winds is prohibited, the lowlands on the poleward side of a mountain range are made colder than they would otherwise be, and the lowlands on the equatorward side are made warmer.

Other Lesser Controls of Climate.   Local climates are affected by other lesser controls. Forests moderate the temperature somewhat. The effect of forests on rainfall has been greatly exaggerated: rainfall is produced by forces which can be affected by the vegetation to only a very minor degree. Evaporation is greater over a forest than over bare ground, so that a forest cover permits the moisture from the ocean to penetrate farther inland than would be the case if no forests were present. But agricultural land is probably fully as effective as a forest in providing moisture for evaporation.

Among the many other minor controls affecting temperature and humidity are soils, and even the works of man, such as cities.

III. The Köppen Classification of Climates

The Köppen classification of climates is a quantitative system based on monthly and annual means of temperature and rainfall. Unlike many other climatic classifications, the lines which are used to limit the climatic types are given exact definitions and so are subject to checking and revision on the basis of new data. The boundaries, being isarithms (that is, connecting points of equal value), reveal the arrangement of the climatic elements much as contours reveal the shape of a hillside. The direction of greatest climatic difference is always at right angles to the boundary lines. The values which are used in the definitions of these boundaries are based on temperature, on precipitation, or on combinations of these. This is not only because temperature and rainfall are among the most important climatic elements but also because these data are the only ones which are available for a large number of stations throughout the world. The Köppen system has become an international standard, and therefore it is presented in this book without modification.

The History of the Classification.   Dr. Wladimir Köppen developed and perfected the classification which bears his name over a period of more than fifty years. His first attempt at a world classification included only temperature distinctions. In 1900 temperature and moisture were both considered. Eighteen years later a revised statement of the climatic classification was published, this time in essentially its present form. With minor variations of definition, the system formed the basis of a book on world climatology, published in 1923.* Important revisions were introduced, however, on a wall map published by Köppen and Geiger in 1928. On this map certain changes in definition were made which were later discarded. The wide use of the wall map and the reproduction of its lines and definitions elsewhere have led to considerable confusion. In 1931 a second edition of Köppen's book was published, with still further revisions.† This last publication remains the latest pronouncement, and the definitions contained in it were used in the preparation of a handbook of climatology.‡

Main Outlines of the System.   Köppen recognizes five major divisions of the world's climates. These divisions were originally intended to correspond with A. de Candolle's five principal vegetation groups.§ The five climatic divisions, identified by capital letters, are: *A*, rainy climates with no winters (no cool or cold season); *B*, dry climates; *C*, rainy climates with mild winters; *D*, rainy climates with severe winters; and *E*, polar climates with no warm season.

These various major categories are then subdivided. The *B*, or dry climates, are separated into semiarid, *BS* (*S* from the word *steppe*, or dry grassland), and arid, *BW* (*W* from the German *Wüste*, meaning "desert"). The polar deserts, or *E* climates, are subdivided into the marginal or tundra type, *ET*, and the climates of continuous frost, *EF*. The rainy climates, *A*, *C*, and *D*, are subdivided on the basis of the distribution of rainfall through the year. Those with no marked dry seasons are identified by the small letter *f* (from the German *feucht*, meaning "moist"), those with winter dry

---

* These four publications are: W. Köppen, *Die Klimate der Erde* (Berlin, 1923); "Klassification der Klimate nach Temperatur, Niederschlag, und Jahreslauf," *Petermann's Mitteilungen*, vol. 64 (1918), pp. 193–203, 243–248; "Versuch einer Klassification der Klimate, vorzugsweise nach ihren Beziehungen zur Pflanzenwelt," *Geographische Zeitschrift*, vol. 6 (1900), pp. 593–611; and "Die Wärmezonen der Erde, nach der Dauer der heissen, gemässigten und kalten Zeit, und nach der Wirkung der Wärme auf die organische Welt betrachtet," *Meteorologische Zeitschrift*, vol. 1 (1884), pp. 215–226.

† Ibid. *Grundriss der Klimakunde*, Berlin, 1931.

‡ W. Köppen and R. Geiger, *Handbuch der Klimatologie* (in five volumes by various authors, still incomplete).

§ A. de Candolle, "Constitution dans le règne végétal des groupes physiologiques applicables à la géographie ancienne et moderne," *Archives des sciences physiques et naturelles*, Geneva (May, 1874).
De Candolle recognized as his five major plant groups: (1) megatherms, plants needing continuously high temperature and abundant moisture; (2) xerophytes, plants which tolerate dryness and need at least a short hot season; (3) mesotherms, plants needing a moderate amount of heat and a moderate supply of moisture; (4) microtherms, plants needing less heat, less moisture, and tolerant of shorter summers and colder winters; (5) hekistotherms, plants of the polar zone beyond the limits of the forest. It is now recognized that this classification of plants is quite inadequate. Any classification of climates, however, would recognize Köppen's basic categories, so that this historical relation to De Candolle is irrelevant.

seasons are indicated by the small letter *w,* and those with summer dry seasons are indicated by the small letter *s.**

Still further subdivision is made on the bases of other significant features of temperature and rainfall (section Definition of Symbols).

Procedure in Classifying a Climate.   Since all these various letters have quantitative definitions, it is possible to determine from the statistics of temperature and rainfall the proper symbols to describe a climate.   Climatic data for numerous stations are given in Appendix F.   In classifying each station the following procedure should be used:

1. Is the station *E*? If so, is it *ET* or *EF*? If not—
2. Is the station *B*? If so, is it *BS* or *BW*? If one of these, what small letters must also be used? If not—
3. Is it *A, C,* or *D*? If *A,* is it *f, m,* or *w*? If one of these, what other small letters must also be used. If *C,* is it *f, s,* or *w,* and is it *a, b,* or *c*? If *D,* is it *f, s,* or *w,* and is it *a, b, c,* or *d*? What other small letters must also be used?

Definitions of the Symbols.   The following definitions are arranged under the five major types and in the order *E, B, A, C,* and *D*.   The figures are given in Fahrenheit degrees and inches, with the equivalents in centigrade and centimeters given in parentheses.†

E Climates

E: warmest month below 50° (10°).   *ET:* warmest month below 50° (10°) and above 32° (0°).   *EF:* warmest month below 32° (0°).

B Climates

Several formulas are used to identify the dry climates.   This is necessary because the effectiveness of the rainfall in providing moisture in the ground for plants varies with the rate of evaporation, which, in turn, varies with the temperature and with the other elements previously listed (pp. 465–471).   The formulas for the identification of the semiarid and arid climates must therefore take into account the total annual rainfall and the temperature, and they must also show that if the rain comes chiefly in the hot season its effectiveness is decreased, and that if it comes chiefly in the cold season its effectiveness is increased.

The phrase "chiefly in summer" is interpreted as meaning that at least 70 per cent of the total annual rainfall comes in the summer six months (April to September, inclusive, in the Northern Hemisphere).   "Chiefly in winter" means that at least 70 per cent comes in the winter six months (October to March, inclusive, in the Northern

---

* Note that there is an important distinction between capital and small letters.   Capital *W* and capital *S* are used only with the *B* climates; small *w* and small *s* are used throughout the system, in every case to indicate the presence of a dry season.   Similarly, *F* is used only with *E* climates and must not be confused with *f*.   It is important, in writing the climatic symbols, to distinguish carefully between capital and small letters.

† Definitions from W. Köppen, *Grundriss der Klimakunde* (Berlin, 1931), pp. 127–126.

Hemisphere). If less than 70 per cent is concentrated in either six-month period, then the rainfall is said to be evenly distributed.

There are two sets of formulas. One set gives us the humid limits of the dry climates, *BS/H*; the other set gives us the limits between arid and semiarid, *BW/BS*. There are three formulas in each set—one for evenly distributed rain, one for summer rain, and one for winter rain.

In these formulas *r* is the amount of rain which marks the humid boundary of the *B* climates, the amount of rain less than which is considered deficient; *r'* is the amount of rain which marks the limit between arid and semiarid, less than which is considered arid; *t* is the average annual temperature. The formulas are based on an empirical relationship between the temperature in degrees centigrade and the rainfall as measured in centimeters. They can therefore be used only with centigrade degrees and centimeters.

	BS/H	*BW/BS*
Rainfall evenly distributed	$r = 2(t + 7)$	$r' = t + 7$
Rainfall chiefly in summer	$r = 2(t + 14)$	$r' = t + 14$
Rainfall chiefly in winter	$r = 2t$	$r' = t$

These formulas were used in the preparation of the numerical tables on pages 482 and 484, which are given in degrees Fahrenheit and inches. Table II gives the *BS/H* boundary; Table III gives the *BW/BS* boundary.*

The following small letters are also used with the *BW* and *BS* climates:

h: average annual temperature over 64.4° (18°).
k: average annual temperature under 64.4° (18°).
k': temperature of the warmest month under 64.4° (18°).
s: indicates that at least 70 per cent of the rain falls in the winter six months.
w: indicates that at least 70 per cent of the rain falls in the summer six months.

(The absence of *s* or *w* indicates that the rainfall is evenly distributed.)

LETTER COMBINATIONS IN THE *B* CLIMATES

BSh, BShs, BShw; BSk, BSks, BSkw; BSk', BSk'w
BWh, BWhs, BWhw; BWk, BWks, BWkw; BWk', BWk'w

(The small letter *n* is sometimes added to these to indicate the presence of frequent fogs. This letter, however, is not given exact definition and cannot be identified from the climatic data given in this book.)

---

* These tables were prepared by Dr. Henry M. Kendall.

TABLE II. For the Determination of the *BS/H* Boundary

AVERAGE ANNUAL TEMPERATURE	AT LEAST 70 PER CENT IN WINTER	EVEN DISTRIBUTION	AT LEAST 70 PER CENT IN SUMMER
32	0.00	5.52	11.02
33	0.44	5.96	11.46
34	0.86	6.38	11.88
35	1.32	6.82	12.34
36	1.74	7.26	12.76
37	2.18	7.70	13.20
38	2.62	8.14	13.64
39	3.06	8.58	14.08
40	3.50	9.02	14.52
41	3.94	9.46	14.96
42	4.38	9.90	15.40
43	4.82	10.34	15.84
44	5.26	10.78	16.28
45	5.68	11.20	16.70
46	6.12	11.64	17.14
47	6.56	12.08	17.58
48	7.00	12.52	18.02
49	7.44	12.96	18.46
50	7.88	13.40	18.90
51	8.32	13.84	19.34
52	8.74	14.26	19.76
53	9.18	14.70	20.20
54	9.62	15.14	20.64
55	10.06	15.58	21.08
56	10.50	16.02	21.52
57	10.94	16.46	21.96
58	11.38	16.90	22.40
59	11.82	17.34	22.84
60	12.26	17.78	23.28
61	12.68	18.20	23.70
62	13.12	18.64	24.14
63	13.56	19.08	24.58
64	14.00	19.52	25.02
65	14.44	19.96	25.46
66	14.88	20.40	25.90
67	15.30	20.82	26.32
68	15.74	21.26	26.76
69	16.18	21.70	27.20
70	16.62	22.14	27.64
71	17.06	22.58	28.08
72	17.50	23.02	28.52
73	17.94	23.46	28.96

TABLE II (*continued*)

AVERAGE ANNUAL TEMPERATURE	AT LEAST 70 PER CENT IN WINTER	EVEN DISTRIBUTION	AT LEAST 70 PER CENT IN SUMMER
74	18.38	23.90	29.40
75	18.82	24.34	29.84
76	19.24	24.76	30.26
77	19.68	25.20	30.70
78	20.12	25.64	31.14
79	20.56	26.08	31.58
80	21.00	26.52	32.02
81	21.44	26.96	32.46
82	21.88	27.40	32.90
83	22.30	27.82	33.32
84	22.74	28.26	33.76
85	23.18	28.70	34.20

TABLE III. For the Determination of the *BW/BS* Boundary

AVERAGE ANNUAL TEMPERATURE	AT LEAST 70 PER CENT IN WINTER	EVEN DISTRIBUTION	AT LEAST 70 PER CENT IN SUMMER
32	0.00	2.76	5.51
33	0.22	2.98	5.73
34	0.43	3.19	5.94
35	0.66	3.42	6.17
36	0.87	3.63	6.38
37	1.09	3.85	6.60
38	1.31	4.07	6.82
39	1.53	4.29	7.04
40	1.75	4.51	7.26
41	1.97	4.73	7.48
42	2.19	4.95	7.70
43	2.41	5.17	7.92
44	2.63	5.39	8.14
45	2.84	5.60	8.35
46	3.06	5.82	8.57
47	3.28	6.04	8.79
48	3.50	6.26	9.01
49	3.72	6.48	9.23
50	3.94	6.70	9.45
51	4.16	6.92	9.67
52	4.37	7.13	9.88
53	4.59	7.35	10.10

TABLE III (*continued*)

AVERAGE ANNUAL TEMPERATURE	AT LEAST 70 PER CENT IN WINTER	EVEN DISTRIBUTION	AT LEAST 70 PER CENT IN SUMMER
54	4.81	7.57	10.32
55	5.03	7.79	10.54
56	5.25	8.01	10.76
57	5.47	8.23	10.98
58	5.69	8.45	11.20
59	5.91	8.67	11.42
60	6.13	8.89	11.64
61	6.34	9.10	11.85
62	6.56	9.32	12.07
63	6.78	9.54	12.29
64	7.00	9.76	12.51
65	7.22	9.98	12.73
66	7.44	10.20	12.95
67	7.65	10.41	13.16
68	7.87	10.63	13.38
69	8.09	10.85	13.60
70	8.31	11.07	13.82
71	8.53	11.29	14.04
72	8.75	11.51	14.26
73	8.97	11.73	14.48
74	9.19	11.95	14.70
75	9.41	12.17	14.92
76	9.62	12.38	15.13
77	9.84	12.60	15.35
78	10.06	12.82	15.57
79	10.28	13.04	15.79
80	10.50	13.26	16.01
81	10.72	13.48	16.23
82	10.94	13.70	16.45
83	11.15	13.91	16.66
84	11.37	14.13	16.88
85	11.59	14.35	17.10

TABLE IV. For the Determination of the *Am/Aw* Boundary

YEARLY RAINFALL IN INCHES	RAINFALL OF DRIEST MONTH IN INCHES	YEARLY RAINFALL IN INCHES	RAINFALL OF DRIEST MONTH IN INCHES	YEARLY RAINFALL IN INCHES	RAINFALL OF DRIEST MONTH IN INCHES
39.5	2.36	59.5	1.56	79.5	0.76
40	2.34	60	1.55	80	0.74
40.5	2.32	60.5	1.53	80.5	0.72
41	2.30	61	1.51	81	0.70
41.5	2.29	61.5	1.48	81.5	0.68
42	2.26	62	1.47	82	0.66
42.5	2.24	62.5	1.45	82.5	0.63
43	2.22	63	1.42	83	0.61
43.5	2.20	63.5	1.41	83.5	0.59
44	2.18	64	1.38	84	0.58
44.5	2.16	64.5	1.36	84.5	0.56
45	2.14	65	1.34	85	0.54
45.5	2.12	65.5	1.33	85.5	0.51
46	2.10	66	1.30	86	0.50
46.5	2.08	66.5	1.28	86.5	0.48
47	2.07	67	1.26	87	0.46
47.5	2.04	67.5	1.24	87.5	0.44
48	2.02	68	1.22	88	0.42
48.5	2.00	68.5	1.20	88.5	0.40
49	1.98	69	1.18	89	0.37
49.5	1.96	69.5	1.15	89.5	0.36
50	1.94	70	1.13	90	0.34
50.5	1.92	70.5	1.11	90.5	0.32
51	1.90	71	1.10	91	0.29
51.5	1.88	71.5	1.08	91.5	0.28
52	1.86	72	1.06	92	0.26
52.5	1.85	72.5	1.03	92.5	0.24
53	1.82	73	1.02	93	0.22
53.5	1.80	73.5	1.00	93.5	0.20
54	1.78	74	0.98	94	0.18
54.5	1.77	74.5	0.96	94.5	0.16
55	1.75	75	0.94	95	0.14
55.5	1.73	75.5	0.92	95.5	0.11
56	1.70	76	0.90	96	0.09
56.5	1.68	76.5	0.88	96.5	0.07
57	1.66	77	0.86	97	0.06
57.5	1.64	77.5	0.84	97.5	0.04
58	1.63	78	0.81	98	0.02
58.5	1.60	78.5	0.80	98.5	0.00
59	1.58	79	0.78		

A CLIMATES

> *A:* temperature of the coldest month above 64.4° (18°).
>> *f:* rainfall of the driest month is at least 2.4 in. (6 cm.).
>> *m:* short dry season exists, but is compensated by heavy rains during the rest of the year (see *w*).
>> *w:* dry season exists which is not compensated by rains during the rest of the year. The dry season comes during the low-sun period of the hemisphere.
>> *w':* used if the rainfall maximum comes in autumn of the hemisphere.
>> *w'':* used if there are two distinct maxima of rainfall, separated by two dry seasons.
>> *s:* used when the dry season comes during the high-sun period.

The distinction between *m* and *w* (*w'*, *w''*, and *s*) depends upon the amount of rain in the driest month and the total annual rainfall. As the total annual rainfall increases, smaller and smaller amounts of rain in the driest month can be compensated. If the total annual rainfall is 100 inches (exactly 98.5 in.), one month can be completely dry and still merit the symbol *m*; or if the total annual rainfall is 200 inches, two months can be entirely dry. The distinction between *m* and *w* is given in Table IV, in which the amount of rain in the driest month varies inversely with the total annual rainfall. If the rainfall of the driest month is less than the amount shown in the second column, the symbol *w* (*w'*, or *w''*, or *s*) is used; if the rainfall is more, but less than 2.4 (*f*), the symbol *m* is used.*

After *f* or *m* the letter *w*, *w'*, *w''*, or *s* is sometimes used to indicate the season of less rain.

> *i:* range of temperature between the coldest and warmest months less than 9° (5°).
> *g:* hottest month comes before the solstice.

LETTER COMBINATIONS IN THE *A* CLIMATES

> *Afi, Afwi, (w', w'', s)*
> *Am, Ami, Amwi (w', w'', s)*
> *Aw, Awi, Aw', Aw'', As (i); Awg, Awgi,* etc.

C CLIMATES

> *C:* temperature of the coldest month below 64.4° (18°) but above 26.6° (−3°); temperature of the warmest month over 50° (10°).
>> *f:* no dry season; difference between rainiest and driest month less than that required for *s* or *w*; or, in the case of winter rain and summer drought, driest month of summer receives more than 1.2 in. (3 cm.).
>> *s:* dry season in summer; rainiest month of winter receives at least three times as much rain as the driest month of summer, and the driest month of summer receives less than 1.2 in. (3 cm.).
>> *w:* dry season in winter; rainiest month of summer receives at least ten times as much rain as the driest month of winter.

*The table was prepared by Dr. Henry M. Kendall.

a: hot summers; temperature of the warmest month over 71.6° (22°).

b: cool summers; temperature of the warmest month under 71.6° (22°), but with at least four months above 50° (10°).

c: cool, short summers; only one to three months above 50° (10°).

i: range of temperature between the coldest and warmest months less than 9° (5°).

g: hottest month comes before the summer solstice.

t′: hottest month delayed until autumn.

x: maximum rainfall in spring or early summer; late summer dry.

s′: maximum rainfall in autumn.

(*n* is used, as elsewhere, to indicate frequent fogs.)

LETTER COMBINATIONS IN THE *C* CLIMATES

Cfa, Cfb, Cfc; Cfbi, Cfci, Cfx
Csa, Csb; Csbt′n, Cs′
Cwa, Cwb; Cwbi, Cwg

D CLIMATES

D: temperature of the coldest month below 26.6° (−3°), and temperature of the warmest month above 50° (10°).

f, s, and *w:* defined exactly as in the *C* climates.

a, b, c: defined exactly as in the *C* climates.

d: temperature of the coldest month less than −36.4° (−38°).

LETTER COMBINATIONS IN THE *D* CLIMATES

Dfa, Dfb, Dfc, Dfd
Dsb
Dwa, Dwb, Dwc, Dwd

REFERENCES

1. BLODGET, L. *Climatology of the United States and of the Temperate Latitudes of the North American Continent.* Philadelphia, 1857.

2. MAURY, M. F. *Explanations of Sailing Directions to Accompany the Wind and Current Charts,* Eighth Edition. Washington, D. C., 1858–1859.

3. WARD, R. deC. *Climates of the United States.* Boston, 1925.

4. KENDREW, W. G. *Climate.* Oxford, 1930.

5. KÖPPEN, W. *Grundriss der Klimakunde.* Berlin, 1931.

6. National Research Council, Bulletin 79, *Physics of the Earth, III, Meteorology.* Washington, D. C., 1931.

7. NAMIAS, J. *An Introduction to the Study of Air Mass and Isentropic Analysis.* Milton, Massachusetts (Blue Hill Meteorological Observatory), 1940.

8. United States Department of Agriculture. *1941 Yearbook of Agriculture: Climate and Man.* Washington, D. C., 1941.

9. WILLETT, H. C. *Descriptive Meteorology.* New York, 1944.

10. LANDSBERG, H. E. "Climatology," in BERRY, F. A. JR., BOLLAY, E., and BEERS, N. R. (eds.), *Handbook of Meteorology*. New York, 1945, pp. 927–997.

11. THORNTHWAITE, C. W. "An Approach Toward a Rational Classification of Climate," *Geographical Review*, Vol. 38 (1948), pp. 55–94.

12. GEIGER, R. *The Climates Near the Ground*. Cambridge, Massachusetts, 1950.

13. LANDSBERG, H. E., and JACOBS, W. C. "Applied Climatology," in American Meteorological Society, *Compendium of Meteorology*. 1951, pp. 976–992.

14. SHAPLEY, H. (ed.), *Climatic Change* (third edition). Cambridge, Massachusetts, 1954.

15. KIMBLE, G. H. T. *Our American Weather*. New York, 1955.

16. PÉDELABORDE, P. *Les Moussons,* Paris, 1958. Translated into English by M. J. CLEGG, *The Monsoon* (London, 1963).

17. ODISHAW, H., and RUTTENBERG, S. *Geophysics and the IGY*. Washington, D. C., 1958.

18. TAYLOR, J. A., and YATES, R. A. *British Weather in Maps*. London, 1958.

19. HARE, F. K. "The Westerlies," *Geographical Review*, Vol. 50 (1960). pp. 345–367.

20. TREWARTHA, G. T. *The Earth's Problem Climates*. Madison, Wisconsin, 1961.

21. REITER, E. R. *Meteorologie der Strahlströme*. Vienna, 1961. Translated into English, *Jet-Stream Meteorology* (Chicago, 1963).

22. KENDREW, W. G. *The Climates of the Continents,* (fifth edition). Oxford, England, 1961.

23. RIEHL, H. *Jet Streams of the Atmosphere*. Fort Collins, Colorado, 1962.

24. RIEHL, H. *Introduction to the Atmosphere*. New York, 1965.

The Lithosphere

1. Tectonic Forms

The Earth's Crust. The geologists recognize three major types of rocks which make up the solid crust of the earth. There are the *igneous* rocks, which have cooled and solidified from a previously molten condition. These are crystalline: coarsely crystalline where they have cooled slowly at great depths below the surface; finely crystalline, or even glassy, where they have cooled more rapidly near or at the surface. There are many kinds of igneous rocks, depending on the minerals in them. *Sedimentary* rocks make up the second major type. These are derived from the erosion of earlier rocks and were accumulated as unconsolidated deposits either in the water or on the land. The deposits range from coarse material to fine: gravels, sands, and muds. In the course of time and deep burial under later deposits, the layers of gravel, sand, or mud were gradually consolidated into rock: into conglomerate, sandstone, shale, or limestone. The third major division of rocks includes those which have been altered from either igneous or sedimentary types as a result of pressure or heat, or both. These are known as *metamorphic* rocks. Such a process rearranges the crystal structure of the igneous rocks into more compact forms. Similarly, the individual rock particles of the sedimentary strata are melted and solidified again as tightly fitted crystals. The result in either case is a rock mass more compact and more resistant to the processes of erosion. The coarsely crystalline igneous rocks are changed to gneiss, sandstone to quartzite, shale to slate or schist, and limestone to marble.*

From the point of view of the effect of these rock types on the shape of

---

*For a more exact discussion of rock types see any modern textbook in geomorphology, such as references 16, 21, or 24, listed at the end of this appendix.

the surface of the earth the most important distinction is between those which are massive and those which are arranged in layers, or strata. Igneous rocks may be either massive or stratified; sedimentary rocks are always stratified; metamorphic rocks may be either.

Deformation of the Earth's Crust.   The rock crust of the earth has been subjected to stresses and strains throughout geologic history. Mountain ranges have been raised up only to be worn down again countless times. While certain sections of the lithosphere have remained more stable than others, there is no part which does not bear the record of some deformation. The crust of the earth is raised, lowered, broken, crumpled, or folded by these movements.

Four chief types of *tectonic* forms—that is, forms produced by forces from within the earth—are recognized. On the spheroidal surface of the planet a gentle uplift usually results in the formation of a simple *dome*. This is probably the commonest of the tectonic forms. Some mountain ranges are the result of the erosion of domes (Figure 27); on a large scale the Laurentian Upland of northeastern North America represents a dome structure of continental proportions.

Where the forces which disturb the earth's crust are stronger, the rocks may be crumpled in the process of deformation. A *folded* structure is the result of compression which wrinkles the rock strata. Among the examples of this are strata with simple, open folds with horizontal axes. But there are many examples where the folding has been more intense: where the *anticlines,* or upfolds, have toppled over into the *synclines,* or downfolds, or where the axes of the folds have themselves been warped from the horizontal (Figure 7, p. 386). The Jura Mountains furnish a standard example of simple folding, while the Appalachians are somewhat more complex; and still more complex are the Alps, which are noted for the complicated distortions of the rock layers.

Actual breaking of the earth's crust is known as *faulting*. This is the third chief kind of tectonic deformation. The rock masses may be broken into blocks which are raised or lowered with reference to one another. The result is the formation of *block mountains* or of *rift valleys*. These tectonic forms are repeated in many parts of the world, the middle valley of the Rhine (Figure 28), Death Valley in California, the Dead Sea–Red Sea rift, and the lakes of eastern Africa being a few well-known examples. Earthquakes are produced by the slipping which takes place along fault lines.

These tectonic forms are produced very slowly as measured by human time. The old popular phrase "convulsions of nature" implies violent movements. In the last century, however, geologists have come gradually to realize that sudden spectacular movements are rare and that most of the

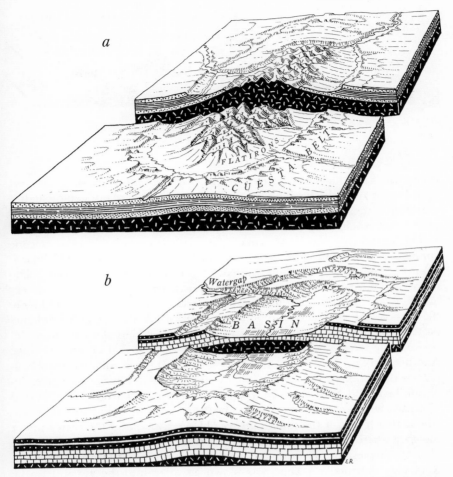

Figure 27. Block diagrams illustrating the landforms characteristically associated with the erosion of a structural dome: (a) where the rocks exposed in the center are relatively resistant; (b) where the rocks exposed in the center are relatively weak.

deformations take place only very slowly.   *Volcanoes,* however, the fourth type of tectonic form, are quite different.

Volcanoes.   There are two chief kinds of volcanoes.   Where the molten material which pours out from within the earth emerges quietly, a broad dome is piled up around the crater or fissure.   One of the finest examples of the *dome volcano* is furnished by the island of Hawaii, which has been built

Figure 28. A generalized cross section of the rift valley of the Rhine and the adjoining block mountains of the Vosges and the Black Forest.

up by successive flows of lava to a height of more than thirty thousand feet above the floor of the Pacific Ocean. Such volcanoes are not explosive, but the lava in them is of a kind which cools slowly and flows great distances after it has reached the surface.

The second type of volcano is explosive. It builds around its crater a cone composed of alternating flows of lava and falls of ash and dust. Of the *cone volcanoes,* Fujiyama in Japan is noted for the perfection of its form. The eruptions of cone volcanoes are violent and destructive. Vesuvius, for example, after lying dormant for many centuries, in the year 79 A.D. suddenly blew its old cone to pieces and built a new one inside the rim of the old one. At this time the neighboring towns of Pompeii and Herculaneum were destroyed, the former being buried under from 25 to 30 feet of ash and dust. Another striking example of the explosion of a long-dormant conical volcano is that of Krakatoa, formerly located on an island in Sunda Strait, between Java and Sumatra. In 1883, with but little warning, it exploded violently, with a concussion that was heard in Australia, 2200 miles distant. About two thirds of the mountain was blown away, and the water under the spot where the central peak had stood was found to be 1000 feet deep after the explosion. Enormous "tidal" waves produced by this cataclysm were very destructive. Dust was blown 20 miles into the air and in the course of a few weeks drifted entirely around the world, giving vivid colors to the sunset skies. Dust from Krakatoa has been identified on the snow surfaces of the polar regions.

II. Destructional Forms

The Destructional Forms. As soon as the tectonic forces begin to raise a portion of the earth's crust above the sea, the exposed land is attacked by various processes of destruction. Since these processes result from the contacts with the atmosphere, the particular combination of processes in any one area is largely controlled by the climatic conditions. All these processes, however, in the long run have the effect of reducing the elevations and filling the low places of the lithosphere. Erosion proceeds by *weathering* (rock fracture and decay), *corrasion* (wearing away of exposed surfaces), and *transportation* (movement of loose material). Corrasion and transportation can be accomplished in six different ways, each of which produces a peculiar set of landforms. These six processes are (1) running water, (2) direction action of gravity on slopes, (3) glaciers, (4) wind, (5) solution, and (6) waves and currents. We shall consider in turn the landforms produced by each of these.

The Products of Weathering. The first step in the wearing down of the land is the breaking up of solid rock into pieces under the influence of the atmosphere. This is known as weathering. It proceeds by two different methods: the rocks are physically broken, or *disintegrated;* or the rocks are attacked chemically and the minerals are transformed, or *decomposed.* Disintegration is hastened by the expansion and contraction which come from heating and cooling, or by frost action, or, to a lesser extent, by the prying action of tree roots or the burrowing of animals. The physical fracturing of the rocks reaches a maximum in the deserts, where there is a great contrast between the temperatures of day and night, and in the polar regions or high mountains, where frost action is most active. Decomposition requires the presence of water, and since most chemical processes go on more rapidly at higher temperatures this type of weathering is most active in the rainy tropics.

The result of weathering is the production of a mantle of loose material at the surface of the earth. This mantle is more or less thick, depending on the strength of the weathering processes, the resistance of the rock to these processes, the length of time the rock has been exposed to them, and the rate of removal. Such a mantle of loose material is known as *regolith*. The regolith which is chiefly the result of disintegration is generally coarse, whereas the mantle produced by decomposition is generally fine.

Landforms Produced by Running Water. In most parts of the world the landforms produced by running water are of dominant importance. Where this is the case the surface features may be described under four headings: the valleys, the interfluves, the stream pattern, and the relief. Pages 493 through 502 deal with these elements as produced by running water.

V-Shaped Valleys. When a portion of the earth's crust is raised rapidly enough and far enough above the sea, the streams of water which flow over its surface cut rapidly downward and headward to excavate V-shaped valleys. The slope of the stream channel in such valleys is steep and is usually interrupted by falls and rapids. However, as the stream cuts down in the valley bottom, the sides of the valley are changed both by the move-

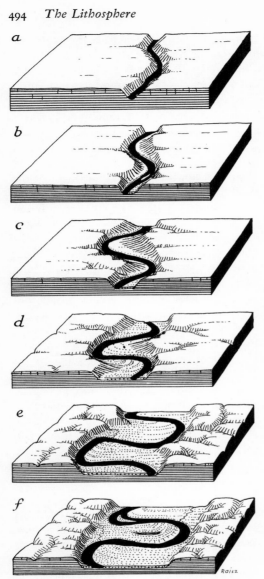

Figure 29. Series of block diagrams illustrating the stages in the evolution of a valley from youth to old age.

ment of regolith on the steep slopes and by the headward cutting of tributaries. The transverse profile of the valley depends on the ratio between the rate of downward cutting of the main stream and the rate of valley-side erosion. Where erosion on the valley side is relatively slight, as in the dry lands, the **V** is narrow and canyon-like; but where the valley-widening processes are very active, as in the rainy tropics, especially where the forest has been removed, the V becomes broad and open. In all V-shaped valleys the stream occupies the whole bottom (Figure 29).

Baselevel and Grade. Streams, however, cannot cut down their valley bottoms indefinitely. No stream can cut below the body of water into which it flows; nor can any stream reduce its valley bottom to the level of the body of water into which it is flowing, except at its mouth, for it must maintain a slope on which to flow. The level below which a stream cannot cut at its mouth is known as *baselevel*. After the stream reaches baselevel at its mouth, little by little it establishes a slope on which it is just able to flow. An equilibrium is reached between three variable elements: slope, volume of water, and load. A change in any one of these elements necessitates readjustment of the others to maintain this equilibrium. When a stream has developed this balance, it is said to be *graded*.*

Floodplain Scroll Valleys. The valleys remain V-shaped until the streams establish grade. But as soon as downward cutting ceases, the streams must expend their energy in lateral cutting at the base of the valley sides. At each river bend the current swings against the outside bank, and by *sapping,* or undercutting, it pushes back and steepens the valley side. The lateral movement of the river, however, leaves exposed a small piece of flat valley bottom on the inside of each bend. The first bits of valley flat to appear are scroll-shaped in outline (Figure 29, *b* and *c*). As the river swings from one side of its valley to the other, the scrolls appear on alternate sides, each of them isolated by the river and by the steep valley slopes behind them. Since these flats are submerged during flood water, they are included under the general term "floodplain," or that portion of the valley bottom covered by water during flood. Valleys of this kind are called floodplain scroll valleys.

Floodplain Valleys. All stages of gradation may be seen between the floodplain scroll valley and a third type, the floodplain valley. Little by little the valley sides are pushed back and the floodplain scrolls become more extensive. From the somewhat irregular swings of the river in its earlier stage, more regular meanders are gradually developed, the width of these meanders being proportional to the size of the river. Since the meanders tend to migrate downstream, they not only cut against the valley slopes on the outside of each bend but they also begin to undercut the upstream side of each spur which, in the floodplain scroll valley, extends from the valley slope into the inside of each river bend (Figure 29, *d*). When the spurs are eliminated, the flats lose their scroll-shaped outline and become continu-

* For classical discussions of these concepts see references 1 and 4; for more recent studies which modify many older ideas see references 17, 22, and 23.

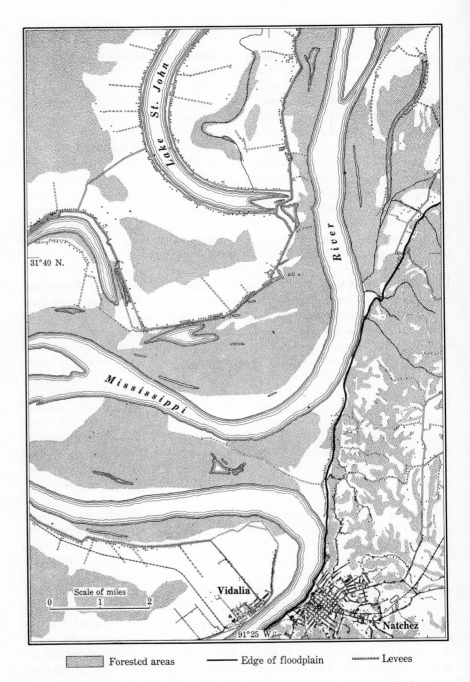

Map 100. Topography of a floodplain (from the Natchez Quadrangle, Mississippi, United States Geological Survey).

ous, and the river is able to meander freely across a wide and unobstructed floodplain (Figure 29, *e*).

A number of distinctive features characterize valleys of this type. The floodplain is bordered by sharply defined *valley bluffs,* which are especially steep where the river swings against them (Figure 29,*f*). Since the floodplain is covered at high water, it is built up of the loose silts and sands deposited by the water and known as *alluvium.* During a flood the greatest amount of deposition takes place along the immediate edges of the channel, for here the largest checking of the current is felt. In the course of time the edge of the channel is built up higher than the rest of the plain. These highest parts of the floodplain, the last to be covered by water in time of flood, are called *natural levees.* Back from the channel, near the margins of the floodplain, are the lowest places—the *back marshes,* which may remain wet even during low water (Map 100).

All these various features of river floodplains are arranged in crescentic patterns. Rivers seldom flow in straight lines, unless controlled by man; on a floodplain they meander, and not uncommonly whole meanders are cut off during high water, and the river channel is shifted to another position. As a result the typical floodplain is marked by a confused array of abandoned channels, or oxbow lakes, each bordered by natural levees, and all arranged in characteristic crescentic plan.

Interfluves. During the development of these various types of valleys the interfluves also pass through a sequence of forms. At first much of the initial surface of the land remains undissected. The land between the main V-shaped valleys is flat-topped, and the divides between neighboring streams are ill-defined or entirely absent. The slopes of the V-shaped valleys begin to retreat away from the rivers. The interfluve then develops four elements. At the divide the initial surface becomes gently convex. This upper surface ends sharply where the free face of the underlying bedrock is exposed, and it is this free face which is most rapidly worn back. At the base of the free face is a debris slope, or *colluvial base.* And between this and the river banks there is a *pediment,* smooth and concave. Eventually the initial surface disappears, and only low, rounded swells separate the drainage basins.[*]

The Cycle of Erosion. The ideal succession of landforms developed during the wearing down of an upraised surface toward baselevel is called a cycle of erosion. As formulated by William Morris Davis, the landforms pass through stages known as *youth, maturity,* and *old age.*[†] When the streams are flowing vigorously and turbulently in V-shaped valleys, they are said to be

[*] References 17, 22, and 23.
[†] References 4 and 5.

Figure 30. Valley and interfluve profiles: (a) youthful interfluves and mature valleys; (b) mature interfluves and youthful valleys.

youthful. When grade is established along the valley bottoms and the floodplain scroll valley makes its appearance, the valleys are described as mature. When the river occupies a broad floodplain across which it meanders freely, it is said to be old. According to Davis's concept the interfluves would during the same time be gradually worn down to gently sloping convex surfaces. The late stage of old age he called a *peneplain,* an almost featureless plain surmounted by only a few erosion remnants known as *monadnocks.*

Modern geomorphologists recognize that there is also a cycle of interfluve forms, which goes on independently of the valley development. The retreat of hillsides parallel to their initial position results in the formation of wide concave areas of pediment, surmounted, in the late stages, by only a few erosion remnants which stand abruptly above the pediment. The parallel retreat of valley sides, or of scarps produced by tectonic movements, permits remnants of earlier erosion surfaces to remain in the landscape even in the stage of old age. The resulting plain is described as a *pediplain.**

These ideal landform sequences, however, are almost always interrupted. In the first place, for every foot of rock material removed from an uplifted surface by erosion, the underlying rock column rises some nine to eleven feet. This is because the earth's crust sinks when weight is placed on it and rises when weight is removed. The result is a continuing succession of uplifts that return the valley forms again and again to the youthful stage. This is called *rejuvenation.* The landforms of a region always carry the record of several cycles.

Associations of Valley and Interfluve Forms. The simple cycle is complicated in many cases by variations in the association of valley and interfluve forms. Valleys, for example, may be youthful while the interfluves are mature; or interfluves may remain youthful while valleys are old. Only rarely is it possible to find both valleys and interfluves that are in the same stage. Where the uplift which initiates a cycle of erosion is slight, so that baselevel lies only a short distance below the initial surface, the streams may develop floodplain scrolls and so advance their valleys to maturity or even old age while the central portions of the interfluves remain undissected and youthful (Figure 30, *a*). On the other hand, if uplift is very great or if it is continuous, the interfluves may develop the sharp divides of maturity while

* References 22 and 23.

the streams are still deepening their youthful V-shaped valleys (Figure 30, *b*). All the various stages between these extremes may be observed in different parts of the world.

Some Complex Valley Forms. As a result of various kinds of earth movement, or from other causes which we cannot discuss here, valleys of greater complexity are developed. Since the cycle of erosion can be interrupted at any stage, valleys may be composite in character. For example, the rejuvenation of an old stream results in the preservation of the meanders of old age in the youthful V-shaped valley which follows; in other words, it results in the development of *intrenched meanders*. Or a wide mature valley, if rejuvenated, may be transformed into a valley with an upper flare and lower V. On the other hand, valleys may become *aggraded*: a decrease of slope (by depression of the land instead of uplift), a decrease of the volume of water, or an increase of load may cause a stream to fill up its valley bottom. Aggraded youthful valleys are especially noticeable because of the contrast between the steep valley sides and the flat bottom. This is a valley type which is very common in the desert, where many streams flow only after a rain and most of the time are dry.

Complex Valleys Produced by Rock Structure. Where valleys are being excavated through stratified rocks of varying degrees of resistance the stronger layers project on the valley sides as cliffs. If the strata lie in a horizontal or nearly horizontal position, the *cliff and platform* type of valley is produced; if the strata are inclined, the valleys between the outcrops of resistant layers become *asymmetrical*.

Interfluve Forms Produced by Rock Structure. The forms of the interfluves are similarly affected by the rock structure (Figure 31). Horizontal strata produce flat-topped interfluves, or *mesas*. Tilted rock layers produce ridgelike *cuestas*. The erosion of a dome structure produces a series of infacing cuestas (Figure 27), whereas the erosion of a structural basin produces a series of outfacing cuestas.*

Stream Patterns. The third of the four major headings under which landforms produced by running water can be described (section 6) is the stream pattern. The arrangement of the valleys and interfluves is a function of the stream pattern. The commonest type of pattern, developed where the rock structure does not interfere with the free development of the streams,

---

*Some writers prefer to distinguish between steeply sloping ridges, where the rock layers are very steeply inclined and are called *hogbacks,* and ridges where one slope is scarcely distinguishable, so gentle is the dip of the resistant stratum. They reserve the term "cuesta" for this latter type (reference 16).

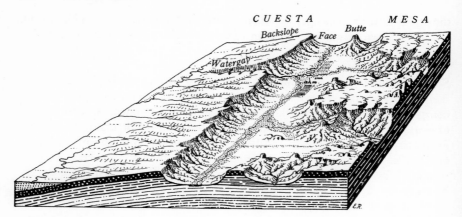

Figure 31. Block diagram illustrating the characteristics of mesas and cuestas.

is *dendritic;* that is, branching like a tree (Figure 32, *a*).   Around a dome the dendritic pattern can be arranged in radial fashion, but elsewhere the main streams may lie roughly parallel to one another.   The dendritic pattern is first elaborated and later simplified during the cycle of erosion: in youth the main streams are relatively straight, with few and only short tributaries; in maturity the fullest development of the drainage is reached, with many small tributaries joining the larger main stream and with numerous examples of drainage rearrangement resulting from the capture of one stream by the tributaries of another; in old age only a few master streams have survived the competition, and these are large, with a few large tributaries.

The second type of drainage pattern is formed where rock strata of varying degrees of resistance are inclined at an angle, so that the more resistant beds come to the surface to form cuesta ridges separated by asymmetrical valleys.   Because of the relative ease of stream erosion on the weaker beds, the valleys are quickly excavated along the outcrops of these strata between the upstanding cuestas.   The main streams may cross the ridges through deep, relatively youthful water gaps.   The resulting drainage pattern is one of striking parallelism—of long, straight valleys, in strict accordance with the arrangement of the rock strata, joined by short right-angled jogs where the rivers cross the resistant beds.   This is known as *trellis* drainage (Figure 32, *b*).

Where the cuestas are arranged around the margins of a dome in circular plan, the trellis pattern is curved and is described as *annular.*

Relief.   These various features developed by running water may be constructed in various degrees of relief.   They may occur in miniature in a

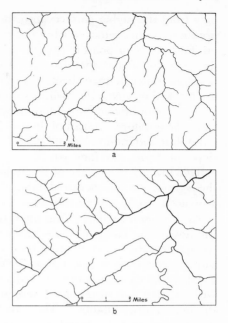

Figure 32. Stream patterns: (a) dendritic; (b) trellis.

plain where the relief is slight, or they may be built on a grand scale in a mountain region with very high relief. There is no essential difference in form between the Grand Canyon of the Colorado and the gully which develops in a plowed field after a heavy rain.

During an uninterrupted cycle of erosion the surface is changed from one of slight initial relief to one of considerable relief, and again to an ultimate surface of slight relief. As soon as the main streams feel the effects of rejuvenation they start the work of downward cutting. During youth, therefore, the local relief is gradually increased. The amount of this increase in the long run depends on the depth of baselevel below the surface; in other words, on the amount of uplift. The maximum relief is reached when the interfluves become mature, when the tributaries have extended headward to dissect the last remnants of the initial surface. After the streams become graded the relief gradually decreases as long as the land remains undisturbed by earth movements.

Landforms Developed in Arid Climates. Even in dry climates the sculpturing by running water is of dominant importance in producing landforms. The rare but violent desert rains give rise to floods which do the work of erosion and deposition quickly. The chief contrast with the work of running water in rainy lands, however, is the absence of a regional baselevel. Since most desert streams do not reach the ocean, they can carry material only from the higher surfaces into the desert basins, or *bolsons*. The waste products are not removed from the region as a whole, but are accumulated not far from their point of origin. The sequence of desert landforms therefore consists of the vigorous erosion of the elevations and in the gradual accumulation of a great sheet of alluvium. At first the mouths of the valleys are marked by *alluvial fans* where they enter the basins. Later these coalesce to form a continuous compound alluvial fan around the piedmont. At this stage the landforms consist of three chief parts (Figure 33, *b*): (1) the rapidly crumbling mountains, deeply dissected by youthful streams; (2) the gentle slopes of the alluvial fans, which emerge from the mouths of the valleys and extend toward the center of the bolson in long, sweeping curves; and (3) the *playa*, or the salt-incrusted flat at the center of the bolson, in which water may accumulate temporarily after the heavy rains in the mountains.

As the desert sequence continues, the bolson is gradually buried beneath the advancing fans. In some cases a higher bolson may be dissected by streams leading to neighboring basins at lower levels (Figure 33, *c*). In the late stages, however, the bolson is filled with a great sheet of waste material, while the mountains are reduced to rocky pediments thinly mantled with the fans and surmounted here and there by a few island-like *inselberge*, the mountain remnants.* These rocky platforms are called *hamadas* (Figure 33, *c*, *d*, and *e*). Wind action reaches a maximum in these areas (see section 30).

The Direct Action of Gravity on Slopes. The direct action of gravity on slopes is the second of the six chief processes of corrasion and transportation. The movement of the regolith on the slopes begins as soon as the streams develop valley sides and the interfluves are dissected by tributaries. The effect of this movement is to change the interfluve profiles from the sharp concavity of running-water excavation to a rounded convexity.

Three kinds of regolith movement can be observed, which we shall describe as *creep, flow,* and *slide*. Earth creep is perhaps the most common of these. Any occurrence which causes the waste mantle to expand produces a movement out at right angles to the slope, and the subsequent contraction then takes place under the influence of gravity directly downward. The result is a gradual downhill movement. Wetting and drying produce rapid earth creep, and earth creep is at a minimum in those climates where the ground remains either permanently dry or permanently wet. Freezing and thawing are also active aids of earth creep. The presence of burrowing animals is another but quite different cause of creep.

Earth flow is a smooth, downward semiliquid movement, generally re-

*Reference 9.

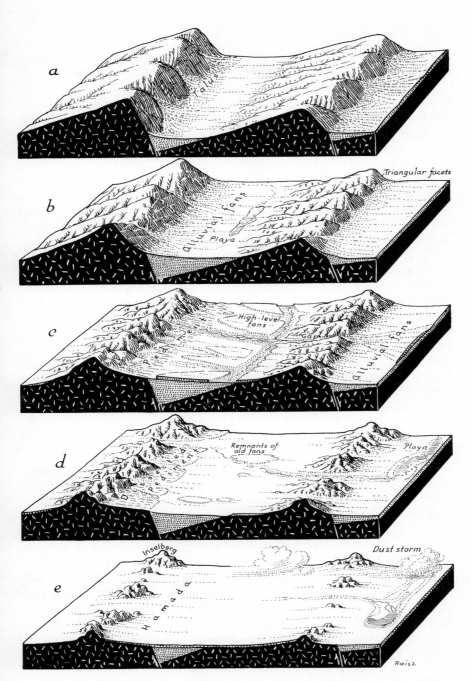

Figure 33. Series of block diagrams illustrating a sequence of landforms in an arid climate.

stricted to the waterlogged regolith of the rainy tropics. The effect of earth
flow is to produce concave rather than convex slopes.

The presence of trees tends to retard both flow and creep, and so to maintain steeper slopes than would otherwise form. The gentlest slopes of the
old-age interfluves would theoretically be developed in the tropical grasslands, where wetting and drying would be extreme and yet where no retaining network of tree roots would hold back the movement of regolith.

The third type of regolith movement is generally limited to mountainous
areas. This is the slide, or *avalanche*. Where the geologic structure is favorable the loose regolith forming on the steep slopes stands perilously balanced
until some slight jar gives it a start. Slides are most common in the spring
in middle-latitude mountains, when the frost begins to melt and when there
is plenty of water to aid the movement. Slides occur more frequently on
shady slopes where the ground does not dry out quickly. Starting high up,
perhaps with a single boulder, a larger and larger mass of the waste mantle
begins to move. With destructive violence the avalanche rushes into the
valley bottom, forming there a jumbled accumulation of boulders and
broken tree trunks, arranged in a series of low concentric ridges, perhaps
blocking the stream to form a temporary lake. The *avalanche scar* on the
valley side and the pile of debris below are forms often repeated in mountain areas (Figure 6, p. 386). Man sometimes creates avalanches through
oversteeping slopes in connection with excavating for roads, railroads, and
canals.

Glaciers.   During a recent period of geologic history somewhat cooler and
stormier climates produced great accumulations of ice in various parts of
the world. This period is known as the *Pleistocene*. In order to produce
glaciers it is necessary that more snow should fall during the winter than is
melted during the summer; heavy snowfall and cool summers, then, are the
climatic conditions which lead to glaciation. As the snow piles up to greater
and greater depths, ice is gradually formed underneath. As this ice increases in thickness, it tends to spread, either downhill, if it lies on a steeply
inclined slope, or out in all directions from a center of accumulation, if it
lies on a flattish surface. In this way the great ice sheets came into existence. In the course of long periods of time, as measured by human stand-
ards, the ice grew to great thicknesses and extended by further accumulation
in the directions of heavier snowfall. Near the margins of the ice sheets,
at least, there was considerable outward movement, and the resulting grind-
ing and scraping over the hills and through the valleys of the preglacial
surfaces brought about important changes in the character of the landforms.

The distribution of the ice sheets during the Pleistocene is shown on page

342 (Map 76). At present large ice sheets exist only in Greenland and Antarctica; but high mountains, even on the equator, have smaller glaciers.

Forms of Glacial Erosion by Ice Sheets.   In hilly areas the work which the ice accomplished was largely that of erosion. The loose rock material at the surface was scraped off and dumped into the valleys as irregular masses of heterogeneous debris. The bedrock, exposed on the preglacial ridges, was smoothed, rounded, and polished. Passing over a preglacial hill, the scraping action of the ice was concentrated on the side toward which the ice was moving. The contour of the hill was smoothed and rounded; but on the lee side, where the ice, in moving away, plucked from the slopes any loose or broken fragments of rock, steep, jagged cliffs were formed. The characteristic *rock hill* of a glaciated upland therefore has a relatively gentle slope in the direction from which the ice came; a rounded summit, composed in many instances of bare, smooth rock; and a jagged cliff on the lee side. Many of the preglacial valleys, however, were completely filled with the rock debris scraped from the hills. Except for the rock hills, the ice left such hilly country rougher than before, although, perhaps, with less total relief; and with the melting back of the glacier, the many small depressions, produced both by ice gouging in bedrock and by irregular deposition, were left as lakes and marshes.

Glacial Deposition.   The enormous amount of debris picked up and carried by the ice was deposited on the lowlands, and, especially near the margins of the glaciated area, formed a covering in some places hundreds of feet deep over the preglacial surface. As long as the climatic conditions over the glacier favored snow accumulation, the ice itself, at least near the margins, continued to move outward in great tongues, or lobes. The actual position of the margin of the glacier, however, was dependent on two things: the rate of advance and the rate of melting. If the summers were cool and the melting slow, the ice front would advance; but if the summers were warmer, melting might go on so much faster than the rate of advance that the actual front of the ice would retreat. Cycles of wetter and drier and hotter and cooler years apparently prevailed during the glacial period, as they do now, for the ice advanced and retreated many times, and the rate of advance and retreat was very irregular.*

Moraines.   Along the glacier front, where melting was active, the rock debris contained in the ice was dropped in irregular piles. If the rates of advance and melting were balanced and the ice front remained stationary for a period of years, a belt of little hills was built up, following the lobate

* Reference 21.

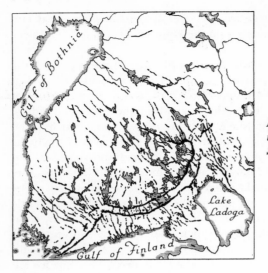

Map 101. RHe two, large moraines and the chief eskers of Finland (after J. J. Sederholm).

pattern of the ice margin (Map 101). These hilly belts are called *moraines*. In some cases the moraines had extremely rough surfaces, composed of knobby hills and deep depressions—described as *knob and basin moraines*. In other places only *sag and swell moraines* were formed. Moraines are best developed on plains, and near the margins of the glaciated areas where the supply of rock material was large.

Outwash. Moraines were deposited directly from the ice, but much of the material carried by the melting glaciers was spread out by floods of water. Glacial outwash filled in around the moraines and buried the pre-existing landforms under a mantle of waterlaid sands and gravels even beyond the limits of the ice.

The water which poured from the melting glacier deposited its load under three different sets of circumstances. Where the valleys sloped away from the front of the ice, as in the case of the Mississippi system, ready-made drainage channels were provided, and the floods were concentrated in them. Hundreds of miles beyond the limits of glaciation the floods of glacial waters filled the valleys. Broad floodplains were developed as the reinforced streams advanced their valleys more rapidly than their smaller tributaries in the cycle of erosion. Such outwash deposits are called *valley trains*. Except for the prematurely old main valleys, this type of outwash leaves the preglacial landforms untouched.

On the other hand, in areas where surfaces without adequate preglacial valleys lay beyond the melting ice, the torrential waters were not concentrated. They spread an apron of sand or gravel in front of the moraine.

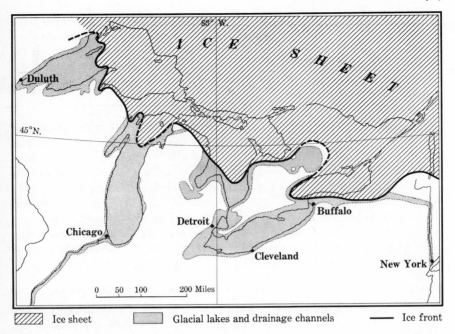

Map 102. A stage in the retreat of the last ice sheet from the Great Lakes Region, showing formation of glacial lakes ponded against the ice front, and the temporary drainage channels by way of the Illinois and Mohawk rivers (after F. B. Taylor).

The resulting plain, sloping gently away from the former position of the ice front, is called an *outwash plain*. Not uncommonly such surfaces are pitted with innumerable small depressions, resulting from the subsequent melting of ice masses buried under the sands. When an outwash plain has been deposited over a country previously mantled with moraines, landforms of the most varied kinds are mixed together in heterogeneous confusion.

Glacial Lakes. A very different situation was presented when the water found a surface sloping toward the ice instead of away from it. In this case a lake was formed, with one side held in by the ice itself and with an outlet over a low place in the divide. The present Great Lakes of North America are bordered by lake plains which were formed in this way when the outlet through the St. Lawrence River was blocked (Map 102).* The lake waters spread over much of northern Ohio and eastern Michigan, finding outlets at various times through the present site of Chicago to the Illinois River and through the Mohawk Valley to the Hudson. Similarly, when the outlet to

*Reference 6.

Hudson Bay was blocked, the waters of the Red River of the North were ponded in the basin of the present Lake Winnipeg. A glacial lake, referred to as Lake Agassiz, extended southward along the Red River Valley as far as the northern part of South Dakota. The lake plains are among the flattest surfaces in existence in the world; and in glaciated regions they provide exceptionally good agricultural lands.

Other Glacial Forms. In addition to these widespread forms of glacial deposition, there are a number of more unusual forms, which, nevertheless, are of great importance locally. The *drumlins* are rounded, elongated hills that loom conspicuously above their surroundings and are composed of an unstratified mixture of boulders and clay. *Kames* are small, knobby hills of stratified sand and gravel, commonly associated with moraines and not easily distinguished from morainic hills by surface form alone. *Eskers* are long, narrow ridges of irregular height, some of which can be traced for scores of miles across the country (Map 101). They are composed of coarse gravels with faint stratification and are believed to mark the courses of subglacial streams.

Glacial Forms in Mountains. Glacial forms in mountains differ in many ways from those produced by continental ice sheets. Since the glaciers are mostly confined to the valleys, the ice erosion results in a sharpening of the peaks and a steepening of the valley sides. The *glacial trough* is the most striking feature developed by valley glaciers. Here we find that whatever the preglacial form of the valley, the ice gouges it out, scraping away the spurs, steepening the sides, and deepening and widening the bottom. The characteristic profile of a glaciated valley is that of a flattened U. The deep excavation of the main valley leaves the former tributaries perched high on the cliffed sides as *hanging valleys* (Figure 34, *d*). In the bottom of the trough horseshoe moraines, marking the places where the ice front hesitated during its retreat, act as dams to hold back little valley lakes. Where the glaciers were big enough to reach the piedmont and spread terminal moraines on the neighboring lowlands or gouge out rock basins in the valley bottoms, large *marginal lakes* were formed, extending up-valley for many miles. A number of these lakes appear on the map of the southern Andes (Map 89, p. 385); they are common in other parts of the world where similar alpine scenery has been developed,—for example, the lakes of the southern Alpine piedmont in Italy (Map 38, p. 184).

The most spectacular alpine scenery, however, is produced at higher altitudes. The snow field in which the ice of a valley glacier has its origin is commonly located high on the mountain slopes at the valley head. As the ice forms and moves off downgrade it plucks away the rocks loosened by frost. The plucking action, quite similar to that which takes place on the

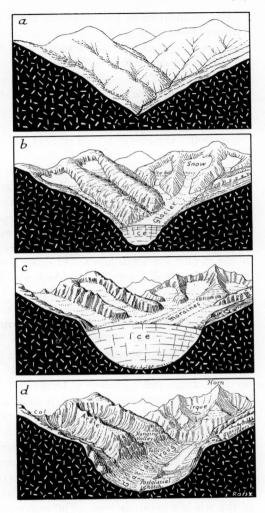

Figure 34. A series of diagrams illustrating the development of glacial landforms in high mountains.

lee side of a rock hill covered by a continental ice sheet (see Forms of Glacial Erosion by Ice Sheets), results in the hollowing out of an amphitheater backed by steepened cliffs. Vigorous glaciation produces great semicircular amphitheaters near the mountain crest at the head of each valley. In many cases small remnant glaciers still survive at these high levels; but where the ice has melted entirely away the almost vertical rock walls overlook the exposed floor of the basin, in which is nestled, among the smoothed and polished rocks of the glacier bed, a little lake of crystal-clear, ice-cold water. The lake occupying such an ice-gouged basin is called a *tarn;* the whole amphitheater is known as a *cirque* (Figure 34, *d*).

The sculpturing of the mountain crests by the headward erosion of the cirques develops a jagged sky line. Glaciers gouging out their amphitheaters on opposite sides of a range push back the head walls until only a knife-edge of crumbling rock separates them. Here the divide is lowered to form a *col.* Knife-edge divides, or *arêtes,* also separate the neighboring cirques on the same side of the range. Meanwhile between the cols, and towering high above the neighboring cirques, stand massive pyramids of frost-fractured rock. These are the *horns* which produce the characteristic "saw-tooth" sky line of alpine scenery.

Postglacial Mountain Forms. Since the glacial period a deluge of rock fragments from the towering walls of the cirques and horns has partially obscured the glacial forms in some localities. Frost action of high altitudes is very active. Especially in the spring large quantities of broken rock fall from the cliffs and accumulate as *talus cones* at the base. Loosened fragments of rock break off and clatter noisily down into the valley. In some of the cirques the accumulation of waste is so great that huge *rock streams* are formed, descending into the amphitheater bottoms and filling them with a tumbled confusion of rock piled on rock.

Landforms Produced by Wind. Landforms produced by wind are of much less importance than those developed by the processes already discussed. Wind erosion can be effective only where there is a supply of dry sand or dust to abrade the exposed rock surfaces. In the dry lands, especially in the late stages (see Landforms Developed in Arid Climates), wind-sculptured forms are not uncommon, but elsewhere they are rare. Wind sweeping over the fans of the desert bolsons, or over the ergs which succeed them in the dry-land sequnce, picks up whatever loose material is available. Some of the material is too heavy to be carried far; this is rolled or skipped into dunes. The very fine particles, however, are lifted high into the air and may even be carried beyond the limits of the deserts. Great accumulations of fine wind-blown material, known as *loess,* are found on the lee sides of the world's great deserts. The removal of the finer particles from the desert fans is known as *deflation.* Little by little the surface comes to be mantled with only the coarser pieces that are too large to be moved by the wind. These fragments are fitted tightly together to form what is known as the *desert pavement.*

Dunes are also formed in rainy lands where a large supply of dry sand is available, as along a sea or lake shore.

Karst. Landforms resulting from rock solution are also narrowly limited in their distribution. Only certain kinds of rocks are sufficiently soluble to permit such development. Of the soluble rocks, limestone is the chief kind,

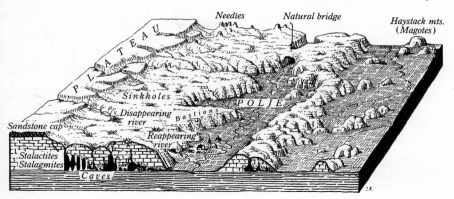

Figure 35. Block diagram showing some characteristic karst landforms.

although not all limestones are soluble and each limestone layer is of a somewhat different degree of solubility. Where solution can go on rapidly enough, caverns are formed underground; and the collapse of the cave roofs marks the surface of the earth with pitlike depressions, or *sinks* (Figure 35). The surface streams find entrance into these underground caverns and disappear, leaving only dry valleys above ground. Such areas may, as a result, be deficient in moisture at the surface. Lands pockmarked in this way with sinks, and by larger basins known as *poljes* and *uvalas,* are called *karst* lands after the type locality where such forms are developed on a spectacular scale, on the Karst Plateau, near the head of the Adriatic Sea in Yugoslavia (Map 96, p. 415).*

Shorelines. The relative changes of level between the land and the sea are most noticeable along the shores. So unstable are the relations of land and sea and so rapid are the processes of shoreline development by waves and currents that these modifications can be observed in historical time. Many are the ancient seaports which now are separated from open water by miles of delta or coastal plain.

In general two major classes of shorelines may be recognized. There are *shorelines of submergence* (Figure 36) and *shorelines of emergence* (Figure 37).†
The former class is the result of either a depression of the land or a rise of the water; it is characterized by a greatly indented shore, with numerous bays, inlets, promontories, and islands. Where pre-existing river-cut valleys are drowned by submergence, leaving the interfluves to extend seaward as promontories or strings of islands, the descriptive term *ria shore* is used (Map 34, p. 178). Where a glacial trough is submerged, the result is described as

*See reference 10.
† Reference 7.

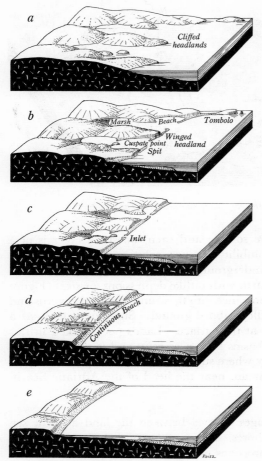

Figure 36. A series of block diagrams illustrating the development of a shore-line of submergence.

a *fiord* (Map 89, p. 385). The shorelines of emergence, on the other hand, are relatively straight, with few indentations or promontories. Commonly these are *coastal-plain shores;* but in some places mountainous shores are emergent, in which case the land rises abruptly from the water's edge. Evidences of emergence can be seen in the raised terraces (see section Shore Modifications) now well above the sea level (Map 103).

Shore Modifications. The waves and currents along shores produce rapid changes on the land. The formation of terraces is one of the most important of these modifications. Actual cutting by the waves is confined to a horizontal zone between the wave crests at high tide and the wave troughs at

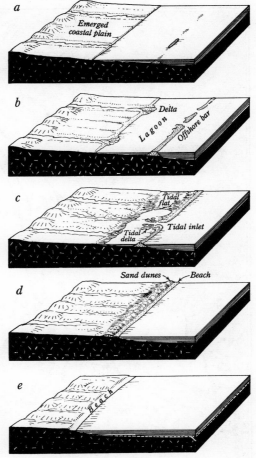

Figure 37. A series of block diagrams illustrating the development of a shore-line of emergence.

low tide. This zone of cutting, however, results in the development, by sapping, of a steep *wave-cut cliff.* Under the water, and not visible unless raised on an emerging shore, is a *wave-cut terrace,* continued on its seaward edge by a *wave-built terrace* composed of the material cut from the land.

Whether shorelines are emergent or submergent, in the long run the waves transform them into shores of very similar appearance. The accompanying diagrams illustrate the sequence of forms of a shoreline of submergence (Figure 36). First the promontories are cliffed, and then spits and bay-head bars appear across the indentations. Beaches are eventually formed across the mouths of the bays, festooned from headland to headland and enclosing half-moon-shaped marshy lagoons. Later the headlands are

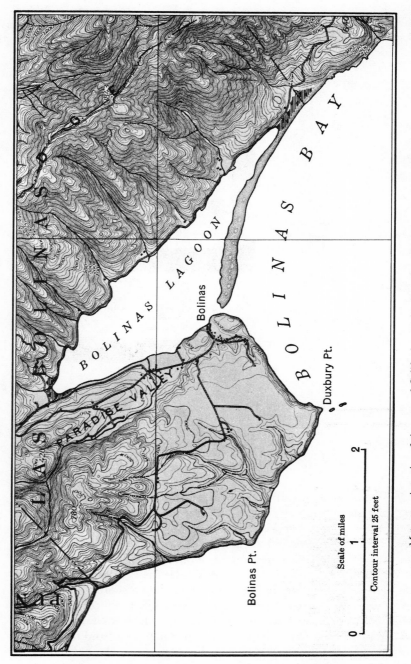

Map 103. A portion of the coast of California—a shoreline of recent emergence following local subsidence (from Tamalpais quadrangle, California, United States Geological Survey).

farther worn back and the bays filled until a straight shore is produced. A shoreline of emergence (Figure 37) is quickly protected by an *off-shore bar,* behind which a lagoon forms. In the rainy tropics this lagoon, like the smaller lagoons of the indented coast, is filled with mangrove, but in the middle latitudes it is commonly covered with salt-marsh grass. Little by little the bar retreats landward until eventually a straight shore again appears, with no lagoon. All these various stages can be observed on the shores of the lakes or the oceans.

Deltas. The building of deltas by streams is dependent on various factors. Submergence and emergence are balanced against the rate of delta growth; and delta growth, in turn, is determined by the amount of alluvium brought by the river, by the nature of the body of water into which the stream is flowing, and by other things. Marked shore currents greatly affect the shape of the growing delta. As a general rule rivers entering seas with strong tides do not build deltas, for the washing of the water in and out of the river mouths keeps them free from silt. On the other hand, deltas form rapidly in seas with small tidal range, such as the Caribbean and the Gulf of Mexico or the Mediterranean.

REFERENCES

Geomorphology

1. GILBERT, G. K. *Geology of the Henry Mountains,* United States Geological Survey Report. Washington, D. C., 1877.

2. GILBERT, G. K. *Lake Bonneville,* United States Geological Survey, Monograph I. Washington, D. C., 1890.

3. POWELL, J. W. *Physiography of the United States,* National Geographic Society, Monograph No. 1. Washington, D. C., 1895.

4. DAVIS, W. M. *Geographical Essays.* Boston, 1909.

5. DAVIS, W. M. "Meandering Valleys and Underfit Rivers," *Annals of the Association of American Geographers,* Vol. 3 (1913), pp. 3–28.

6. LEVERETT, F., and TAYLOR, F. B. *The Pleistocene of Indiana and Michigan and the History of the Great Lakes,* United States Geological Survey, Monograph LIII. Washington, D. C., 1915.

7. JOHNSON, D. W. *Shore Processes and Shoreline Development.* New York, 1919.

8. CRESSEY, G. B. *The Indiana Sand Dunes and Shore Lines of the Lake Michigan Basin,* Geographic Society of Chicago, Bulletin No. 8. Chicago, 1928.

9. DAVIS, W. M. "Rock Floors in Arid and in Humid Climates," *Journal of Geology,* Vol. 38 (1930), pp. 1–27, 136–158.

10. DAVIS, W. M. "The Origin of Limestone Caverns," *Bulletin of the Geological Society of America,* Vol. 41 (1930), pp. 475–628.

11. MATTHES, F. E. *Geologic History of the Yosemite Valley,* United States Geological Survey, Professional Paper 160. Washington, D. C., 1930.

12. ASHLEY, G. H. "Studies in Appalachian Mountain Sculpture," *Bulletin of the Geological Society of America,* Vol. 46 (1935), pp. 1395–1436.

13. CRESSEY, G. B. "The Land Forms of Chekiang," *Annals of the Association of American Geographers,* Vol. 28 (1938), pp. 259–276.

14. SHARPE, C. F. S. *Landslides and Related Phenomena: A Study of Mass-Movements of Soil and Rock.* New York, 1938.

15. IRELAND, H. A., SHARPE, C. F. S., and EARGLE, D. H. *Principles of Gully Erosion in the Piedmont of South Carolina,* United States Department of Agriculture, Technical Bulletin No. 633. Washington, D. C., 1939.

16. LOBECK, A. K. *Geomorphology: An Introduction to the Study of Landscapes.* New York, 1939.

17. BRYAN, K. "The Retreat of Slopes," *Annals of the Association of American Geographers,* Vol. 30 (1940), pp. 254–268.

18. THORNTHWAITE, C. W., SHARPE, C. F. S., and DOSCH, E. F. *Climate and Accelerated Erosion in the Arid and Semi-Arid Southwest, with Special Reference to the Polacca Wash Drainage Basin, Arizona,* United States Department of Agriculture, Technical Bulletin No. 808. Washington, D. C., 1942.

19. FLINT, R. F. *Glacial Geology and the Pleistocene Epoch.* New York, 1947.

20. SHEPARD, R. P. *Submarine Geology.* New York, 1948.

21. COTTON, C. A. *Geomorphology,* Sixth Edition. New York, 1952.

22. PENCK, W. *Morphological Analysis of Land Forms.* New York, 1953.

23. KING, L. C. "Canons of Landscape Evolution," *Bulletin of the Geological Society of America,* Vol. 64 (1953), pp. 721–753.

24. THORNBURY, W. D. *Principles of Geomorphology.* New York, 1954.

25. BRETZ, J. H., SMITH, H. T. U., and NEFF, G. E. "Channeled Scabland of Washington: New Data and Interpretations," *Bulletin of the Geological Society of America,* Vol. 67 (1956), pp. 957–1049.

26. STRAHLER, A. N. *Physical Geography,* (second edition). New York, 1960.

27. KING, L. C. *The Morphology of the Earth.* New York, 1962.

28. BUDEL, J. "Klimagenetische Geomorphologie," *Geographische Rundschau,* Vol. 15 (1963), pp. 269–285.

Soils

29. GLINKA, K. D. *The Great Soil Groups of the World and Their Development.* Translated from the German by C. F. Marbut. Ann Arbor, Michigan, 1927.

30. MARBUT, C. F. "Soils of the United States," Part III of the *Atlas of American Agriculture,* United States Department of Agriculture. Washington, D. C., 1935.

31. United States Department of Agriculture, *1938 Yearbook of Agriculture. Soils and Men.* Washington, D. C., 1938.

32. KELLOGG, C. E. *The Soils that Support Us.* New York, 1941.

33. JENNY, H. *Foundations of Soil Science.* New York, 1946.

34. KELLOGG, C. E., CLINE, M. G., and Others. *Soil Science,* Vol. 67 (1949), pp. 77–260.

35. KELLOGG, C. E. *Soil Survey Manual,* United States Department of Agriculture, Miscellaneous Publications 274, Second Edition. Washington, D. C., 1951.

36. United States Department of Agriculture, *1957 Yearbook of Agriculture. Soils.* Washington, D. C., 1957.

The Hydrosphere

The Hydrosphere. Water covers 70 per cent of the earth's surface. It not only fills the major depressions of the earth's crust but also submerges the margins of the continents. The oceans are the reservoirs from which is derived not only the water that appears as a visible feature of the landscape in rivers, lakes, and marshes but also the invisible water vapor that plays such a vital part in determining the world's climates (Appendix B). Among the first recorded observations of mankind was the apparently strange fact that "the rivers flow into the sea, yet the sea is not full." The ancients were observing only the visible part of a cycle which is of fundamental importance among the natural processes of our earth. Water is evaporated from the surface of the ocean. Onshore winds carry the water vapor inland, where, later, it is deposited as rain, hail, or snow. When this water reaches the land, it returns again through the rivers to the sea, either directly or indirectly. Not only is the supply of moisture essential to living organisms on the earth, but also, of the six processes of land sculpture listed in Appendix C, only one, the wind, is neither directly nor indirectly dependent on the presence of water.

Two general facts regarding the hydrosphere should be remembered. The first is the peculiar range of the earth's atmospheric temperatures, which permits water to exist on the face of our planet in the form of a liquid. The second is the contrast between fresh and salt water with regard to freezing point and temperature of greatest density. Fresh water is densest at 39.2° F. If this were not true, lakes and rivers would freeze at the bottom instead of at the surface, and the circulation of water in them would be very different. Salt water with a salinity of 3.5 per cent freezes at 28° and also reaches its greatest density at this same temperature. As a consequence the deepest parts, which descend as much as six and one-half miles below sea level, are very cold.*

The Nature of Ocean Water.   The water of the ocean is by no means uniform in character.   There are great differences from place to place, and these differences are of fundamental importance not only in the geography of the oceans themselves but also in the climatic patterns of the whole earth. There are great differences in temperature—from temperatures well over 80° in the equatorial regions to temperatures below 32° in the polar regions. The highest ocean temperatures are in the Persian Gulf and the Red Sea. Where temperatures are high and evaporation is rapid, the salt content of the water is generally higher than it is in areas of low water temperature. Marine organisms are usually more abundant in cool or cold water than in warm or hot water.   And associated with these things are the colors of ocean water, which range from greenish to bluish.

Generally, three major kinds of ocean water can be recognized.   (1) In the high latitudes *polar water* is low in temperature, low in salt content, rich in plankton and other marine organisms, and greenish in color.   (2) In the low latitudes the *tropical* and *subtropical water* is high in temperature, high in salt content, low in organic forms, and blue in color.   (3) In between are the so-called *mixed waters* of the middle latitudes.

Movements of Ocean Water.   As in the case of all phenomena on the face of the earth that are directly or indirectly related to the climatic features, there is a tendency toward regularity in the pattern of arrangement.   Departures from the regular arrangement as regards ocean currents are due to the irregular configuration of the continents and ocean basins.   In both hemispheres there are two major lines of convergence where water masses differing in temperature, salt content, life forms, and color are in contact. These are known as the *polar convergence* and the *subtropical convergence* (see the map of ocean currents—Plate 10).   In the Northern Hemisphere low latitudes the easterly winds produce a west-moving current of water, which, under the influence of the earth's rotation, tends constantly to swing to the right, or north.   In the Southern Hemisphere the swing is to the left, or south.   In the middle latitudes there is an east-moving current of water which, urged on by the prevailing westerly winds, swings to the right, or south, in the Northern Hemisphere, and to the left, or north, in the Southern Hemisphere.   These two currents of water in each hemisphere tend to swing toward each other, meeting along the lines of convergence.   There is relatively little mixing along this line; rather, the denser water sinks under the lighter water.

*For the characteristics of the oceans, and for many references to additional sources, see references 9, 10, 11, and 12.

The warm, west-moving currents of subtropical water strike the continental east coasts in the low latitudes. In the Pacific Ocean a strong equatorial countercurrent is developed, moving eastward between 5° and 10° north of the equator all the way to the coast of Panama and Colombia. In the Atlantic, on the other hand, the countercurrent which returns to the equatorial part of western Africa is relatively weak. The projecting nose of South America splits the west-moving current, deflecting a considerable part of it northward into the Caribbean and the Gulf of Mexico. This strong current of warm tropical and subtropical water emerges between Cuba and Florida as the Gulf Stream, which bathes the east coast of North America as far as about 40° north. It then swings eastward across the Atlantic as the North Atlantic Drift to the shores of Europe north of 35°. The configuration of Norway permits this relatively warm water to penetrate even into the polar ocean, bringing ice-free waters to the northernmost part of Europe. The similar current in the North Pacific, the Kuro Siwo, is not so strong and does not penetrate so far north. The configuration of Alaska and the Aleutian Islands does not permit it to reach the polar sea. The relative weakness of the Kuro Siwo can be matched against the relatively slight development of the equatorial countercurrent in the Atlantic.

The west coasts of the continents between 35° and 15° are bathed by relatively cold water. Here the equatorward-moving currents in both hemispheres tend to swing offshore. Close to the land, the water is being replaced by up-welling from below, and is especially cold.

Cold polar water moves equatorward along the east coasts of the continents in higher middle latitudes, and meets the east-moving water of the middle latitudes along the line of the polar convergence. The continental east coasts are bathed by cold water as far as 40° of latitude; and off the coast of eastern South America this cold water area is especially wide. These several currents are indicated on Plate 10.

The movements of water in the Indian Ocean are complicated by the seasonal shift of the monsoons. In the Northern Hemisphere winter there is a well-developed westerly movement of the subtropical water both north and south of the equator. These currents, striking the east coast of Africa, give rise to a strong equatorial countercurrent. In the Northern Hemisphere summer, on the other hand, the onshore south Asian monsoon reverses the direction of the ocean current north of the equator, and the equatorial countercurrent entirely disappears. The currents in the Bay of Bengal and among the East Indies are similarly reversed by the seasonal shift of the winds.

Ground Water.* Three things can happen to the water that falls on the surface of the land: it can evaporate again, it can run off over the surface,

---

* References 1 through 8.

or it can sink into the ground. These processes are sometimes described as fly-off, run-off, and cut-off. The circumstances which increase or decrease evaporation have already been described (Appendix B). As regards the ratio between run-off and cut-off, the cut-off is greater where the regolith is porous than where it is relatively impervious, it is greater on gentle slopes than on steep slopes, it is greater when the rain falls slowly than when it comes in violent showers, and it is greater where the ground is protected by a cover of vegetation than where the ground is bare.

The water which sinks into the ground and is not used near the surface by plants fills the spaces between the rock particles of the regolith and even the cracks in the bedrock below. This store of water is known as *ground water*. The portion of the bedrock and regolith which is saturated with water is known as the *zone of saturation*, and the top of the zone of saturation is termed the *ground-water table*. Above the ground-water table is the *zone of aeration*, through which the cut-off must sink on its way down to the zone of satura- tion. Water on its way down through the zone of aeration is called *vadose water*. The zone of aeration, however, may be moist even when there is no vadose water actually seeping through it; for just as a blotter may remain damp but not saturated, the upper zone of the regolith may contain con- siderable *soil moisture*, even during a protracted drought.

The ground-water table lies at varying depths below the surface. In general it follows the contour of the surface but without the smaller irregu- larities. The water table rises under the hills and falls under the valleys, but it is farther below the surface under a hill than under a valley. Where the water table reaches the surface of the ground, it forms a marsh; where it rises above the surface, it forms a lake or supports the continued flow of a permanent stream. Even in the dry lands, where the characteristic streams flow only during and for a short time after a rain, ground water is usually to be found not far below the valley floors. Anything which diminishes the cut-off results eventually in a general lowering of the water table: thus the removal of the forest cover of a rainy land may result in the drying up of marshes and the fall of lake levels without any actual decrease in the rain- fall.

The ground water in rainy lands seeps through the regolith toward the valleys to come to the surface again in springs. Because of the varied structure of the regolith and of the bedrock, the movement of ground water is not always uniform. The position and force of water in springs are de- termined by the underlying geologic structure.

Common Wells. The common well is used to tap the supply of ground water. It consists simply of an excavation deep enough to reach the zone of saturation. The ground water seeps into the well, filling it to the height of the water table.

Artesian Wells. In some wells water rises independently of the local ground-water table and may even flow out at the surface. These are *artesian wells*. The true artesian system requires the existence of a special set of geologic conditions, the essentials of which are illustrated in the accompanying cross section (Figure 38). A stratum of porous rock (W)—a sandstone, let us say—is inclined at an angle. Its outcrop is in an area of plentiful ground water (C). This is the intake of the artesian system, where the local ground water not only fills the usual cracks and fissures near the surface but also is absorbed by the porous sandstone. Gradually this layer of rock is saturated, and water seeps underground long distances, even hundreds of miles, from the intake. Overlying the water-bearing stratum is an impervious rock (B)—a shale, for example—through which the imprisoned water cannot make its escape. Thus when a fissure is found, or when man makes a boring, as at D_1, D_2, or D_3, the water rises under pressure until it reaches the level of E. In some cases the system is so placed that water actually flows out at the surface, making a flowing artesian well (D_2 and D_3); but in others the intake is not high enough for this, and the water rises only part way in the boring and must be pumped the remainder of the distance to the surface (D_1). The essential requirements for such a system are tilted layers of rock, among which there is a porous water-bearing stratum under an impervious stratum. Wells may be bored hundreds of miles from the source of water. Obviously, however, the overuse of such a system may remove water faster than it is stored up and may bring about the eventual exhaustion of the supply, as is threatened at D_1.

Hot Springs and Geysers. In many parts of the world there are natural springs the temperature of which varies from slightly warm to hot or even boiling. These are produced where the cracks and fissures in the bedrock are deep enough to bring the ordinary ground water in contact with heated rocks. Few cracks reach depths greater than five miles, but even at that distance below the surface the rock is very hot. Where pools of molten rock lie near the surface, as in volcanic regions, hot springs are common.

Geysers are less common. A geyser is produced in a fissure from which there is no outlet save at the top. Ground water seeping down into such an opening is heated at the lower end. The temperature at the bottom may rise above the boiling point, but the weight of the overlying water does not permit the formation of steam. Eventually the superheated water below is able to force a passage up through the tube, blowing out at the surface in a tall plume of spray.

Hard and Soft Waters. As water sinks through the zone of aeration or seeps through the regolith to emerge again in the rivers, many minerals are picked up in solution. It is the constant addition of mineral matter to the

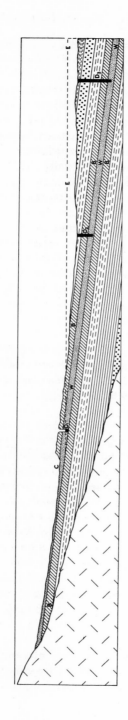

Figure 38. Diagram of an artesian system.

oceans and to the desert lakes that have no surface outlets that gives such bodies of water their high mineral content. Waters which have a considerable amount of mineral matter in solution (chiefly $CaCO_3$, $MgCO_3$, and $FeCO_3$) are said to be *hard*. In general the ground water and the water in rivers is hardest in areas of limestone rock or on plains where movement is slow. The softest waters are found where the rocks are relatively insoluble, as in granitic areas, or in hilly or mountainous country where the run-off is too rapid to permit the dissolving of such mineral matter.

Surface Water. Surface water includes rivers, lakes, marshes, and glaciers. The landforms related to these kinds of surface water have been discussed in Appendix C.

The more or less regular rise and fall of streams with the passage of the seasons is known as the *regimen*. Regimens may be described as regular, irregular, or intermittent. The regimen of a stream bears a close resemblance to the rainfall of its drainage basin, but it is also controlled to a certain extent by a number of other factors. De Martonne* illustrates the factors in regimen by a simple equation:

$$F = P - (C + E^1 + E^2) + S.$$

In this equation F is the flow of the river. This is determined primarily by the rainfall (P), subtracting, however, the amount of water which is cut off by sinking into the ground (C) and the amount which is evaporated directly (E^1) or indirectly through plants (E^2), and adding the amount of water which emerges again from the ground water through springs (S). Any condition that diminishes the values of C and E increases the flow of rivers. Yet since in the long run C and S are very nearly balanced, it follows that the volume of water in the streams must vary largely with P and E. The regimen of a stream, then, reflects closely the climatic conditions; it is most irregular in the w or s climates and most regular in the f climates (see Appendix B). In the case of streams draining areas of considerable snowfall, however, the spring melting is commonly the season of high water. Lakes have the effect of regularizing the flow of water, regardless of the regime of rainfall.

Ice. The following classification of ice forms was suggested by Nordenskjöld.†

A. HIGHLAND GLACIERS

    I. Ice forms and ice motion dependent on the character of the underlying terrain.

---

*Martonne, E. de, *Traité de géographie physique* (Paris, 1926).
† Nordenskjöld, O., and Mecking, L. *The Geography of the Polar Regions*, American Geographical Society, Special Publication No. 8 (New York, 1928), p. 25.

1. Glaciers in distinct catchment basins bordered by dominating ice-free ridges, outlets down-valley (valley glacier). Figure 34.

2. Glacier occupying an isolated catchment basin on the top of a plateau or highland (plateau glacier).

3. Glacier resulting from the accumulation of several converging valley glaciers at the base of a mountain (piedmont glacier).

II. Ice forms and ice motion independent or partially independent of the underlying terrain.

4. Glacier covering most of surface, although the general shape of the underlying terrain is visible in the ice contour (near icecap). Map 89.

5. Glacier covering the whole surface to such a depth that no sign of the underlying terrain is apparent in the ice contour (inland ice). Map 85.

B. LOWLAND GLACIERS

6. Accumulation of glacial ice in a band along the base of a mountain; not fed, as is the piedmont glacier, by converging valley glaciers, but formed in place from snow accumulation (ice foot).

7. Accumulation of glacial ice on the seacoast, extending out into the water so that in some cases its outer margin is floating, and formed in place from snow accumulation (shelf ice). Map 84.

REFERENCES

Water on the Land

1. MEINZER, O. E. *Outline of Ground-Water Hydrology,* United States Geological Survey, Water-Supply Paper 557. Washington, D. C., 1923.

2. JARVIS, C. S., and Others. *Floods in the United States: Magnitude and Frequency,* United States Geological Survey, Water-Supply Paper 771. Washington, D. C., 1936.

3. FOSTER, E. E. *Rainfall and Runoff.* New York 1948.

4. The President's Water Resources Policy Commission. *A Water Policy for the American People* (Vol. 1); *Ten Rivers in America's Future* (Vol. 2); *Water Resources Law* (Vol. 3). Washington, D. C., 1950.

5. THOMAS, H. E. *The Conservation of Ground Water.* New York, 1951.

6. MEIGS, P. "Water Problems in the United States," *Geographical Review,* Vol. 42 (1952), pp. 346–366.

7. United States Department of Agriculture, 1955 Yearbook. *Water.* Washington, D. C., 1955.

8. THOMAS, H. E., and LEOPOLD, L. B. "Ground Water in North America," *Science,* Vol. 143 (1964), pp. 1001–1006.

Water in the Oceans

9. SCHOTT, G. *Geographie des Indischen und Stillen Ozeans.* Hamburg, 1935.

10. JAMES, P. E. "The Geography of the Oceans: A Review of the Work of Gerhard Schott," *Geographical Review,* Vol. 26 (1936), pp. 664–669.

11. SVERDRUP, H. U., JOHNSON, M. V., and FLEMING, R. H. *The Oceans: Their Physics, Chemistry, and General Biology.* New York, 1942.

12. SCHOTT, G. *Geographie des Atlantischen Ozeans,* Fourth Edition. Hamburg, 1944.

13. RUSSELL, R. J. "Instability of Sea Level," *American Scientist,* Vol. 45 (1957), pp. 414–430.

14. STOMMEL, H. *The Gulf Stream. . . .* Berkeley, California, 1958.

15. United States Navy Weather Research Facility. *Oceanography for the Navy Meteorologist.* Norfolk, Virginia, 1960.

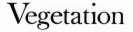

APPENDIX E

Vegetation

By David J. deLaubenfels*

The map of world vegetation (Plate 10, p. 564) divides the plant cover into seven broad categories based on the dominant layer of growth. The use of only seven basic types of vegetation allows the map to be relatively free from possibly confusing detail, while each category differs in some significant way from all the others in its vegetative characteristics. The actual mapping of world vegetation is limited by the lack of adequate data for some parts of the world. Furthermore, because vegetation boundaries are usually far from sharp, their location on maps is often somewhat subjective. The major world patterns of vegetation are, however, quite clear, and a comparison between them and the related patterns of climate and soil should be very instructive. The seven categories include five which represent largely undisturbed formations, while the other two (grassland and parkland) owe their characters in large measure to the results of disturbance.

Rain Forest is distinguished by a luxuriant evergreen canopy and the relative absence of mechanisms for dormancy. There is little or no vegetation in the world that is not prepared in some degree to withstand unfavorable conditions for growth, but a rain forest is not normally subject to severe or regularly unfavorable periods. Included within rain forest are luxuriant and evergreen but xerophytic types with small, tough or needle-like leaves. The year around sameness of these xerophytic formations that grow in tropical highland and middle latitude marine areas suggests the absence of severe unfavorable seasons, but the thick leaves imply chronically poor

*Reproduced from P. E. James, *One World Divided,* New York, 1964.

growing weather. The luxuriance is achieved by prolonged, even though slow, growth during each year. The rain forest is distinctly denser in growth than the following vegetation types, although in some areas rain forest blends through a gradual transition into seasonal forest.

Seasonal Forest has a tree canopy that displays well developed mechanisms for regular dormancy. It lacks the luxuriance of the rain forest where frequently, when the two come together, there is a distinct change from a complex growth, for the most part of sensitive trees, to a uniform stand of a few hardy tree species. Seasonal forest regularly becomes dormant during a part of the year as a result of seasonally unfavorable conditions for growth— either excessive cold or drought. Trees withstand either type of prolonged stress in one of two ways: sensitive leaves are discarded and the tree stands bare (deciduous); or the leaves themselves are adapted to endure by means of a thick cuticle, surface hairs, resin, reduced surface, etc. (xerophytic). Normally a seasonal forest is made up of trees of which some use one method of defense and some the other—for this condition the terms mixed or semideciduous are used. Because seasonal forests are dominated at most by a few kinds of trees, and not uncommonly by just one (e.g., oak, eucalyptus), it is no surprise that forests which are all deciduous, or all evergreen-xerophytic, are widespread.

Woodland is characterized by a cover of trees whose crowns do not mesh, with the result that branches extend to the ground. Woodland normally grows in the semiarid zones of the world, although essentially the same kind of formation is also found on the cold margins of the seasonal forests. Continuous brush is included in the areas mapped as woodland. Brush intermingles with woodland in complex mosaics as a rule, apparently because of variable amounts of disturbance or because of edaphic differences.

Desert vegetation has a discontinuous cover of plants. While bushes and herbaceous plants such as grass grow among and between the trees of a woodland, bare ground becomes dominant in desert vegetation. Deserts are characterized by a great variety of plant forms: trees in the less arid parts, bushes, herbaceous plants, and many bizarre growths that have in one way or another become adapted to survive under virtually continuous stress. It should be noted that desert grasslands cover extensive areas; the fact that herbaceous plants are the rule does not make such an area any less of a desert.

Tundra is the name applied to all areas which are too cold to allow trees to grow. There are actually three major kinds of tundra. The most typical is a prostrate cover of plants crowded together on the surface, which in a less extreme form becomes simply brush. Alternatively there may be grass and other herbaceous plants—essentially a grassland. Finally, in the most difficult areas climatically there may be what amounts to desert vegetation. None of these sub-formations is unique in the larger sense, and tundra can well be thought of as simply a cold desert. Where other deserts tend to meet the tundra, as in inner Asia, there may be difficulty in distinguishing tundra from other vegetation formations.

Parkland refers to areas where clumps of trees alternate with grassland, but where neither becomes an extensive, uninterrupted stand. Parkland normally results from the disturbance of forest or woodland. Not only may the forest be opened up in this way, but the trees may also be stunted to a smaller size than they achieve through uninterrupted growth. There are limited areas where rain forest alternates with parkland, but in general it appears to alternate with seasonal forest, and frequently borders on grassland.

Grassland is a cover of herbaceous plants where grass and grass-like plants are most prominent. Individual stands may be dominated by clump types, prostrate types, or upright but sod-forming types three feet and more high; but all types coalesce into a continuous cover, as they must in order to form a true grassland. It is generally thought that the world's great grasslands are the result of fires because they alternate with seasonal forest and woodland, and often lie between the two. Sharp boundaries are likely to be edaphically controlled; otherwise a zone of parkland, in most cases, intervenes between grassland and the woody formations. When fires are controlled in grassland areas the growth reverts to bushes or trees as the seeds become available. A grass desert must not be thought of as a grassland; each is caused by different conditions.

REFERENCES

1. Küchler, A. W. "A Physiognomic Classification of Vegetation," *Annals of the Association of American Geographers,* Vol. 39 (1949), p. 201–210.
2. Küchler, A. W. "Classification and Purpose in Vegetation Maps," *Geographical Review,* Vol. 46 (1956), pp. 155–167.
3. Dansereau, P. *Biogeography, An Ecological Perspective.* New York, 1957.
4. Cain, S. A., and Oliveira Castro, G. M. de. *Manual of Vegetation Analysis.* New York, 1959.
5. Schmithüsen, J. *Allgemeine Vegetationsgeographie.* Berlin, 1959.
6. Eyre, S. R. *Vegetation and Soils, A World Picture.* Chicago, 1963.

Statistics

TABLE 1. The World's Major Urban Centers, by Culture Regions.
Population for whole conurbations for latest available date as reported in
United Nations, *Demographic Yearbook*, 1964.

EUROPEAN

Wien (Vienna), Austria	1,634,000
Bruxelles (Brussels), Belgium	1,041,000
Paris, France	7,369,000
West Berlin, West Germany	2,177,000
Hamburg	1,851,000
München	1,157,000
Athens, Greece	1,853,000
Roma (Rome), Italy	2,329,000
Milano	1,643,000
Napoli	1,198,000
Torino	1,097,000
Madrid, Spain	2,443,000
Barcelona	1,634,000
Stockholm, Sweden	1,162,000
London, United Kingdom	8,187,000
Manchester	2,449,000
Birmingham	2,384,000
Glasgow	1,036,000
Leeds	1,721,000
Liverpool	1,385,000

SOVIET

Praha (Prague), Czechoslovakia	1,011,000
East Berlin, East Germany	1,071,000
Warszawa (Warsaw), Poland	1,203,000

TABLE I (*continued*)

Moskva (Moscow), U.S.S.R.	6,388,000
Leningrad	3,607,000
Kiev	1,292,000
Baku	1,116,000
Gorky	1,066,000
Tashkent	1,061,000
Kharkov	1,048,000
Novosibirsk	1,013,000

ANGLO-AMERICA

Montreal, Canada	2,205,000
Toronto	1,925,000
New York, U.S.A.	14,115,000
Los Angeles	6,489,000
Chicago	5,959,000
Philadelphia	4,554,000
Detroit	3,538,000
San Francisco-Oakland	2,839,000
Boston	2,413,000
Washington	2,250,000
St. Louis	2,180,000
Baltimore	1,811,000
Pittsburgh	1,804,000
Cleveland	1,785,000
Minneapolis	1,377,000
Milwaukee	1,150,000
Houston	1,140,000
Buffalo	1,054,000

LATIN AMERICA

Buenos Aires, Argentina	7,000,000
Rio de Janeiro, Brazil	3,223,000
São Paulo	3,165,000
Santiago, Chile	2,271,000
Bogota, Colombia	1,681,000
Habana, Cuba	1,463,000
Mexico City, Mexico	3,118,000
Lima, Peru	1,436,000
Montevideo, Uruguay	1,203,000
Caracas, Venezuela	1,589,000

NORTH AFRICA–SOUTHWEST ASIA

Teheran, Iran	2,317,000
Istanbul, Turkey	1,467,000

TABLE I (*continued*)

| Cairo, United Arab Republic (Egypt) | 3,518,000 |
| Alexandria | 1,588,000 |

SOUTH ASIA

Calcutta, India	4,580,000
Bombay	4,538,000
Delhi	2,630,000
Madras	1,834,000
Bangalore	1,347,000
Ahmedabad	1,316,000
Hyderabad	1,293,000
Kharagpur	1,060,000
Karachi, Pakistan	1,913,000
Lahore	1,296,000

SOUTHEAST ASIA

Djakarta, Indonesia	2,907,000
Surabaja	1,008,000
Singapore, Singapore	1,820,000
Manila, Philippines	1,139,000
Bangkok, Thailand	1,608,000
Saigon, South Vietnam	1,336,000

EAST ASIA

Shanghai, China (Mainland)	6,900,000
Peking	4,010,000
Tientsin	3,220,000
Shenyang (Mukden)	2,411,000
Wuhan	2,146,000
Chungking	2,121,000
Canton	1,840,000
Haerhpin (Harbin)	1,552,000
Dairen	1,508,000
Nanking	1,419,000
Hsi-an (Sian)	1,310,000
Tsingtao	1,121,000
Chengtu	1,107,000
Taiyuan	1,020,000
Taipei, China (Taiwan)	1,028,000
Tokyo, Japan	10,428,000
Osaka	3,197,000
Nagoya	1,859,000
Yokohama	1,590,000
Kyoto	1,324,000

TABLE I (*continued*)

Kobe	1,181,000
Kitakyushu-Kokura-Yahata	1,052,000
Seoul, South Korea	2,983,000
Pusan	1,270,000

AFRICA, SOUTH OF THE SAHARA

Johannesburg, South Africa	1,153,000

AUSTRALIA–NEW ZEALAND

Sydney, Australia	2,256,000
Melbourne	2,003,000

TABLE II. Climatic Data for Selected Stations
T. = temperature in degrees Fahrenheit; Rf. = rainfall in inches

		JAN.	FEB.	MAR.	APRIL	MAY	JUNE	JULY	AUG.	SEPT.	OCT.	NOV.	DEC.	YEAR
1.	T.	27.9	28.8	35.6	46.4	57.1	66.5	71.7	69.9	63.2	53.6	42.0	32.5	49.6
	Rf.	3.6	3.4	3.6	3.3	3.2	2.9	3.5	3.6	3.1	3.1	3.3	3.4	40.0
2.	T.	49.8	51.2	57.5	63.9	72.1	78.1	80.6	80.0	76.2	67.0	57.8	51.0	65.4
	Rf.	3.1	3.3	3.4	2.9	3.4	4.8	7.1	6.6	5.0	3.6	2.4	2.9	48.5
3.	T.	25.6	27.0	36.6.	47.4	58.4	68.1	74.0	72.9	66.3	54.8	41.5	30.3	50.2
	Rf.	2.0	2.1	2.6	2.8	3.6	3.3	3.4	3.0	3.1	2.6	2.4	2.1	33.0
4.	T.	-23.1	-11.3	3.8	29.1	46.4	56.7	59.3	54.3	42.4	25.1	0.7	-13.1	22.5
	Rf.	0.8	0.8	0.5	0.7	0.9	1.3	1.6	1.6	1.7	1.3	1.3	1.1	13.6
5.	T.	29.9	31.6	38.9	47.4	56.7	67.2	72.2	70.9	62.4	50.5	39.2	31.6	49.9
	Rf.	0.4	0.5	1.0	2.1	2.4	1.3	1.6	1.4	1.0	1.0	0.6	0.7	14.0
6.	T.	5.5	10.5	23.4	40.5	51.0	57.2	61.1	59.2	50.2	41.1	24.7	14.3	36.5
	Rf.	0.9	0.6	0.7	0.8	1.8	3.2	3.4	2.4	1.4	0.7	0.7	0.8	17.4
7.	T.	18.5	18.7	23.5	30.9	40.1	46.6	49.8	47.3	41.0	33.8	26.4	20.7	33.1
	Rf.	3.3	2.7	3.4	2.4	3.6	3.0	3.3	3.8	6.0	5.9	4.4	3.1	44.9
8.	T.	57.0	60.1	64.9	70.7	73.9	72.3	69.8	69.6	67.8	64.9	61.2	56.8	65.7
	Rf.	0.4	0.3	0.7	0.2	1.2	4.5	6.1	5.2	4.5	1.4	0.5	0.4	25.4
9.	T.	57.9	61.7	67.8	73.0	79.0	81.9	82.2	82.6	78.1	71.4	63.5	57.4	71.4
	Rf.	0.5	0.5	0.7	1.1	1.2	2.3	2.1	2.0	4.4	2.4	1.3	1.0	19.5
10.	T .	13.0	14.7	25.4	41.1	55.1	64.7	69.3	67.0	58.7	46.7	32.7	19.1	42.3
	Rf.	3.7	3.2	3.7	2.4	3.1	3.4	3.7	3.3	3.5	3.3	3.4	3.7	40.4
11.	T.	54.2	57.3	62.8	68.8	75.4	80.6	82.4	82.2	79.2	71.0	61.6	55.6	69.2
	Rf.	4.3	4.2	4.7	5.2	4.6	5.9	6.4	5.8	5.0	3.3	3.1	4.8	57.3
12.	T.	30.6	30.5	38.0	48.5	59.4	68.5	73.5	72.1	66.4	55.8	44.1	34.3	51.8
	Rf.	3.2	3.3	3.4	3.3	3.5	3.5	4.1	4.3	3.4	3.4	3.4	3.3	42.1
13.	T.	50.4	54.4	60.2	66.9	74.6	84.2	89.6	88.0	81.7	70.0	58.6	51.6	69.2
	Rf.	1.0	0.7	0.6	0.4	0.1	0.1	1.3	1.0	0.7	0.5	0.8	0.7	7.9
14.	T.	16.0	18.6	31.5	46.8	58.0	68.5	75.3	72.8	63.8	49.8	33.6	21.8	46.4
	Rf.	0.5	0.5	0.9	1.8	2.5	3.0	2.7	2.1	1.1	0.8	0.5	0.5	16.9
15.	T.	-19.9	-13.0	-13.1	-1.7	21.7	35.3	40.9	38.5	32.1	16.3	0.3	-15.4	10.2
	Rf.	0.1	0.4	0.2	0.3	0.3	0.3	0.9	0.9	0.5	0.7	0.3	0.4	5.3
16.	T.	38.9	41.5	46.3	51.2	56.6	61.4	66.6	66.4	60.9	53.6	45.9	41.0	52.5
	Rf.	6.5	5.5	4.8	3.0	2.3	1.6	0.6	0.6	1.9	3.2	6.5	6.9	43.5
17.	T.	45.8	50.1	54.3	58.1	63.3	69.4	73.2	72.9	69.3	62.9	53.6	46.2	59.9
	Rf.	3.7	3.0	2.6	1.5	0.8	0.1	0	0	0.4	0.9	1.9	3.0	17.9
18.	T.	31.6	33.7	44.2	55.8	66.2	75.0	79.2	77.3	70.1	58.3	45.4	35.6	56.0
	Rf.	2.3	2.6	3.5	3.8	4.5	4.6	3.6	3.5	3.2	2.8	2.9	2.5	39.8

TABLE II (*continued*)

		JAN.	FEB.	MAR.	APRIL	MAY	JUNE	JULY	AUG.	SEPT.	OCT.	NOV.	DEC.	YEAR
19.	T.	12.1	15.2	29.0	45.6	58.6	67.4	72.3	69.4	60.6	48.1	32.1	19.8	44.2
	Rf.	0.9	0.9	1.5	2.3	3.5	4.3	3.5	3.3	3.1	2.3	1.3	1.0	27.9
20.	T.	54.0	54.9	56.5	58.3	60.5	63.5	66.8	68.4	66.9	63.2	59.1	55.6	60.6
	Rf.	1.8	1.9	1.5	0.6	0.3	0.1	0.1	0.1	0.1	0.4	0.9	1.8	9.6
21.	T.	49.4	51.4	52.8	54.3	55.5	57.2	57.3	57.8	59.9	58.9	55.5	50.6	55.0
	Rf.	4.8	3.6	3.1	1.6	0.7	0.1	0	0	0.3	0.9	2.4	4.5	22.0
22.	T.	31.7	34.1	36.5	41.3	46.6	51.3	54.8	55.5	51.7	45.8	38.2	35.4	43.6
	Rf.	7.6	6.5	5.6	5.5	4.1	3.4	4.2	7.1	10.1	12.2	9.5	9.0	84.8
23.	T.	71.0	72.1	71.0	68.5	65.3	63.1	62.2	64.4	68.1	70.3	70.3	70.1	68.0
	Rf.	13.2	7.2	7.7	2.9	0.6	0.4	0.2	0.6	0.9	4.4	8.8	11.6	58.5
24.	T.	73.6	72.5	68.7	61.3	55.0	49.6	48.9	51.1	55.0	59.9	65.8	70.9	61.0
	Rf.	3.1	2.7	4.4	3.5	2.9	2.5	2.2	2.5	3.0	3.5	3.1	3.9	37.3
25.	T.	73.8	72.5	68.5	62.1	55.8	49.6	50.4	51.6	58.6	63.3	68.4	72.3	62.2
	Rf.	4.2	4.2	3.5	1.8	1.0	0.3	0.3	0.5	0.9	2.4	4.0	4.6	27.7
26.	T.	81.0	80.8	80.7	80.2	77.5	75.4	75.9	78.3	82.0	81.7	82.0	81.3	79.8
	Rf.	9.8	8.3	8.3	4.0	2.0	0.3	0.2	1.1	2.2	4.5	5.9	8.1	54.7
27.	T.	69.4	69.4	67.6	64.8	62.6	61.2	60.4	60.3	61.2	63.0	65.3	67.5	64.4
	Rf.	0	0	0	0	0	0	0	0	0.1	0	0	0	0.1
28.	T.	46.6	46.8	46.0	44.2	41.9	39.9	39.0	39.4	40.1	41.7	42.6	44.8	42.7
	Rf.	12.1	9.7	11.7	11.2	9.0	9.4	9.5	8.4	9.0	9.4	9.8	10.2	119.4
29.	T.	72.7	74.3	73.6	70.2	66.0	62.6	61.2	61.0	61.3	63.0	65.7	70.0	66.8
	Rf.	0	0	0	0	0.1	0.2	0.3	0.4	0.4	0.2	0.1	0	1.7
30.	T.	79.9	80.1	79.7	79.9	80.1	80.1	80.6	81.7	82.8	82.8	82.2	80.6	80.9
	Rf.	9.2	9.0	9.6	8.5	7.0	3.6	2.2	1.4	2.0	4.1	5.5	7.7	69.8
31.	T.	75.2	75.4	76.3	77.8	79.1	78.1	77.9	77.8	78.3	78.2	77.5	76.3	77.3
	Rf.	2.7	1.5	1.8	1.8	3.6	7.9	8.8	9.6	7.4	6.6	7.0	4.7	63.4
32.	T.	54.6	54.5	54.5	54.5	54.6	54.7	54.5	54.6	54.8	54.6	54.5	54.6	54.6
	Rf.	4.1	4.2	5.1	7.4	5.0	1.5	0.8	1.4	2.9	3.6	3.7	3.8	43.5
33.	T.	58.8	57.6	54.5	47.9	41.2	35.4	35.1	38.3	43.5	48.8	53.1	56.3	47.5
	Rf.	0.6	0.4	0.3	0.6	0.6	0.5	0.7	0.4	0.2	0.4	0.5	0.9	6.1
34.	T.	67.3	66.0	61.9	56.1	50.5	46.0	46.0	48.2	52.2	56.1	61.0	65.7	56.4
	Rf.	0	0.1	0.2	0.6	2.6	3.3	3.1	2.2	1.3	0.5	0.2	0.2	14.3
35.	T.	61.9	60.4	57.9	53.1	49.6	45.5	45.7	46.4	48.0	52.0	55.0	59.0	52.9
	Rf.	2.4	3.0	5.5	9.4	15.2	17.0	16.1	13.2	8.7	5.2	5.0	4.1	104.8
36.	T.	8.1	9.7	17.4	30.0	41.5	52.7	59.5	55.2	45.7	33.8	21.4	12.2	32.3
	Rf.	0.9	0.7	1.1	0.7	1.2	1.8	2.5	2.4	2.1	1.6	1.2	0.9	17.1

TABLE II (*continued*)

		JAN.	FEB.	MAR.	APRIL	MAY	JUNE	JULY	AUG.	SEPT.	OCT.	NOV.	DEC.	YEAR
37.	T.	19.2	22.8	32.7	47.8	63.5	72.5	76.1	73.8	62.6	49.5	36.0	26.6	48.6
	Rf.	0.5	0.4	0.4	0.7	0.7	0.8	0.5	0.5	0.5	0.5	0.6	0.6	6.6
38.	T.	24.1	23.8	24.0	27.6	33.0	39.7	41.1	40.4	38.0	31.4	28.9	25.2	31.4
	Rf.	18.7	15.1	17.0	10.2	8.3	7.8	11.3	14.0	16.9	14.8	16.0	21.2	171.3
39.	T.	26.2	30.6	41.0	52.2	62.2	68.9	72.9	72.0	63.5	52.9	39.7	30.9	51.1
	Rf.	1.3	1.1	1.6	1.7	2.4	3.5	2.7	2.0	1.5	1.7	1.9	1.6	23.0
40.	T.	50.5	52.2	54.3	57.6	60.3	66.7	70.0	71.1	68.4	62.2	56.5	51.6	60.1
	Rf.	3.6	3.5	3.4	2.5	1.9	0.7	0.1	0.2	1.4	3.2	4.3	4.0	28.8
41.	T.	12.6	15.6	24.3	38.1	53.2	60.1	64.4	60.4	49.8	38.6	27.0	17.6	38.5
	Rf.	1.3	1.2	1.4	1.3	1.8	2.6	3.2	3.1	2.2	2.1	1.7	1.6	23.5
42.	T.	34.9	39.4	43.2	49.3	56.1	61.7	64.6	63.9	58.5	50.0	42.4	38.1	50.2
	Rf.	1.5	1.4	1.6	1.7	1.9	2.1	2.2	2.1	1.9	2.3	1.9	2.0	22.6
43.	T.	29.8	29.8	31.1	36.3	42.8	48.6	51.6	50.5	45.5	39.2	33.8	30.0	39.1
	Rf.	3.8	3.3	2.7	2.4	1.9	1.9	1.9	2.0	3.5	3.4	3.7	3.5	34.0
44.	T.	44.6	46.8	50.9	56.7	64.4	70.9	76.1	75.6	69.6	61.7	52.7	46.4	59.7
	Rf.	3.2	2.7	2.9	2.6	2.2	1.5	0.7	1.0	2.5	5.0	4.4	3.8	32.5
45.	T.	30.6	32.9	39.7	49.3	60.4	68.0	72.1	71.1	63.9	55.0	43.7	35.8	51.9
	Rf.	1.0	0.8	1.1	1.1	1.2	1.9	1.4	1.3	1.4	1.5	1.5	1.1	15.3
46.	T.	24.4	23.4	27.9	37.8	48.7	57.4	61.9	58.5	50.4	41.4	32.2	25.5	40.8
	Rf.	1.2	1.1	1.1	1.2	1.7	2.0	2.7	2.8	2.0	2.1	2.7	1.6	22.2
47.	T.	44.7	44.8	45.1	48.1	52.4	55.6	58.9	59.2	56.4	51.7	47.5	45.4	50.8
	Rf.	5.9	5.1	4.4	3.7	3.2	3.5	3.9	4.8	4.5	5.8	5.4	6.5	56.7
48.	T.	61.3	65.6	76.8	87.3	93.1	92.6	86.4	84.4	84.3	79.3	69.4	61.7	78.5
	Rf.	0.7	0.5	0.4	0.1	0.3	4.7	12.0	11.0	6.3	2.3	0.3	0.2	38.8
49.	T.	−0.6	2.3	14.9	33.6	52.3	63.7	68.0	63.0	51.8	35.8	16.9	5.0	33.9
	Rf.	0.7	0.5	0.5	0.6	1.3	1.6	2.0	1.8	1.1	1.2	1.0	0.9	13.2
50.	T.	77.9	77.9	78.1	79.5	79.7	79.2	78.6	79.0	79.7	79.9	79.3	78.4	78.9
	Rf.	13.0	12.8	7.8	5.1	4.0	3.7	2.6	1.7	2.9	4.5	5.5	8.5	72.1
51.	T.	56.5	57.7	61.2	66.0	71.8	77.7	82.0	83.1	80.8	76.1	67.3	60.6	70.1
	Rf.	7.3	5.7	3.9	2.2	0.8	0.1	0	0	0.3	2.1	5.3	7.5	35.2
52.	T.	75.5	75.7	79.5	83.1	85.8	84.0	81.4	80.8	80.9	82.4	80.6	77.4	80.6
	Rf.	0.1	0.1	0	0	0.7	19.9	24.2	14.5	10.6	1.9	0.4	0	72.4
	Rf.	0.1	0.1	0	0	0.7	19.9	24.2	14.5	10.6	1.9	0.4	0	72.4
53.	T.	57.9	59.0	65.5	74.1	82.4	86.1	89.6	90.2	86.5	79.5	70.1	61.5	75.2
	Rf.	2.7	1.9	0.9	0.5	0	0	0	0	0	0.1	1.4	2.9	10.4
54.	T.	66.6	71.2	80.2	85.6	86.1	85.1	83.7	83.2	83.2	79.3	73.5	66.5	78.7
	Rf.	0.4	1.0	1.4	2.2	5.6	11.9	12.7	13.4	10.0	4.9	0.6	0.2	64.3
55.	T .	53.2	54.9	60.9	63.7	66.3	68.1	68.6	68.6	68.9	66.1	61.0	54.7	62.9
	Rf.	0.7	2.3	10.6	31.3	50.8	103.6	107.4	81.5	49.4	16.8	2.3	0.3	457.0
56.	T.	80.5	82.0	84.2	85.0	83.6	80.0	79.0	79.2	79.9	80.4	81.1	80.7	81.3
	Rf.	0.8	0.8	1.7	3.7	11.4	27.8	25.3	12.5	9.2	12.9	6.7	1.9	114.7
57.	T.	79.5	80.4	81.8	82.7	82.8	81.6	81.2	81.2	81.2	80.5	80.0	79.5	81.0

TABLE II (*continued*)

		JAN.	FEB.	MAR.	APRIL	MAY	JUNE	JULY	AUG.	SEPT.	OCT.	NOV.	DEC.	YEAR
	Rf.	3.2	1.9	4.3	9.7	10.9	7.3	4.4	3.2	4.8	13.4	11.8	5.1	80.0
58.	T.	40.1	42.6	50.4	61.9	71.4	79.7	85.5	85.5	76.6	66.6	55.2	44.6	63.3
	Rf.	1.8	1.9	3.8	6.0	6.5	9.5	7.1	3.8	2.8	3.2	1.9	1.1	49.4
59.	T.	60.0	58.7	63.0	70.4	76.8	80.9	82.0	81.5	80.5	76.3	69.3	62.7	71.8
	Rf.	1.3	1.6	2.7	5.3	11.6	15.9	13.8	14.1	9.8	4.9	1.8	1.1	83.9
60.	T.	61.3	64.7	75.0	85.0	91.8	92.4	86.2	83.6	83.6	79.7	70.3	62.9	78.0
	Rf.	0.4	0.3	0.3	0.2	0.6	2.6	8.3	7.3	3.2	0.3	0.1	0.3	23.9
61.	T.	65.3	68.4	75.0	80.6	84.7	86.8	84.3	82.4	82.0	80.0	74.0	67.4	77.6
	Rf.	0.6	0.4	0.3	0.1	0.1	0.6	2.8	1.7	0.6	0	0.1	0.2	7.5
62.	T.	76.2	77.7	81.1	85.3	89.8	90.0	87.6	86.0	85.2	82.3	78.9	76.7	83.1
	Rf.	1.1	0.3	0.3	0.6	1.8	2.0	3.8	4.5	4.8	11.1	13.6	5.3	49.2
63.	T.	30.9	31.5	36.7	46.8	54.1	60.8	67.8	71.6	65.1	54.7	45.0	36.0	50.1
	Rf.	2.7	2.6	3.5	3.8	4.7	5.0	5.3	7.0	8.5	6.6	3.2	2.4	55.3
64.	T.	8.1	14.0	29.7	46.9	60.1	70.5	76.5	74.5	61.3	48.4	29.1	14.0	44.4
	Rf.	0.2	0.3	0.7	1.1	2.2	3.4	5.8	5.3	3.3	1.5	0.9	0.2	24.9
65.	T.	22.8	22.3	31.6	37.2	43.9	50.0	57.6	62.6	58.8	50.4	39.4	29.3	42.1
	Rf.	1.3	1.0	2.2	2.9	3.7	3.7	3.8	4.3	5.5	3.8	3.3	2.3	37.8
66.	T.	57.3	57.4	58.9	60.4	61.7	60.9	58.8	59.3	59.3	59.5	59.1	57.8	59.2
	Rf.	5.6	2.1	3.4	5.6	6.8	12.8	11.9	7.8	8.1	11.0	9.0	8.7	92.8
67.	T.	79.0	81.0	83.7	85.8	84.2	82.2	81.5	81.7	81.7	81.1	80.2	78.8	81.7
	Rf.	0.9	0.1	0.3	1.7	8.3	12.6	11.1	11.0	13.3	11.1	3.7	3.1	77.2
68.	T.	79.8	80.1	81.1	82.3	82.6	81.7	81.8	81.8	81.7	81.5	80.8	80.1	81.3
	Rf.	18.4	9.6	8.0	4.1	5.9	7.3	6.5	8.1	9.4	10.0	14.7	17.7	119.7
69.	T.	37.4	38.8	44.4	54.5	61.9	68.9	75.6	77.7	71.4	60.4	50.5	41.4	56.9
	Rf.	2.2	2.8	4.4	4.9	5.7	6.5	5.3	5.7	8.7	7.4	4.2	2.1	59.9
70.	T.	-2.9	2.1	12.9	30.2	46.6	59.0	64.0	59.2	48.4	31.8	12.7	1.6	30.5
	Rf.	1.1	0.8	0.8	0.7	1.5	2.7	3.0	2.3	1.4	2.4	1.4	1.9	20.0
71.	T.	-58.2	-48.1	-23.8	9.5	36.3	56.1	59.9	51.6	36.1	5.7	-34.1	-51.3	3.3
	Rf.	0.2	0.1	0.1	0.2	0.3	0.9	1.1	1.0	0.5	0.3	0.3	0.2	5.2
72.	T.	-45.9	-33.2	-9.2	16.7	41.4	59.5	66.4	58.8	42.6	16.7	-20.0	-40.4	12.8
	Rf.	0.2	0.2	0.1	0.2	0.5	1.1	1.3	1.7	0.9	0.5	0.4	0.3	7.4
73.	T.	37.8	39.4	46.0	56.1	65.5	73.4	80.4	80.2	73.0	63.5	52.0	42.1	59.1
	Rf.	2.0	2.3	3.5	3.7	3.5	7.2	6.0	5.7	4.4	3.2	2.1	1.4	45.0
74.	T.	49.3	50.4	52.5	55.8	61.0	67.9	73.4	74.7	70.3	63.7	56.8	51.8	60.6
	Rf.	4.0	2.6	3.3	2.0	1.7	0.7	0.1	0.1	1.1	3.4	4.1	3.9	27.0
75.	T.	71.5	70.2	68.9	66.0	61.2	57.4	57.2	61.2	67.6	72.4	72.5	71.8	66.5
	Rf.	5.9	4.0	3.1	0.6	0.3	0	0	0	0.1	0.9	3.3	5.2	23.4
76.	T.	54.1	56.8	62.4	70.2	76.8	81.9	83.5	82.6	78.1	71.4	65.1	57.9	70.1
	Rf.	0.3	0.2	0.2	0.1	0	0	0	0	0	0	0.2	0.2	1.2
77.	T.	69.9	70.3	68.1	63.2	58.9	55.7	54.7	55.6	57.9	61.2	64.4	67.9	62.3
	Rf.	0.7	0.6	0.9	1.9	3.8	4.5	3.6	3.4	2.3	1.6	1.1	0.8	25.2

TABLE II (*continued*)

		JAN.	FEB.	MAR.	APRIL	MAY	JUNE	JULY	AUG.	SEPT.	OCT.	NOV.	DEC.	YEAR
78.	T.	71.1	71.1	71.3	70.3	69.8	69.4	68.6	68.6	69.4	70.1	70.1	70.2	70.0
	Rf.	2.6	3.6	5.8	9.7	8.5	5.1	2.9	3.1	3.1	3.5	5.0	5.1	58.0
79.	T.	81.3	82.3	82.4	82.4	81.5	80.3	78.6	77.9	79.1	80.1	81.2	81.4	80.7
	Rf.	0.4	0.3	1.2	4.1	11.5	20.0	35.6	36.6	28.5	12.6	5.1	1.4	157.3
80.	T.	66.5	65.4	63.3	59.8	54.4	50.7	50.5	54.3	59.4	62.7	63.5	65.1	59.6
	Rf.	6.2	5.2	4.4	1.7	0.8	0.1	0.3	0.5	1.0	2.6	5.0	5.4	33.2
81.	T.	72.5	75.2	81.0	81.0	92.5	93.4	89.6	87.8	89.2	88.9	82.0	74.7	84.0
	Rf.	0	0	0	0	0.1	0.3	1.8	2.6	0.7	0.2	0	0	5.7
82.	T.	75.6	73.9	69.5	62.9	54.7	48.9	49.3	54.1	61.3	66.9	70.7	75.0	63.6
	Rf.	2.8	3.1	3.0	1.3	0.9	0.3	0.4	0.4	0.7	1.5	1.7	2.4	18.0
83.	T.	80.9	82.2	83.3	82.5	81.8	79.3	78.0	77.7	78.4	79.5	81.4	81.5	80.5
	Rf.	1.1	2.1	3.7	5.7	10.5	18.6	10.7	2.8	5.3	7.8	2.6	0.8	71.7
84.	T.	72.1	73.3	71.1	66.0	58.5	53.0	53.4	54.0	58.2	62.9	65.8	70.2	63.2
	Rf.	0.2	0.3	0.4	0.6	1.0	1.1	0.8	0.9	0.6	0.4	0.2	0.2	6.7
85.	T.	69.4	69.7	68.0	65.1	61.6	59.3	57.9	58.4	59.8	61.8	64.5	67.6	63.6
	Rf.	1.2	1.3	1.8	2.0	2.4	1.7	1.9	2.1	2.2	2.1	2.1	1.7	22.5
86.	T.	73.6	73.9	73.6	72.3	72.1	70.9	70.2	70.7	71.1	70.7	72.3	73.0	72.0
	Rf.	1.6	2.7	5.9	9.1	8.1	4.5	2.6	3.3	7.6	8.9	5.9	2.0	62.2
87.	T.	73.9	74.1	69.8	63.9	57.9	53.5	51.7	54.0	57.1	61.9	66.9	71.1	63.0
	Rf.	0.7	0.6	1.0	1.7	2.8	3.1	2.6	2.5	2.0	1.7	1.2	1.0	20.9
88.	T.	77.2	76.5	74.3	70.3	64.5	60.2	58.5	60.4	65.4	69.8	73.6	76.4	68.9
	Rf.	6.3	6.2	5.6	3.6	2.8	2.6	2.3	2.1	2.0	2.6	3.7	4.8	44.6
89.	T.	83.8	83.4	84.0	84.1	81.8	78.9	77.4	79.4	82.6	85.3	85.8	85.1	82.6
	Rf.	15.9	12.9	10.1	4.1	0.7	0.1	0.1	0.1	0.5	2.2	4.8	10.3	61.8
90.	T.	70.3	70.9	69.2	65.8	60.6	55.8	54.3	56.1	59.2	62.6	65.8	68.7	59.9
	Rf.	0.7	0.5	0.9	1.3	1.2	1.1	0.9	0.8	0.8	0.7	0.7	0.4	10.0
91.	T.	67.5	67.6	64.6	59.4	54.1	50.4	48.7	51.1	54.1	57.7	61.3	64.9	58.4
	Rf.	1.8	1.8	2.1	2.2	2.1	2.0	1.8	1.7	2.4	2.6	2.2	2.2	24.9
92.	T.	83.3	82.0	76.6	68.1	59.7	54.4	52.6	58.2	65.5	73.3	79.0	82.3	68.6
	Rf.	1.8	1.7	1.2	0.7	0.7	0.6	0.4	0.4	0.4	0.7	1.0	1.6	11.2
93.	T.	71.7	71.3	69.3	64.7	58.8	54.6	52.7	55.0	59.2	63.5	67.1	70.1	63.1
	Rf.	3.7	4.2	4.8	5.6	5.1	4.8	4.8	3.0	2.9	3.2	2.8	2.9	47.8
94.	T.	21.7	9.3	-7.4	-24.0	-27.0	-29.4	-33.7	-34.2	-29.4	-14.1	8.6	23.7	-11.3

SOURCES OF CLIMATIC DATA

1. CLAYTON, H. H. *World Weather Records,* Smithsonian Miscellaneous Collections, Vol. 79. Washington, D. C., 1927.

2. United States Weather Bureau. "Normals of Daily Temperature for the United States," *Monthly Weather Review,* Supplement No. 25 (Washington, D. C., 1925), and idem. "The Daily, Monthly, and Annual Normals of Precipitation in the United States, . . . ," *Monthly Weather Review,* Supplement No. 34. Washington, D. C., 1930.

3. NORDENSKJÖLD, O., and MECKING, L. *The Geography of the Polar Regions,* American Geographical Society, Special Publication No. 8. New York, 1928.

4. Minas Geraes (Brazil), Commissão Geographica e Geologica. *Boletim de Normaes de Temperatura, Chuva, e Insolação.* Belo Horibonte, 1923.

5. KÖPPEN, W., and GEIGER, R. *Handbuch der Klimatologie* (in five volumes). Berlin.

6. KENDREW, W. G. *The Climates of the Continents.* Oxford, 1922.

7. VOZNESENSKĬ, A. V. *Karta klimatov U.S.S.R., Trudy po Selsko-khoz.* Meteorologii, No. 21. Leningrad, 1930 (quoted by L. I. Prasolov, "The Climate and Soils of Northern Eurasia as Conditions of Colonization," in *Pioneer Settlement,* American Geographical Society, Special Publication No. 14. New York, 1932).

8. Chinese official statistics, quoted by G. B. Cressey, *China's Geographic Foundations.* New York, 1934.

9. HANN, J. *Handbuch der Klimatologie,* pp. 82–83. Hamburg, 1908.

CLIMATIC STATIONS FOR WHICH DATA ARE GIVEN
ON PAGES 537-54

The number in parentheses refers to the source of the data; the letter symbols are those of the Köppen classification (see Appendix B, Definitions of the Symbols).

NORTH AMERICA

1. Boston, U.S.A. . . . . (2) *Cfa*
2. Charleston, U.S.A. . . . . (1) *Cfa*
3. Chicago, U.S.A. . . . . . . (1) *Dfa*
4. Dawson, Canada . . . . . (1) *Dfc*
5. Denver, U.S.A. . . . . (1) *BSkw*
6. Edmonton, Canada . . . . (1) *Dfb*
7. Ivigtut, Greenland . . . . (1) *ET*
8. León, Mexico . . . . (1) *BShw*
9. Monterrey, Mexico . . . . (1) *BSh*
10. Montreal, Canada . . . . (1) *Dfb*
11. New Orleans, U.S.A. . . (2) *Cfa*
12. New York, U.S.A. . . . . . (1) *Cfa*
13. Phoenix, U.S.A. . . . . . . (1) *BWh*
14. Pierre, U.S.A. . . . . (2) *BSkw*
15. Point Barrow, Alaska . . (2) *ET*
16. Portland (Oregon), U.S.A. . . . . (1) *Csb*
17. Sacramento, U.S.A. . . . (2) *Csa*

18. St. Louis, U.S.A. . . . . . . (1) *Cfa*
19. St. Paul, U.S.A. . . . . . . (1) *Dfa*
20. San Diego, U.S.A. . . . . (1) *BSksn*
21. San Francisco, U.S.A. . . (1) *Csbt'n*
22. Sitka, Alaska . . . . (1) *Cfbs'*

SOUTH AMERICA

23. Belo Horizonte, Brazil . . (4) *Cwa*
24. Buenos Aires, Argentina (1) *Cfa*
25. Córdoba, Argentina . . . (1) *Cwa*
26. Cuiabá, Brazil . . . . (1) *Awi*
27. Iquique, Chile . . . . (1) *BWh(k)*
28. Islote de los Evangelistas, Chile . . . . (1) *ET*
29. Lima, Peru . . . . (5) *BWhsn*
30. Manaus, Brazil . . . . (5) *Ami*
31. Port-of-Spain, Trinidad (1) *Amwi*
32. Quito, Ecuador . . . . (5) *Cfbi*
33. Santa Cruz, Argentina . (1) *BWk'*

34. Santiago, Chile ...... (1) *Csb*
35. Valdivia, Chile ...... (5) *Cfbs*

EUROPE

36. Arkhangelsk, U.S.S.R. . (1) *Dfc*
37. Astrakhan, U.S.S.R. ... (1) *BSk*
38. Ben Nevis, Great Britain (6) *ET*
39. Bucuresti, Romania ... (1) *Dfa*
40. Lisboa, Portugal ..... (1) *Csb*
41. Moskva, U.S.S.R. ..... (1) *Dfb*
42. Paris, France .... (1) *Cfb*
43. Reykjavik, Iceland .... (5) *Cfc*
44. Roma, Italy .... (1) *Cs'a*
45. Sulina, Romania ...... (1) *Cfa*
46. Uppsala, Sweden ..... (1) *Dfb*
47. Valentia, Ireland ...... (1) *Cfb*

ASIA

48. Allahabad, India ...... (1) *Cwg*
49. Barnaul, U.S.S.R. .... (7) *Dfb*
50. Batavia (Jakarta), Java (1) *Amwi*
51. Beirut, Lebanon ...... (1) *Csa*
52. Bombay, India .... (1) *Awg*
53. Bushire, Iran .... (1) *BShs*
54. Calcutta, India .... (1) *Awg*
55. Cherrapunji, India .... (1) *Cwb*
56. Cochin, India .... (1) *Amgi*
57. Colombo, Ceylon .... (1) *Amw''i*
58. Hankow, China ...... (8) *Cfa*
59. Hong Kong, China .... (1) *Cwa*
60. Jaipur, India .... (1) *BShw*
61. Karachi, Pakistan ... (6–1) *BWhw*
62. Madras, India .... (1) *Aw'*
63. Miyako, Japan .... (1) *Cfb(a)*
64. Mukden, Manchuria .. (1) *Dwa*
65. Nemuro, Japan .... (1) *Dfb*
66. Nuwara Eliya, Ceylon . (1) *Cfbgi*
67. Saïgon, Viet Nam ..... (1) *Awgi*

68. Sandakan, British North
    Borneo .... (1) *Afsi*
69. Tokyo, Japan .... (1) *Cfa*
70. Tomsk, U.S.S.R. .... (1–6) *Dfc*
71. Verkhoyansk, U.S.S.R. (7) *Dwd*
72. Yakutsk, U.S.S.R. ..... (7) *Dwd*
73. Zi-ka-wei (Shanghai),
    China .... (1) *Cfa*

AFRICA

74. Algiers, Algeria .... (1) *Csa*
75. Bulawayo, Rhodesia ... (1) *BShw*
76. Cairo, Egypt .... (9) *BWhs*
77. Capetown, South Africa (1) *Csb*
78. Entebbe, Uganda ..... (1) *Amw''i*
79. Freetown, Sierra Leone (1) *Amgi*
80. Johannesburg, South
    Africa .... (1) *Cwb*
81. Khartoum, Sudan .... (1) *BWhw*
82. Kimberley, South Africa (1) *BSkw*
83. Lagos, Nigeria .... (1) *Aw''gi*
84. O'Okiep, South Africa . (1) *BWks*
85. Port Elizabeth, South
    Africa .... (1) *Cfb*
86. Yaunde, Cameroon .... (6) *Amw''i*

AUSTRALIA

87. Adelaide .... (1) *Csa*
88. Brisbane .... (1) *Cfa*
89. Darwin .... (1) *Awgi*
90. Eucla .... (5) *BSk*
91. Melbourne .... (5) *Cfb*
92. Stuart .... (1) *BWhw*
93. Sydney .... (1) *Cfa*

ANTARCTICA

94. Framheim, Little Amer-
    ica .... (3) *EF*

References

As a guide to students who wish to become familiar with geographic writings the following suggestions and lists of references are offered. In the first place the student should become familiar with the chief geographical bibliographies. The most important of these is the *Bibliographie géographique internationale,* published annually since 1891 by Armand Colin in Paris. Many geographical societies in many countries collaborate in preparing this bibliography. In the United States the American Geographical Society of New York maintains a current list of writings. Since 1938 this Society has published monthly (except July and August) its *Current Geographical Publications: Additions to the Research Catalogue of the American Geographical Society.* These and many other geographical bibliographies are listed and described in J. K. Wright and E. T. Platt, *Aids to Geographic Research,* American Geographical Society Research Series, No. 22, Second Edition, New York, 1947.

For lengthy lists of geographic writings arranged by topics or branches of geography, the student is directed to P. E. James and C. F. Jones (editors), *American Geography, Inventory and Prospect,* Syracuse, New York, 1954.

The following references provide a selected list of readings in geography. For references dealing with maps, see the list at the end of Appendix A; for those dealing with climatology, see the end of Appendix B; for those dealing with landforms and soils, see the end of Appendix C; for those dealing with hydrography and oceanography, see the end of Appendix D; and for those dealing with vegetation, see the end of Appendix E.

A. HISTORY OF GEOGRAPHIC THOUGHT

BUNBURY, E. H. *A History of Ancient Geography.* London, 1883.
MILL, H. R. *The Realm of Nature.* London, 1892.
BEAZLY, C. R. *The Dawn of Modern Geography,* Oxford, 1897; reprinted New York, 1949.

HERBERTSON, A. J. "The Major Natural Regions: An Essay in Systematic Geography," *Geographical Journal*, Vol. 25 (1905), pp. 300–312.

DAVIS, W. M. "An Inductive Study of the Content of Geography," *Bulletin of the American Geographical Society*, Vol. 38 (1906), pp. 67–84.

VIDAL DE LA BLACHE, P. *Principes de géographie humaine.* Paris, 1922.

SAUER, C. O. "The Morphology of Landscape," *University of California Publications in Geography*, Vol. 2 (1925), pp. 19–53.

HETTNER, A. *Die Geographie—Ihre Geschichte, ihr Wesen, und ihre Methoden.* Breslau, 1927.

DICKINSON, R. E., and HOWARTH, O. J. R. *The Making of Geography.* Oxford, 1933.

KIMBLE, G. H. T. *Geography in the Middle Ages.* London, 1938.

HARTSHORNE, R. *The Nature of Geography: A Critical Survey of Current Thought in the Light of the Past.* Lancaster, Pennsylvania, 1939. Available in Central Office, Association of American Geographers, 1146 16th St., N.W., Washington, D. C., 20036.

AHMAD, N. *Muslim Contributions to Geography.* Lahore, 1947.

STAMP, L. D., and WOOLDRIDGE, S. W. (editors). *London Essays in Geography.* London, 1951.

TAYLOR, G. (editor). *Geography in the 20th Century.* New York, 1951.

JAMES, P. E., and JONES, C. F. (editors). *American Geography, Inventory and Prospect.* Syracuse, New York, 1954.

Géographie française au milieu de XXme siècle. Paris, 1957.

ACKERMAN, E. A. *Geography as a Fundamental Research Discipline.* Chicago, 1958.

HARTSHORNE, R. *Perspective on the Nature of Geography.* Chicago, 1959.

PLATT, R. S. *Field Study in American Geography,* Chicago, 1959.

DE JONG, G. *Chorological Differentiation as the Fundamental Principle of Geography,* Groningen, Netherlands, 1962.

LEIGHLY, J. (editor). *Land and Life, A Selection from the Writings of Carl Ortwin Sauer.* Berkeley, California, 1963.

SKELTON, R. A. *History of Cartography,* Cambridge (Mass.), 1964.

CHORLEY, R. J., DUNN, A. J., and BECKINSALE, R. P. *The History of the Study of Landforms, or the Development of Geomorphology,* London and New York, 1964.

BROEK, J. O. M. *Geography: Its Scope and Spirit,* Columbus (Ohio), 1965.

ACKERMAN, E. A. (chairman). *The Science of Geography,* Report of the *ad hoc* Committee on Geography, National Academy of Sciences—National Research Council, Washington, D.C., 1965.

B. THE WORLD AS A WHOLE OR LARGER PARTS

MARSH, G. P. *The Earth as Modified by Human Action.* New York, 1874.

WHITTLESEY, D. S. *The Earth and the State.* New York, 1939.

SPENCER, J. E. *Asia, East by South; A Cultural Geography.* New York, 1954.

CRESSEY, G. B. *Land of the 500 Million; A Geography of China.* New York, 1955.

THOMAS, W. L., JR. and others (editors). *Man's Role in Changing the Face of the Earth.* Chicago, 1956.

EAST, W. G., and MOODIE, A. E. (editors). *The Changing World, Studies in Political Geography.* London and New York, 1956.

GINSBURG, N. (editor). *The Pattern of Asia.* New York, 1958.

James, P. E.   *Latin America* (3rd ed.).   New York, 1959.
Kimble, G. H. T.   *Tropical Africa.*   New York, 1960.
Hoffman, G. W. (editor).   *A Geography of Europe* (2nd ed.).   New York, 1961.
Cressey, G. B.   *Asia's Lands and Peoples* (3rd ed.).   New York, 1963.
Dasman, R. F.   *The Last Horizon.*   New York, 1963.
Harrison Church, R. J., Clarke, J. I., Clarke, P. J. H., and Henderson, H. J. R.   *Africa and the Islands.*   New York, 1964.
Hance, W. A.   *The Geography of Modern Africa.*   New York, 1964.
Lydolph, P. E.   *Geography of the U.S.S.R.*   New York, 1964.
James, P. E.   *One World Divided.*   New York, 1964.

C. AREAL STUDIES

Group I

Huntington, E.   *The Pulse of Asia.*   Boston, 1907.
Gautier, E. F.   *Le Sahara.*   Paris, 1923.
Montagne, R.   *La civilisation du désert: Nomades d'Orient et d'Afrique.*   Paris, 1947.
Lebon, J. H. G.   "The New Irrigation Era in Iraq," *Economic Geography,* Vol. 31 (1955), pp. 47–59.
Davies, D. H.   "Observations on Land Use in Iraq," *Economic Geography,* Vol. 33 (1957), pp. 122–134.
Clarke, J. I.   "Studies of Semi-Nomadism in North Africa," *Economic Geography,* Vol. 35 (1959), pp. 95–108.
Cressey, G. B.   *Crossroads, Land and Life in Southwest Asia.*   New York, 1960.
Gabriel, A.   *Die Wüsten der Erde und ihre Erforschung.*   Berlin, 1961.
Cuny, H.   *Les déserts dans le monde.*   Paris, 1961.
Lewis, R. A.   "The Irrigation Potential of Soviet Central Asia," *Annals of the Association of American Geographers,* Vol. 52 (1962), pp. 99–114.
Gulick, L. H., Jr.   "Irrigation Systems of the Former Sind Province, West Pakistan," *Geographical Review,* Vol. 53 (1963), pp. 79–99.
Ebert, C. H. V.   "Water Resources and Land Use in the Qatif Oasis of Saudi Arabia," *Geographical Review,* Vol. 55 (1965), pp. 496–509.

Group II

Wallace, A. R.   *A Narrative of Travels on the Amazon and Rio Negro.*   London, 1853.
Wood, W. H. A.   "Rivers and Man in the Indus-Ganges Alluvial Plain," *Scottish Geographical Magazine,* Vol. 40 (1924), pp. 1–16.
Vlieland, C. A.   "The Population of the Malay Peninsula: A Study in Human Migration," *Geographical Review,* Vol. 24 (1934), pp. 61–78.
Price, A. G.   *White Settlers in the Tropics,* American Geographical Society, Special Publication No. 23.   New York, 1939.
Dobby, E. H. G.   "Settlement Patterns in Malaya," *Geographical Review,* Vol. 32 (1942), pp. 211–232.
Geddes, A.   "The Population of India . . . ," *Geographical Review,* Vol. 32 (1942), pp. 562–573.

RUSSELL, J. A.   "Fordlandia and Belterra, Rubber Plantations on the Tapajos River, Brazil," *Economic Geography,* Vol. 18 (1942), pp. 125–145.

PENDLETON, R. L.   "The Belgian Congo: Impressions of a Changing Region," *Geographical Review,* Vol. 39 (1949), pp. 371–400.

MONBEIG, P.   *Pionniers et Planteurs de São Paulo.*   Paris, 1952.

JAMES, P. E.   "Trends in Brazilian Agricultural Development," *Geographical Review,* Vol. 43 (1953), pp. 301–328.

WAGLEY, C.   *Amazon Town, A Study of Man in the Tropics.*   New York, 1953.

GINSBURG, N., and ROBERTS, C. F., JR.   *Malaya.*   Seattle, 1958.

JOHNSTON, B. F.   *The Staple Food Economies of Western Tropical Africa.*   Stanford, California, 1958.

LOWENTHAL, D.   "Population Contrasts in the Guianas," *Geographical Review,* Vol. 50 (1960), pp. 41–58.

AUGELLI, J. P., and TAYLOR, H. W.   "Race and Population Patterns in Trinidad," *Annals of the Association of American Geographers,* Vol. 50 (1960), pp. 123–138.

FOSBERG, F. R., GARNIER, B. J., and KÜCHLER, A. W.   "Delimitation of the Humid Tropics," *Geographical Review,* Vol. 51 (1961), pp. 333–347.

SOPHER, D. E.   "Population Dislocation in the Chittagong Hills," *Geographical Review,* Vol. 53 (1963), pp. 337–362.

Group III

WAIBEL, L.   "Vegetation and Land Use in the Planalto Central of Brazil," *Geographical Review,* Vol. 38 (1948), pp. 529–554.

BUCHANAN, K.   "The Northern Region of Nigeria, The Geographical Background of its Political Destiny," *Geographical Review,* Vol. 43 (1953), pp. 451–473.

DAVIS, C. M.   "Fire as a Land-Use Tool in Northeastern Australia," *Geographical Review,* Vol. 49 (1959), pp. 552–560.

MCMASTER, D. N.   "Change of Regional Balance in the Bukoba District of Tanganyika," *Geographical Review,* Vol. 50 (1960), pp. 73–88.

COLE, M. M.   "Cerrado, Caatinga and Pantanal: The Distribution and Origin of the Savanna Vegetation of Brazil," *Geographical Journal,* Vol. 126 (1960), pp. 168–179.

COLE, M. M.   *South Africa.*   New York, 1961.

PRESCOTT, J. R. V.   "Population Distribution in Southern Rhodesia," *Geographical Review,* Vol. 52 (1962), pp. 559–565.

FLOYD, B. N.   "Land Apportionment in Southern Rhodesia," *Geographical Review,* Vol. 52 (1962), pp. 566–582.

COLE, M. M.   "The Rhodesian Economy in Transition and the Role of Kariba," *Geography,* Vol. 47 (1962), pp. 15–40.

Group IV

AHLMANN, H. W.   "The Geographical Study of Settlements . . . ," *Geographical Review,* Vol. 18 (1928), pp. 93–128.

ALMAGIÀ, R.   "The Repopulation of the Roman Campagna," *Geographical Review,* Vol. 19 (1929), pp. 529–555.

SEMPLE, E. C. *The Geography of the Mediterranean Region: Its Relation to Ancient History.* New York, 1931.

BROEK, J. O. M. *The Santa Clara Valley, California: A Study in Landscape Changes.* Utrecht, 1932.

TORBERT, E. N. "The Specialized Commercial Agriculture of the Northern Santa Clara Valley," *Geographical Review,* Vol. 26 (1936), pp. 247–263.

UNGER, L. "Rural Settlement in the Campania," *Geographical Review,* Vol. 43 (1953), pp. 506–524.

DICKINSON, R. E. *The Population Problem of Southern Italy, An Essay in Social Geography.* Syracuse, New York, 1955.

MELAMID, A. "The Geographical Distribution of Communities in Cyprus," *Geographical Review,* Vol. 46 (1956), pp. 355–374.

NAYLON, J. "Land Consolidation in Spain," *Annals of the Association of American Geographers,* Vol. 49 (1959), pp. 361–373.

PARSONS, J. J. "The Cork Oak Forests and the Evolution of the Cork Industry in Southern Spain and Portugal," *Economic Geography,* Vol. 38 (1962), pp. 195–214.

STANISLAWSKI, D. *Portugal's Other Kingdom, The Algarve.* Austin, Texas, 1963.

SHAW, D. J. "The Problem of Land Fragmentation in the Mediterranean Area: A Case Study," *Geographical Review,* Vol. 53 (1963), pp. 40–51.

JENSEN, R. G. "Soviet Subtropical Agriculture, A Microcosm," *Geographical Review,* Vol. 54 (1964), pp. 185–202.

Group V

GALLOIS, L. *Régions naturelles et noms de pays, étude sur la région parisienne.* Paris, 1908.

DEMANGEON, A. *La Picardie. . . .* Paris, 1925.

GOLDTHWAITE, J. W. "A Town that Has Gone Downhill," *Geographical Review,* Vol. 17 (1927), pp. 527–552.

OGILVIE, A. G. (editor). *Great Britain, Essays in Regional Geography.* Cambridge, England, 1928.

JAMES, P. E. "The Blackstone Valley: A Study in Chorography in Southern New England," *Annals of the Association of American Geographers,* Vol. 19 (1929), pp. 67–109.

EAST, G. *An Historical Geography of Europe.* London, 1935.

TORBERT, E. N. "The Evolution of Land Utilization in Lebanon, New Hampshire," *Geographical Review,* Vol. 25 (1935), pp. 209–230.

KENDALL, H. M. "A Survey of Population Changes in Belgium," *Annals of the Association of American Geographers,* Vol. 28 (1938), pp. 145–164.

FRIIS, H. R. "A Series of Population Maps of the Colonies and the United States, 1625–1790," *Geographical Review,* Vol. 30 (1940), pp. 463–470.

BROWN, R. H. *Mirror for Americans, Likeness of the Eastern Seaboard, 1810.* New York, 1943.

TREWARTHA, G. T. *Japan: A Physical, Cultural and Regional Geography,* Madison, Wisconsin, 1945.

TREWARTHA, G. T. "Types of Rural Settlement in Colonial America," *Geographical Review,* Vol. 36 (1946), pp. 568–596.

BROWN, R. H. *Historical Geography of the United States.* New York, 1948.

STAMP, L. D.   *The Land of Britain: Its Use and Misuse.*   London, 1950.

PRUNTY, M., JR.   "Land Occupance in the Southeast: Landmarks and Forecast," *Geographical Review,* Vol. 42 (1952), pp. 439–461.

BRUSH, J. E.   "The Hierarchy of Central Places in Southwestern Wisconsin," *Geographical Review,* Vol. 43 (1953), pp. 380–402.

KLIMM, L. E.   "The Empty Areas of the Northeastern United States," *Geographical Review,* Vol. 44 (1954), pp. 325–345.

MONKHOUSE, F. J.   *A Regional Geography of Western Europe.*   London, 1959.

HO, P-T.   *Studies on the Population of China, 1368–1953.*   Cambridge, Massachusetts, 1959.

TASKIN, G. A.   "The Soviet Northwest: Economic Regionalization," *Geographical Review,* Vol. 51 (1961), pp. 213–235.

PRUNTY, M., JR.   "The Woodland Plantation as a Contemporary Occupance Type in the South," *Geographical Review,* Vol. 53 (1963), pp. 1–21.

HOUSTON, J. M.   *A Social Geography of Europe.*   London, 1963.

WATSON, J. W., and SISSONS, J. B. (eds.).   *The British Isles, A Systematic Geography,* London, 1964.

Group VI

WEBB, W. P.   *The Great Plains.*   New York, 1931.

BOWMAN, I.   "Jordan Country," *Geographical Review,* Vol. 21 (1931), pp. 22–55.

BROWN, R. H.   "Belle Fourche Valleys and Uplands," *Annals of the Association of American Geographers,* Vol. 23 (1933), pp. 127–156.

THORNTHWAITE, C. W.   "The Great Plains," Chapter V in CARTER GOODRICH and others, *Migration and Economic Opportunity: the Report of the Study of Population Redistribution.*   Philadelphia, 1936, pp. 202–250.

MALIN, J. C.   *Winter Wheat in the Golden Belt of Kansas: A Study in Adaptation to Subhumid Geographical Environment.*   Lawrence, Kansas, 1944.

MALIN, J. C.   "Grassland, 'Treeless,' and 'Subhumid': A Discussion of Some Problems of the Terminology of Geography," *Geographical Review,* Vol. 37 (1947), pp. 241–250.

DAVIS, C. M.   "Merino Sheep on the Australian Riverina," *Geographical Review,* Vol. 44 (1954), pp. 475–494.

MALIN, J. C.   *The Grassland of North America* (2nd ed.).   Lawrence, Kansas, 1956.

JACKSON, W. A. D.   "The Virgin and Idle Lands of Western Siberia and Northern Kazakhstan: A Geographical Appraisal," *Geographical Review,* Vol. 46 (1956), pp. 1–19.

ALBRECHT, W. A.   "Soil Fertility and Biotic Geography," *Geographical Review,* Vol. 47 (1957), pp. 86–105.

MEINIG, D. W.   *On the Margins of the Good Earth, The South Australian Wheat Frontier, 1869–1884.*   Chicago, 1962.

JACKSON, W. A. D.   "The Virgin and Idle Lands Program Reappraised," *Annals of the Association of American Geographers,* Vol. 52 (1962), pp. 69–79.

HEWES, L.   "A Traverse Across Kit Carson County, Colorado, with Notes on Land Use On the Margin of the Old Dust Bowl, 1939–1940 and 1962," *Economic Geography,* Vol. 39 (1963), pp. 332–340.

LOEFFLER, M. J. "Beet-Sugar Production on the Colorado Piedmont," *Annals of the Association of American Geographers,* Vol. 53 (1963), pp. 364–390.

Group VII

ALBRIGHT, W. D. "Gardens of the Mackenzie," *Geographical Review,* Vol. 23 (1933), pp. 1–22.

LEPPARD, H. M. "The Settlement of the Peace River Country," *Geographical Review,* Vol. 25 (1935), pp. 62–78.

LLOYD, T. "The Mackenzie Waterway: A Northern Supply Route," *Geographical Review,* Vol. 33 (1943), pp. 415–434.

HARE, F. K. "Climate and Zonal Divisions of the Boreal Forest Formation in Eastern Canada," *Geographical Review,* Vol. 40 (1950), pp. 615–635.

PLATT, R. R. *Finland and its Geography.* New York, 1955.

HUMPHRYS, G. "Schefferville, Quebec: A New Pioneering Town," *Geographical Review,* Vol. 48 (1958), pp. 151–166.

KOHN, C. F., and SPECHT, R. E. "The Mining of Taconite, Lake Superior Mining District," *Geographical Review,* Vol. 48 (1958), pp. 528–539.

Group VIII

NORDENSKJÖLD, O., and MECKING, L. *The Geography of the Polar Regions,* American Geographical Society, Special Publication No. 8. New York, 1928.

FRIIS, H. R. "Greenland: A Productive Arctic Colony," *Economic Geography,* Vol. 13 (1937), pp. 75–92.

KIMBLE, G. H. T., and GOOD, D. (editors). *Geography of the Northlands.* New York, 1955.

GOULD, L. M. "Antarctic Prospect," *Geographical Review,* Vol. 47 (1957), pp. 1–28.

REED, J. C. "The United States Turns North," *Geographical Review,* Vol. 48 (1958), pp. 321–335.

SONNENFELD, J. "An Arctic Reindeer Industry: Growth and Decline," *Geographical Review,* Vol. 49 (1959), pp. 76–94.

SONNENFELD, J. "Changes in an Eskimo Hunting Technology, An Introduction to Implement Geography," *Annals of the Association of American Geographers,* Vol. 50 (1960), pp. 172–186.

Group IX

BOWMAN, I. *The Andes of Southern Peru.* New York, 1916.

UNSTEAD, J. F. "The Lötschental: A Regional Study," *Geographical Journal,* Vol. 79 (1932), pp. 298–317.

GARNETT, A. "Insolation, Topography, and Settlement in the Alps," *Geographical Review,* Vol. 25 (1935), pp. 601–617.

JAMES, P. E. "Regional Planning in the Jackson Hole Country," *Geographical Review,* Vol. 26 (1936), pp. 439–453.

PEATTIE, R.   *Mountain Geography.*   Cambridge, Massachusetts, 1936.

PARSONS, J. J.   *Antioqueño Colonization in Western Colombia,* Ibero-Americana, No. 32. Berkeley, California, 1949.

LEWIS, N. N.   "Lebanon—The Mountain and Its Terraces," *Geographical Review,* Vol. 43 (1953), pp. 1–14.

HAGEN, T., WAHLEN, F. T., and CORTI, W. R.   *Nepal: The Kingdom in the Himalayas.* Bern, Switzerland, 1961.

WAGNER, P. L.   "Natural and Artificial Zonation in a Vegetation Cover: Chiapas, Mexico," *Geographical Review,* Vol. 52 (1962), pp. 253–274.

EYRE, J. D.   "Mountain Land Use in Northern Japan," *Geographical Review,* Vol. 52 (1962), pp. 236–252.

DYER, D. R.   "Population of the Quechua Region of Peru," *Geographical Review,* Vol. 52 (1962), pp. 337–345.

Reference Maps

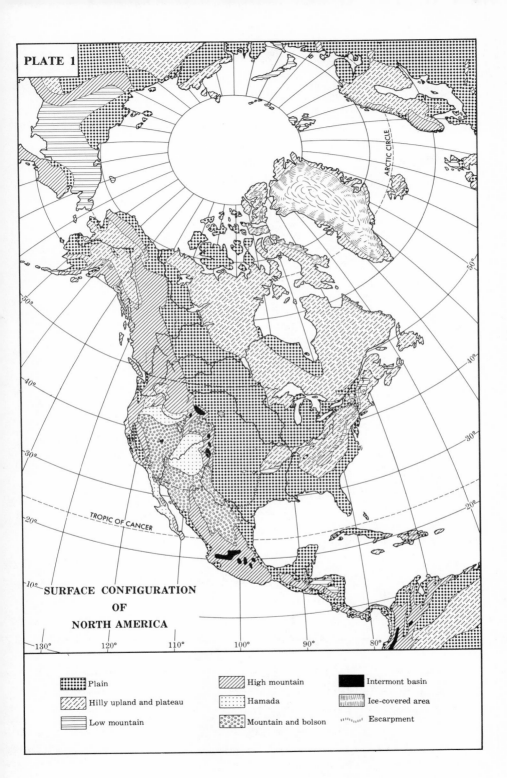

PLATE 1

SURFACE CONFIGURATION
OF
NORTH AMERICA

ARCTIC CIRCLE

TROPIC OF CANCER

Plain

Hilly upland and plateau

Low mountain

High mountain

Hamada

Mountain and bolson

Intermont basin

Ice-covered area

Escarpment

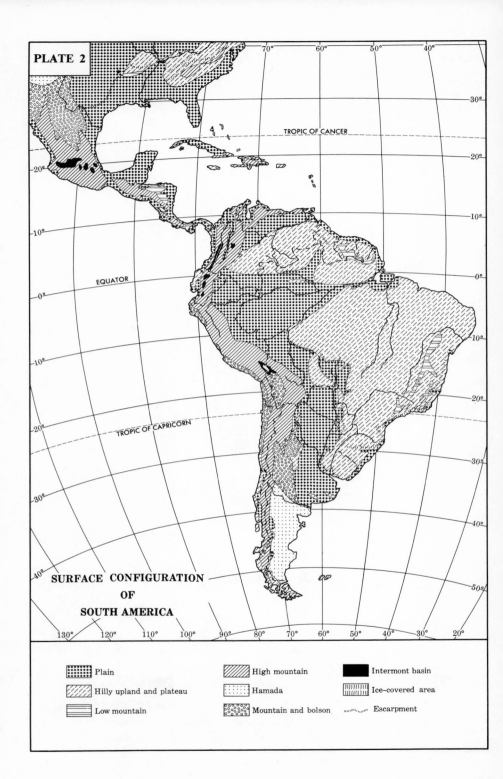

PLATE 2

TROPIC OF CANCER

EQUATOR

TROPIC OF CAPRICORN

SURFACE CONFIGURATION

OF

SOUTH AMERICA

Plain	High mountain	Intermont basin
Hilly upland and plateau	Hamada	Ice-covered area
Low mountain	Mountain and bolson	Escarpment

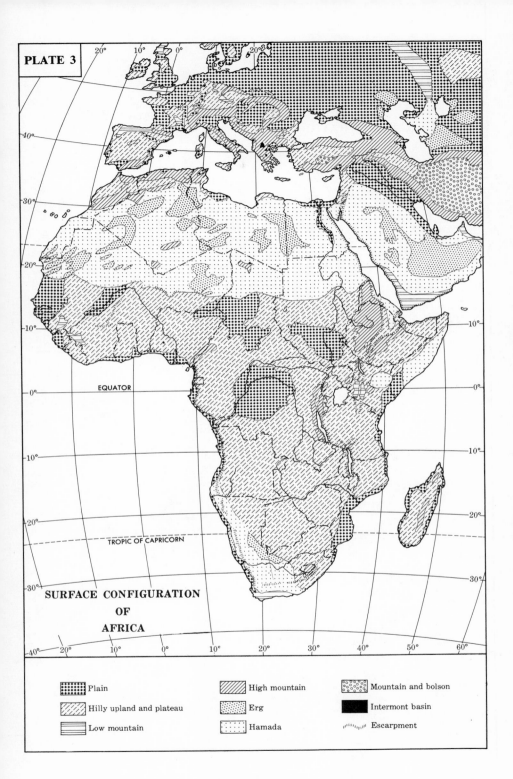

PLATE 3

EQUATOR

TROPIC OF CAPRICORN

SURFACE CONFIGURATION

OF

AFRICA

░ Plain	▨ High mountain	▧ Mountain and bolson
▨ Hilly upland and plateau	▨ Erg	■ Intermont basin
☰ Low mountain	⋮ Hamada	⌒⌒ Escarpment

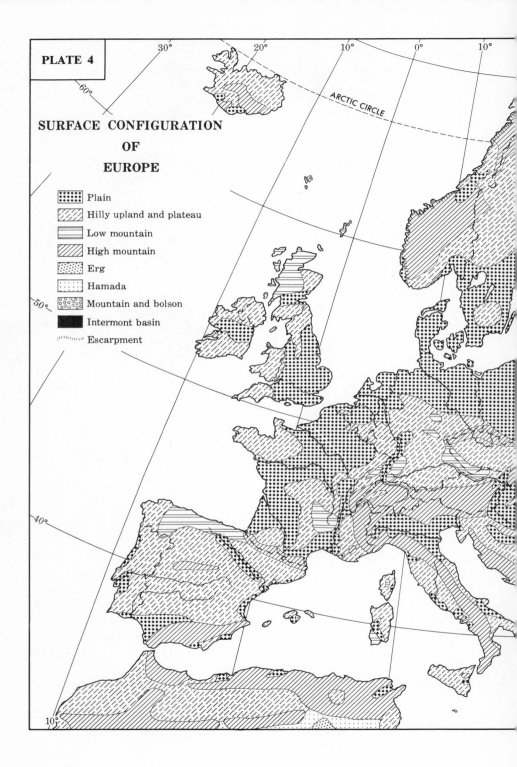

PLATE 4

SURFACE CONFIGURATION
OF
EUROPE

Plain	
Hilly upland and plateau	
Low mountain	
High mountain	
Erg	
Hamada	
Mountain and bolson	
Intermont basin	
Escarpment	

ARCTIC CIRCLE

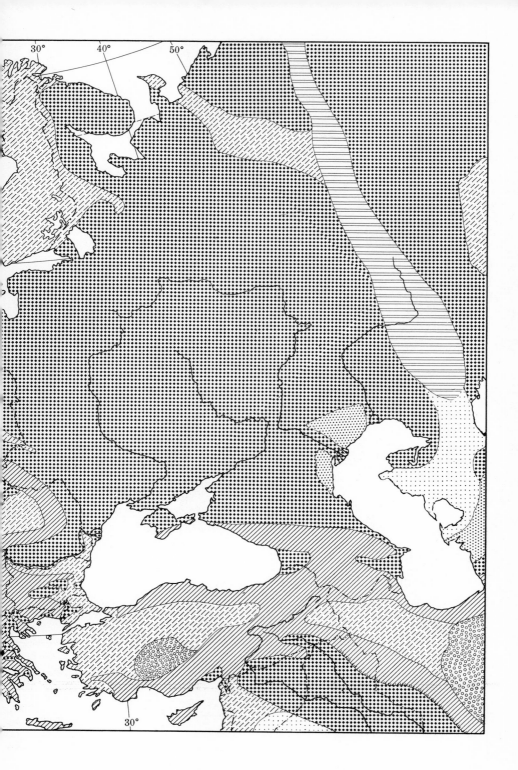

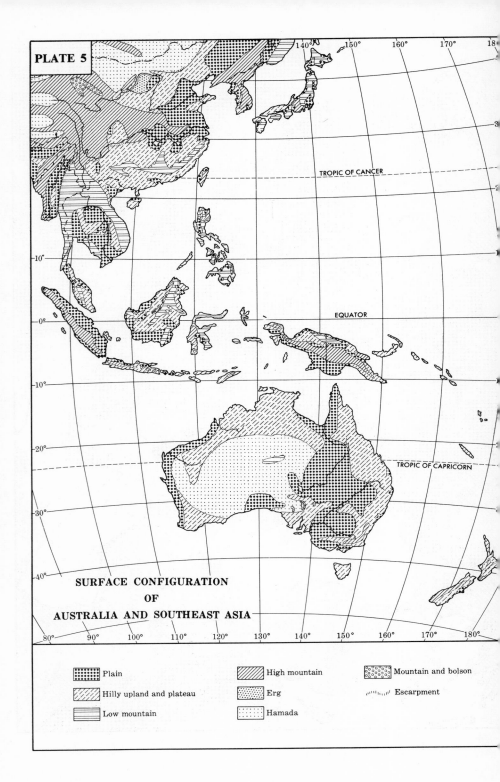

PLATE 5

140° 150° 160° 170° 18

150° 160° 170°

TROPIC OF CANCER

-10°

EQUATOR

-0°

-10°

-20°

TROPIC OF CAPRICORN

-30°

-40°

SURFACE CONFIGURATION
OF
AUSTRALIA AND SOUTHEAST ASIA

80° 90° 100° 110° 120° 130° 140° 150° 160° 170° 180°

Plain	High mountain	Mountain and bolson
Hilly upland and plateau	Erg	Escarpment
Low mountain	Hamada	

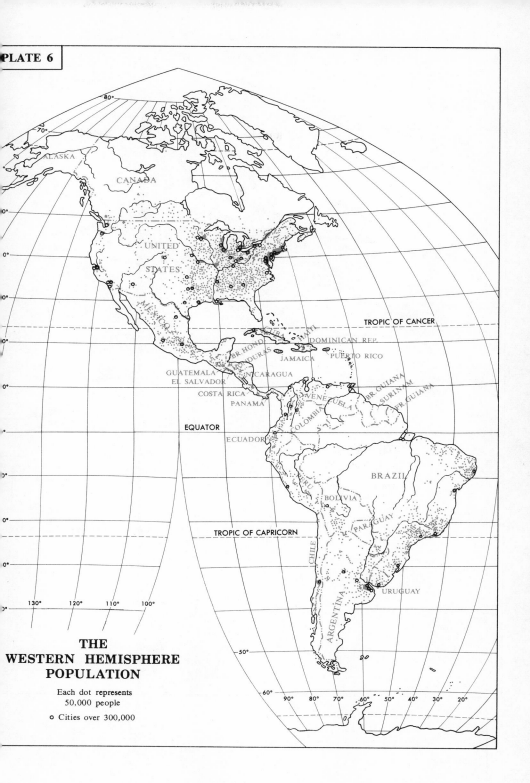

PLATE 6

80°
70°

ALASKA

CANADA

UNITED
STATES

MEXICO

TROPIC OF CANCER

BR. HOND.
HONDURAS
GUATEMALA
EL SALVADOR
NICARAGUA
COSTA RICA
PANAMA

CUBA HAITI
DOMINICAN REP.
JAMAICA PUERTO RICO

BR. GUIANA
SURINAM
FR. GUIANA
VENEZUELA
COLOMBIA

EQUATOR

ECUADOR

PERU

BRAZIL

BOLIVIA

TROPIC OF CAPRICORN

PARAGUAY

CHILE

URUGUAY

ARGENTINA

130° 120° 110° 100°

50°

60° 90° 80° 70° 60° 50° 40° 30° 20°

THE
WESTERN HEMISPHERE
POPULATION

Each dot represents
50,000 people

o Cities over 300,000

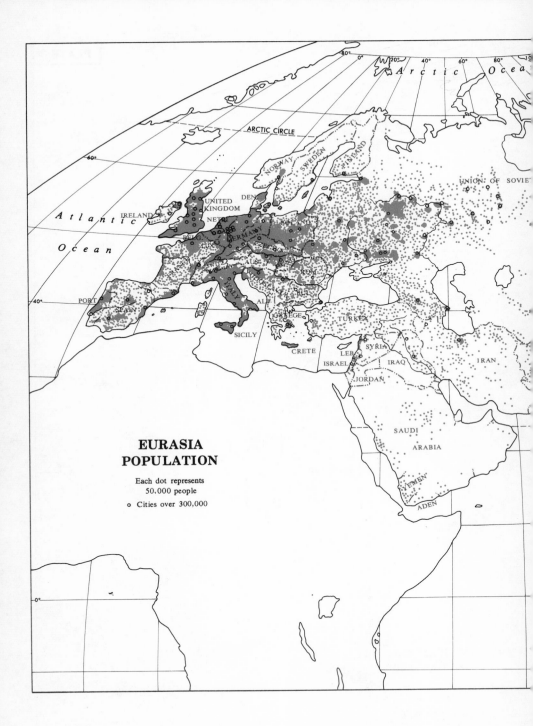

EURASIA
POPULATION

Each dot represents
50,000 people

o Cities over 300,000

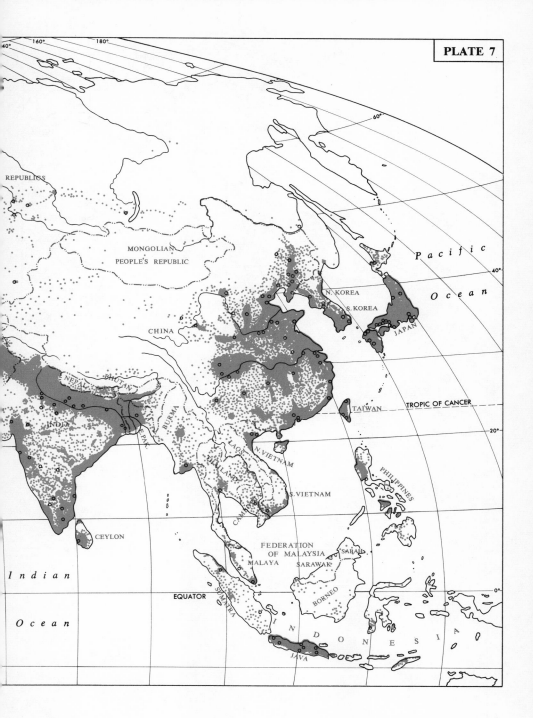

PLATE 7

REPUBLICS

MONGOLIAN
PEOPLE'S REPUBLIC

CHINA

NEPAL   BHUTAN

INDIA

E. PAK.

BURMA

CEYLON

LAOS   N. VIETNAM

THAILAND

CAM.   S. VIETNAM

FEDERATION
OF MALAYSIA
MALAYA   SARAWAK   SABAH

SUMATRA

EQUATOR

BORNEO

INDONESIA

JAVA

N. KOREA
S. KOREA

JAPAN

TAIWAN   TROPIC OF CANCER

PHILIPPINES

Pacific

Ocean

Indian

Ocean

40°

60°

40°

20°

0°

160°   180°

60°

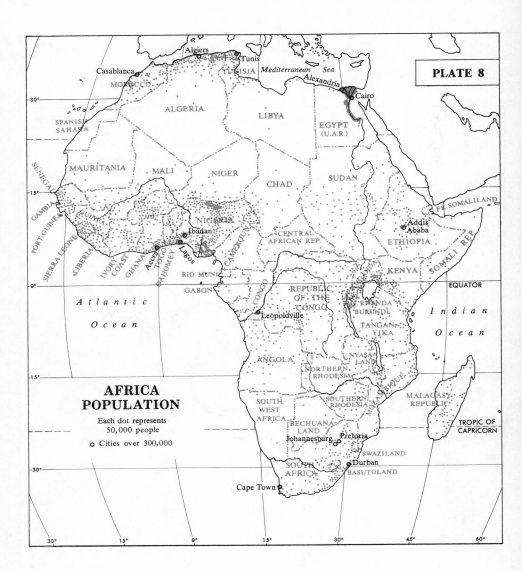

PLATE 8

AFRICA
POPULATION

Each dot represents
50,000 people

○ Cities over 300,000

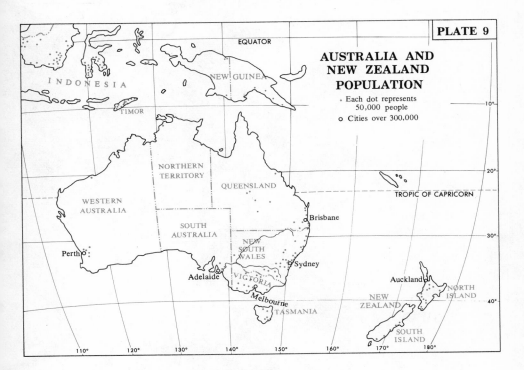

PLATE 9

AUSTRALIA AND
NEW ZEALAND
POPULATION

· Each dot represents
  50,000 people
o Cities over 300,000

EQUATOR

INDONESIA

NEW GUINEA

TIMOR

NORTHERN
TERRITORY

QUEENSLAND

TROPIC OF CAPRICORN

WESTERN
AUSTRALIA

SOUTH
AUSTRALIA

Brisbane

Perth

NEW
SOUTH
WALES

Adelaide

VICTORIA

Sydney

Auckland

NORTH
ISLAND

NEW
ZEALAND

Melbourne

TASMANIA

SOUTH
ISLAND

10°

20°

30°

40°

110° 120° 130° 140° 150° 160° 170° 180°

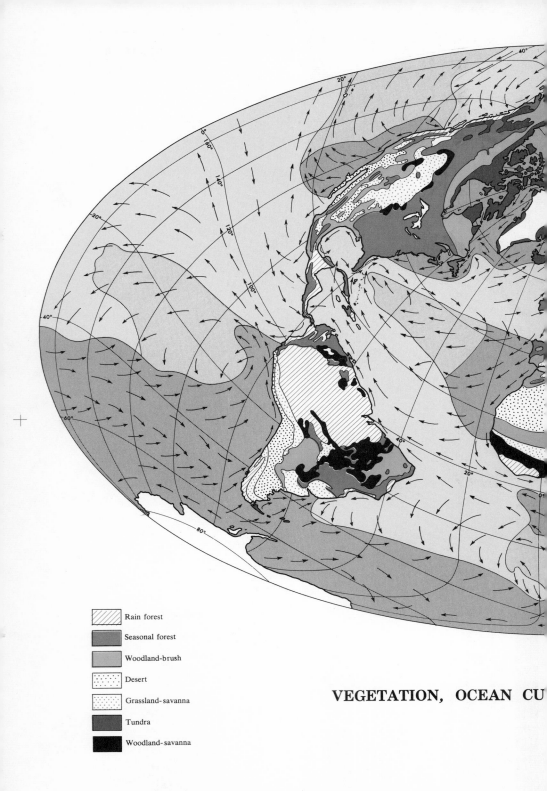

Rain forest

Seasonal forest

Woodland-brush

Desert

Grassland-savanna

Tundra

Woodland-savanna

VEGETATION, OCEAN CU

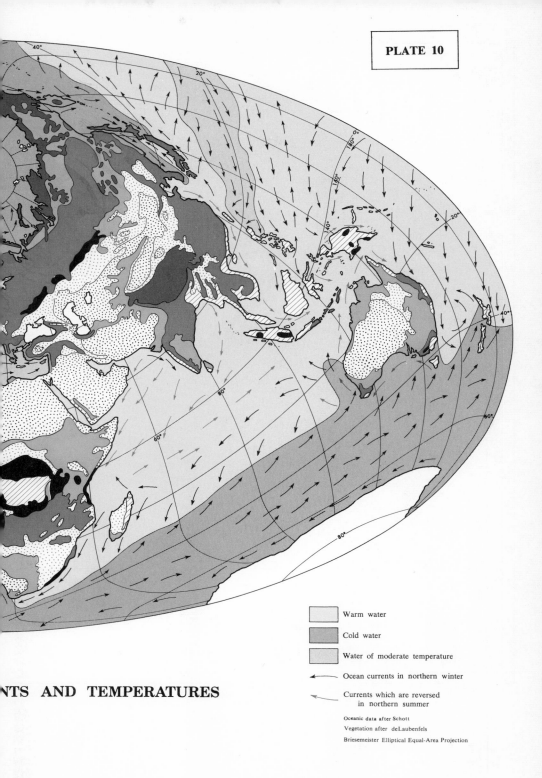

PLATE 10

NTS AND TEMPERATURES

Warm water

Cold water

Water of moderate temperature

Ocean currents in northern winter

Currents which are reversed
in northern summer

Oceanic data after Schott

Vegetation after deLaubenfels

Briesemeister Elliptical Equal-Area Projection

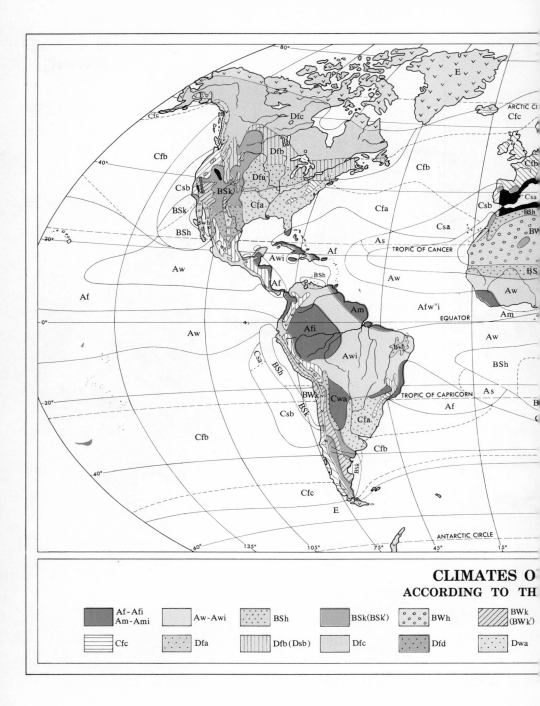

CLIMATES O

ACCORDING TO TH

Af-Afi Am-Ami	Aw-Awi	BSh	BSk(BSk')	BWh	BWk (BWk')
Cfc	Dfa	Dfb (Dsb)	Dfc	Dfd	Dwa

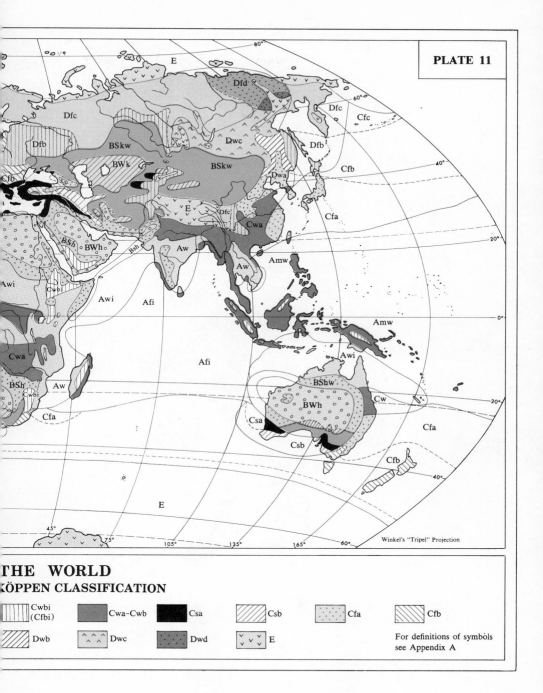

PLATE 11

THE WORLD
KÖPPEN CLASSIFICATION

Cwbi (Cfbi)	Cwa-Cwb	Csa
Dwb	Dwc	Dwd

Csb   Cfa   Cfb

E

For definitions of symbols
see Appendix A

Winkel's "Tripel" Projection

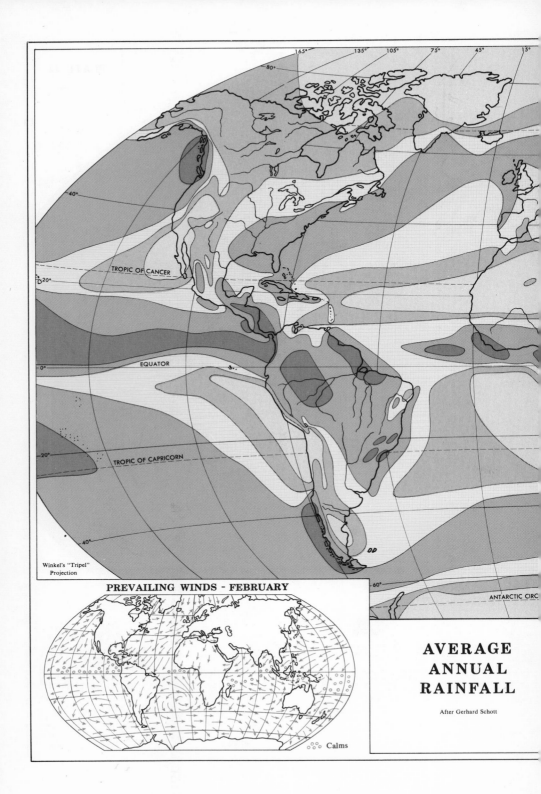

165°　　135°　105°　　75°　　45°　　15°

80°

40°

TROPIC OF CANCER

D 20°

EQUATOR

20°

TROPIC OF CAPRICORN

40°

Winkel's "Tripel"
Projection

60°

ANTARCTIC CIRC

PREVAILING WINDS - FEBRUARY

○°○ Calms

AVERAGE
ANNUAL
RAINFALL

After Gerhard Schott

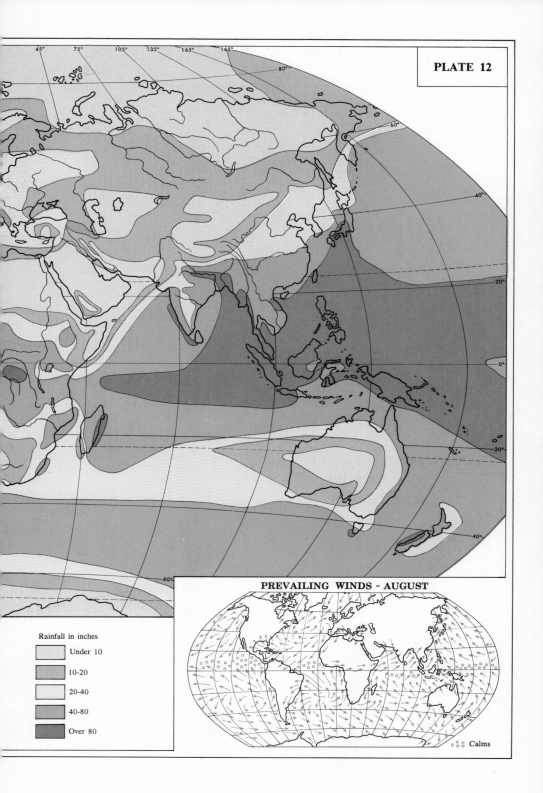

PLATE 12

Rainfall in inches

Under 10

10-20

20-40

40-80

Over 80

PREVAILING WINDS - AUGUST

Calms

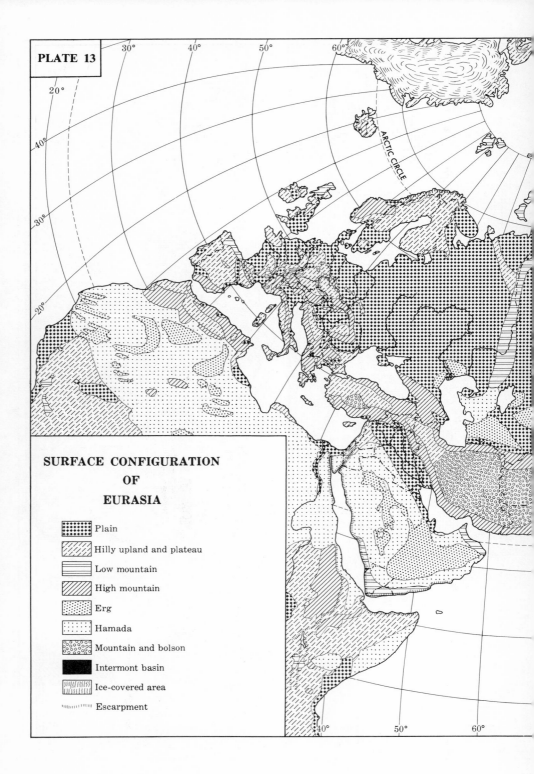

PLATE 13

ARCTIC CIRCLE

SURFACE CONFIGURATION
OF
EURASIA

Plain
Hilly upland and plateau
Low mountain
High mountain
Erg
Hamada
Mountain and bolson
Intermont basin
Ice-covered area
Escarpment

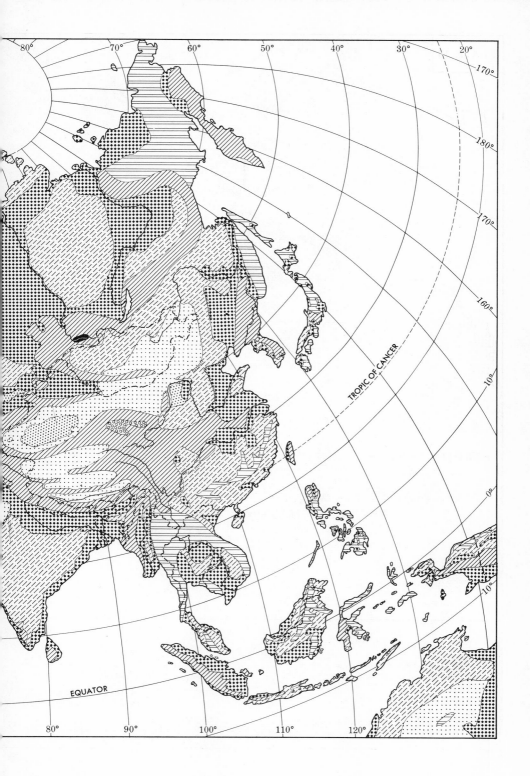

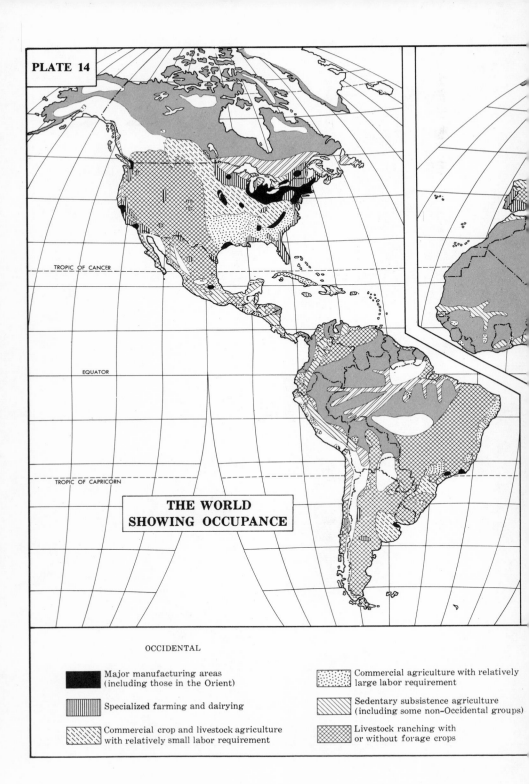

PLATE 14

TROPIC OF CANCER

EQUATOR

TROPIC OF CAPRICORN

**THE WORLD
SHOWING OCCUPANCE**

OCCIDENTAL

◼ Major manufacturing areas
(including those in the Orient)

▥ Specialized farming and dairying

▦ Commercial crop and livestock agriculture
with relatively small labor requirement

⬚ Commercial agriculture with relatively
large labor requirement

▧ Sedentary subsistence agriculture
(including some non-Occidental groups)

▦ Livestock ranching with
or without forage crops

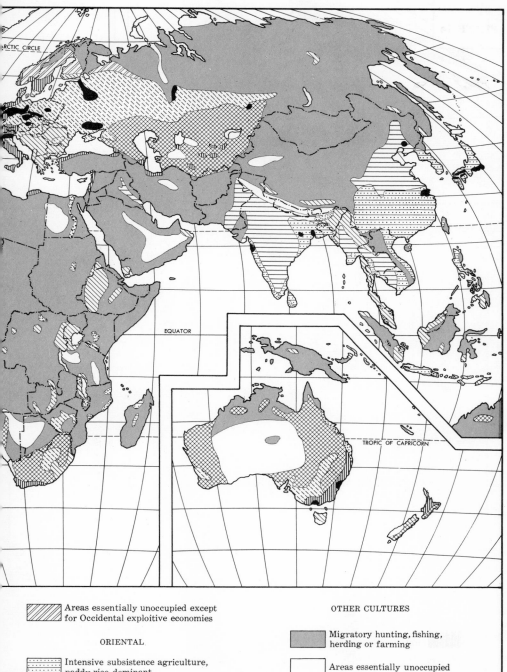

ARCTIC CIRCLE

EQUATOR

TROPIC OF CAPRICORN

Areas essentially unoccupied except
for Occidental exploitive economies

OTHER CULTURES

ORIENTAL

Migratory hunting, fishing,
herding or farming

Intensive subsistence agriculture,
paddy rice dominant

Areas essentially unoccupied

Intensive subsistence agriculture,
without paddy rice

Index

CONVERSION SCALES

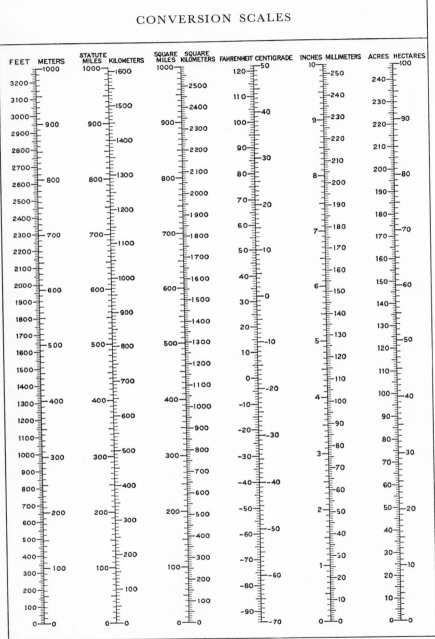

Courtesy, American Geographical Society